Elements of Water Supply and Waste-Water Disposal

NEW YORK · JOHN WILEY & SONS, INC.

London · Chapman & Hall, Limited

Elements of Water Supply and Waste-Water Disposal

GORDON MASKEW FAIR

Abbott and James Lawrence Professor of Engineering
and
Gordon McKay Professor of Sanitary Engineering
Harvard University

JOHN CHARLES GEYER

Professor of Sanitary Engineering
The Johns Hopkins University

Library of Congress Catalog Card Number: 58-6071

Printed in the United States of America

Preface

Engineering and, with it, the teaching of engineering are in transition. No longer are engineers satisfied with "workable knowledge" alone. Effective design and effective operation of engineering works ask, above all, for a fuller understanding and application of scientific principles. Progress in water engineering towards more scientific goals, too, has been steady and encouraging. The results of scientific research are being incorporated with remarkable success in new designs and in new operating schedules. Scientific thinking is making for better engineering including better economy.

The study of scientific principles, which has motivated the preparation of this book, is best accomplished in the classroom; the application of these principles is a matter of practice. To give reality to scientific thinking and afford the student the satisfaction of being concerned with real problems, however, it is suggested that the study of this textbook be supplemented by the following teaching aids: (1) visits to existing municipal and industrial water works and waste-water works, especially works under construction; (2) projection of lantern slides of noteworthy systems; (3) examination of plans and specifications of a variety of installations, including neighborhood works that can be visited; (4) assignment of readings in the periodicals listed in the Appendix to this book; and (5) examination of the catalogues and technical bulletins of manufacturers and suppliers of pertinent equipment.

To give emphasis to the scientific principles on which water supply and waste-water disposal are based, the present volume, like its larger protoype, *Water Supply and Waste-Water Disposal,** dispenses with

* John Wiley and Sons, New York, 1954.

the usual functional treatment of the subject matter in which water supply and waste-water disposal are considered separate subjects. There is joint discussion instead. However, it remains possible to develop a series of readings oriented specifically towards water supply and towards waste-water disposal for those who prefer to take up these subjects one at a time. The following sequences of readings are suggested for such purpose:

Water Supply. Sections 1–1 to 1–5; 1–8 and 1–9; 2–1 to 2–7; 3–1 to 3–10; 3–14; 3–16; 4–1 to 4–13; 5–1 to 5–19; 6–1 to 6–10; 7–1 to 7–9; 11–1 to 11–17; 12–1 to 12–4; 12–9 and 12–10; 13–1 to 13–14; 14–1 to 14–9; 15–1 to 15–13; 17–1 and 17–2; 18–1 to 18–21; 19–1 to 19–3; 19–16; 20–1 to 20–6.

Waste-Water Disposal. Sections 1–1 to 1–3; 1–6 to 1–9; 2–1 to 2–5; 2–8 and 2–9; 3–1 to 3–3; 3–8 and 3–9; 3–11 to 3–16; 8–1 to 8–5; 9–1 to 9–10; 10–1 to 10–9; 11–1 to 11–9; 11–11; 11–13 to 11–17; 12–1 and 12–2; 12–5 to 12–10; 13–1 to 13–17; 14–1 to 14–4; 14–8 and 14–9; 15–1 to 15–5; 15–13; 16–1 to 16–11; 17–1 to 17–19; 18–1 to 18–12; 19–1 to 19–16; 20–1; 20–7 to 20–14.

That there is much overlapping within these sequences testifies to the essential unity of the subject matter.

The present volume shares much of its purpose, content, and statement with our larger work *Water Supply and Waste-Water Disposal.* However, in order to direct the new book more specifically to satisfying the wants and needs of undergraduate students of civil and sanitary engineering, some subject matter has been simplified, some recast, and some shortened. A new feature of the present volume is the collection of 175 problems at the end of the book. Their solution can be supplemented by the analysis of existing water-supply and waste-water disposal systems with the aid of plans of the works and information obtained by personal inquiry.

In preparing chapters concerned with concepts of water chemistry, the authors have had the advice of Professor J. C. Morris. This is gratefully acknowledged, as is the encouragement and assistance of their other colleagues at Harvard and Hopkins. Once again Mrs. William Hutchinson, Secretary of Dunster House, Harvard College, has our thanks for preparing the typescript.

Gordon M. Fair
John C. Geyer

Harvard University
The Johns Hopkins University
December 10, 1957

Contents

1 Water Supply and Waste-Water Disposal Systems

1-1. Community Sanitary Works and Facilities. Water is introduced into municipalities for many purposes: (1) for drinking and culinary uses; (2) for bathing and washing; (3) for heating and air-conditioning systems; (4) for the watering of lawns and gardens; (5) for street sprinkling; (6) for recreational use in swimming and wading pools; (7) for display in fountains and cascades; (8) for the creation of hydraulic and steam power; (9) for numerous and varied industrial processes; (10) for the protection of life and property against fire; and (11) for the removal by water carriage of offensive and potentially dangerous wastes from household (sewage) and industry (industrial wastes). To provide for these varying uses, which average about 100 gallons per capita per day (gpcd) in the residential communities and 140 gpcd in the industrial cities of North America, the supply of water must be satisfactory in quality and adequate in quantity, readily available to the user, relatively cheap, and easily disposed of after it has served its purposes. The engineering works that make possible this manifold use of water are: (*a*) the water works, or water-supply system, and (*b*) the waste-water works, or waste-water disposal system.[1]

The water works collect water from its natural source, purify it if necessary, and deliver it to the consumer. The waste-water works

[1] The terms *sewage works* and *sewerage system* are, strictly speaking, more limited in concept than the terms *waste-water works* and *waste-water disposal system*. As a general rule, however, they are employed to describe the collection and disposal of all types of water-carried wastes and also of storm-water runoff.

collect the sewage or spent water of the community—about 70 per cent of the water supplied, together with varying amounts of entering ground and surface water. Surface runoff resulting from rainstorms and melting snow and ice is either collected by the system of drains that also carries away the waste waters of household and industry (combined sewerage), or the runoff is collected in an independent or separate system of storm drains (separate sewerage). The collected sewage or waste water is discharged, when required after suitable treatment, usually into a natural drainage channel, or receiving body of water, of the region; more rarely onto land. Often the same body of water must serve both as a source of water and as a recipient of sewage and storm drainage. It is this dual use of water in nature and within communities and industrial premises that establishes the most impelling reasons for water sanitation. The pollution of water by waste matters from household and industry, as well as other sources, not only makes the water unattractive (unsightly and malodorous) but carries with it the danger of adding disease-producing organisms such as the causative agents of typhoid fever and dysentery.

1-2. Interdependence of Water Supply and Waste-Water Disposal. The interdependence of water supply and waste-water disposal is the more pronounced the greater the urbanization of a region and the farther advanced its sanitary economy. The connecting link between water supply and waste-water disposal is the plumbing system, or system of water supply and drainage within dwellings, commercial establishments, and industries. Refuse collection is essentially independent of the two, except as garbage is ground and discharged into sewers and except as refuse incinerators are operated in connection with sewage-treatment works. Figure 1-1 illustrates, from the point of view of the householder, the progress from the individualistic practices of rural populations to the communal services that are provided for the urban dweller. The associated problems of sanitation are briefly indicated.

1-3. Background in History. The history of water supply and waste-water disposal has its roots in antiquity. There the design, construction, and management of public water supplies and waste-water disposal systems were allied to the growth of capital cities and religious or trade centers. Developed as installations of considerable magnitude and complexity, their remnants stand as monuments to sound, yet daring, feats of early engineering. Notable among the

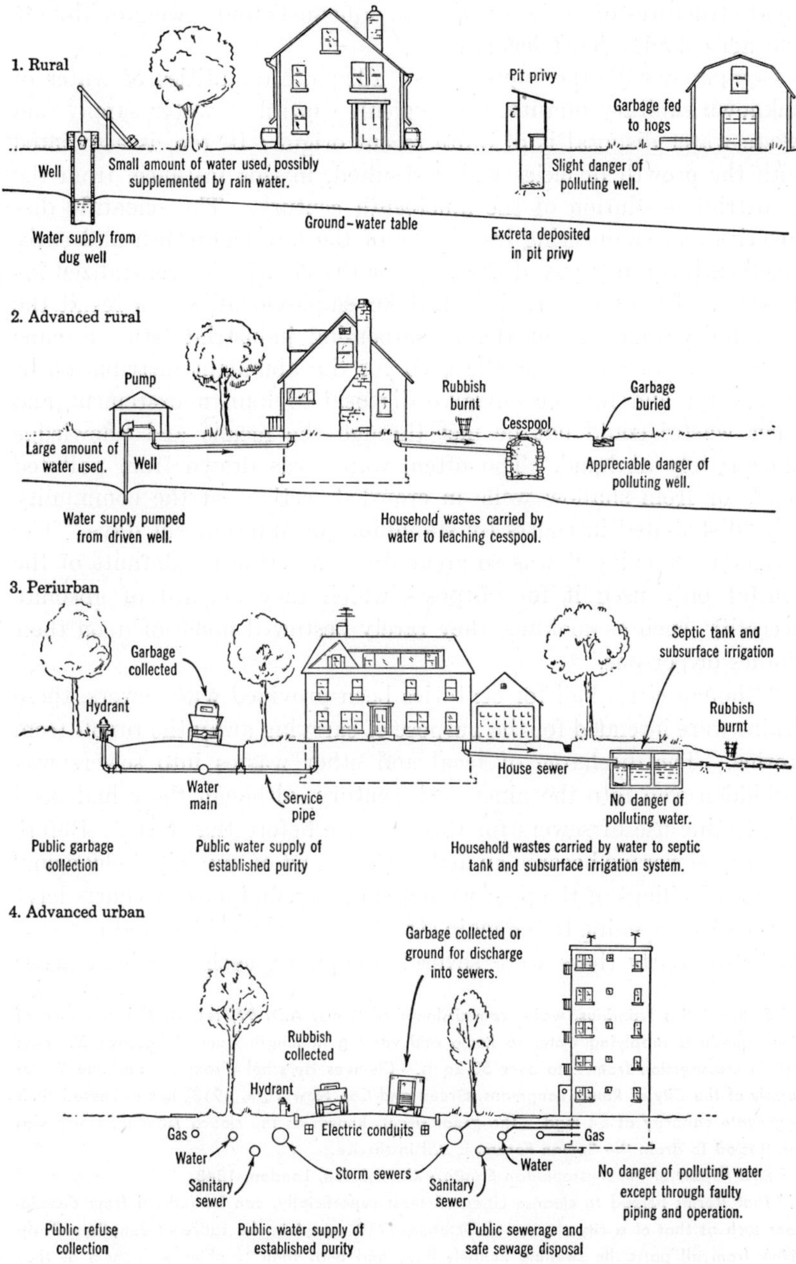
1. Rural
Well
Small amount of water used, possibly supplemented by rain water.
Pit privy
Garbage fed to hogs
Slight danger of polluting well.
Ground-water table
Water supply from dug well
Excreta deposited in pit privy
2. Advanced rural
Pump
Large amount of water used.
Well
Rubbish burnt
Cesspool
Garbage buried
Appreciable danger of polluting well.
Water supply pumped from driven well.
Household wastes carried by water to leaching cesspool.
3. Periurban
Garbage collected
Hydrant
Septic tank and subsurface irrigation
Rubbish burnt
House sewer
Water main
Service pipe
No danger of polluting water.
Public garbage collection
Public water supply of established purity
Household wastes carried by water to septic tank and subsurface irrigation system.
4. Advanced urban
Garbage collected or ground for discharge into sewers.
Rubbish collected
Hydrant
Electric conduits
Gas
Water
Sanitary sewer
Storm sewers
Sanitary sewer
Water
Gas
No danger of polluting water except through faulty piping and operation.
Public refuse collection
Public water supply of established purity
Public sewerage and safe sewage disposal

Figure 1-1. Rural and urban water-supply and waste-water disposal.

great structures of antiquity are the aqueducts and sewers of Rome [2] and her colonial dependencies.

Compared with the supplying of adequate quantities of water of unknown sanitary quality, the hygienic control of water supply and waste-water disposal is of quite recent origin. It, too, is associated with the growth of cities which resulted, in this instance, from the industrial revolution of the nineteenth century. The scientific discoveries and engineering inventions of the late eighteenth and early nineteenth century paved the way for the creation of centralized industries. To these, people flocked for employment. As a result the community facilities of the mushrooming industrial cities became overtaxed. In particular the need for the abundant distribution of safe water and for the effective disposal of human excrement and other wastes could not be met through the means and knowledge immediately at hand. Too often, water was drawn from polluted rivers or from shallow wells in crowded sections of the community and "distributed in courts by standpipes on intermittent days. The fatigue of fetching it was so great that they (the inhabitants of the courts) only used it for purposes which they deemed of absolute necessity, such as cooking; they rarely bestowed much of it on their clothes or persons." [3]

Although cities had for centuries been provided with sewers, these drains were intended for the purpose of carrying away the runoff from storms. The discharge of fecal and other wastes into sewers was forbidden well into the nineteenth century, although there had been clandestine use of sewers for this purpose before that time.[4] Before sanitary sewerage became an accepted method of municipal cleansing, "many dwellings of the poor were arranged round narrow courts having no other opening to the main street than a narrow covered passage. In these courts there were several occupants, each of whom accu-

[2] Sextus Julius Frontinus, water commissioner of Rome, A.D. 97, reports the existence of nine aqueducts supplying water to Rome and varying in length from 10 to over 50 miles and in cross-section from 7 to over 50 sq ft. Clemens Herschel (*Frontinus and the Water Supply of the City of Rome,* Longmans, Green and Co., New York, 1913) has estimated their aggregate capacity at 84 mgd. The great sewer, known as the *cloaca maxima,* which was constructed to drain the Roman Forum, is still in service.

[3] *First Report of the Metropolitan Sanitary Commission,* London, 1848.

[4] That storms helped to cleanse cities, at least superficially, can be judged from descriptions such as that of a city shower of October, 1710, cased in the satire of Jonathan Swift: "Now from all parts the swelling kennels flow, and bear their trophies with them as they go: Filth of all hues and odour, seem to tell what street they sail'd from, by their sight and smell."

mulated a heap. In some cases, each of these heaps was piled up separately in the court, with a general receptacle in the middle for drainage. In others a pit was dug in the middle of the court for the general use of all the occupants. In some the whole courts up to the very doors of the houses were covered with filth."[5] In the great cities of the world, large numbers of people inhabited basements and cellars. "In very many cases the vaults and privies were situated on the same or a higher level, and their contents frequently oozed through walls into the occupied apartments beside them." The privies themselves were often "too small in size and too few in number, and without ventilation or seat covers."[6]

Search for a remedy for foul conditions such as these ultimately led to the suggestion that human excrement be discharged into existing storm drains. The system of combined sewers was thereby created, and the early drainage works of most metropolitan communities were elaborated in accordance with this scheme. The storm drains had justifiably been constructed so as to terminate in the nearest water courses. When sewage was emptied into the drains, they carried into the water courses quantities of wastes that, more often than not, overtaxed the receiving capacity of those waters. The nuisances that had apparently been so happily removed from dwellings by water carriage of waste matters were concentrated within waters that flowed through or past the communities. First the smaller and then the larger bodies of water, especially during hot weather, began to "seethe and ferment under a burning sun, in one vast open *cloaca*."[7] As a result, "large (surrounding) territories were at once, and frequently, enveloped in an atmosphere of stench so strong as to arouse the sleeping, terrify the weak, and nauseate and exasperate everybody."[8]

To cope with this new situation, many of the smaller streams were converted into sewers; but the larger bodies of water remained open to view and sensory disapprobation, until the discharge of waste

[5] *Report from the Poor Law Commissioners on an Inquiry into the Sanitary Conditions of the Labouring Population of Great Britain,* 1842, *Local Reports,* p. 2. (In this quotation, the past tense replaces the present tense of the original.)

[6] *Report of the Council of Hygiene and Public Health of the Citizens' Association of New York upon the Sanitary Condition of the City,* 1865. (In this quotation, the past tense replaces the present tense of the original.)

[7] W. Budd, *Typhoid Fever,* 1873, relative to the condition of the Thames during the hot months of 1858 and 1859.

[8] E. C. Clark, *Report on the Main Drainage Works of the City of Boston,* 1885, quoting excerpts from one of the annual reports of the Board of Health.

matters into them was diminished by interception of the dry-weather flow and treatment of the collected waste waters.

The men who guided communities out of these difficulties did so by awakening the social and sanitary consciousness of the people and of their representatives in government. They included doctors, lawyers, engineers, writers,[9] and statesmen. Especially noteworthy are these men.

Sir Edwin Chadwick, British lawyer and statesman, whose studies and crusades, beginning in 1840, led to the organization of health and related commissions and whose inventive genius suggested the use of tile sewers and the separate system of sewerage.[10]

Lemuel Shattuck, Boston bookseller and principal author of the *Report of the Sanitary Commission of Massachusetts* (1850), which underlies the creation of the first engineering division in an American state board of health (1886).

John Snow and William Budd, British physicians, who demonstrated between 1849 and 1857 the role of fecal pollution of drinking water in the spread of cholera and typhoid fever.

James Simpson, British engineer, who in 1829 built the filters of the Chelsea (London) Water Company for the purpose of improving the quality of Thames River water.

James P. Kirkwood, American engineer, who in 1871 built the first sizeable water filters at Poughkeepsie, N. Y.

Sir John Bazelgette, British engineer, who started the main drainage of London in 1850.

Julius W. Adams, American engineer, who in 1857 constructed the first comprehensive system of sewerage in Brooklyn, N. Y.

Sir Robert Rawlinson, British engineer, who, as Sanitary Inspector of the General Board of Health (1848), conducted the engineering studies necessary for the construction of water supplies and waste-water works in industrial Britain.

Hiram F. Mills, American engineer, who as engineer-member of the Massachusetts State Board of Health gave direction to its newly formed engineering division (1886) and supported the researches of this division in the Lawrence Experiment Station.

More recent developments in water supply and waste-water disposal are discussed later in this book in connection with individual subject matters.

9 Charles Dickens, in commenting upon the slums of London at a public meeting in 1850, said that he "knew of many places in London unsurpassed in the accumulated horrors of their neglect by the *dirtiest* old spots in the *dirtiest* old towns under the *worst* old governments in Europe."

10 His advocacy of the separation of storm drainage from sanitary sewerage is epitomized in the slogan: "The rain to the river and the sewage to the soil."

Water Supply Systems

1-4. General Features of Water-Supply Systems. Water-supply systems generally comprise (1) collection works; (2) purification works, where needed; and (3) transportation and distribution works. Their relative functions and positions in a surface-water supply are outlined in Figure 1-2. The collection works either tap a source of water that is continuously adequate in quantity to satisfy present and reasonable future demands, or they convert an intermittently inadequate source into a continuously adequate supply by storing surplus water for use during periods of insufficiency. If the water is not satisfactory in quality at the point of collection, purification works render the collected water suitable for the purposes it is to serve. Polluted and hence potentially infected water is disinfected; esthetically un-

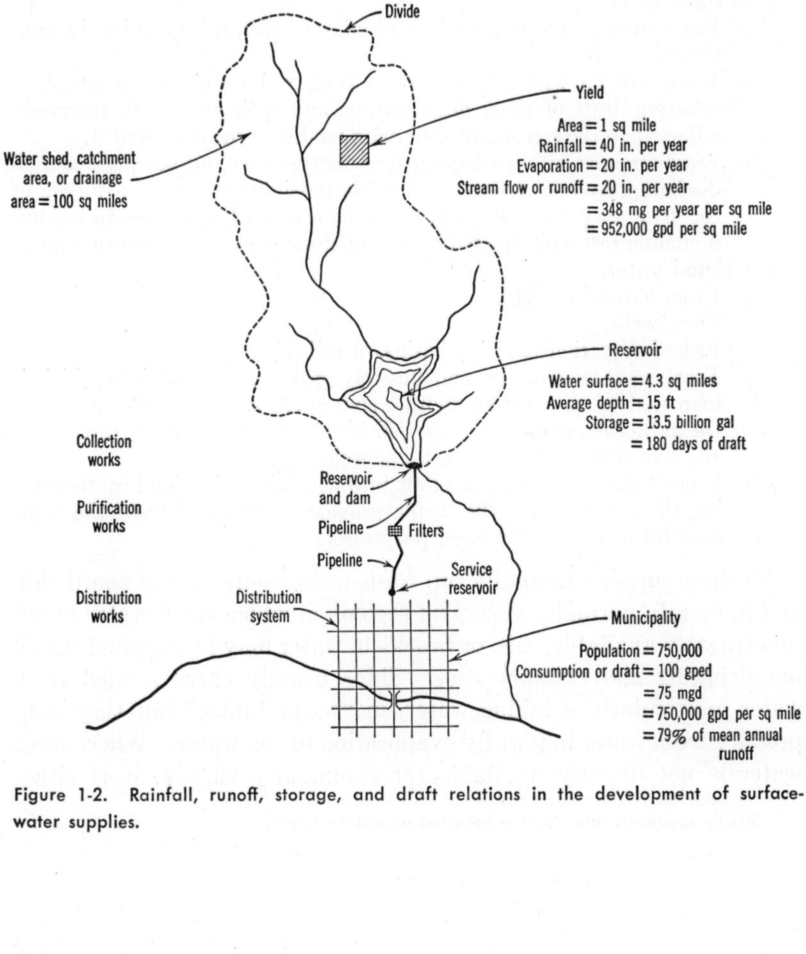

Figure 1-2. Rainfall, runoff, storage, and draft relations in the development of surface-water supplies.

attractive or unpalatable water is treated to make it attractive and palatable; water containing iron or manganese is subjected to deferrization or demanganization; corrosive water is stabilized chemically to render it non-corrosive; and excessively hard water is softened. The transportation and distribution works convey the collected and purified water to the community and there dispense it to consumers in ample volume and at adequate pressure. The amount of water delivered is measured so that an equable charge can be made for its use.

1-5. Sources of Supply. The source of water determines the nature of the collection, purification, and distribution works. Sources of water and their development may be classified as follows:

1. Rain water.[11]
   a. From roofs, stored in cisterns for small individual supplies.
   b. From larger, prepared catchment areas, or "catches," stored in reservoirs, for large communal supplies.
2. Surface water.
   a. From streams, natural ponds, and lakes of adequate capacity, by continuous draft.
   b. From streams with adequate flood flow, by intermittent, seasonal, or selective draft of clean flood waters, and their storage in reservoirs adjacent to the stream, or otherwise readily accessible from it.
   c. From streams with inadequate dry-weather flow but adequate annual discharge, by continuous draft made possible through the storage of the necessary proportion of flows in excess of daily use in an impounding reservoir created by a dam thrown across the stream valley.
3. Ground water.
   a. From natural springs.
   b. From wells.
   c. From infiltration galleries, basins, or cribs.
   d. From wells or galleries and possibly springs, the flow into which is increased by water from another source (1) spread on the surface of the gathering ground, (2) carried into charging basins or ditches, or (3) lead into diffusion galleries or wells.
   e. From wells or galleries, the flow into which is maintained by recharging the ground with the water previously removed from the same area for cooling and related purposes.

All these supplies normally tap fresh-water sources. On board ship and in certain normally very arid regions in which fresh water is not immediately available, salt, or brackish, water may be supplied for all but drinking and culinary uses. Ships usually carry needed fresh water, particularly drinking water, in "water tanks," but they may produce fresh water in part by evaporation of sea water. Where fresh water is not directly available for community supply, it is either

[11] Strictly speaking, rain water is collected as surface runoff.

hauled in by road, rail, or water, or it is supplied entirely or in part by evaporation of salt or brackish water. Some brackish or saline waters are economically amenable to desalting by ion-exchange processes as well as chemical precipitation methods.

Municipal supplies may be drawn from a single source or from a number of different ones. The water from multiple sources is ordinarily mixed before distribution to the community, provided that the component waters or their mixtures are safe and satisfactory in quality. Dual public water supplies of unequal quality are unusual in North America. They are frowned upon by health authorities because of the ever-present hazard of their being interconnected, wittingly or unwittingly.

Waste-Water Disposal Systems

1-6. General Features of Waste-Water Disposal Systems. The disposal of waste waters requires the construction and operation of: (1) collection works and (2) disposal works. The latter are preceded by treatment works where needed. The complex of structures is called the *sewerage* or drainage system. The relative functions and positions of the component parts are outlined in Figure 1-3. If the collection works transport in the same conduits (1) waste matters from households and industries and (2) storm-water runoff, the conduits are called *combined sewers* [12] and form part of a *combined system* of sewerage. If the two kinds of waste waters are collected separately, the resulting *sanitary sewers* and *storm sewers* (or storm drains) create a *separate system* of sewerage. The water-carried wastes originating in households are *domestic sewage;* those coming from manufacturing establishments are *industrial wastes* or *trade wastes.* The addition of storm water creates *combined sewage. Municipal sewage* generally includes both domestic and industrial wastes. Combined sewerage systems are common in the older cities of the world [13] in which they evolved from the existing system of storm drains.

The collection works consist of one or more branching systems of conduits designed to remove the sewage or storm water by "free" flow as through the branches and stem of an underground river system. The main collector of many combined systems is, in fact, a stream

[12] The word sewer is derived ultimately from the Latin words ex, out, and *aqua,* water. In the eighteenth and early nineteenth centuries, the common form of the word was *shor.*

[13] The sewerage systems of London, England; Paris, France; New York, N. Y.; and Boston, Mass.; are examples of this evolution.

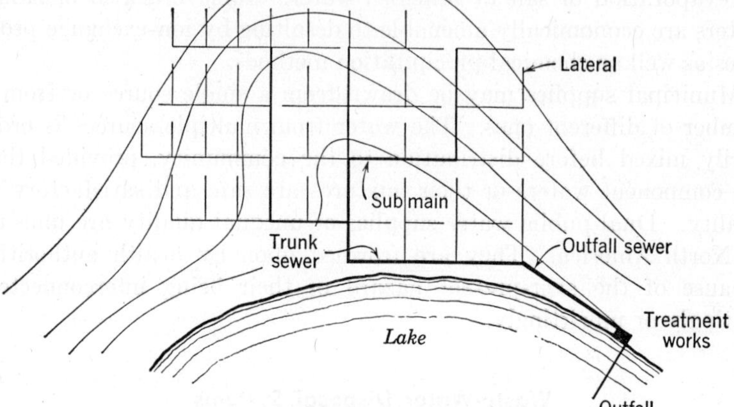

a. Sanitary sewerage system

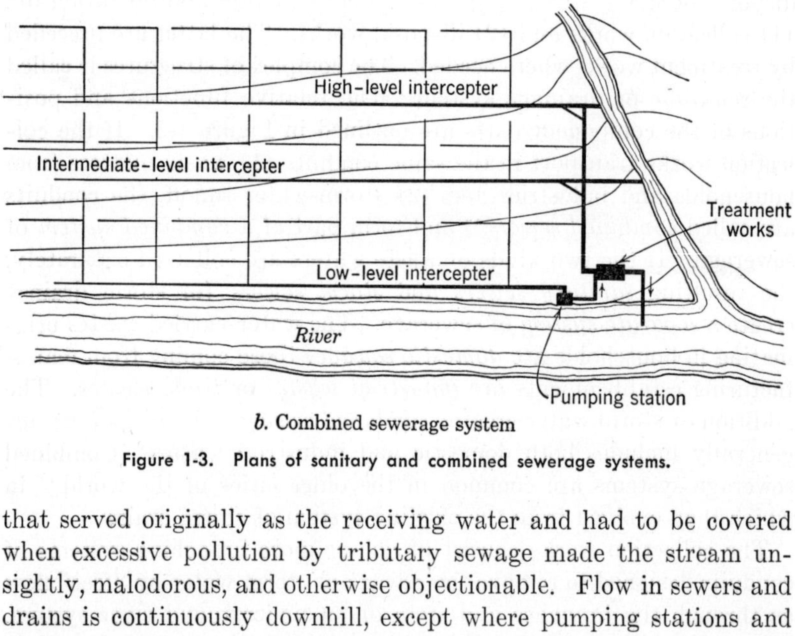

b. Combined sewerage system

Figure 1-3. Plans of sanitary and combined sewerage systems.

that served originally as the receiving water and had to be covered when excessive pollution by tributary sewage made the stream unsightly, malodorous, and otherwise objectionable. Flow in sewers and drains is continuously downhill, except where pumping stations and force mains are interpolated in the system (1) in order to lift waste waters from a deep sewer to one near the ground surface and so to avoid the construction of uneconomically deep conduits in flat country or bad ground; or (2) in order to transfer waste waters from one drainage area, or *sewer district,* to another. Sewers are laid below ground for reasons of convenience. They are not intended to flow under pressure. Hydraulically, sewers are designed as "open channels," flowing partly full or, at most, just filled. Of the various formulas characterizing open-channel flow, American engineers commonly employ either the Chezy formula with Kutter's velocity coefficient or the Manning formula.[14] Vitrified-clay pipes are generally used for small sewers, and concrete or masonry pipes or conduits of special shapes for large ones.

Each branching system collects the sewage, storm runoff, or both from the area it is intended to serve and conducts it to the point of disposal. Here the collected waste waters are treated, if necessary.

Ordinarily they are discharged into a water course that constitutes a natural drainage channel of the region or a natural receiver of drainage waters. This final emptying of waste waters into a *receiving body of water* is called disposal by *dilution.* In semiarid regions or places otherwise suited for it, terminal discharge may be on land. This is called disposal by *irrigation.* Treatment of waste waters prior to final disposal aims at the removal of unsightly and putrescible matter from the carrying water and at the destruction of the disease-producing organisms that it may contain. The degree of treatment is predicated upon the economical conservation of the water and land resources of the region.

1-7. Sources and Nature of Waste Waters. *Sanitary sewage* is the spent water supply of the community. *Domestic sewage* is the waste water from kitchen, bathroom, lavatory, toilet, and laundry. In addition to the mineral and organic matter already in the water dispensed to the community, domestic sewage contains an imposed burden of human excrement, paper, soap, dirt, food wastes (garbage), and numerous other substances. Some of these waste matters are carried in suspension; others are taken into solution; still others are, or become, so finely divided that they possess the properties of colloidal (dispersed, ultramicroscopic) particles. A large portion of the waste matters is organic in nature and, because of its high energy value, subject to attack by saprophytic microorganisms, i.e., organisms that feed upon dead organic matter. Domestic sewage, therefore, is unstable, decomposable, or putrescible; it may give rise to offensive odors, notably those of hydrogen sulfide, and other objectionable conditions associated with decomposition. Pathogenic organisms (1) discharged by persons harboring intestinal parasites or suffering from

[14] See Section 9-3.

infectious diseases, particularly typhoid, paratyphoid, the dysenteries, and other gastrointestinal infections, or (2) excreted by carriers of these diseases, are always potentially present in domestic sewage and render it dangerous.

The nature of *industrial wastes* depends upon the industrial processes in which they originate. Industrial waste waters vary in nature from relatively clean rinse waters to waste liquors that are heavily laden with organic or mineral matter, or with corrosive, poisonous, flammable, or explosive substances. Some industrial wastes are so objectionable that they should not be admitted to the public sewerage system; others contain so little and such unobjectionable foreign matter that it is safe to discharge them into a storm drain or directly into a natural body of water. Some industrial wastes adhere to sewers and clog them; acids and hydrogen sulfide destroy cement, concrete, and metals; hot wastes crack tile and concrete; poisonous chemicals, quite apart from their immediate danger to man, interfere with biological treatment processes and kill the organisms that normally populate receiving waters; flammable or explosive substances, such as gasoline, endanger the structures through which sewage flows; and toxic gases or vapors create hazards to workmen and operators of sewage works. Industrial wastes become part of sanitary sewage when they are permitted to enter the public sewerage system.

All sewage contains some ground water that gains entrance into the sewers through their many joints.[15] In combined systems, storm runoff adds the washings from streets, roofs, gardens, parks, and yard areas. These are chiefly dirt, dust, sand, gravel, and other gritty substances that are heavy and inert. Leaves and other debris enter the system at certain seasons of the year. Storm drains receive, in addition to surface runoff from rain, ice, and snow, water that has been used to cleanse streets, fight fires, or flush the water distribution system through hydrants; sometimes, also, waste water from fountains, wading and swimming pools, and similar sources.

Sanitary sewage flows from the premises in which it originates through one or more service connections to the public sewer. The service pipes are called *house* or *building drains* inside the building and *house* or *building sewers* outside (Figure 8-1). Storm water from roofs and paved areas, if taken into a *property drain,* is discharged into the street gutters or directly into the storm sewer. In combined

[15] Clay sewer pipe, 8 to 24 in. in diameter, is 2, 2½, or 3 ft long; above that 2½ or 3 ft long. Concrete sewer pipe, 8 to 24 in. in diameter, is 2, 2½, 3, or 4 ft long.

systems of sewerage, roof water may be carried into the house drain and water from yard areas into the house sewer. Storm water that is not otherwise channeled travels over the ground until it reaches the street gutter along which it flows to a storm-water inlet or catch basin, whence it is piped to a manhole. In separate systems, connections to the wrong sewer, made by mistake or in violation of regulations, carry some storm water into sanitary sewers and some sewage into storm drains. The dry-weather flow in combined sewers is primarily sewage and ground water; the flow during and immediately following a heavy rainstorm is predominantly storm runoff.

1-8. Management of Water and Waste-Water Works. The development of water and waste-water works from the ground up, or their improvement and extension, progresses from preliminary investigations through their financing, design, and construction to their operation, maintenance, and repair. All these steps involve political and financial activities as well as those of a more strictly engineering nature. A concept of the magnitude of the engineering activity and responsibility involved in the design and construction of water-supply and waste-water works is given by their cost.

a. Cost of water supplies. The per capita investment in physical plant for water supplies depends upon many factors: the nature, proximity, and abundance of a suitable water source; the need for water treatment; the availability and cost of labor and materials; the size and requirements of the system; the habits of the people; and the characteristics of the area served. Because of wide differences in these factors, the first cost of water-supply systems varies considerably. For communities in excess of 10,000 population, costs in North America lie ordinarily between $50 and $300 per capita, with much of the investment in smaller communities chargeable to fire-protection needs. Of the various portions of the system, the collection and transportation works represent about a third of the cost, the distribution works slightly more than a half, and the purification works about a tenth, the remainder being invested in real estate. The first cost of water-filtration plants is about $150,000 per mgd capacity, and the cost of water treatment, excluding fixed charges, lies in the vicinity of $25 per mg (million gallons). Including interest and depreciation as well as charges against operation and management, water costs from $50 to $300 per mg and is charged for accordingly. As one of our most prized commodities, water is remarkably cheap. It sells for as low as 2 cents a ton delivered to the premises of large consumers and costs the small consumer as little as 4 cents a ton.

b. Waste-water disposal systems. The per capita investment in sewerage systems varies with the type of system; the topography, hydrology, and geology of the area served; the nature and proximity of receiving waters; the need for sewage treatment; the availability and cost of labor and materials; and the size and characteristics of the community.

The first cost of sanitary sewers lies ordinarily between $20 and $80 per capita in North American communities. The cost of storm drains and combined sewers, depending upon local conditions, is about three times as great. The first cost of sewage-treatment plants varies with the degree of treatment provided. Primary treatment works cost about $100,000, and complete treatment works about $300,000, per mgd capacity. Plants handling combined sewage are about one-third more expensive than those treating domestic sewage alone. The cost of treatment, excluding fixed charges, is close to $20 per mg for primary treatment and about twice that amount for complete treatment. Including interest and depreciation, as well as charges against operation and management, the removal of domestic sewage and its safe disposal costs from $50 to $200 per mg. Comparisons with the cost of water supply will show that complete sewage treatment works are relatively twice as expensive as water purification works, whereas collection systems for domestic sewage are about half as expensive as distribution systems for water. Sewer rentals, corresponding to charges for water, are employed when it is desired to place the cost of sewerage upon a "value received" basis. Rentals may cover part or all of the cost of the service rendered and are generally related to the water bill.

No general values can be assigned to the cost of separate treatment of industrial waste waters. When they are discharged into municipal sewerage systems, the cost of their treatment can be estimated in terms of the load that they impose on the municipal works, as measured by the suspended solids, the putrescible matter, or a combination of these two with the volume of waste water.

1-9. Importance and Accomplishments of Water Supply and Waste-Water Disposal. In 1950, more than 17,000 water works in the United States and Canada supplied about 17 billion gallons of water a day to communities with a total population of about 110 millions.[16] The annual value of this product places the water-works industry in the top ten largest industries of the continent, and the tonnage of water

[16] This information is provided by the American Water Works Association.

delivered (almost 70 million tons daily) is many times the weight of all other industrial products. About 100,000 people are employed directly by the industry. Much of this water finds its way into public sewers. The number of sewered communities is close to 10,000 with a population in excess of 80 millions.

Since the turn of the century, there has been about a fourfold increase in water works and a tenfold increase in sewerage systems. These advances include, in addition to economic benefits, an enhancement of human comfort and well-being which cannot readily be measured although it is very real. At the same time, great strides have been made in the protection of the public against water-borne diseases. Through the purification and protection of their waters, cities supplied with water from polluted streams have seen their annual death rate from typhoid fever drop from well over 100 per 100,000 to well below 1 per 100,000. At such a level there is no longer reason to suspect that the disease is acquired from drinking the water of the community.

How acceptable a supply of good water can be to a community that has lacked it is well illustrated by the celebration in 1848 on Boston Common of the introduction into that city of a new supply of water from Lake Cochituate. For this celebration, James Russell Lowell was prompted to write a poem that includes the words: "My name is Water: I have sped through strange, dark ways, untried before, by pure desire of friendship led, Cochituate's ambassador; he sends four royal gifts by me, long life, health, peace, and purity."

Of house drainage, Stobart[17] has well said: "There is no truer sign of civilization and culture than good sanitation. It goes with refined senses and orderly habits. A good drain implies as much as a beautiful statue. And let it be remembered that the world did not reach the Minoan[18] standard of cleanliness again until the great sanitary movement of the late nineteenth century."

[17] J. C. Stobart, *The Glory That Was Greece* (revised by F. N. Pryce), Appleton-Century Co., New York, p. 29, 1935.

[18] Named after King Minos of Crete. Archeologists have found that the palace of Knossos on this island contained bathrooms, a latrine flushed by rain water, and tile drains.

2 Quantities of Water and Waste Water

2-1. Required Estimates. Both management and design of water-supply and waste-water disposal systems require a knowledge of the quantities of water needed and waste water produced and their relation to the population served. Per capita figures generalize the experience. They are useful in comparing the records of different communities and in estimating the future needs of a growing community or area. Water supply and waste-water disposal systems, at the time of their construction, are made large enough to satisfy the needs of the community for a reasonable number of years in the future without requiring important additions or changes. Determination of the design capacity calls for the exercise of skill in the interpretation of social and economic trends, as well as the use of sound judgment in the analysis of past experience for the purpose of predicting future requirements. Among the estimates to be made by the designer are the following:

1. The number of years during which the proposed system and its component structures and equipment are to be adequate. This is called the *period of design.*
2. The number of people to be served as determined by estimates of population and required service.
3. The rate of water use and related sewage flow as reflected by estimates of per capita water consumption and sewage discharge as well as industrial and commercial requirements.
4. For storm and combined sewerage, in particular, the area to be served and the allowances to be made for rainfall and runoff.[1]

[1] This aspect of the problem is considered in Chapter 10.

2-2. Period of Design. In fixing upon a period of design, consideration is given to the following factors:

1. The useful life of the structures and equipment employed, taking into account obsolescence as well as wear and tear.
2. The ease, or difficulty, of extending or increasing the works, including a consideration of their location.
3. The anticipated rate of growth of the population, with due regard to increases in commercial and industrial needs.
4. The rate of interest that must be paid on bonded indebtedness.
5. The change in the purchasing power of money during the period of retirement of indebtedness.
6. The performance of the works during their early years when they are not loaded to capacity.

TABLE 2-1. Design Periods for Water-Supply and Sewerage Structures

Type of Structure	Special Characteristics	Design Period—yr
Water Supply		
Large dams and conduits	Hard and costly to enlarge	25–50
Wells, distribution systems, and filter plants	Easy to extend	
	When growth and interest rates are low *	20–25
	When growth and interest rates are high *	10–15
Pipes more than 12 in. in diameter	Replacement of smaller pipes is more costly in long run	20–25
Laterals and secondary mains less than 12 in. in diameter	Requirements may change fast in a limited area	Full development
Sewerage		
Laterals and submains less than 15 in. in diameter	Requirements may change fast in a limited area	Full development
Main sewers, outfalls, and intercepters	Hard and costly to enlarge	40–50
Treatment works	When growth and interest rates are low *	20–25
	When growth and interest rates are high *	10–15

* The dividing line is in the vicinity of 3% per annum.

The longer the useful life (1), the greater the difficulty of extensions (2), the smaller the rate of growth (3), the lower the rate of interest (4), the greater the likelihood of inflation (5), and the better the early performance (6), the farther into the future can the design be projected with economic justification. The lengths of design periods often employed in practice are indicated in Table 2-1.

Population Estimates

2-3. Population Growth. The best source of information on the population living in a given community or area at a designated time is an official census or enumeration. The government of the United

States has made a decennial census since 1790. Additional data are sometimes available through special surveys conducted by public authorities or private agencies for governmental, social, or commercial purposes. Since 1930, the U. S. Census has recorded the population as of April 1. Prior census dates are 1 January, 1920, 15 April, 1910, and 1 June, 1830 to 1900.

Census data are published by the Bureau of the Census in the Department of Commerce. The subdivisions for which population data are made available include states, counties, metropolitan districts, cities, and towns, wards, and census tracts. Populations are increased by births, decreased by deaths, increased or decreased by migration, and increased by annexation. All four elements are influenced by social and economic factors some of which are inherent in the community concerned while others are country wide and even world wide in scope.

Recognizing that there are certain stable values toward which birth and death rates will move, and that annexations or extensions of services can be accounted for by following the development of the individual population groups, the most important and least predictable element of population change is the commercial and industrial activity of an individual community. This element may produce sharp rises, slow growth, stationary conditions, or even marked declines in population.[2]

Were it not for these manifold and varying influences, populations would trace the growth curve that is characteristic of all forms of life within a limited space. This curve is S-shaped (Figure 2-1), early growth taking place at an increasing rate, late growth at a decreasing rate as a saturation value or upper limit is approached. What the future holds for a given population depends upon the point that has been reached on the growth curve.

2-4. Methods of Estimating Population. Two types of population estimates are needed in the management and design of sanitary works:

[2] Examples are furnished by the growth of Detroit, Mich. (automobile industry), the decline of Lowell, Mass. (textile industry), and the growth of Miami, Fla. (recreation).

Census Year	1910	1920	1930	1940	1950
Population of Detroit	466,000	994,000	1,560,000	1,623,000	1,839,000
Population of Lowell	106,000	113,000	100,000	101,000	97,000
Population of Miami	5,500	30,000	111,000	172,000	247,000

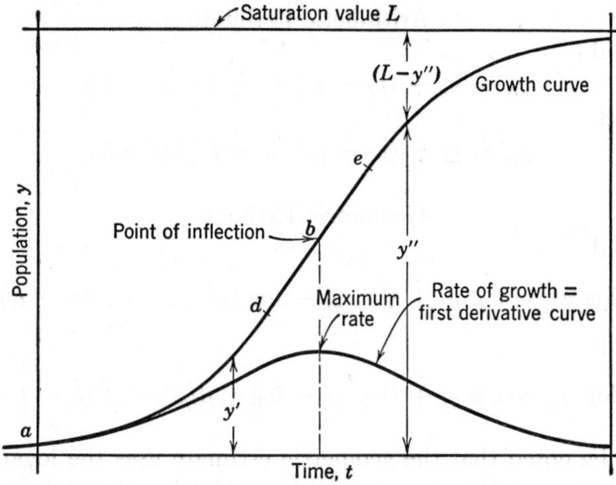

Figure 2-1. Curve of population growth. Note geometric increase from a to b; straight-line increase from d to e (approximately); and first-order increase from b to c.

(a) estimates of midyear populations for current years and the recent past, and (b) forecasts of population for the period of design.

a. Estimates for current and past years. These are either intercensal estimates for the years between two censuses or postcensal estimates for the years since the last census. Mathematically, the midyear values are readily interpolated, or extrapolated, on the basis of arithmetic or geometric change. Growth is *arithmetic* if the population increase dy in the time interval dt is a constant amount k_a, irrespective of the size of the population; i.e., $dy/dt = k_a$. Growth is *geometric* if the population increase dy in the time interval dt is proportional to the size of the population y; i.e., $dy/dt = k_g y$, where k_g is the proportionality factor. Integration of these relationships between the limits y_e (the population of the earlier census) and y_l (the population of the later census) and the limits t_e (the date of the earlier census) and t_l (the date of the later census) yields the following values for k_a and k_g:

$$k_a = (y_l - y_e)/(t_l - t_e) \quad \text{for arithmetic growth} \qquad 2\text{-}1$$

$$k_g = (\log_e y_l - \log_e y_e)/(t_l - t_e) \quad \text{for geometric growth} \qquad 2\text{-}2$$

Integration between the limits y_m (the desired midyear population) and y_e or y_l, and between the limits t_m (the desired date) and t_e or t_l, gives the midyear population as follows:

Arithmetic Estimate

Intercensal

$$y_m = y_e + (y_l - y_e)(t_m - t_e)/(t_l - t_e) \qquad 2\text{-}3$$

Postcensal

$$y_m = y_l + (y_l - y_e)(t_m - t_l)/(t_l - t_e) \qquad 2\text{-}4$$

Geometric Estimate

Intercensal

$$\log y_m = \log y_e + (\log y_l - \log y_e)(t_m - t_e)/(t_l - t_e) \qquad 2\text{-}5$$

Postcensal

$$\log y_m = \log y_l + (\log y_l - \log y_e)(t_m - t_l)/(t_l - t_e) \qquad 2\text{-}6$$

It will be noted that the geometric estimate uses the logarithms of the populations in the same way the populations themselves are used in the arithmetic estimate; also, that arithmetic increase is analogous to growth by simple interest, geometric increase to growth by compound interest. The lower portion of the S-shaped growth curve (Figure 2-1) is approximated by geometric increase (concave upward) and the central portion by arithmetic increase (straight line). The upper portion is concave downward. It is analogous to a *first-order* chemical reaction.[3] Choice of method is best determined by an examination of the population curve that is obtained when all available census figures are plotted on arithmetic-coordinate paper.

Example 2-1. A city[4] recorded a population of 111,000 in the earlier decennial census and 171,000 in the later one. Estimate the midyear (1 July) populations (*a*) for the fifth intercensal year and (*b*) for the ninth postcensal year by the arithmetic-increase method and the geometric-increase method. Assume a census date of 1 April.

a. Intercensal estimate for fifth year. $t_m - t_e = 5.25$ yr; $t_l - t_e = 10.00$ yr; and $(t_m - t_e)/(t_l - t_e) = 5.25/10.00 = 0.525$.

Arithmetic	Geometric
$y_l = 171{,}000$	$\log y_l = 5.23300$
$y_e = 111{,}000$	$\log y_e = 5.04532$
$y_l - y_e = 60{,}000$	$\log y_l - \log y_e = 0.18768$
$0.525(y_l - y_e) = 31{,}500$	$0.525(\log y_l - \log y_e) = 0.09853$
$y_m = 142{,}500$	$\log y_m = 5.14385$
	$y_m = 139{,}300$

[3] The first-order reaction is formulated for first-stage BOD in Section 19-6. Its application to population data is indicated in Figure 2-1 and involves an estimate of the limiting population, or saturation value *L*.

[4] The figures used are rounded values for Miami, Fla., 1930 and 1940.

b. Postcensal estimate for ninth year. $t_m - t_l = 9.25$ yr; $t_l - t_e = 10.00$ yr; and $(t_m - t_l)/(t_l - t_e) = 9.25/10.00 = 0.925$.

Arithmetic	Geometric
From (*a*) $y_l - y_e = 60{,}000$	$\log y_l - \log y_e = 0.18768$
$0.925(y_l - y_e) = 55{,}500$	$0.925(\log y_l - \log y_e) = 0.17360$
$y_l = 171{,}000$	$\log y_l = 5.23300$
$y_m = 226{,}500$	$\log y_m = 5.40660$
	$y_m = 255{,}000$

Note that the geometric estimates are higher for postcensal years and lower for intercensal years.

Current estimates of the nation's population are made by the Bureau of the Census by adding the differences between births and deaths and between immigration and emigration to the last census population. For states and other large population groups, current (postcensal) estimates can be made on a proportionate basis, by assuming, for example, that the local increase equals the national increase times the ratio of the local to the national intercensal increase.

b. Forecasts for the period of design. Long-range forecasts of population differ appreciably from postcensal estimates in their method of attacking the problem. Instead of dealing with the results of the last two censuses only, the full record of population growth is quite generally employed, in order to identify the long-term swing rather than short-term fluctuations. Forecasting methods include especially (1) mathematical curve fitting, and (2) graphical studies.

S-shaped curves, like the growth curve, can be described by a number of different equations that seek a rational biological basis for their selection. One of the best known is the *logistic* curve of Verhulst.[5] Ordinarily, mathematical curve fitting is of most value in the study of large population groups, or nations.

Plots of population against time generally exhibit trends that are readily sketched in by eye. In the hands of a skilled interpreter of population growth this extension of the population curve will yield forecasts that are reasonably close to actual experience. For this reason, graphical forecasts are much used by engineers. In extending the population curve, judgment is sometimes aided by sketching in the growth experience of similar, but larger, communities that have reached the last census figure of the population under consideration in the not too distant past (see Figure 2-2).[6] It should be realized, how-

[5] See Raymond Pearl, *Medical Biometry and Statistics*, W. B. Saunders Co., Philadelphia, Chapter 18, 1940.

[6] The populations recorded in Figure 2-2 are those of *A*, Hartford, Conn.; *B*, Columbus, Ohio; *C*, Providence, R. I.; and *D*, Newark, N. J.; all prior to 1930.

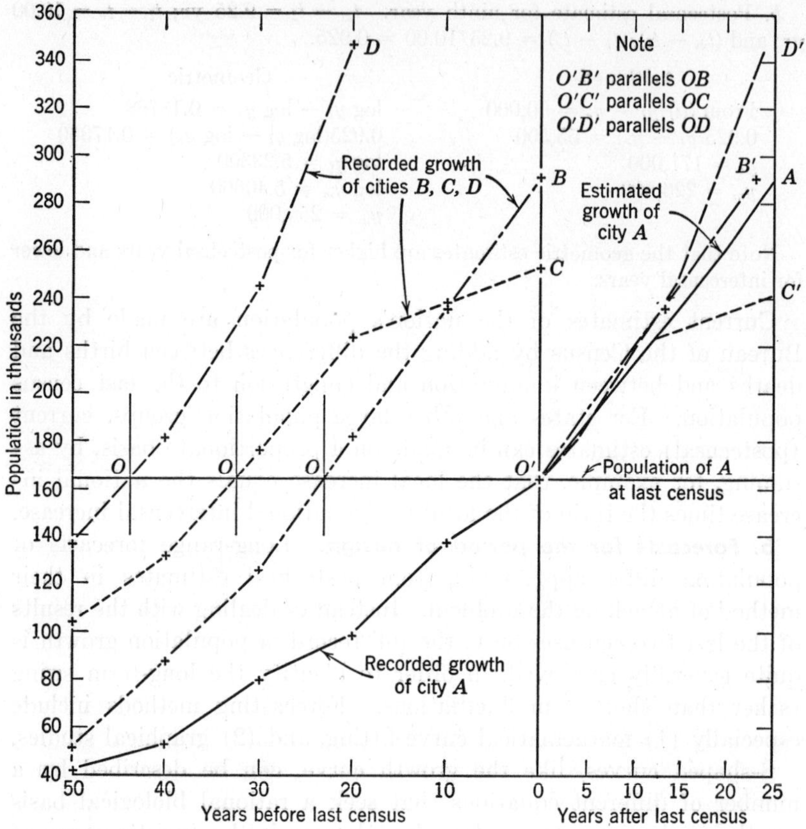

Figure 2-2. Graphical estimation of growth of a city by comparison with past growth of similar but larger cities.

ever, that the historical periods involved in such a comparison are quite unlike and that the future development of a community of a given size may be very different from the past development of a like community of similar size.

A somewhat different method for forecasting population involves the projection into the future, not of the growth curve, but of its first derivative, the rate-of-growth curve. For convenience the rate of growth is then generally expressed as the intercensal percentage increase in population, adjusted if necessary to account for variations in census dates. Comparisons can again be made with the rate of growth of other, larger populations. Plotting rate of growth against population density provides additional information. Forecasts of future population, like postcensal forecasts, can also be proportioned to national estimates made by the Bureau of the Census.[7]

Arithmetic scales are most generally useful in plotting population data. A logarithmic (geometric) scale for the population or rate of growth, however, often straightens out the curve and aids in its projection.

2-5. Population Distribution or Density. Distribution of water and collection of sewage within a community require estimates of the density of the population and the nature of occupancy or the use of the different types of areas that compose the community. For these purposes, population density is generally expressed as the number of persons per acre. A classification of areas and expected population densities is shown in Table 2-2.

TABLE 2-2. Common Population Densities

	Persons Per Acre
1. Residential areas	
a. Single-family dwellings, large lots	5–15
b. Single-family dwellings, small lots	15–35
c. Multiple-family dwellings	35–100
d. Apartment or tenement houses	100–1,000
2. Mercantile and commercial areas	15–30
3. Industrial areas	5–15
4. Total, exclusive of parks, playgrounds, and cemeteries	10–50

Values of this kind are determined by an analysis of the present and possible future subdivision of typical blocks. Census data on population distribution within communities may be had for the larger cities of the United States from an analysis of census tract reports; for the smaller cities, from an analysis of ward reports.

Water Consumption

2-6. Uses and Averages. Service pipes deliver water to dwellings, mercantile or commercial properties, industrial establishments, and public buildings. The water used is classified accordingly. The quantities delivered in North American communities approximate the values shown in Table 2-3, with wide variations to be expected because of differences in (1) climate, (2) standard of living, (3) extent of

[7] See Robert C. Schmitt, Forecasting population by the ratio method, *J. Am. Water Works Assoc.*, *46*, 960 (1954).

TABLE 2-3. Normal Water Consumption

Class of Consumption	Quantity, gpcd: Normal Range	Average
Domestic or residential	20–80	50
Commercial	10–130	20
Industrial	20–80	50
Public	5–20	10
Water unaccounted for	5–30	10
Total	60–240	140

sewerage, (4) type of mercantile, commercial, and industrial activity, (5) cost of water, (6) availability of private water supplies, (7) quality of water for domestic, industrial, and other uses, (8) pressure in the distribution system, (9) completeness of meterage, and (10) management of the system.

Extremes of heat and cold increase water consumption: hot and arid climates by more bathing, air conditioning, and irrigation; cold climates by water being bled through faucets in order to keep service pipes and building distribution systems from freezing. Higher standards of cleanliness, larger numbers of plumbing fixtures, and more lawn and garden sprinkling, car washing, and air conditioning, associated with greater wealth, result in heavier use of water. Certain commercial enterprises, like hotels and restaurants, use more water than others; so do industrial establishments [8] like breweries, canneries, laundries, paper mills, railroad yards, and steel mills.

The lower the cost of water, the higher, ordinarily, is its consumption, particularly for industrial purposes. Rough rules based upon an analysis of North American experience are (1) that consumption varies inversely as the water rate for manufacturing purposes, and (2) that an increase in rates reduces consumption by about one-half the percentage increase in rates.

Use of the public supply is encouraged when the water delivered is clean, palatable, and of unquestioned safety for drinking and culinary uses; when it is soft for washing and cool for condensing purposes; and when it meets the quality standards of industry. Poor water drives consumers to private, sometimes dangerous, sources. The flow of water through faucets and similar outlets, as well as through leaks in mains and faulty plumbing, is akin to flow through an orifice and so varies about as the square root of the pressure head. In distribu-

[8] Industrial water requirements are discussed in Chapter 20.

tion systems, therefore, high pressures result (1) in rapid discharge of fixtures and increased waste of water, and (2) in increased leakage. Operating pressures in excess of about 60 psig are no longer as important for fire fighting as they were before the advent of the motor pumper.

Introduction of meterage encourages thrift and normalizes the demand. The cost of metering water, including the reading and repair of the meter, is substantial. The cost of meterage, therefore, must be balanced against the value of the water made available by reduction of waste. In some instances this reduction may permit the postponement of otherwise needed extension of, or addition to, the existing supply.

There is some leakage from all distribution systems. In a well-managed system, leakage is checked carefully and continuously. Controllable leakage is detected in various ways: (1) observation of water running in gutters, moist pavement, persistent seepage, excessive flow in sewers, abnormal drop in pressure, and unusually green vegetation (in dry climates); (2) use of sounding rods driven into the ground to test for moist earth; (3) employment of devices that report the sound of running water; (4) inspection of premises for leaky plumbing; and (5) water-waste surveys that involve isolating comparatively small sections of the system by closing valves on mains that supply these sections and measuring the water flowing to them, usually through a single connection and at night, by means of (*a*) Pitot tubes, (*b*) by-pass meters around the controlling valves, or (*c*) meters on one or more hose lines between hydrants that straddle a closed valve.

As North American cities grow, their per capita use of water commonly increases by about one-tenth the percentage increase in population. If a city increases its population by 50%, therefore, water consumption per person is expected to rise by 5%. Water uses for summer air conditioning will undoubtedly mount in the future. The expanding use of dishwashers, automatic home laundries, and garbage grinders, too, will produce further increases in the per capita rate of consumption.

The quantities of water used under rural conditions and the resulting amounts of waste water vary in magnitude from the values common to urban areas to much smaller amounts. The minimum use of piped water in dwellings is about 20 gpcd, the average about 50 gpcd. The water requirements of rural schools, overnight camps, and rural factories (excluding manufacturing uses) are about 25 gpcd, of restaurants about 10 gpcd on a patronage basis, and of work or construction camps about 45 gpcd. By contrast, resort hotels need about 100 gpcd and rural sanatoria or hospitals about twice this amount.

On farms, livestock and irrigation needs are additional. The drinking-water requirements of farm animals vary from 20 gpcd for dairy cows and 12 gpcd for horses, mules, and steers, to 4 gpcd for hogs and 2 gpcd for sheep. Chickens consume but 0.04 gpcd and turkeys but 0.07 gpcd. The over-all water requirements for dairy cows, including water for cleansing and cooling, are about 35 gpcd. Greenhouses may need as much as 70 gpd per 1,000 sq ft, and garden crops about half this amount.

Military water requirements vary from an absolute minimum of 0.5 gpcd for troops in combat through 2 to 5 gpcd for troops on the march or in bivouac and 15 gpcd for troops in temporary camps up to 50 or more gpcd for permanent military installations.

The quantities of waste water are of the same order of magnitude, but due allowance must be made for waters that do not reach the waste-disposal system.

2-7. Variations in Demand. Water consumption changes with the seasons, with the days of the week, and with the hours of the day. The smaller the community, the greater, in general, is the variation in its demand for water. The shorter the period of flow, furthermore, the greater is the departure from the average. For purposes of comparison, these variations are expressed as ratios to the average demand. The following values are indicated by experience:

Ratio	Normal Range	Average
Maximum day:average day	(From 1.2 to 2.0):1	1.5:1
Maximum hour:average hour	(From 2.0 to 3.0):1	2.5:1

The rate at which water should be supplied to extinguish fires and prevent conflagrations is determined by factors such as the bulk, congestion, fire resistance, and content of buildings. In North America, the protection of property against fire is the purpose of the National Board of Fire Underwriters, a fact-finding organization supported by fire-insurance companies. Among many other activities, this board grades public water supplies on adequacy for fire protection.[9] Careful and continuing analyses of water demands experienced during fires have led this organization to formulate general standards from which

[9] *Standard Schedule for Grading Cities and Towns of the United States,* National Board of Fire Underwriters, New York, 1956.

the designer should depart only after careful study and for good and sufficient reasons. Standard fire flows take into account probable loss of water from connections that are broken during a large fire. The general requirements of the National Board are summarized in Chapter 7.

It is hardly conceivable that the maximum rate of draft of water for general community purposes will be exerted at the same time as a serious conflagration is being fought. For this reason the coincident draft during fire fighting need not be assumed to equal the maximum hourly rate. A value in excess of the average daily rate, such as the maximum daily rate (150% of the average), appears to be reasonable.

Example 2-2. The four typical water-works systems shown in Figure 2-3 serve a community with an estimated future population of 100,000. Determine the required capacities of their constituent structures for an average water consumption of 100 gpcd and a distributing reservoir so sized that it can provide enough water to care for differences between hourly and daily flows, fire demands, and emergency water requirements. Fundamental calculations are:

a. Average daily draft $= 100 \times 100{,}000/1{,}000{,}000 = 10$ mgd.
b. Maximum daily draft = coincident draft $= 1.5 \times 10 = 15$ mgd.
c. Maximum hourly draft $= 2.5 \times 10 = 25$ mgd.
d. Fire flow to high-value district $= 1{,}020\sqrt{100}\,(1 - 0.01\sqrt{100}) = 9{,}180$ gpm, or $9.180 \times 1.44 = 13.2$ mgd; see Section 7-2.
e. Coincident draft plus fire flow $= 15.0 + 13.2 = 28.2$ mgd > item *c*.
f. Provisions for breakdowns and repairs of pumps, and water purification units by installing at least one reserve unit give the following capacities:
Low-lift pumps: $2 \times$ average daily draft $= 2.0 \times 10 = 20$ mgd.
High-lift pumps: $3 \times$ average daily draft $= 3.0 \times 10 = 30$ mgd.
Filters and the like: $1.6 \times$ average daily draft $= 1.6 \times 10 = 16$ mgd.
The resulting capacities of the four systems shown in Figure 2-3 are summarized below that figure.

The rates of water use and waste-water production under rural conditions are determined by the water requirements and discharge capacities of different fixtures.

Waste-Water Flows

2-8. Sources of Flow and Averages. The flow in sewers includes one or more of the following: the spent water of the community, ground-water seepage,[10] and storm-water runoff.

[10] Also called infiltration, but usually identified as seepage in this book.

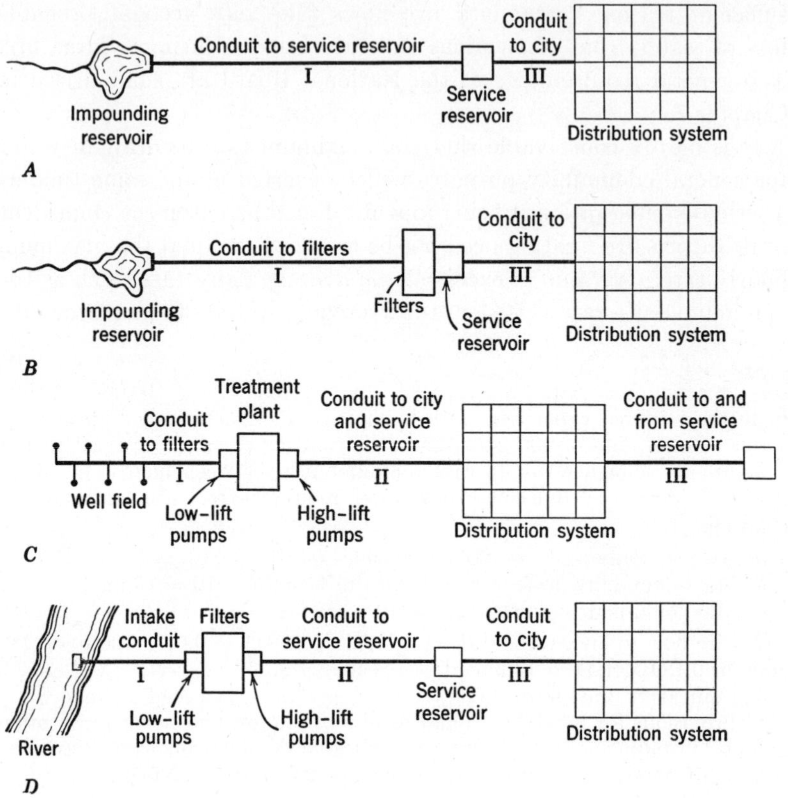

Figure 2-3. Capacity requirements for the constituent structures of four typical water-works systems. The service reservoir is assumed to take care of hourly fluctuations, fire drafts, and emergency reserve.

Structure	Required capacity	Capacity of system, mgd A	B	C	D
1. River or well field	Maximum day	....	....	15.0	15.0
2. Conduit I	Maximum day	15.0	15.0	15.0	15.0
3. Conduit II		....	....	....	15.0
4. Conduit III	Coincident draft and fire	28.2	28.2	28.2	28.2
5. Low-lift pumps	Maximum day plus reserve	....	....	20.0	20.0
6. High-lift pumps	Maximum day plus reserve	....	....	30.0	30.0
7. Filters or treatment plant	Maximum day plus reserve	....	16.0	16.0	16.0
8. Distribution system to high-value district	Coincident draft and fire	28.2	28.2	28.2	28.2

a. Spent water. The spent water of the community is that portion of the public supply which is discharged into sewers from the collecting systems of all types of buildings. Water drawn from private water sources for air conditioning, industrial processes, and similar uses may also become spent water. Ordinarily, 60 to 70% of the total water supplied becomes waste water. The remainder is used up in watering lawns and gardens, flushing streets, fighting fires, generating steam, and satisfying miscellaneous household, commercial, and industrial needs. Commercial areas may be assumed to discharge about 25,000 gpd per acre. Industrial waste waters vary widely in quantity.

b. Ground water. Water enters street and building sewers from the ground through joints and manholes that are not watertight and through cracks in the pipes. The amount of seepage depends upon the height of the ground-water table above the invert of the sewers, the permeability of the soil, and the workmanship exercised in the construction of manholes and sewers as well as their connections to buildings. Seepage rates are stated in various ways to suit the convenience of the designer. Common allowances are:

A: 500 to 5,000 gpd per acre; average 2,000.
B: 5,000 to 100,000 gpd per mile of sewer; average 30,000.
C: 500 to 5,000 gpd per mile of sewer per inch diameter (average 2,500) plus 100 gpd per manhole.

These allowances can be explained in terms of rainfall, infiltration into the ground, and area drained. Conversion from A to B follows from the length of sewers per acre in North American communities (namely, 115 ft for average development and 300 ft for full development), the diameter of the sewer (normally about 12 in.), and the spacing of manholes (generally less than 400 ft).

Example 2-3. Find A, B, and C for an annual rainfall of 48 in., one-half of which filters into the ground and eventually reaches the sewers.

$A = 48 \times 1/2 \times 1/12 \times 43{,}560 \times 7.5/365 = 1{,}800$ gpd per acre.

$B = 1{,}800 \times 5{,}280/300 = 32{,}000$ gpd per mile for full development.

For a 12-in. sewer and $5{,}280/350 = 15$ manholes per mile, $C = (32{,}000 - 15 \times 100)/12 = 2{,}500$ gpd per mile per inch diameter.

No allowance is made for seepage when sewers are provided with underdrains that have a free outlet. The amount of seepage is determined by gaging sewers in the early morning hours and making an allowance for the small quantities of spent water received at that time. The initial tightness of the system is established by gagings made before properties are connected to the sewers.

c. Storm water. Runoff from precipitation is intended to be discharged into storm drains or combined sewers. The amounts received are large and overshadow the flow of sanitary sewage in combined systems. Separate sanitary sewers should be free of storm water but are not. Illicit connections and manhole covers that are not tight permit entrance of some runoff. Amounts vary with the degree of enforcement of regulations and the effectiveness of countermeasures. Rates up to 70 gpcd and averaging 30 gpcd are reported. Gagings of flows in sanitary sewers will record illicit storm water as the difference between the normal dry-weather flow and the discharge immediately following intense rains.

2-9. Variations in Flow. The rate of flow in storm and combined sewers is determined by the rate of runoff from precipitation. In sanitary sewers, flow varies with water consumption, but fluctuations are smaller for the following reasons: (1) only a portion of the sewage is derived from the water supply; (2) fluctuations of this portion are damped by the seepage of a relatively steady amount of ground water; and (3) open-channel flow in sewers creates further damping effects. Rising waters are stored and falling waters are supplemented by release of stored water. The instantaneous flow at a given point, finally, is a composite of upstream waters that were discharged at time intervals increasing with the distance from the given point. The resulting *time of concentration* produces an averaging of peak discharges analogous to that associated with flood flows in rivers and storm sewers. Hence some formulations of expected variations in flow are like flood-flow formulas (Section 3-16). The Maryland Department of Health, for example, has proposed design flows for sanitary sewers of:

$$Q = 3.2Q_{\mathrm{ave}}^{5/6} \qquad 2\text{-}7$$

where Q is the design flow and Q_{ave} the average flow (1 to 16 mgd). Wider variations in flow are expected, therefore, from small areas or small numbers of people than from large ones. Harmon [11] has generalized North American experience as follows:

$$Q_{\mathrm{max}}/Q_{\mathrm{ave}} = (18 + \sqrt{P})/(4 + \sqrt{P}) \qquad 2\text{-}8$$

where Q_{max} is the maximum rate of flow of domestic sewage, Q_{ave} is the average rate of flow of domestic sewage, and P is the population

[11] W. G. Harmon, Forecasting sewage discharge at Toledo, *Eng. News-Rec.*, *80*, 1235 (1918).

in thousands. Other ratios, frequently used for the flow of domestic sewage from small areas, are:

Maximum daily flow = 2 × average daily flow.

Maximum hourly flow = 1.5 × maximum daily flow = 3 × average daily flow.

Example 2-4. Estimate the average and peak rates of flow in a district sanitary sewer serving 9,000 people in a community of 45,000 with an average water consumption of 140 gpcd and draining an area of 600 acres.

a. Spent water: 0.7 × 140 = 100 gpcd.

b. Maximum hour: 3 × 100 = 300 gpcd. By Equation 2-8, $Q_{\max} = 100[(18 + \sqrt{9})/(4 + \sqrt{9})] = 300$.

c. Proportion of total population served: 100 × 9,000/45,000 = 20%.

d. Average population density: 9,000/600 = 15 persons per acre.

e. Storm water: 30 gpcd (assumed).

f. Infiltration: 2,000 gpd per acre (assumed).

g. Average rate of flow: 15(100 + 30) + 2,000 = 4,000 gpd per acre, if storm water is included.

h. Peak rate of flow: 15(300 + 30) + 2,000 = 7,000 gpd per acre.

In sanitary and combined sewers, the minimum flow is fully as significant as the maximum flow, because velocities are decreased as flows drop off and the sewers may then be unable to meet their main responsibility: the removal of waste matters without nuisance caused by the deposition and decomposition of suspended solids and the clogging of the system. Expressed as ratios to the average, minimum hourly flows may be expected to be about as follows:

Minimum daily flow = ⅔ × average daily flow.

Minimum hourly flow = ½ × minimum daily flow = ⅓ × average daily flow.

3 Hydrology

3-1. The Cycle of Water. Hydrology[1] is the science or classified body of knowledge pertaining to the properties, distribution, and behavior of water in nature. As such, it is a basic science for water supply and waste-water disposal.

The study of hydrology may be divided into three branches that treat of water in its different forms above, on, and below the earth's surface: (1) atmospheric water or precipitation, (2) surface water or runoff, and (3) subsurface water or percolation.

Precipitation, runoff, and percolation are stages in the cycle of water, which is without beginning or end. Of the water precipitating upon the earth, part falls directly upon water surfaces; part flows over the surface of the ground and finds its way into brooks and rivers, and into ponds, lakes, and reservoirs, or into the ocean; and part percolates into the ground. In addition, part is immediately returned to the atmosphere by evaporation from water surfaces, land surfaces, and vegetation.

Of the water that soaks into the ground, part is held by capillarity near the surface, some of it ultimately evaporating directly from the ground into the atmosphere, and some being taken up by vegetation to be returned in large measure to the atmosphere by transpiration.[2]

[1] From the Greek words *hydōr*, water, and *logos*, science.

[2] Transpiration is evaporation or exhalation of water or water vapor from plant cells, such as leaf cells. It corresponds to perspiration in animals. The term evapotranspiration is used to describe all water lost to the atmosphere, whether by evaporation, transpiration, or other processes.

The remainder of the infiltering water passes through the soil until it meets and forms part of the underlying ground water. Most of the ground water is eventually discharged at the surface of the earth as springs or seepage outcrops, or passes, at or below the water line, into streams and standing bodies of water, including the oceans.

The water flowing in brooks and rivers is known as *runoff*. It is derived either directly from precipitation as surface runoff or indirectly as dry-weather flow from the lowering of lakes, ponds, and reservoirs, and from ground-water seepage.

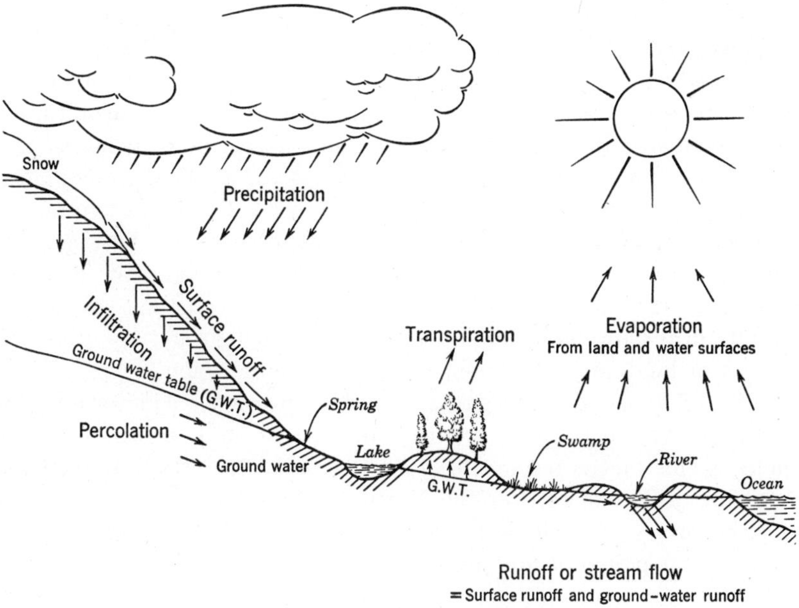

Figure 3-1. The water cycle.

Figure 3-1 shows diagrammatically the various phases of the cycle of water. Evaporation and precipitation are the driving forces in the cycle of water, with solar radiation as the source of energy. Runoff and percolation shift the scene of evaporation, or upward motion of water, laterally along the earth's surface. Atmospheric circulation accomplishes a similar shift for precipitation.

3-2. Causes of Precipitation. Atmospheric moisture reaches the earth's surface chiefly in the form of precipitation as rain, snow, hail, or sleet. The most important causes of precipitation are external and dynamic cooling. By dynamic cooling is meant the reduction in temperature accompanying the expansion of air when it rises or is driven to higher altitudes.

The upward movement of moist air essential to precipitation is brought about in three principal ways: (1) by convective currents which cause *convective* rainfalls; (2) by hills and mountain ranges which produce *orographic* rainfall; and (3) by cyclonic circulation which is responsible for *cyclonic* rainfall.

Convective precipitation is exemplified by the so-called tropical rainstorm in which warm, moist air rises almost vertically to altitudes of lower temperature and pressure. Orographic precipitation is encountered when horizontal currents of moist air strike hills or mountain ranges that deflect the currents upward. Cyclonic precipitation is associated with the unequal heating of the earth's surface and the creation of pressure differences that cause air to flow from points of higher pressure to points of lower pressure. There are two major temperature effects: (1) the difference in temperature between the equator and the poles, which produces so-called planetary circulation; and (2) the unequal heating of land and water masses, which results in the formation of secondary areas of high and low pressure on sea or land and consequent atmospheric circulation.

The difference in relative rotary speed between the equator and the poles deflects to the east tropical air currents moving towards the poles. This fact is responsible for the general easterly movement of cyclonic disturbances over the North American continent as well as for the rotary or cyclonic motion of the horizontal air currents that converge at points of low pressure.

In the continuous planetary circulation of the atmosphere between the equator and the poles, warm, moisture-laden, tropical air masses travel towards the poles, are cooled, precipitate their moisture, and are ultimately transformed into cold, dry, polar air. A return movement carries heavy, polar air masses towards the equator. Heaviest precipitation takes place when tropical air masses collide with polar air masses. The light, warm, tropical air is forced up and over the colder air, cools, and precipitates its moisture. Collisions between tropical and polar air masses normally produce the protracted general rainfalls and the accompanying floods of the central and eastern United States. When, for unknown reasons, polar air does not move southward in the usual manner, there may be serious droughts.

Commonly the three types of precipitation—convective, orographic, and cyclonic—do not occur independently. Most precipitation in the temperate regions of the earth results from the combined activity of two or more causative agents.

About one-fourth to one-third of the water that falls on continental areas reaches the oceans as runoff. The balance is returned to the air by evaporation and transpiration. Of this vaporized water, a small part is reprecipitated, but the major part is carried away to the oceans. The streamflow from continents represents the net water loss from the circulating air masses as they precipitate and re-evaporate moisture in their course across the continents.

3-3. Measurement of Precipitation. Of the many thousands of stations of the U. S. Weather Bureau, all but a few hundred are "cooperative observer" stations at which only limited records are kept. At these stations, rainfall is measured in cylindrical can gages, 2 ft high and 8 in. in diameter (see Figure 3-2). A funnel-shaped receiver concentrates the catch in a collecting tube which is so proportioned that a depth of 1 in. on a measuring stick inserted in the tube equals 0.1 in. of rainfall.

At the official Weather Bureau stations, recording gages are used. These register rainfall rates as well as quantities of precipitation. Rainfall rates need to be known in the design of storm sewerage systems, and continuous rainfall records are essential in forecasting flood stages on streams. The two types of continuous-recording gages shown in Figure 3-2 are in common use.

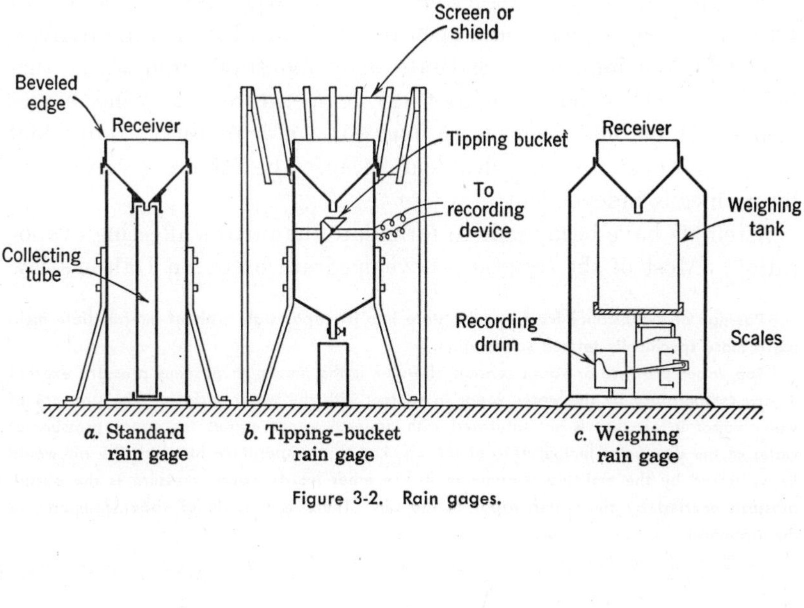

Figure 3-2. Rain gages.

Snowfall is measured with the standard rain gage by removing the receiving funnel and using the can after the fashion of a "cookie cutter" to collect samples of snow from undrifted areas. The snow is melted by the addition of a known amount of warm water, and the quantity of precipitation is recorded in inches of water. The water equivalent of snow varies greatly. On an average, 10 in. of snow equal 1 in. of water.

In regions where melting of the winter's accumulation of snow produces a major part of the annual runoff, or where spring thaws may cause serious floods, more accurate methods for determining the snowfall on a water shed are desirable. Two methods have been developed. The older one is to select representative sampling stations along a snow course laid out across the drainage area. An observer walks the course periodically and samples the snow blanket at each station with a hollow-tube collector. The water content of the sample is determined by weighing it or by melting the snow. In the newer methods, batteries of shielded snow gages are used. Four or five of these gages are spaced some 200 or 300 ft apart in a location that is typical of average conditions on the water shed.

3-4. Evaporation. Evaporation is the process by which water passes from the liquid or solid [3] state into the vapor state. By evaporation, water is lost from water surfaces and moist earth surfaces. This is of importance in determining the storage requirements for impounding reservoirs and in estimating the losses of water from lakes, ponds, and open reservoirs, and from swamp areas.

The factors influencing the rate of evaporation from water surfaces are: (1) vapor pressure,[4] (2) temperature, (3) wind movements, (4) barometric pressure, and (5) water quality. Individual effects, however, are not clear cut because the factors involved are by no means independent.

Attempts have been made to formulate the factors affecting evaporation. Most of the equations developed are based on Dalton's law

[3] Passage of a substance from its solid state into its vapor state without intermediate melting is more specifically termed *sublimation*.

[4] The vapor pressure or vapor tension of water is the maximum gaseous pressure exerted at any temperature by the water vapor in contact with the water surface. The pressure of water vapor in air that is not saturated with aqueous vapor equals the vapor pressure of water at the dew-point temperature of the air, i.e., the temperature at which the air would be saturated by the moisture actually in it. In other words, vapor pressure is the partial pressure exerted by the water vapor in the air. There is a table of vapor pressures in the Appendix.

and include a wind factor and sometimes a pressure factor. A typical formula [5] is:

$$E = C(V - v)[1 + (w/K)][1 - (p/k)] \qquad 3\text{-}1$$

where E is the evaporation in a given interval of time; V is the vapor pressure at the water temperature; v is the vapor pressure at the dew-point temperature of the air; w is the wind velocity; p is the barometric pressure; and C, K, and k are coefficients.

In Rohwer's formula,[6] pressures are expressed in inches of mercury, wind velocity in miles per hour, evaporation in inches per 30-day month; and C, K, and k have magnitudes of 15, 3.7, and 79, respectively.

Example 3-1. Estimate the evaporation for a month during which the following averages obtain: water temperature = 60 F; maximum vapor pressure $V = 0.52$ in.; air temperature = 80 F; relative humidity = 40%; vapor pressure $v = 1.03 \times 0.40 = 0.41$ in.; wind velocity $w = 8$ mph; and barometric pressure = 30 in.

By Equation 3-1, $E = 15(0.52 - 0.41)(1 + 2.2)(1 - 0.38) = 3.3$ in.

Evaporation from surfaces of snow and ice proceeds much as it does from water surfaces. At temperatures below freezing, the wind factor seems to be particularly important.

Evaporation from land surfaces is of two types: (1) rapid evaporation from recently wetted surfaces and (2) relatively slow evaporation from moist soil.

Much larger volumes of water are returned to the atmosphere over continents by transpiration than by evaporation. There are two reasons for this: (1) the exposed surface area of plant leaves is tremendous as compared with the ground surface and free water surfaces, and (2) plants have the ability to draw water from considerable depths within the soil and yield it to the atmosphere by transpiration.

The effect of vegetation, particularly forest cover, upon the water cycle is the subject of much argument. Such factual data as have been gathered indicate that the effects of different types of vegetal cover, such as grass, brush, and forests, are much the same and that, depending upon the circumstances, the water losses to the atmosphere

[5] There is a second type of equation which relates evaporation to the difference between incoming solar radiation and heat accounted for as back radiation, heat storage in the water, and heat lost in other ways.

[6] C. Rohwer, Evaporation from free water surfaces, *U. S. Dept. Agr. Tech. Bull.* *271*, 78 (1931).

from barren areas may or may not be greater than losses from growth-covered areas. The beneficial effect of vegetal cover in reducing soil erosion is not necessarily related to the effect that growing plants exert upon the water cycle, and the two should not be confused.

3-5. Measurement of Evaporation and Transpiration. Measurements of evaporation from water surfaces, a matter of importance in water-supply studies, are commonly made by exposing pans of water to the air and recording the evaporation losses by systematic observations or by means of self-registering devices. Both floating pans and land pans have been used. The standard equipment adopted by the Weather Bureau consists of a 4-ft galvanized iron pan, 10 in. in depth, exposed on an open platform of spaced 2-in. by 4-in. timbers, raised slightly above ground for circulation of air all around the pan. Typical land and floating pans are illustrated in Figure 3-3. Results are affected by the location of the pan, its area, depth, color, and material. The proportion of lake pan to land pan evaporation is about 0.7:1. In the greater part of the United States, the mean annual evaporation from water surfaces equals or exceeds the mean annual rainfall. Transpiration and evaporation from land surfaces is called *consumptive use.*

3-6. Percolation. The term percolation describes the passage of water into, through, and out of the ground. Water below the surface of the earth is known as subsurface water and is encountered in various conditions shown in Figure 3-4.

Of the different kinds of subsurface water, only ground water, i.e., water in the saturated zone, is available for the development of water supplies from subsurface sources provided that this water will flow in

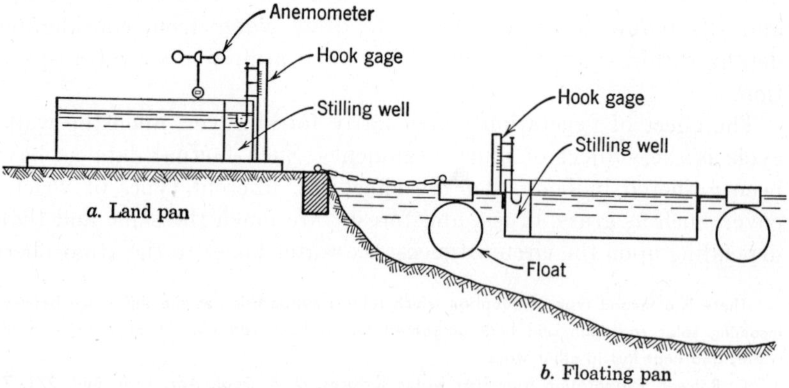

Figure 3-3. Evaporating pans.

Under-Saturated Zone or Zone of Aeration	Soil water is near enough to the surface to be reached by the roots of common plants. Some soil water remains after plants begin to wilt.
	Stored or pellicular water adheres to soil particles and is not moved by gravity.
	Gravity or vadose* water moves down by gravity throughout zone.
Suspended Water	Capillary water occurs only in the capillary fringe at bottom of the zone of aeration.
Saturated Zone Ground Water or Phreatic† Water	Free water occurs below the water table. Movement controlled by the slope of the water table.
	Confined or artesian water occurs beneath a confining stratum. Moves laterally as water in a pressure conduit.
	Fixed ground water occurs in subcapillary openings of clays, silts, etc. Not moved by gravity.
	Connate‡ water entrapped in rocks at the time of their deposition.

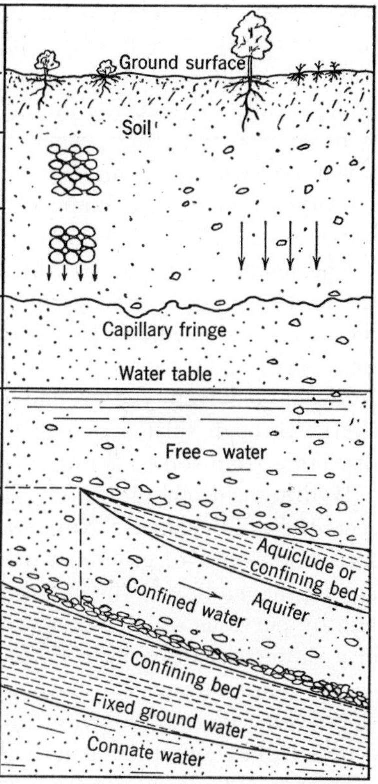

* From the Latin *vadosus* full of something going.
† From the Greek *phreas* a well. ‡ From the Latin *connatus* born together.

Figure 3-4. Occurrence and distribution of subsurface water. After C. F. Tolman, *Ground Water*, McGraw-Hill Book Co., New York, 1937.

adequate quantities into collection works that are economically justified. The penetration of ground water into sewerage systems, called seepage or infiltration, is an element of sewerage design.

Ground water is derived from two sources: (1) precipitation that filters into the ground, or seeps through cracks or solution passages into rock formations, and penetrates deep enough to reach the ground-water table; and (2) surface water from streams, swamps, ponds, lakes, and reservoirs that filters into the ground when the soil is permeable and the elevation of the ground-water table is lower than that of the free water surface.

The water table is the upper limit of the zone of saturation. It is overlain by the capillary fringe in which the water is held by capillary action. The depth of the fringe varies from a foot or so in sand to as much as 10 ft in clay. The fringe is of importance in lifting water to, or close to, the surface. It may be significant in relieving ground water of pollution that spreads out along the water table and is lifted into the fringe, where it is trapped and destroyed. When a water-bearing stratum dips below an impervious stratum, there is no water table, except immediately below the intake area where the water is still free. A piezometric surface is created instead.

The maximum depth to which subsurface water can penetrate in the earth's crust is set by the depth of porous rock. This is estimated at 2 to 8 miles. Below this depth, the pressures are so great that plastic flow closes the interstices. In nature, subsurface water is discharged from the ground in two ways: (1) by hydraulic discharge through springs or seepage outcrops; and (2) by evaporative discharge from soil or through vegetation.

Hydraulic discharge takes place whenever the water table intersects the land surface. Numerous geologic and hydraulic conditions force the return of ground water in the form of springs. Important among them are: (1) the outcropping of an impervious stratum overlain by pervious soil or other water-bearing formations; (2) overflow of a subterranean basin in limestone or lava; (3) leakage from artesian systems through faults that obstruct flow; and (4) steep surface slopes that cut into the water table. Seepage into streams ordinarily occurs throughout their length in humid regions.

Evaporative discharge from soil occurs in much the same way as does evaporation from water surfaces. It is commonly confined to the belt of soil water, but it affects ground water when the capillary fringe reaches the land surface. Transpiration takes place either from the belt of soil water, or from the capillary fringe and, therefore, from ground water when the roots of plants are able to penetrate to it.

Experiments have been made to determine the amount of infiltration into various types of soil supporting different kinds of vegetation. The variables entering into the problem are so many, however, that ground-water flow and yield cannot be predicated upon observations of rainfall. Values in the vicinity of 50% of the rainfall are common. Annual percolation is best expressed in inches, just as rainfall is. The methods available for measuring the flow of ground water are discussed in Chapter 5.

3-7. Runoff. Runoff, or stream flow, is the water that is gathered into rivulets, brooks, and rivers. The water that is derived directly from precipitation and passes over the ground into water courses is known as the *surface, storm,* or *flood runoff.* The surface runoff then consists of the precipitation minus the losses from infiltration, evaporation, and the like. The water that flows in streams during dry spells, or when precipitation takes the form of snow that remains on the ground without melting, is known as the *dry-weather flow* or *runoff.* It is made up of surface water that is discharged gradually from lakes, ponds, swamps, and other backwaters, in which it has accumulated during wet weather, and of ground water that seeps out of the soil into stream beds when the water level of the stream drops below the level of the ground-water table. The dry-weather yield of streams from surface sources comes from *natural storage;* that from the soil, from *ground-water storage.* In some river basins with headwaters at high altitudes, the summer runoff is augmented by waters from melting snowfields. These constitute an additional variety of natural storage. Unless the snow melt, or surface storage, provides water during droughts, streams lying above the ground-water table at all stages of flow are *ephemeral* (short-lived), whereas those lying above the summer ground-water level are *intermittent.*

Runoff studies form the basis for the investigation of surface-water supplies, storm and combined sewerage systems, and waste-water disposal by dilution. Stream-flow data are obtained by various methods of stream gaging, based upon measurements by current meters, floats, weirs, chemical methods, and slope methods.

3-8. Statistical Hydrology. Our knowledge of the laws that govern hydrological phenomena is not sufficient to provide exact solutions for hydrological problems. The best we can do is to estimate future behavior on the basis of past experience. This process requires familiarity with statistical methods and in particular with the analysis of frequency distributions. A frequency distribution is traced by a series of observations arranged in ascending or descending order of magnitude, irrespective of the order of occurrence of individual observations. Such a numerical arrangement is called an array.

It is a curious and important fact that the arrays of many types of observations and measurements trace a bell-shaped curve like that shown in Table 3-1. The tendency of arrays to reach a maximum, mode, or magnitude of greatest frequency is called a central tendency or tendency towards an average value, of which the mode, the arithmetic mean, and the median, or midmost value, are exam-

TABLE 3-1. Short Table of Areas of the Normal Frequency Curve. Values of A/n from the Center out to Stated Values of x/σ

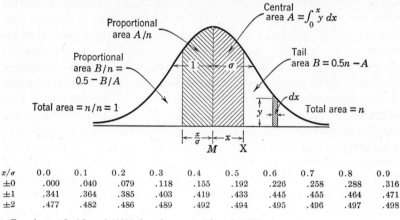

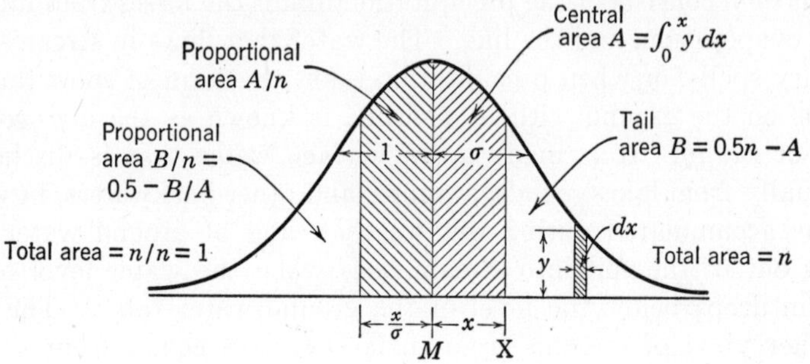

x/σ	0.0	0.1	0.2	0.3	0.4	0.5	0.6	0.7	0.8	0.9
± 0	.000	.040	.079	.118	.155	.192	.226	.258	.288	.316
± 1	.341	.364	.385	.403	.419	.433	.445	.455	.464	.471
± 2	.477	.482	.486	.489	.492	.494	.495	.496	.497	.498

For $x/\sigma = \pm 3$, $A/n = 0.49865$; for $x/\sigma = \pm 4$, $A/n = 0.49997$.

ples. The tendency of arrays to depart or deviate from this central value is called deviation, variability, variation, or scatter. As we shall see, variability is best measured by the standard deviation or root mean square of all the deviations from the mean. The tendency of some arrays to be asymmetric is called skewness. Mathematically, the bell-shaped curve is well described by the equation for the *normal frequency curve*. This curve is also called the Gaussian or normal probability curve. Probability is synonymous with relative frequency. It is the ratio of the number of observations of given magnitude or range in magnitude to the total number of observations in the collection. The normal equation is an integration of the equation $dy/dx = -cxy$ and reads as follows:

$$y = \frac{n}{\sigma\sqrt{2\pi}} e^{-\frac{1}{2}(x/\sigma)^2} \qquad 3\text{-}2$$

where y is the number or frequency of observations of magnitude X; x is the deviation of any magnitude, X, from the central, or arithmetic mean, magnitude M, i.e., $x = X - M$;[7] n is the total number of observations; π and e are well known mathematical constants; $\sigma = \sqrt{\Sigma x^2/(n-1)}$ is the standard deviation from the mean, as meas-

[7] Since the curve is symmetrical, the central magnitude must equal the median and arithmetic mean of all the observations ($M = \Sigma x/n$), and the sum of the deviations from the mean must equal zero ($\Sigma x = 0$).

ured by the distance from the arithmetic mean to the points of inflection of the curve; and y/n is the probability of occurrence of any deviation x. What this equation and the curve it describes say is that most observations are normally crowded around the mean and that fewer and fewer observations depart farther and farther from the mean in a symmetrical fashion.

As derived from Equation 3-2, $\sigma = \sqrt{\Sigma x^2/n}$. This presupposes that the origin of the curve is at the true mean rather than at the calculated mean. However, it can be shown that $\sigma = \sqrt{\Sigma x^2/(n - 1)}$ yields a more probable value when deviations, as they have to be, are measured from the calculated mean. As n becomes large there is little difference between the two expressions.

Examination of Equation 3-2 shows that a normal frequency distribution of n observations is described completely by the arithmetic mean M and the standard deviation σ. To the statistically initiate, therefore, the arithmetic mean and standard deviations are parameters that completely generalize the collection of numerical data analyzed.

Engineers find it generally more convenient to work with the area under the frequency curve rather than the ordinates of the curve. Integration [8] of Equation 3-2 permits the calculation of a generalized table of the areas under the normal frequency distribution (Table 3-1) known as the probability integral table. As suggested by Hazen,[9] this table can be used to develop a system of coordinates on which frequency distributions that are normal will plot as straight lines. The companion scale to the probability scale can be (1) arithmetic, for true Gaussian normality, or (2) logarithmic, for geometric or functional normality. In the first instance, the frequency distribution is fitted by a normal curve when the data, as

[8] Measuring the area A from the center out,

$$A = \int_0^x y\, dx$$

where y has the magnitude shown in Equation 3-2. Replacing $e^{-\frac{1}{2}(x/\sigma)^2}$ by the convergent series:

$$1 - \left(\frac{x}{\sigma\sqrt{2}}\right)^2 + \frac{1}{2!}\left(\frac{x}{\sigma\sqrt{2}}\right)^4 - \frac{1}{3!}\left(\frac{x}{\sigma\sqrt{2}}\right)^6 + \cdots$$

$$\frac{A}{n} = \frac{1}{\sqrt{\pi}}\left[\left(\frac{x}{\sigma\sqrt{2}}\right) - \frac{1}{3}\left(\frac{x}{\sigma\sqrt{2}}\right)^3 + \frac{1}{5 \times 2!}\left(\frac{x}{\sigma\sqrt{2}}\right)^5 - \cdots\right]$$

[9] Allen Hazen, Storage to be provided in impounding reservoirs, *Trans. Am. Soc. Civil Engrs., 77,* 1539 (1914).

observed, are plotted on an arithmetic scale against their cumulative frequency. In the second instance, the observed data do not array themselves in a straight line when they are plotted on an arithmetic scale but their logarithms do, or they themselves do when they are plotted on a logarithmic scale against their cumulative frequency. Logarithmic or geometric normality implies that the observations have a lower limit at or near zero. This is true of many hydrological phenomena.

The position of the straight line of best fit for an arithmetically normal distribution is defined by the following requirements:

1. It must pass through the intersection of the arithmetic mean M with the 50% frequency, since half the observations must lie to either side of the mean and the mean and median are almost of the same magnitude.
2. It must pass through the intersection of $M \pm \sigma$ with the 84.1% and 15.9% frequency respectively, since, in accordance with Table 3-1, 34.1% of the observations must lie within $x/\sigma = 1$ of the mean and $50 \pm 34.1 = 84.1\%$ and 15.9% respectively.

For a geometrically normal distribution the position of the straight line of best fit is defined by the following requirements:

1. It must pass through the intersection of the geometric mean M_g (antilog of the mean of the logarithms of the observations) with the 50% frequency, and the geometric mean and the median are almost identical.
2. It must pass through the intersection of $M_g \times \sigma_g$ (the geometric standard deviation) with the 84.1% and M_g/σ_g with the 15.9% frequency respectively.

In geometric normality, therefore, the logarithms of the observations behave in the same way as the observations themselves do in arithmetic normality.

Plotting data on arithmetic-probability or logarithmic-probability paper will give the following information:

1. Approach to a straight line on arithmetic-probability paper indicates arithmetic normality of the frequency distribution. Departure from a straight line is a sign of skewness. A skewed series may approach a straight line on logarithmic-probability paper.
2. The approximate magnitude of the arithmetic or geometric mean of the series can be read at the 50% frequency from a straight line plotted by eye. However, it will pay to calculate the mean as one point on the fitted straight line and pass the line through it at the 50% frequency.
3. The approximate magnitude of the standard deviation can be found from a reading of $M + \sigma$ or $M_g \times \sigma_g$ at the 84.1% and $M - \sigma$ or M_g/σ_g at the 15.9% frequencies respectively.
4. The expected frequency of any observation of a given magnitude (and vice versa) can be read from the plot.

5. Two or more series plotted to the same scale are readily compared. The ratio of the standard deviation to the mean σ/M, called the coefficient of variation, c_v, is a dimensionless, analytical measure of the relative variability of different series.

3-9. Rainfall and Runoff Analysis. The designer of water-supply and waste-water disposal systems is concerned, in particular, with two types of rainfall and runoff records: (1) records of the amounts of water collected by a given water shed in fixed calendar periods, such as days, weeks, months, and years, and (2) records of the intensities and durations of rainstorms and flood flows in a given drainage area. Studies of the yield of water in different calendar periods underlie the safe and economic development of surface-water supplies by continuous draft and by storage. They cast some light, too, upon the possible production of ground water and are needed in gaging the pollutional load that can safely be imposed upon a body of water into which sewage and industrial wastes are discharged. Studies of rainfall intensities and flood runoff are the starting points for the design of storm and combined sewers and their appurtenances. They provide, too, the information needed for the proper dimensioning of spillways and diversion conduits for dams and similar structures, for the location and protection of water and waste-water works that lie in the flood plains of streams, and for the proper proportioning of works that collect rain water.

3-10. Annual Rainfall and Runoff. Both rainfall and runoff form frequency distributions that are skewed to the right. Skewness is induced by the constraint imposed by a lower limit of annual rainfall or runoff. This limit is generally greater than zero but smaller than the recorded minimum. It stands to reason that there must be an upper limit as well, but its value is less circumscribed than that of the lower limit and, from the standpoint of water supply, also less important. In spite of these acknowledged facts, most records of rainfall and runoff can be generalized with fair success as arithmetically normal series and somewhat better as geometrically normal series. Reasonably accurate comparisons can be had, therefore, in terms of the arithmetic mean M and standard deviation σ or the geometric mean M_g and standard deviation σ_g. For ordinary purposes, mean annual values and coefficients of variation, $c_v = \sigma/M$, will indicate the comparative safe yields of water supplies that are developed with and without storage. Draft is then best expressed for comparative purposes in terms of the mean annual rainfall or runoff, whatever the basis of measurement happens to be.

a. Rainfall. In those portions of the North American continent in which municipal development has taken place on a significant scale, mean annual rainfalls generally exceed 10 in. They range thence to almost 80 in. For the well-watered regions, the coefficient of variation is as low as 0.1; for the arid regions it is as high as 0.5. This means that a deficiency as great as half the mean annual rainfall is expected to occur in the arid regions as often as a deficiency of only one-tenth the mean annual rainfall, or less, in the well-watered ones.[10] High values of c_v, therefore, signify reduced maintainable drafts or increased storage requirements.

b. Runoff. Losses by evaporation and transpiration, together with unrecovered infiltration, reduce the magnitude of annual runoff below that of annual rainfall. So much depends upon the seasonal distribution of rainfall, however, that it is impossible to establish a direct and reliable relationship between the two. There is likewise no direct relationship between their variability. On the North American continent, the mean annual runoff from catchment areas that contribute flow to water supplies ranges from about 5 to 40 in., and the coefficients of variation lie between 0.15 and 0.75. The fact that the mean annual runoff is usually less than half the mean annual rainfall, whereas the variation in stream flow is about half again as great as the variation in precipitation, militates against the establishment of direct runoff-rainfall ratios.

Example 3-2. Analyze the 26-year record of a stream[11] in the northeastern United States and of a rain gage[11] situated in a neighboring valley and covering the identical period of observation (Table 3-2).

a. The arrayed data produce the results shown in Table 3-3.

b. Each year of record covers $100/26 = 3.85\%$ of the experience. The values in each array are plotted on probability paper at $100k/(n+1) = 100k/27\%$ in Figure 3-5. This method of plotting locates identical points whether the left-hand or right-hand scales of the probability paper are employed. Only an arithmetic plot is shown. On it, the arithmetically normal curve of best fit is a straight line, the geometrically normal curve a curved line. The straight line passes through the intersection of the mean with the 50% frequency and through that of $M \pm \sigma$ with the 84.1% or 15.9%

[10] Reference to the probability integral, Table 3-1, will show that deficiencies, or negative deviations from the mean, equal to or greater than $c_v M = \sigma$ are to be expected $50.0 - 34.1 = 15.9\%$ of the time or $1/0.159 =$ once in 6.3 years since $x/\sigma = 1.0$. These calculations, however, are only approximately true because normality is assumed where skewness exists.

[11] The Westfield Little River which supplies water to the city of Springfield, Mass., the rain gage being situated at the West Parish filtration plant. The years of record are 1906 to 1931 (Table 3-2).

TABLE 3-2. Record of Annual Rainfall and Runoff (Example 3-2)

Order of Occurrence	Rainfall, in.	Runoff, in.	Order of Occurrence	Rainfall, in.	Runoff, in.
1	43.6	26.5	14	48.9	25.4
2	53.8	35.5	15	*66.3* (max.)	39.9
3	40.6	28.3	16	42.5	23.3
4	45.3	25.5	17	47.0	26.4
5	*38.9* (min.)	21.4	18	48.0	29.4
6	46.6	25.3	19	41.3	25.5
7	46.6	30.1	20	48.0	23.7
8	46.1	22.7	21	45.5	23.7
9	41.8	20.4	22	59.8	*41.9* (max.)
10	51.0	27.6	23	48.7	32.9
11	47.1	27.5	24	43.3	27.7
12	49.4	21.9	25	41.8	*16.5* (min.)
13	40.2	20.1	26	45.7	23.7

TABLE 3-3. Statistical Parameters of Rainfall and Runoff (Example 3-2)

	Rainfall	Runoff	Runoff-Rainfall Ratio, %
1. Length of record, n, yr	26	26	. . .
2. Arithmetic mean, M, in.	46.8	26.6	57
3. Median, M_d, in.	46.3	25.5	55
4. Geometric mean, M_g, in.	46.5	26.1	56
5. Arithmetic standard deviation, σ, in.	6.0	5.8	97
6. Coefficient of variation, c_v, %	12.9	21.8	169
7. Geometric standard deviation, σ_g	1.13	1.24	110

value. The curve of geometric normality is traced by values read from a similar straight line of best fit passing through M_g at 50% and through $M_g \times \sigma_g$ at 84.1% and M_g/σ_g at 15.9% on logarithmic-probability paper.

c. Examination of the results and the plot (Figure 3-5) shows the following:

1. Both records are fitted approximately by an arithmetically normal distribution and somewhat better by a geometrically normal distribution.

2. A little over half the annual rainfall appears as stream flow. The range of recovery is from 39 to 70%.

3. Runoff is more variable than rainfall; about 1.7 times as much, as measured by c_v.

4. The probable lower limits of rainfall and runoff are fairly well defined by the plot, namely 30 in. for rainfall and 10 in. for runoff.

5. The magnitudes of maximum and minimum yields expected once in 2, 5, 10, 20, 50, and 100 years, i.e., 50, 20, 10, 5, 2, and 1% of the time, as read from the curves of best fit, are summarized in Table 3-4.

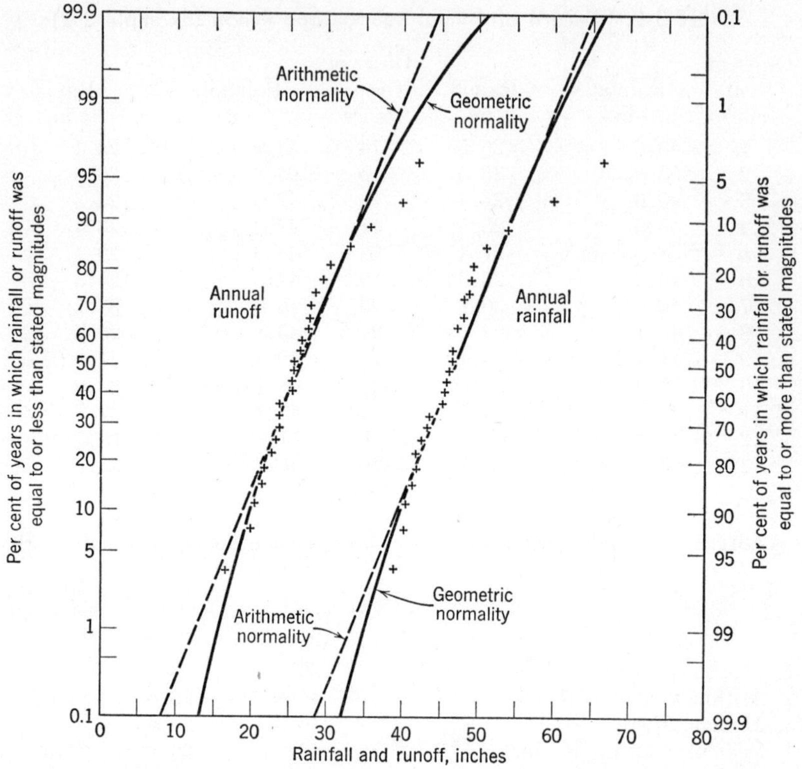

Figure 3-5. Frequency distribution of annual rainfall and runoff plotted on arithmetic-probability paper.

TABLE 3-4. Expected Rainfall and Runoff Frequencies (Example 3-2)

Maximum values may be exceeded, minimum values may not be reached.

Frequency, once in stated number of years	By Arithmetic Normality				By Geometric Normality			
	Rainfall, in.		Runoff, in.		Rainfall, in.		Runoff, in.	
	Max.	Min.	Max.	Min.	Max.	Min.	Max.	Min.
2	47	47	27	27	47	47	26	26
5	52	42	31	22	52	42	32	22
10	54	39	34	19	54	40	35	20
20	56	37	35	17	56	38	37	18
50	59	35	39	15	59	36	41	17
100	60	33	40	13	61	35	43	16

3-11. Storm Rainfall. Storms sweeping over the country deposit their moisture in fluctuating amounts during different intervals of time and over varying areas. For a particular storm, a recording rain gage measures the quantity of precipitation collected in specified intervals of time at the point at which the gage is situated. Even if it is placed within the catchment or drainage area under investigation, the gage can reflect but imperfectly the conditions of precipitation that prevail over all portions of the area, especially if the area is large. As usual in such circumstances, reliance must be placed upon the statistical averaging of experience to offset individual departures from the norm. Given the records of one or more recording rain gages within or reasonably near the area studied, it is found that rainfall varies in intensity (1) during the course or duration of individual storms; (2) throughout the area covered by individual storms; and (3) from storm to storm. These variations establish respectively: (1) the time-intensity, or intensity-duration relationship of individual storms; (2) the areal distribution of individual storms; and (3) the frequency of storms of specified intensity and duration.

3-12. Intensity of Storms. The intensity, or rate, of rainfall is conveniently expressed in inches per hour; and it happens that an inch of water distributed over an acre in an hour equals closely a cubic foot per second. The most intense rainfall frequently occurs near the beginning of the storm; but it may be experienced at any time during the progress of the storm. By convention, the storm intensity is expressed as the arithmetic mean rate of precipitation during a specified period. This makes it a progressive mean covering increasing periods of time. The intensity is highest for short periods and declines steadily with the length of the period to which the mean is applied. Analysis of time-intensity relationships is illustrated in Example 3-3.

Example 3-3. Given a rain-gage record for successive periods of a storm,[12] find the arithmetic mean rate, or intensity, of precipitation for various durations. The gage record is shown in Columns 1 and 2 of Table 3-5. The necessary calculations are added in Columns 3 to 7. It should be noted that Columns 5 to 7 are independent of the preceding Columns.

In this example the maximum rate of rainfall was experienced during the 5-min interval between the 30th and 35th minute.

3-13. Frequency of Intense Storms. The greater the intensity of storms, the rarer is their occurrence or the lesser their frequency. The highest intensity of specified duration that is reported in a station record of n years has a frequency of once in n years and is called the

[12] Storm of October 27–28, 1908, at Jupiter, Fla.

TABLE 3-5. Time and Intensity of a Storm Rainfall (Example 3-3)

Rain-Gage Record				Time-Intensity Relationship		
Time from Beginning of Storm, min (1)	Cumulative Rainfall, in. (2)	Time Interval, min (3)	Rainfall during Interval, in. (4)	Duration of Rainfall, min (5)	Maximum Total Rainfall, in. (6)	Arithmetic Mean Intensity, in. per hr (7)
5	0.31	5	0.31	5	0.54	6.48
10	0.62	5	0.31	10	1.07	6.42
15	0.88	5	0.26	15	1.54	6.16
20	1.35	5	0.47	20	1.82	5.46
25	1.63	5	0.28	30	2.55	5.10
30	2.10	5	0.47	45	3.40	4.53
35	2.64	5	0.54	60	3.83	3.83
40	3.17	5	0.53	80	4.15	3.11
45	3.40	5	0.23	100	4.41	2.65
50	3.66	5	0.26	120	4.59	2.30
60	3.83	10	0.17			
80	4.15	20	0.32			
100	4.41	20	0.26			
120	4.59	20	0.18			

Column 6 records maximum rainfall in stated consecutive periods. The magnitudes are obtained from Column 4 by finding the value, or combination of consecutive values, that produces the largest rainfall for the indicated period. Column 7 = Column 6 × 60/Column 5.

n-year storm. The next highest value has a frequency of twice in n years or once in $n/2$ years and is called the $n/2$-year storm.

By pooling all observations irrespective of their association with individual storm records, a generalized intensity-duration-frequency relationship is obtained. Some effort can be saved in the preparation of records of storm rainfall for analysis if, at the outset, storms of low intensity are eliminated from consideration. The following empirical relationships are useful in indicating the lower limits of the intensities that should ordinarily be included in the analysis of North American station records:

$$i = 0.6 + 12/t \quad \text{for the northern United States} \qquad 3\text{-}3$$

$$i = 1.2 + 18/t \quad \text{for the southern United States} \qquad 3\text{-}4$$

Here i is the intensity of rainfall in inches per hour and t is its duration in minutes. For a duration of 10 min, for example, intensities below 3 in. per hr in the southern states need not receive attention. The storm recorded in Example 3-2 exhibits double this intensity.

There are many different patterns of storm-rainfall analysis. All procedures start, however, from a summary of experience such as that shown in Example 3-4. The data included in such a summary may then be used directly, or after smoothing (generally graphical) operations that generalize the experience. The developed intensity-duration-frequency relationships may be expressed in tabular or graphical form or as equations.

Example 3-4. The number of storms of varying intensity and duration recorded by a rain gage[13] in 45 years are listed in Table 3-6. Determine the time-intensity values for the 5-year storm.

TABLE 3-6. Record of Intense Rainfalls (Example 3-4)

Duration, min	Number of Storms of Stated Intensity (in. per hour) or More												
	1.0	1.25	1.5	1.75	2.0	2.5	3.0	4.0	5.0	6.0	7.0	8.0	9.0
5							123	47	22	14	4	2	1
10					122	78	48	15	7	4	2	1	
15				100	83	46	21	10	3	2	1	1	
20			98	64	44	18	13	5	2	2			
30	99	72	51	30	21	8	6	3	2				
40	69	50	27	14	11	5	3	1					
50	52	28	17	10	8	4	3						
60	41	19	14	6	4	4	2						
80	18	13	4	2	2	1							
100	13	4	1	1									
120	8	2											

If it is assumed that the 5-year storm is equaled or exceeded in intensity $45/5 = 9$ times in 45 years, the generalized time-intensity values may be interpolated from the summary by finding (a) for each specified intensity the duration that is equaled or exceeded by 9 storms and (b) for each specified duration the intensity that is equaled or exceeded by 9 storms. Interpolation proceeds along the broken diagonal line both vertically and horizontally with the results shown in Table 3-7. The values for the first 60 min are plotted on double logarithmic paper in Figure 3-6. A straight line drawn through the values shifted by 2 min to the right identifies the equation of the 5-year storm rainfall as $i = A/(t + d)^n = 26/(t + 2)^{0.66}$.

TABLE 3-7. Calculation of Storm Frequencies (Example 3-4)

a. Duration, min	5	10	15	20	30	40	50	60	80	100
a. Intensity, in. per hr	6.50	4.75	4.14	3.50	2.46	2.17	1.88	1.66	1.36	1.11
b. Intensity, in. per hr	1.0	1.25	1.5	1.75	2.0	2.5	3.0	4.0	5.0	6.0
b. Duration, min	116.0	89.9	70.0	52.5	46.7	29.0	25.7	16.0	9.3	7.5

[13] Record for New York City from 1869 to 1913.

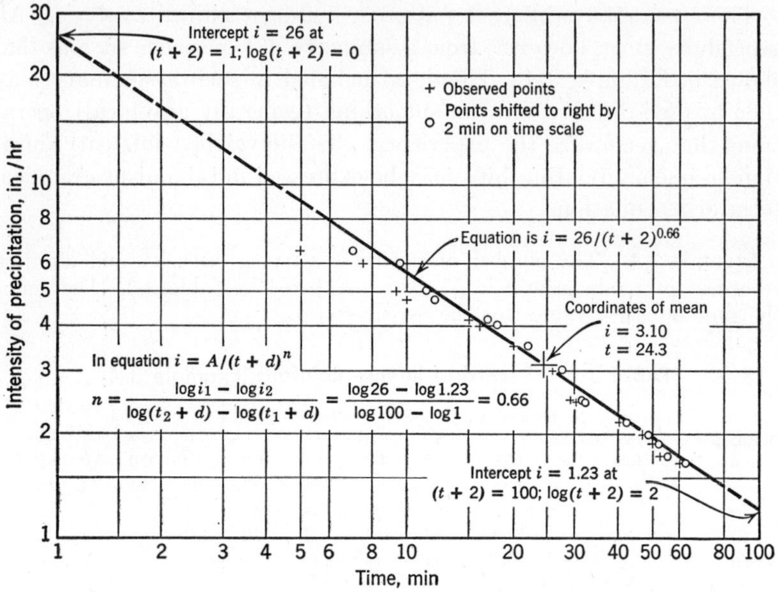

Figure 3-6. Intensity-duration of 5-year rainstorm.

Similar plotting of the 1-year, 2-year, and 10-year storms would yield lines of good fit essentially parallel to that of the 5-year storm. It is a common experience that the intercepts a of these lines on the i-axis at $(t + d) = 1$ themselves plot as a straight line against the recurrence interval T on double logarithmic paper. Hence $A = CT^m$ where c and m are determined in the same fashion as A and n, and the complete formulation of the intensity-duration-frequency (recurrence interval) relationship becomes

$$i = CT^m/(t + d)^n \qquad 3\text{-}5$$

3-14. Storm Runoff or Flood Flows. The flood waters that descend the water courses of a drainage basin or that are collected by the storm drains or combined sewers of a municipal drainage district are derived from the rains that fall upon the tributary water shed. The highest rates of discharge ordinarily prevail at a specified point in the drainage system when storm runoff begins to reach it from the entire tributary area. This time is called the *time of concentration.* Since rainfall decreases in intensity with duration, the shorter the time of concentration the higher is the rate of discharge per unit area. The time is shortest for small, broad, steep areas with rapidly shedding surfaces. It is increased by dry soil, surface inequalities or indentations, vegetal cover, and storage in water courses and adjacent areas.

The volume of runoff associated with a given storm is reduced by infiltration, freezing, and storage. It is increased by thawing of ice and snow, and by the release of water from storage on purpose, or as the result of the failure of dams or the collapse of log, ice, or debris jams. Velocity and direction of storms affect the rate of discharge appreciably. Maximum rates obtain when storms move down stream at velocities that will carry them to the point of discharge in about the time of concentration. The runoff resulting from the most intense rainfall will then reach the point of discharge from all parts of the water shed at nearly the same instant to produce the maximum possible flood crest.

Many ways have been devised for estimating the storm runoff, or flood flow, that is to be provided for in engineering designs. They may be classified as follows:

1. Statistical analyses based upon observed records of adequate length. Obviously these present the most direct answer. Unfortunately the records available for analysis seldom permit the determination of critical magnitudes by generalization within the actual experience. Resort must then be had to extrapolation, a practice always fraught with danger. The record of one or more adjacent, similar basins may serve in the absence of a record for the basin itself. The statistical analysis of flood flows is quite like that of annual runoff (Section 3-10). The frequency distribution of flood runoff approaches geometric normality and can be generalized in geometric terms.
2. "Rational" estimates relating runoff to rainfall; as far as possible, with the benefit of at least brief records of actual runoff measurements. This is the preferred procedure in calculating runoff from sewered areas that are to be developed as part of a municipal drainage scheme.
3. Calculations based upon empirical formulations that are applicable to existing water-shed conditions. These formulations are varied in structure and must be selected with full appreciation of the limitations of their derivation. At best, they should be applied as checks of statistical or rational methods.

Some engineers prefer to avoid the implications of probability analysis and to rely entirely on graphical or purely empirical methods of attack. A much-used method involves the analysis of the peak floods irrespective of the time interval in which they occur. In any one year, for example, there may be a flood second to the maximum for that year but larger than the maximum of some other year. If the peak floods—up to some three or four times the number of years of record—are arranged and numbered in order of decreasing magnitudes, they form the basis for the *flood-expectancy* curve for which frequency of occurrence, ordinarily expressed in terms of the *average recurrence interval* I, is the abscissa and the flood magnitude is the ordinate. For the kth term in a series of n intervals of time,

$$I = \frac{n}{k} \qquad \text{3-6}$$

The 5th value in a series covering 30 years, for example, is equaled or exceeded on the average once in every 6 years, i.e., it has a recurrence interval of 6 years.

3-15. Rational Estimates of Runoff from Rainfall. There are two general ways of estimating runoff from rainfall. One is called the *rational* method; the other, the *unit hydrograph* method.

a. The rational method. This method postulates that

$$Q = cia \qquad \text{3-7}$$

where Q is the rate of runoff at a specified point and time, a is the drainage area tributary to the specified point at the specified time, i is the average intensity of rainfall over the tributary drainage area for the specified time, and c is the coefficient of runoff or ratio of rate of runoff to rate of rainfall applicable to the particular situation.

Of the three factors included in Equation 3-7, a is ascertained from a map of the region or specific water shed, i is determined by means outlined in Section 13 of this chapter, and c is estimated from the characteristics of the catchment area. The time of concentration involved in the determination of i is found (1) for flood discharge by estimating the average velocities of flow obtaining in the principal drainage channels of the tributary area and calculating elapsed time from the quotient of length and velocity; and (2) for runoff from sewered areas by estimating the time required for runoff to enter the sewerage system from adjacent surfaces (called the *inlet time*) and adding to it the time of flow in the sewers or storm drains proper. Since rapid inflow from tributaries creates flood waves in the main stem of a river system, flood velocities are assumed to be from 30 to 50% higher than normal rates of flow.

The selection of suitable values for c in estimating runoff from sewered areas is discussed in connection with the design of storm drains and combined sewers (Chapter 10). In the translation of rainfall into flood flows, c varies seasonally, regionally, and locally. For the eastern United States, Bernard[14] has suggested limiting values, c_{max}, varying approximately from 0.3 to 1.5, the highest values applying to the northern portion of the country where melting snow and ice may contribute to the immediate runoff from spring rains. Bernard has further suggested reducing the limiting coefficient to that of the selected flood frequency in accordance with the relation

$$c = c_{max} (T/100)^m \tag{3-8}$$

on the assumption that the limiting coefficient has a frequency of once in 100 years. In Equation 3-8, T is the frequency of occurrence in years and m a coefficient, both in accordance with their significance in Equation 3-5.

b. The unit hydrograph. In dry weather, or when precipitation is frozen, the residual hydrograph or base flow of a stream is traced by water released from storage in the ground or in ponds, lakes, reservoirs, and backwaters of the stream. Immediately after a rainstorm, the rate of discharge rises above base flow by the amount of surface runoff reaching the drainage system. That portion of the hydrograph which rises above the base flow and can be isolated from it is a measure of the true surface runoff (see Figure 3-7). The *unit hydrograph* method is an outcome of investigations into the geometric properties of the surface-runoff portion of the hydrograph in their relation to an *effective rain* that has fallen during a *unit* of time such as a day or

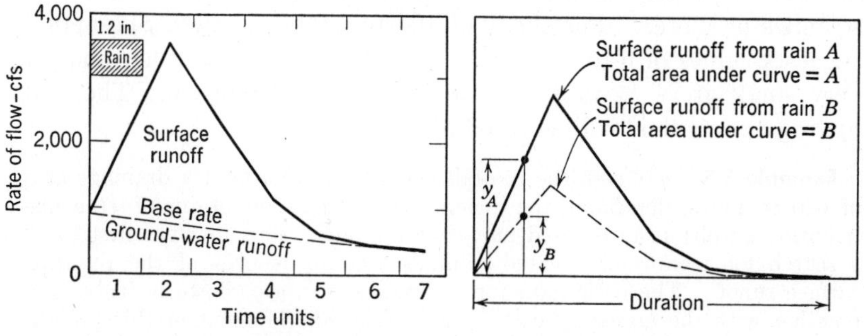

Figure 3-7. Origin and geometric properties of the unit hydrograph. (*a*) Hydrograph resulting from unit-time rain. See Example 3-5. (*b*) Distribution graph showing geometric properties of unit hydrograph; $y_A : A = y_B : B$; base duration is constant.

[14] M. Bernard, Modified rational method of estimating flood flows, Appendix A of *Low Dams*, National Resources Committee, Washington, 1938.

an hour. An effective rain is one that actually produces surface runoff.

The important geometric properties of the unit hydrograph of surface runoff are illustrated in Figure 3-7 as follows:

1. The length of abscissa, which measures time duration above base flow, is substantially constant for all unit-time rains.
2. The ordinates, which measure rates of discharge above base flow at the end of each time unit in a sequence of such units, are proportional to the total runoff resulting from unit-time rains irrespective of the individual magnitudes of these rains.
3. The ratios to the total area under the hydrograph of individual areas—ratios which measure the amount of water discharged in a given interval of time—are constant for all unit hydrographs of the same drainage area. These distribution ratios are generally referred to as the *distribution graph,* even when they are not presented in graphical form.
4. Rainstorms extending over several units of time, with or without interruption, create a hydrograph composed of a series of unit hydrographs superimposed in such manner as to distribute the runoff from each unit-time rain in accordance with the successive distribution ratios derived from unit-time rainfalls.

These geometric properties do not apply when runoff originates in melting snow or ice, or when the speed of flood waves in the stream is changed appreciably if the river stage is varied by fluctuating flows. Time is an important element of the procedure, and the method requires that rainfall data be available for unit times that are shorter than the time of concentration of the drainage area. Unit times of a day can be employed successfully only for large water sheds (1,000 sq miles or more). For sheds of 100 to 1,000 sq miles, Sherman[15] suggests values of 6 to 12 hr; for sheds of 20 sq miles, 2 hr; and for very small areas ¼ to ⅓ of the time of concentration. The unit hydrograph method is illustrated in Example 3-5.

Example 3-5. *a.* Given the rainfall and runoff records of a drainage area of 620 sq miles, determine the generalized distribution of runoff (the distribution graph) from isolated unit-time rainfalls. This involves first of all a search for records of isolated rainfalls and for records of the resulting surface runoff. The basic data for a typical storm are shown in Table 3-8, together with the necessary calculations. The development of this table is straightforward, with the exception of Column 4, which records the estimated base flow. This can be derived only from a study of the general hydrograph of the stream in connection with all related hydrological observations of the region.

b. Apply the average estimate of runoff distribution to the observed rainfall sequence that is presented in Table 3-9.

[15] O. E. Meinzer, *Hydrology,* McGraw-Hill Book Co., New York, p. 524, 1942.

TABLE 3-8. Observations and Calculations for Unit Hydrograph (Example 3-5)

Sequence of Time Units (1)	Observed Rainfall, in. (2)	Runoff, cfs: Observed Total (3)	Runoff, cfs: Estimated Base Flow (4)	Estimated Distribution of Surface Runoff: cfs (5) = (3) − (4)	Estimated Distribution of Surface Runoff: % (6) = 100(5)/6200	Average Distribution Ratio for 10 Storms, % (7)
1	1.20	1,830	870	960	15.5	16
2	0.03	3,590	800	2,790	45.0	46
3	0.00	2,370	690	1,680	27.1	26
4	0.00	1,220	600	620	10.0	10
5	0.00	640	510	130	2.1	1
6	0.00	430	410	20	0.3	1
7	0.00	350	350	0	0.0	0
Totals	....	.....	...	6,200	100.0	100

TABLE 3-9. Application of Unit Hydrograph Method (Example 3-5)

Sequence of Time Units (1)	Rainfall, in.: Observed (2)	Rainfall, in.: Estimated Loss (3)	Net (4) = (2) − (3)	Average Runoff Distribution Ratio, % (5)	Distributed Runoff for Stated Time Units, in.: 1st (6)	2nd (7)	3rd (8)	5th (9)	Compounded Runoff: in. (10)	Compounded Runoff: cfs * (11)
1	1.8	1.3	0.5	16	0.08	....	....	....	0.08	1,300
2	2.7	1.6	1.1	46	0.23	0.18	....	....	0.41	6,900
3	1.6	1.1	0.5	26	0.13	0.50	0.08	....	0.71	11,900
4	0.0	0.0	0.0	10	0.05	0.29	0.23	....	0.57	9,500
5	1.1	0.2	0.9	1	0.01	0.11	0.13	0.14	0.39	6,500
6	0.0	0.0	0.0	1	0.00	0.01	0.05	0.42	0.48	8,000
7	0.0	0.0	0.0	0	0.00	0.01	0.01	0.23	0.25	4,200
8	0.0	0.0	0.0	0	0.00	0.00	0.00	0.09	0.09	1,500

* Rate of runoff in cubic feet per second = inches × 26.88 × 620 sq miles = 16,700 cfs if the time unit is a day. For other time units multiply by reciprocal ratio of length of time to length of day.

The calculations in Table 3-9 need little explanation except Column 3, the estimated loss of rainfall due principally to infiltration. This estimate is made on the basis of all available information for the region. Column 5 is identical with Column 7 of Table 3-8. Column 6 is the net rain of 0.5 in. during the first time unit multiplied by the distribution ratio of Column 5. Columns 7, 8, and 9 are similarly derived for the net rains during the subsequent time units. Column 10 gives the sums of Columns 6 to 9, and Column 11 converts these sums from inches to cubic feet per second. If the base flow is estimated and added to the surface runoff shown in Column 11 the complete hydrograph is constructed.

The unit hydrograph method has the important property of tracing the full hydrograph resulting from a storm rather than being confined to a determination of the peak flow alone. For small drainage areas, the method depends upon the availability of the readings of a recording rain gage. Many refinements in procedure and aids to the rationalization of the various steps are being developed by hydrologists and engineers.

3-16. Flood-Flow Formulas. The basis of flood-flow formulas is an empirical evaluation of drainage-basin characteristics and hydrological factors that rationally fall within the framework of the relation $Q = cia$ (Equation 3-7). In most of the formulas used by engineers, frequency relations are implied even if they are not expressed in exact terms. Variation of rainfall intensities with time of concentration, furthermore, is often introduced indirectly as a function of the size of area drained. Equation 3-7 is thereby reduced to the expression $Q = Ca^m$, where m is less than 1. This follows from the relative changes in i and a with t; namely, $i = A/(t + d)^n$ and $a = kt^2$ where k is an area coefficient. For d close to zero, therefore, $i = \text{constant}/(a^{n/2})$, and, substituting i in Equation 3-7, $Q = \text{constant } a^{1-n/2} = Ca^m$, where $m = 1 - n/2$. Since n varies from 0.4 to 1.0, m must and does vary in different formulations from 0.8 to 0.5. The value of C comprehends the initial rate of rainfall, the runoff-rainfall ratio of the particular water shed, and the frequency factor. An example is the Fanning formula which is listed in Table 3-10 together with other flood-flow formulas in which certain of the component variables or their influence upon runoff are individualized.

TABLE 3-10. Examples of Flood-Flow Formulas

Individualized Variable	Author and Region	Formula
None	Fanning, New England	$Q = Ca^{5/6}$, where $C = 200$ for a in sq miles
Rainfall intensity and slope of water shed	McMath, St. Louis, Mo.	$Q = cia^{4/5}s^{1/5}$, where s = slope in ft per 1,000 and $c = 0.75$ for a in acres
Shape of water shed	Dredge or Burge, India	$Q = Ca/l^{2/3}$, where l = length of area in miles and $C = 1{,}300$ for a in sq miles
Shape, slope, and surface storage	Kinnison and Colby, New England	$Q = (0.000036h^{2.4} + 124)a^{0.95}/(rl^{0.7})$, where h = median altitude of drainage basin in ft above the outlet; r = % of lake, pond, and reservoir area; l = average distance in miles to outlet; and a = sq miles
Frequency of flood	Fuller, U. S. A.	$Q = Ca^{0.8}(1 + 0.8 \log T)(1 + 2a^{-0.3})$, where T = number of years in the period considered, and C varies from 25 to 2,000 for a in sq miles

These examples are presented for the purpose of showing the form that flood-flow formulas may take. They are not necessarily the best of their type or widely applicable.

Fuller's formula is of particular interest because it incorporates a frequency factor and is country-wide in scope. It was developed in sequence as follows:

1. The average annual 24-hr flood:

$$Q_{\text{ave}} = Ca^{0.8} \qquad 3\text{-}9$$

2. The most probable maximum 24-hr flood in T years:

$$Q_{\max} = Q_{\text{ave}}(1 + 0.8 \log T) \qquad 3\text{-}10$$

3. The most probable peak discharge in T years:

$$Q = Q_{\max}(1 + 2a^{-0.3}) \qquad 3\text{-}11$$

Inspection of these equations suggests the nature of their graphical derivation from observed flood flows. For the United States C varies from 25 to 200. It should be noted that the maximum flood in T years

TABLE 3-11. Fuller's Flood Frequency Values

Type of Structure	Damage in Case of Failure	Values of $(1 + 0.8 \log T)$
Temporary works during construction	Slight	1.5–2
Minor permanent structures	Slight	2–3
Temporary works	Considerable	2–3
Major permanent structures	Material	3–5
Major permanent structures	Material and disastrous	5–6

is the most probable value to occur in that period rather than the value that is equaled or exceeded once in that period. Since Fuller assumes that the most probable value is the arithmetic mean of the group of "exceeding" values, flood flows calculated by his formula are generally higher than those determined by common statistical procedures for equal periods. Fuller [16] recommends using the values of the frequency factor $(1 + 0.8 \log T)$ shown in Table 3-11.

[16] W. E. Fuller, Flood flows, *Trans. Am. Soc. Civil Engrs.*, *77*, 564 (1914).

4 Collection of Surface Water

4-1. Sources of Surface Water. In North America, by far the largest volume of water for municipal use is taken from surface sources. The quantities of surface water that can be gathered vary directly with the size of the catchment area, or water shed, and with the difference between the amount of water precipitated and lost by evapotranspiration (Figure 1-2). Where the surface-water and ground-water sheds do not coincide, there may be a loss of ground water to an adjacent catchment area, or there may be a slight gain.

The use and development of surface sources may take one of three forms: (a) continuous draft, (b) selective draft, and (c) impoundage.

a. Continuous draft. Communities situated on or near streams, ponds, or lakes may take their supplies from these sources by continuous draft if stream flow and pond, or lake, capacity are sufficient at all seasons of the year to permit withdrawal of the requisite volumes of water.[1] The collecting works for such supplies include ordinarily (1) an intake structure in the form of a crib, gatehouse, or intake tower; (2) an intake conduit; and (3) in many places, a pump-

[1] Examples of continuous draft from streams are the water supplies of Montreal, P. Q., St. Lawrence River; Philadelphia, Pa., Delaware and Schuylkill rivers; Pittsburgh, Pa., Allegheny River; Cincinnati, Ohio, and Louisville, Ky., Ohio River; Kansas City, Mo., Missouri River; Minneapolis and St. Paul, Minn., Mississippi River; St. Louis, Mo., Missouri and Mississippi rivers; and New Orleans, La., Mississippi River.

Examples of continuous draft from lakes are furnished by Burlington, Vt., Lake Champlain; Syracuse, N. Y., Lake Skaneateles; Toronto, Ont., Lake Ontario; Buffalo, N. Y., and Cleveland, Ohio, Lake Erie; Detroit, Mich., Lake St. Clair; Chicago, Ill., and Milwaukee, Wis., Lake Michigan; and Duluth, Minn., Lake Superior.

ing station. On small streams that serve communities of moderate size, an intake or diversion dam may have to be constructed to create sufficient depth of water to submerge the intake pipe and protect it against ice. When intakes are situated in the immediate vicinity of the community, the water drawn must generally be lifted from the source to the distribution system and prior to that to purification works which are generally needed (Figure 4-1).

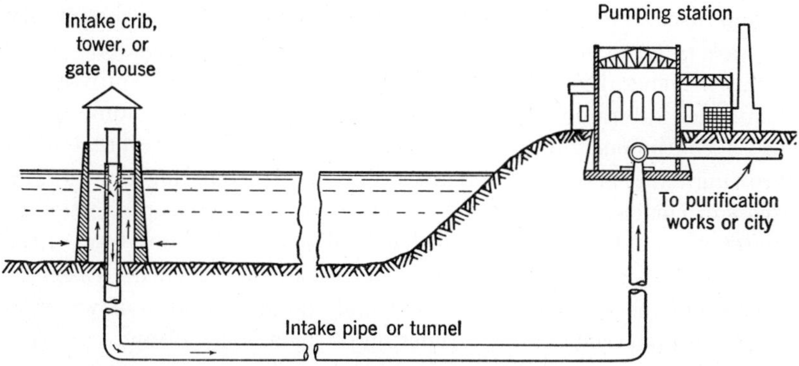

Figure 4-1. Continuous draft of water from large lakes and streams.

Waters drawn from large streams are commonly polluted by the wastes from upstream communities and must usually be purified before use. Cities situated on large lakes must protect themselves against their own discharges of sewage and industrial-process waters as well as those of neighboring municipalities. Intakes are, therefore, placed as far away from shore as economically feasible, and purification plants ordinarily become necessary parts of the water-supply system. Treatment of the sewage of the community is generally indicated.

b. Selective draft. It may be desirable to leave low-water flows in streams undisturbed in order to meet existing water needs of the valley or because the pollution carried by the stream is too highly concentrated to permit satisfactory purification. Only flood waters in excess of basic needs, or cleaner in composition, may then be led into reservoirs constructed in meadow lands adjacent to the stream or otherwise available nearby.[2] The amount of water so stored must

[2] London, England, meets part of its water needs from the Thames River by storing relatively clean flood waters in large basins surrounded by dikes in the Thames Valley. The Boston, Mass., Metropolitan Water Supply diverts the freshets of the Ware River through a

equal the demand for water during the season of unavailable stream flow. If draft is confined to a quarter year, for example, the reservoir must hold at least three-fourths of the annual supply. In spite of its selection, the stored water may have to be purified.

c. Impoundage. In search of clean water and water that can be brought to the community by gravity, engineers have developed supplies from upland streams. Ordinarily these streams are tapped near their source in high and sparsely settled regions. To be of use, their annual discharge must equal or exceed the demands of the community they are to serve, and, since their flows during the dry portions of the year will generally fall short of concurrent municipal requirements, their flood waters must generally be stored in sufficient volume to assure a continuous supply. The necessary reservoirs are created by throwing dams across the stream valley and impounding the flows in excess of current use (Figure 4-2). In this way a large proportion of the total annual runoff can be utilized. The area draining toward the impoundage is known as the catchment area or water shed. Economical development of its capacity depends upon the value of water in the region concerned and is a function of the amount of and variation in runoff, the accessibility of the catchment area, the interference with existing water rights, and the factors that influence the cost of a dam and reservoir. Storage must include allowances for evaporation from the new-water surface created by the impoundage and may have to sustain established minimum flows in the stream below the dam (compensating water). The supplementation of surface storage by increased ground storage in the flooded area and the gradual dissipation of surface storage by siltation are also allowed for when these effects are significant.

Intake structures are either incorporated in the impounding dams or kept separate from them. Other important parts of impounding reservoirs are (1) spillways which must safely discharge floods in excess of reservoir capacity and (2) diversion conduits which must carry the runoff of the stream that is to be impounded safely past the construction site until the reservoir is completed and its spillway can go into action. The design of these ancillary structures requires the analysis of flood records.

Impounded supplies may be sufficiently safe, attractive, and palatable to permit use of their waters without treatment other than

tunnel (1) to the Wachusett Reservoir which impounds the waters of the previously existing Wachusett supply, and (2) to the subsequently completed Quabbin Reservoir which impounds the neighboring Swift River.

protective disinfection.[3] High color, caused by the decomposition of organic matter in swamps and on the flooded valley bottom, odors and tastes associated with this decomposition or engendered by the growth of algae, especially during the years of initial filling, turbidity (finely divided clay or silt) carried into streams or reservoirs by surface wash, wave action, or bank erosion, and recreational uses of water sheds and reservoirs may call for more complete treatment of the stored flows.[4]

Much of the water flowing in streams or reaching ponds, lakes, and reservoirs in times of drought, or when precipitation is frozen, is made up of seepage from the ground. It is nevertheless classified as surface runoff rather than ground water. Discharge of seepage from the ground and recharge of ground water from surface sources are governed by the relative levels of water on the surface and in the ground (Figure 5-1). Release of water from storage in the ground or from snow persisting until midsummer in high mountains may contribute markedly to the dry-weather flow of a stream and thus be the determining factor in the yield of a given area. Although surface waters are derived from rainfall, the relations between rainfall, runoff, and infiltration are so involved that engineers rightly prefer to base their calculations of yield upon stream gagings. These should extend over a considerable number of years if they are to present adequate information.

4-2. Impounding Reservoirs. In the absence of natural ponds and lakes, intensive utilization of upland water sources requires the construction of impounding reservoirs. The selection of a suitable site for a reservoir depends upon a number of interrelated factors that establish the adequacy, economy, safety, and palatability of the supply. Among desirable factors are the following:

1. The surface topography should be such as to create a high ratio of water storage to dam volume; i.e., a broad and branching valley for the reservoir should impinge upon a narrow gorge for the dam. The topography should also present a favorable site for an adequate spillway and a suitable route for an aqueduct or pipeline.
2. The subsurface geology should be such as to provide useful materials for the construction of the dam and appurtenant structures, safe founda-

[3] Examples of untreated, impounded, upland supplies are the Croton River, Catskill, and Delaware River supplies of New York, N. Y., and the Wachusett and Quabbin supplies of the Metropolitan District of Boston, Mass.

[4] Examples of treated impounded supplies are those of Baltimore, Md.; Providence, R. I.; Hartford, Conn.; Springfield, Mass.; and Springfield, Ill.

tions for the dam and spillway, and tightness against seepage of the impounded waters beneath the dam and through its abutments.

3. The reservoir area, i.e., the area to be flooded, should be sparsely inhabited, not heavily wooded, and not traversed by important roads or by railroads. It should contain little marshland. The area, furthermore, should constitute a reservoir (*a*) of such shape as not to favor short-circuiting of the incoming waters to the intake, and (*b*) of such depth, especially around its margins, as not to create large areas of shallow flowage. Purification of water by storage is an important asset of impounding reservoirs. Narrow reservoirs with their major axis in the direction of prevailing winds are especially subject to short-circuiting. Areas of shallow flowage often support a heavy growth of aquatic vegetation, when they are submerged, or of land plants, when they are uncovered by the lowering of the water surface. Decaying vegetation imparts odors and tastes to the water, supports algal growths, and liberates color.

4. The reservoir should interfere as little as possible with existing water rights; the intake should be as close as possible to the community it is to serve; and the development should preferably be at such elevation as to supply its waters by gravity.

In the development of large reservoirs, the sites of whole villages as well as the agricultural and wood lands of the valley are inundated. When the reservoir area is flooded, the vegetation dies, and the organic matter released to the water from this source, as well as from the topsoil, undergoes decomposition. Algae and other microorganisms flourish. Odors, taste, and color are imparted to the water, and 10 to 15 years must elapse before decomposition of the putrescible substances within the reservoir area has been substantially completed and the reservoir has been stabilized. A state of equilibrium is reached when the water within the reservoir takes its quality from the incoming water. The rate of improvement, when referred to conditions of equilibrium, is approximately 14% annually, which implies 90% improvement in about 15 years.

Since the bettering of water quality, after impounding reservoirs are filled, is due to the gradual stabilization of the organic matter within the flooded area, the improvement is a manifestation of the natural purification of polluted waters and closely analogous to the stabilization of bottom deposits (Chapter 19).

Preparation of the reservoir site to insure reasonable cleanliness of the area to be flooded and provide satisfactory operating conditions includes the following:

1. For the entire reservoir area:
   a. Removing or otherwise destroying dwellings and other structures.
   b. Cleaning barnyards, privies, and cesspools.
   c. Removing manure piles.

d. Cutting trees and brush close to the ground and removing usable timber from the area to be flooded.
e. Burning slash, weeds, and grass.
f. Removing as much muck as possible from swamps that will be submerged, and covering residual muck with clean gravel and sand.
g. Cutting channels to pockets within the reservoir bottom to make them self-draining when the water level is lowered.

2. For a marginal strip extending from the high-water mark reached by wave action down to a vertical depth of about 20 ft:
a. Removing all stumps, roots, and topsoil.
b. Draining all marginal swamps.
c. Creating, if possible, a shore-water depth of at least 8 ft during a considerable part of the growing season of aquatic plants. This can be done by excavation or fill, or by the construction of auxiliary dams on the upper reaches of the reservoir.

The removal from the reservoir site of all topsoil that contains more than 1 or 2% organic matter, a practice called *soil stripping,* is generally more expensive than water treatment and will provide a less satisfactory end product. Furthermore, unstripped reservoirs will, in time, catch up with stripped reservoirs. The benefits of stripping are confined to the first decade and a half of the life of a reservoir.

The management of reservoirs presents a number of problems related to the maintenance of water quality. Among them are the control of water weeds, the prevention and destruction of algal blooms, the bleaching of color and settling of turbidity, and the selection of water of optimum temperature and quality by shifting the depth of draft to suit water conditions. These matters are discussed in other chapters of this book.

Reservoirs situated within the flight range of sea gulls are sometimes polluted by these scavenger birds. The firing of blank cartridges, and, if necessary, the occasional killing of sea gulls as well as other large birds, may frighten the invaders away and postpone their return for significantly long stretches of time. The roosting on reservoirs of mud hens and some varieties of duck can be prevented only by extermination of the offending water fowl. Small reservoirs can be protected against large birds by stretching a network of wires over the water surface at intervals of 200 to 500 ft some 10 to 20 ft above the high-water elevation. Small birds, unfortunately, may find a happy perch upon these wires.

4-3. Dams and Dikes. Some of the factors that govern the selection of a reservoir site also determine the choice of the materials and methods of construction for the dams and dikes that create the impoundage.

a. Earth dams and dikes. Earth embankments that are to serve as dams or dikes are constructed of sand, clay, or silt, and of mixtures of these soils which may also incorporate some gravel and small stones. When permeable materials must constitute the bulk of the dam, a central core of selected impervious material is introduced to provide watertightness. Shells or shoulders of permeable fill to either side supply protection for the core and give the additional weight needed to resist the pressure of the stored waters. The common features of an earth dam with earth-core wall are illustrated in Figure 4-2. Earth cores are used wherever the materials that will render them impervious are available. In the absence of such materials, concrete-core walls must take their place. The shoulders are intended to drain readily and, by proper dispatching of fill from the borrow pits, are ideally graded from fine material adjacent to the core to coarse material at the upstream and downstream faces. Within the range of destructive wave action, the upstream face is protected against erosion, by waves and rainstorms, by means of stone paving or riprap, or by a concrete apron. A wide berm is generally placed at the foot of the protected portion of the slope. The downstream face may receive similar treatment to save it from erosion by stormwater runoff. More commonly, however, it is seeded to grass or planted with covering vines. The slope is broken by berms that subdivide the downstream face into smaller drainage areas and that give access to the slope for mowing the grass and for other maintenance operations. The berms slope inward to gutters which intercept the runoff from rainstorms and conduct it safely down the face of the dam through a system of surface or subsurface drains leading to the stream channel.

Today earth dams and dikes are generally constructed as rolled fills. The hydraulic-fill method which creates an embankment in which the water-carried earth is graded from the coarsest grain sizes at the face of the dam to the finest in the core is no longer favored because it is difficult to control.

b. Masonry and other dams. As shown in Figures 4-3 and 4-4, masonry dams are built as gravity, arched, or reinforced structures. They may include their own spillway by permitting passage of water over their full length or part of it, or they may be of the "non-overflow" variety which is protected by a separate spillway. Constructions of cyclopean masonry and mass concrete embedding large stones have, in the course of time, generally given way to the use of poured concrete.

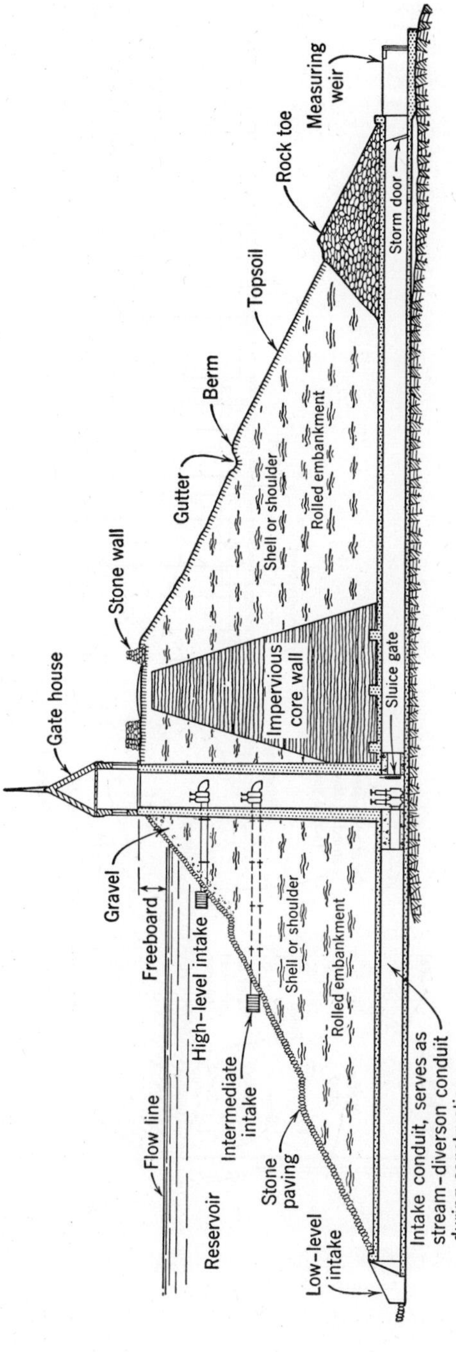

Figure 4-2. Dam and intake tower for an impounded surface-water supply.

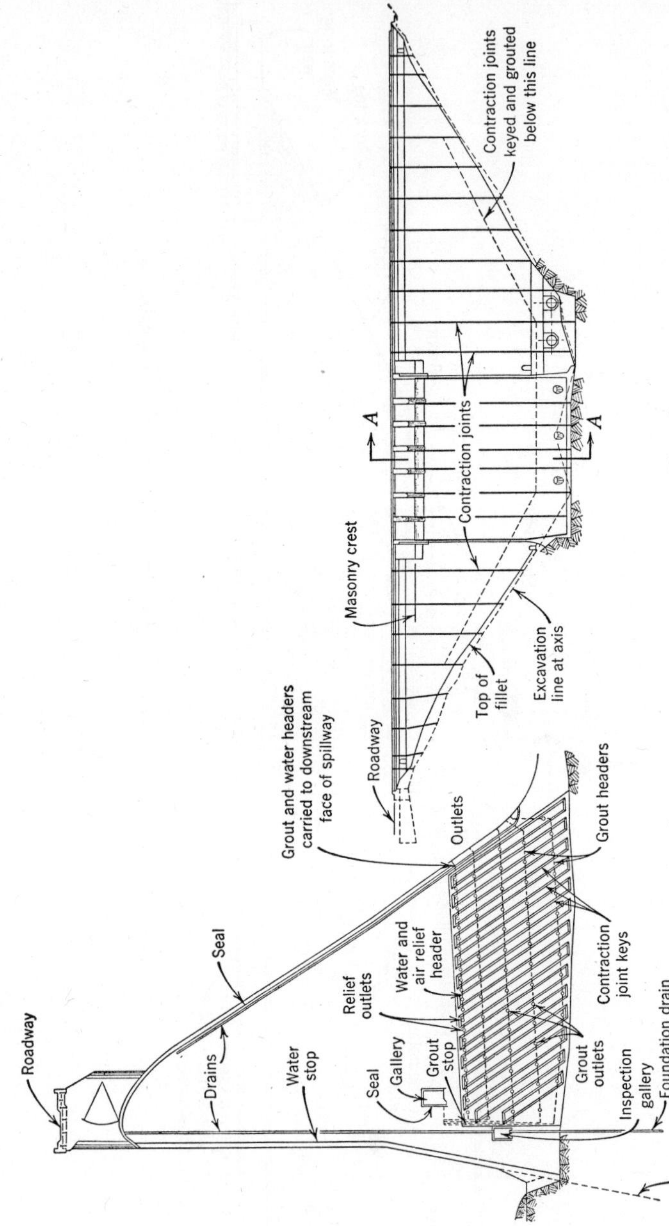

Figure 4-3. Gravity masonry dam. After C. E. Pearce, Design of Hiwassee Dam, *Civil Eng.*, *10*, 433 (1940).

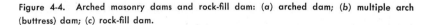

Gravity dams are designed to be in compression under all conditions of loading and can be made to fit almost any location that offers a suitable foundation. Arched dams depend upon arch action to transmit the water thrust laterally to both sides of the valley. Hence, they are adapted to use only in narrow valleys with strong sides. If more than one arch is to be employed, the contact points of the arches must be supported by heavy buttresses. Reinforced-concrete dams are commonly composed of flat slabs that face upstream and lie on a framework of heavy beams and columns. Availability or lack of materials may dictate the construction of timber, rock fill, or steel dams (Figure 4-4).

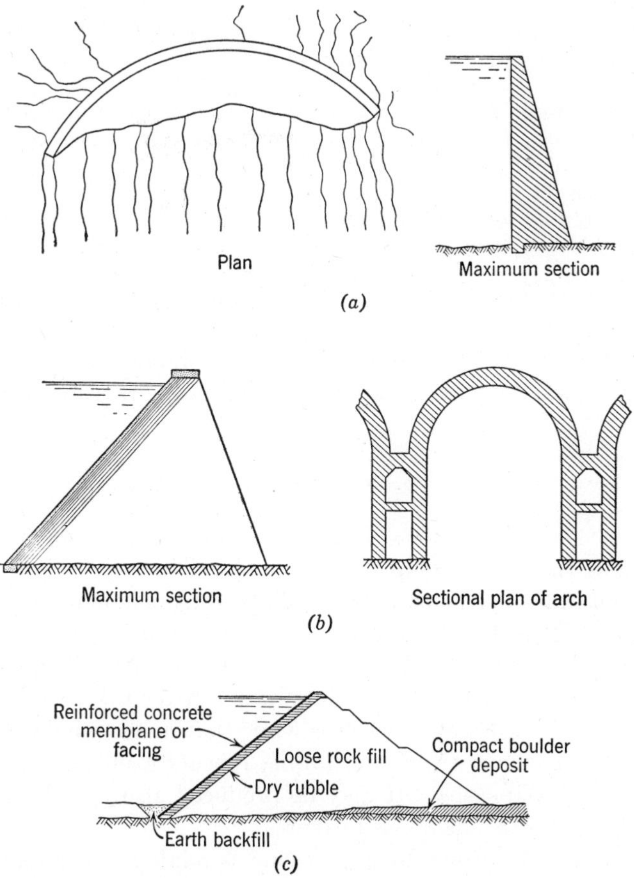

Figure 4-4. Arched masonry dams and rock-fill dam: (*a*) arched dam; (*b*) multiple arch (buttress) dam; (*c*) rock-fill dam.

4-4. Common Dimensions of Dams and Dikes. A first step in the investigation of impounding reservoirs is a comparative study of available dam and reservoir sites. Involved in particular are the determination of the quantities and characteristics of the dam materials that can be provided and of their cost in place. With the aid of maps, a field reconnaissance, and the common dimensionings of different dam types, it is possible to confine detailed designs to the most promising locations, often even to a single site.

a. Freeboard. All dams of the "non-overflow" variety must rise a safe distance above the maximum storage level in order not to be overtopped by waters that rise above the spillway crest in times of storm. This distance is called the *freeboard.* A safe distance is particularly critical for earth dams and dikes. The requisite value is a composite of a number of different factors:

1. Head of water on the spillway crest at maximum rate of discharge.
2. Wind set-up, or increase in elevation of reservoir surface by the drag exerted in the direction of persistent winds.
3. Wave height (trough to crest).
4. Wave run-up, or ride-up on sloping surfaces.
5. Depth of frost (for earth dams only).

Determination of the head on the spillway involves the routing of floods through reservoirs (Section 4-12).

In studies for the dams and dikes for the Zuider Zee in Holland, *wind set-up* was found to be approximated by the relationship

$$h_s = \frac{w^2F}{1{,}400d}\cos\alpha \qquad \text{4-1}$$

where h_s is the wind set-up above pool level in feet, w is the wind velocity in miles per hour, F is the fetch (or maximum clean sweep of the wind towards the dam or dike) in miles, d is the mean depth of water in feet, and α is the angle between the wind direction and a line normal to the structure or shore line. After the wind subsides, the water at the leeward shore falls while that at the windward shore rises. This rhythmic rising and falling repeats itself and is called a *seiche* (pronouced sāsh). It may be produced also by differences in barometric pressures at opposite shores.

Wave height, as shown by Stevenson,[5] is related to the fetch. His

[5] Thomas Stevenson, *Design and Construction of Harbours,* 2nd ed., A. J. Black, Edinburgh, 1874.

formulation has been modified by Molitor[6] to include the wind velocity as follows:

$$h_w = 0.17\sqrt{wF} + (2.5 - \sqrt[4]{F}) \qquad 4\text{-}2$$

The rise of the wave crest above the pool level is approximately three-quarters of the wave height.

In deep water (depth > ½ wave length), *wave velocities* will eventually equal the velocity of the wind and may indeed exceed it. For wave heights between 1 and 7 ft, the wave velocity v in feet per second is approximated by the relationship:

$$v = 7 + 2h_w \qquad 4\text{-}3$$

The run-up of waves on the face of a dam or dike approaches the velocity head of the waves. The height of wave action h_a is a combination of wave height and run-up. It may be approximated as $1.5h_w$, or as

$$h_a = 0.75h_w + v^2/2g \qquad 4\text{-}4$$

Earth dams and dikes must be given a freeboard height above maximum pool level at least equal to the regional depth of frost. Otherwise the material exposed to wetting may freeze and crack. Depth of frost action is discussed in Section 6-7.

Example 4-1. Estimate the height of set-up and wave action for an impoundage with an average depth of 40 ft and a fetch of 25 miles exposed to winds with velocities of 49 mph that strike the dam at an angle of 30° to the normal.

1. By Equation 4-1: $h_s = \dfrac{(49)^2 \times 25}{1{,}400 \times 40} 0.866 = 0.93$ ft.
2. By Equation 4-2: $h_w = 0.17\sqrt{49 \times 25} = 5.95$ ft.
3. By Equation 4-3: $v = 7 + 2 \times 5.95 = 18.9$ fps; or $v^2/2g = 5.55$ ft.
4. By Equation 4-4: $h_a = 0.75 \times 5.95 + 5.55 = 10.0$ ft.

The total freeboard includes, in addition to the allowance for wave action (10 ft), the head on the spillway and the set-up (0.93 ft). Since frost depths commonly do not exceed 5 ft in the United States, no allowance for frost action need be made.

b. Earth dams and dikes. Experience in the design, construction, and maintenance of earth dams has produced certain common dimen-

[6] D. A. Molitor, Wave pressures on sea walls and breakwaters, *Trans. Am. Soc. Civil Engrs., 100,* 984 (1935).

sions and rules of thumb that can form a working basis for the limited objective of this section, namely, arrival at a first estimate of the size of a particular structure. These dimensions and rules of thumb are shown in Figure 4-5.

The slopes of earth dams that are constructed of cohesionless materials, such as sand, may be made uniform from top to bottom. The slope must be less than the angle of internal friction of the grains, a factor of safety of 1.3 to 1.5 in terms of the tangent of the angle commonly being provided. If cohesive materials such as clay are included, the slopes must become progressively flatter.

Dams that can be given dimensions of the order of magnitude indicated in Figure 4-5 will effect the storage of 1 mg of water with about 100 cu yd of earth when the site is good. The relative yardage needed at unusually favorable sites is often half this value, sometimes even less. Justification of a large yardage ratio may be given by the high regional value of water.

The volume of the dam as a whole and of its constituent portions is computed in accordance with common earthwork practice by "average end areas" or "prismoidal formula," or by a combination of the two.

The upstream shoulder of earth dams, because of the buoyant and lubricating effect of the saturating water, is less stable than the downstream shoulder. Hence the upstream slope is generally made flatter. If outward hydrostatic pressure and sloughing of the upstream face are to be avoided when the reservoir is being drawn down rapidly, the shoulder material should drain rapidly. In dams on impervious foundations, water escaping into the downstream shoulder can be safely led away through a broken stone drain at the toe of the structure (Figure 4-2). Entrance to the drain should be through a graded filter. In dams on pervious foundations, underflow is held to a minimum either by placing an impervious blanket between the heel and core of the dam (Figure 4-5) or by carrying the concrete-core wall to bed rock or driving sheet piling to it. The purpose is not so much the prevention of loss of water as the checking of velocities that will carry dam material or subsoil away and cause the dam to fail.

The berms and gutters of the downstream face are placed at vertical intervals of about 30 ft. Design of gutters and drains parallels, in all respects, that of storm-drainage systems for municipal areas (Chapter 10).

c. *Gravity masonry dams.* The forces acting on a gravity masonry dam are readily identified and evaluated as to magnitude, distribu-

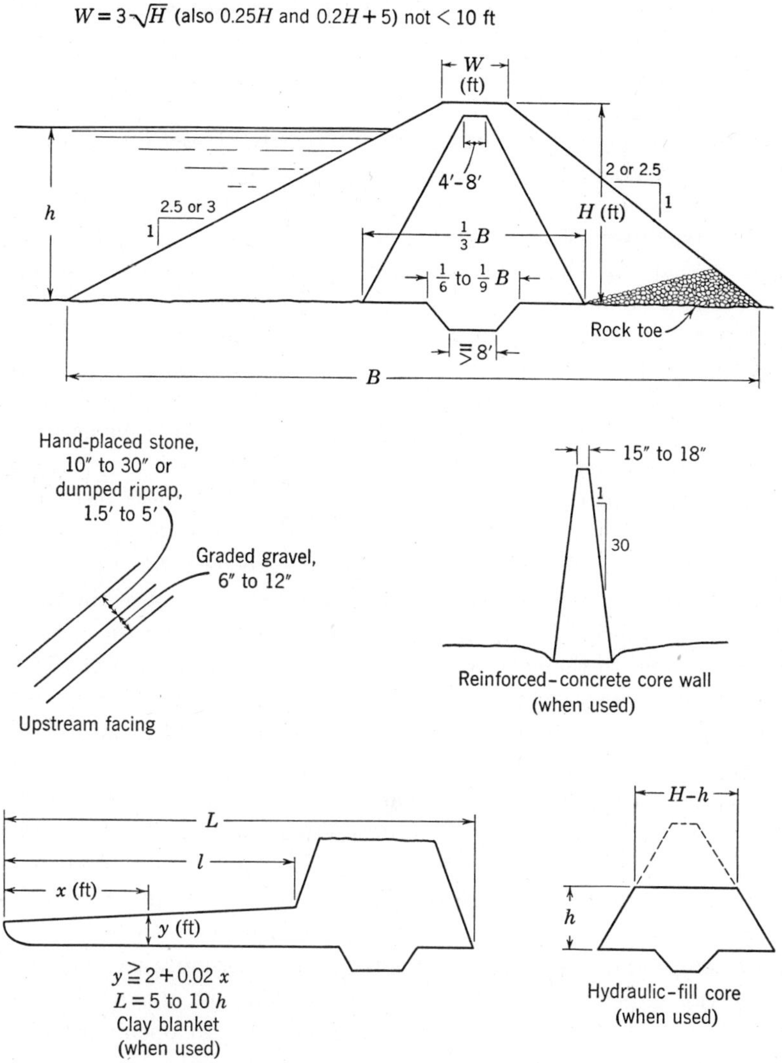

Figure 4-5. Common dimensions of earth dams.

Upstream slope 2.5 on 1, downstream slope 2 on 1 for: (1) homogeneous well-graded material; (2) homogeneous silty clay, or clay, when $H \lesseqgtr 50$ ft; and (3) sand, or sand and gravel, with reinforced-concrete wall.

Upstream slope 3 on 1, downstream slope 2.5 on 1 for: (1) homogeneous coarse silt; (2) homogeneous silty clay, or clay, when $H > 50$ ft; and (3) sand, or sand and gravel, with clay core.

tion, and direction. The structural analysis of such dams, therefore, is straightforward. It need not be detailed in this book because it is commonly covered both in textbooks on hydraulics and in textbooks on structural mechanics. However, a brief consideration of the forces that must be taken into account is of interest. These forces include (1) the weight of the structure; (2) the fluid pressure of water and silt on the face of the dam; (3) the hydrostatic pressure on the base of the structure; (4) ice pressure on the face of the dam at the water line; (5) inertia forces due to earthquakes; and (6) the foundation reaction. Common assumptions are: (1) a unit weight of concrete of 150 lb per cu ft; (2) a unit weight of silt of 90 lb per cu ft; (3) full hydrostatic pressure acting on two-thirds of the area of the base; (4) ice pressures of 20,000 to 50,000 lb per linear foot of dam; and (5) seismic acceleration equaling $0.1g$ to $0.2g$, where g is the acceleration due to gravity.

Ice pressure can be exerted only when the ice sheet is restrained, i.e., when the ice cannot buckle or slide up the face of the dam or the banks of the reservoir. Maximum ice pressure is a function of the crushing strength of the ice (from 100 to 1,000 psi) and of the thickness of the sheet. Buckling is expected to occur when the distance from the dam to the shore exceeds 200 times the thickness of the ice sheet. Ice pressure can be neutralized by using steam or compressed air to maintain a narrow channel of open water at the face of the dam.

Seepage through and beneath masonry dams is obstructed by building metal water stops into the contraction joints and by grouting the foundation beneath the heel of the dam. Uplift on the base of the dam and within it is reduced by installing vertical drains in all contraction joints and in the foundation on the downstream side of the water stops and grout curtain (Figure 4-3). These drains lead to an inspection gallery running the length of the dam just above tail-water height, whence the seepage water is discharged to openings in the downstream face of the structure.

Structural analysis of a gravity section to meet a given set of conditions, including the provision of a roadway over the dam, produces a specific profile. First estimates of the amount of masonry needed at a given site may be had, without detailed computation, by reference to a "practical profile" developed for this purpose on the basis of common assumptions. Such a profile is shown in Figure 4-6. Known

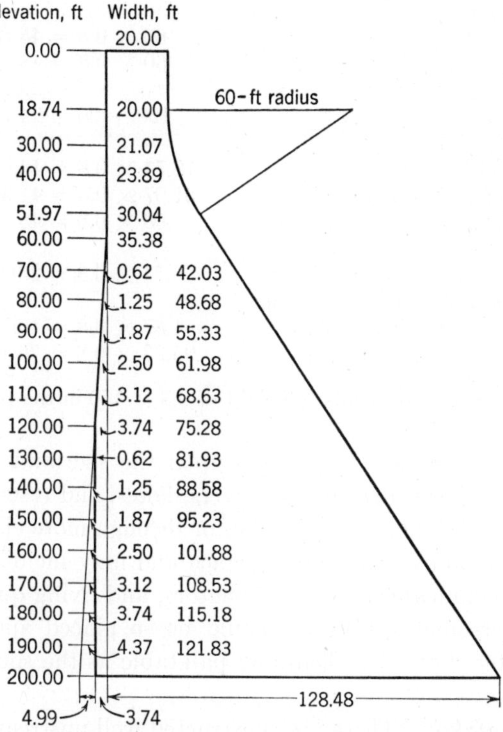

Figure 4-6. Dimensions of masonry dams; Wegmann's Practical Type No. 2.

as "Wegmann's Practical Type No. 2,"[7] this cross-section was developed for zero uplift, masonry weighing 145.8 lb per cu ft, and zero ice pressure except that the top width was made 20 ft. If this width is retained, the profile of a lower dam is obtained by cutting off the unwanted lower portion. If a smaller top width is used, every dimension shown in Figure 4-6 must be reduced in the ratio of the desired width to 20 ft. The proper height is then obtained, as before, by cutting off the unwanted lower portion of the modified structure.

Example 4-2. Estimate the salient dimensions of a dam 120 ft high with top width of 16 ft.

Calculated from Wegmann's Practical Type No. 2 for a ratio of 160/200 = 0.8, the dimensions are:

[7] Edward Wegmann, *The Design and Construction of Dams*, 8th ed., John Wiley and Sons, New York, 1927.

Upstream face	
(a) vertical for	60 × 0.8 = 48 ft
(b) sloping outward for	60 × 0.8 = 48 ft by 3.74 × 0.8 = 2.99 ft
(c) vertical for	120 − 96 = 24 ft
Downstream face	
(a) vertical for	18.74 × 0.8 = 14.99 ft
(b) curved to depth of	51.97 × 0.8 = 41.58 ft
(c) radius of curvature	60 × 0.8 = 48 ft
Base	
(a) width under upstream slope	3.74 × 0.8 = 2.99 ft
(b) intersection of upstream slope and base at distance of	1.87 × 0.8 = 1.50 ft from heel
(c) remaining width of base	95.23 × 0.8 = 76.18 ft

Height of 120 ft corresponds to height of 0.8 × 150 in the profile.

4-5. Water Intakes. Depending upon the size and nature of the installation, water is drawn from rivers, lakes, and reservoirs through relatively simple, submerged intakes or through more elaborate structures that rise above the water surface and may include, in addition to gates, mechanical screens, chlorinators, and living quarters for the operating personnel. Intakes should be so placed and designed as to draw water that is as clean and palatable as the source of supply can provide.

a. River intakes. These are constructed well upstream from points of discharge of the community's sewage and industrial wastes. They are so placed within the river channel as to take advantage of deep water, a stable bottom, and differential water quality (if pollution hugs one shore of the stream, for example), all with due reference to protection against floods, debris, ice, and river traffic.

b. Lake and reservoir intakes. Lake intakes avoid shore waters where possible and are placed with due reference to sources of pollution, prevailing winds, surface and subsurface currents, and shipping lanes. As shown in Figure 4-7, provisions for shifting the depth of draft make it possible to seek the clean bottom water that streams toward lake intakes when the wind is offshore and conversely to open surface ports when onshore winds drive clean surface water to the intake structure. The intake should be placed in water of such depth that bottom sediments are not stirred up by wave action and that ice troubles are minimized.

Reservoir intakes are similar in concept to lake intakes. They are generally placed closer to shore and are often incorporated in the dam that creates the reservoir (Figure 4-2).

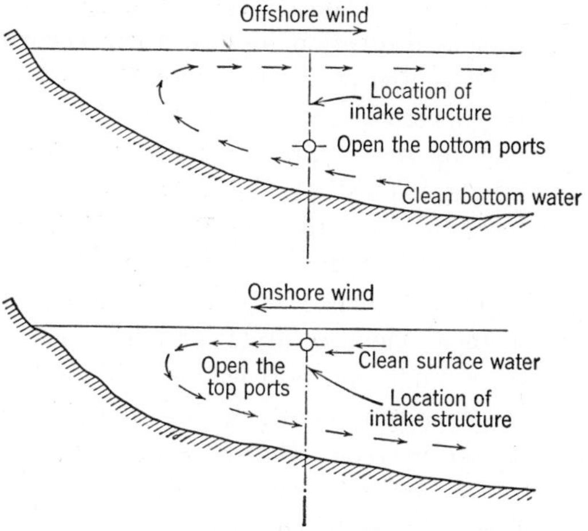

Figure 4-7. Effect of onshore and offshore winds on water quality at intake.

c. Submerged and exposed intakes. Submerged intakes take the form of a crib or a screened bellmouth. The crib protects the conduit against damage. Constructed of heavy timbers, it is weighted with rocks. Within it, the intake pipe rises to draw water through a grating.

Exposed intakes are towerlike structures (Figure 4-1). They may be situated (1) in dams, (2) on the banks of streams and lakes, (3) sufficiently near the shore to be connected to it by bridge or causeway, or (4) at such distances that they can only be reached by boat.

d. Protection against ice. Three types of ice are encountered in cold climates: sheet, frazil,[8] and anchor ice. Frazil ice, depending upon the conditions of its formation, may take the shape of needles, flakes, or formless slush. According to Barnes,[9] frazil is a surface-formed ice that is not permitted to freeze into a surface sheet. Carried to intakes or produced in them from supercooled water, frazil ice attaches itself to metallic racks, screens, conduits, and pumps. An-

[8] A French-Canadian term derived from the French for the forge cinders that fine, spicular frazil ice resembles.

[9] H. T. Barnes, *Natural Ice Formation*, John Wiley and Sons, New York, 1906.

chor ice behaves like frazil ice but is derived from ice crystals that have developed on the bottom and on submerged objects in much the same way that frost forms on vegetation during a clear night. Neither frazil nor anchor ice is normally encountered below sheet ice, which thus offers some protection against their occurrence. Difficulties can also be prevented by heating metallic surfaces or raising the temperature of supercooled water by about 0.1 F, the common order of magnitude of maximum supercooling. Compressed air, backflushing, and light explosives (¼ lb of 60% dynamite) have also been used successfully to free ice-clogged intakes.

e. Intake velocities and depths. Ice troubles are reduced in frequency if intake ports are placed as deep as 25 ft below the water surface and if entrance velocities are kept between 3 and 4 in. per sec. Low velocities will not transport ice and will hold the entraining of leaves and debris to a minimum. At low velocities, too, fish can escape from the intake current. Bottom sediments are kept out of the intake if entrance ports are raised 4 to 6 ft above the lake or reservoir floor. Ports should be provided at numerous other levels as well, in order to permit shifting the draft to optimum water quality. A vertical interval of 15 ft is often chosen. Submerged gratings are given openings of 2 to 3 in. Screens are commonly 2 to 8 meshes to the inch and have face velocities of 3 to 4 in. per sec. Screens are discussed further in Section 13-1.

f. Intake conduits and pumping stations. Constructed as pipes (often with flexible joints) or as tunnels, intake conduits are designed to carry water to the shore at self-cleansing velocities of 3 to 4 fps. Pipelines are generally laid in trenches that are dredged and backfilled. Where they reach the shore line, the pipes must be well protected against disturbance by waves and ice. Conduits on earth foundations beneath dams are subjected to high loads and to the stresses incident to the consolidation of the foundation.

Pumps that draw water through intake conduits are generally placed in a well on shore. Since the suction lift, including friction, should not exceed 15 to 20 ft, pump wells are often quite deep in order to be of service when river, lake, or reservoir levels are lowered appreciably in times of drought. This creates problems of hydrostatic uplift and seepage in times of flood. Large pumping units are generally placed in dry wells.

4-6. Reservoir Outlets. The outlet works of water-supply reservoirs normally include stream-diversion conduits and spillways.

Outlets may be provided, in addition, for low-water regulation (compensating water), development of hydroelectric power, and flood control. Navigation locks and fish ladders or fish elevators complete the list of possible control works.

a. Control conduits. Depending upon the geology and topography of the area, stream-diversion conduits are passed through the dam site or around it. After fulfilling their purpose of by-passing the stream and protecting the dam and valley during construction, they are often incorporated in the intake or outlet system for water supply (Figure 4-2), power development, and stream control (Figure 4-9). Their capacity is determined by flood-flow requirements (Sections 3-14, 3-15, 3-16, and 4-12). Diversion conduits are built as grade aqueducts and tunnels, or as pressure conduits and tunnels. However, no conduit passing through an earth dam can safely be placed under pressure. Gates should, therefore, be installed only at the inlet end of the conduit. If the conduit must work under pressure, consideration should be given to laying it within a larger access conduit. Conduits laid in earth dams or in earth foundations are often equipped with projecting fins or collars to discourage seepage along the outside of the conduit. The projections are designed to increase the path of seepage by 20% or more and to change the direction of seepage to include that of minimum permeability. At its terminus in the toe of the dam, a conduit traversing the dam should be surrounded with rock that, like a rock toe, will permit seepage waters to escape safely.

Flow into the outlet works is controlled by gates that are managed from gate houses. Control structures may also include racks and screens, diversion openings provided with stop logs, Venturi meters, water wheels, and electric generators.

b. Spillways. Spillways may be incorporated into the dam structure or they may be separated from it by a considerable distance.

The spillway section of masonry dams and of earth dams with a masonry spillway is designed as a masonry dam. In cross-section it commonly follows an ogee curve and has a high coefficient of discharge ($C = 3.5$ to 4.0) based on the common weir formula

$$Q = Clh^{3/2} \qquad \text{4-5}$$

where Q is the rate of discharge, l is the length adjusted for contraction, and h is the head. Reduction in length due to contractions is generally estimated at $0.1h$ for each sharp corner and at $0.05h$ for each rounded corner.

Separate spillways take the form of saddle, side-channel, and drop-inlet or shaft structures. Spillways placed in a saddle at some distance from the dam divert flow away from the dam. The spillway may be an open channel that discharges into a natural flood way leading back to the stream below the dam, or it may be a low, overflow ogee weir in advance of the flood way. In accordance with Figure 4-8, the inlet to a spillway channel creates a transition from substantial quiescence to full channel velocity. Maximum discharge

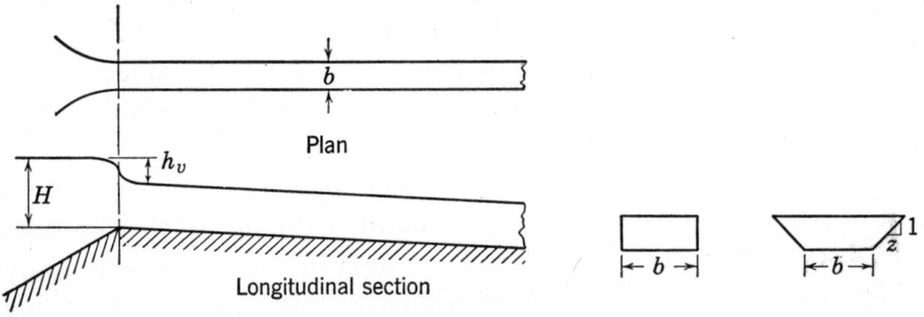

Figure 4-8. Channel spillway.

will be reached when the entrance is smooth and flow is at critical depth. The velocity head h_v at the entrance then equals one-third the height H of the reservoir level above the channel bottom at the entrance, and the rate of discharge through a rectangular channel becomes

$$Q = 3.087CbH^{3/2} \tag{4-6}$$

where b is the width of the channel and C is an entrance coefficient varying from 1.0 for a smooth entrance to 0.8 for an abrupt one. In line with Section 9-6, a trapezoidal channel with side slopes of z (horizontal to vertical) discharges

$$Q = 8.03Ch_v^{1/2}(H - h_v)[b + z(H - h_v)] \tag{4-7}$$

where

$$h_v = \frac{3(2zH + b) - \sqrt{16z^2H^2 + 16zbH + 9b^2}}{10z} \tag{4-8}$$

In accordance with well-known hydraulic principles, best hydraulic efficiency is obtained when a semicircle can be inscribed in the cross-section. Greatest hydraulic efficiency, however, does not necessarily coincide with best economy of construction.

Flow will be uniform below the entrance if frictional resistance is balanced by channel slope. Otherwise non-uniform flow is established. Channel sections are then adjusted to the changing conditions of flow. A weir within the channel produces a backwater curve.

Side-channel spillways are economical of space within the valley of the impounded stream. The crest of the spillway is placed along one hillside next to the dam, and the channel into which the spillway discharges is carried around the end of the dam and safely past its toe. The channel is preferably blasted out of rock. Failing this, it is lined with concrete. The hydraulic principles of design are those incorporated in the dimensioning of wash-water gutters for water filters (Section 15-9).

Shaft or drop-inlet spillways, as shown in Figure 4-9, consist of an overflow lip supported on a riser that discharges into an outlet conduit, which is often the original stream-diversion conduit. The lip is given any desired configuration. A circular lip and trumpet-like transition to the shaft creates a "morning-glory" spillway that must be placed at adequate distance from the shore if it is to be fully effective. A three-sided or semicircular lip is more accessible and can be in contact with the hillside. The capacity of shaft spillways is governed by that of its constituent parts and by the conditions of flow, including the effects of entrained air. Best hydraulic efficiency, as well as maximum flow capacity, is attained when the conduit and riser are flowing full. Model tests are much used to reach a design that will function properly.

Flashboards and gates are added to spillways to take advantage of

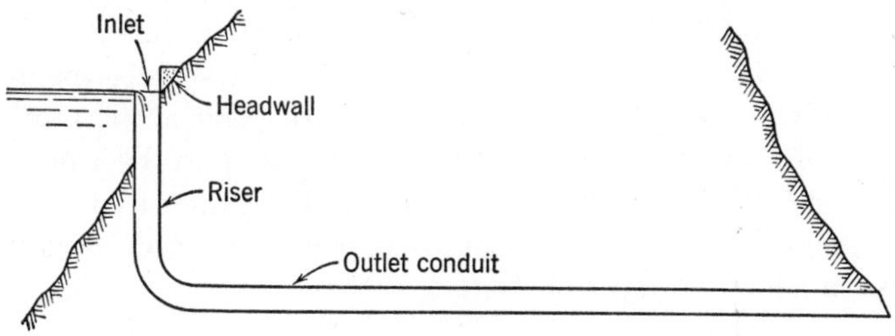

Figure 4-9. Shaft spillway.

storage above crest level, but only when their use will not endanger the structure.

4-7. Storage. In nature, the runoff from drainage areas is stored to a varying extent in lakes and ponds and in the backwaters and channels of streams. There is some storage, too, in the ground adjacent to water courses. This is called *bank storage*.

In the absence of adequate natural storage, engineers resort to the construction of impounding reservoirs or, more rarely, to the excavation of storage basins in lands adjacent to streams. Natural storage, too, can be regulated or developed by control works (gates and weirs) and dams.

Some storage works are designed to serve a single purpose, such as water supply; others are planned to include a number of different functions in serving the broader economy of natural resources. As a matter of wise planning, the multipurpose development of storage works should receive consideration in connection with all storage projects.

There are a number of different ways of calculating the storage from draft and runoff relationships in long-term records of stream flow. To be of use, these records should include at least the average monthly rates of discharge. Storage is determined either by analytical or by graphical methods.

Assuming that the reservoir is full at the beginning of the dry season, or dry period, the maximum amount of water S that must be drawn from storage to maintain a draft or flow D equals the maximum cumulative difference between the draft and runoff Q subsequent to the beginning of the dry period, or:

$$S = \text{maximum value of } \Sigma(D - Q) \qquad 4\text{-}9$$

To find S, therefore, $\Sigma(D - Q)$ is calculated arithmetically or determined graphically. The last is done as a most convincing and useful demonstration by finding $\Sigma(D - Q) = \Sigma D - \Sigma Q$ by the mass-diagram or Rippl [10] method illustrated in Figure 4-10. The shorter the interval of time for which runoff is recorded, the more exact is the result. As the maximum value is approached, therefore, it may be worth while to shift to short intervals of time: from monthly values to daily values, for example. The additional storage indicated by such a shift may equal as much as 10 days of draft.

[10] W. Rippl, The capacity of storage reservoirs for water supply, *Proc. Inst. Civil Engrs.*, *71*, 270 (1883).

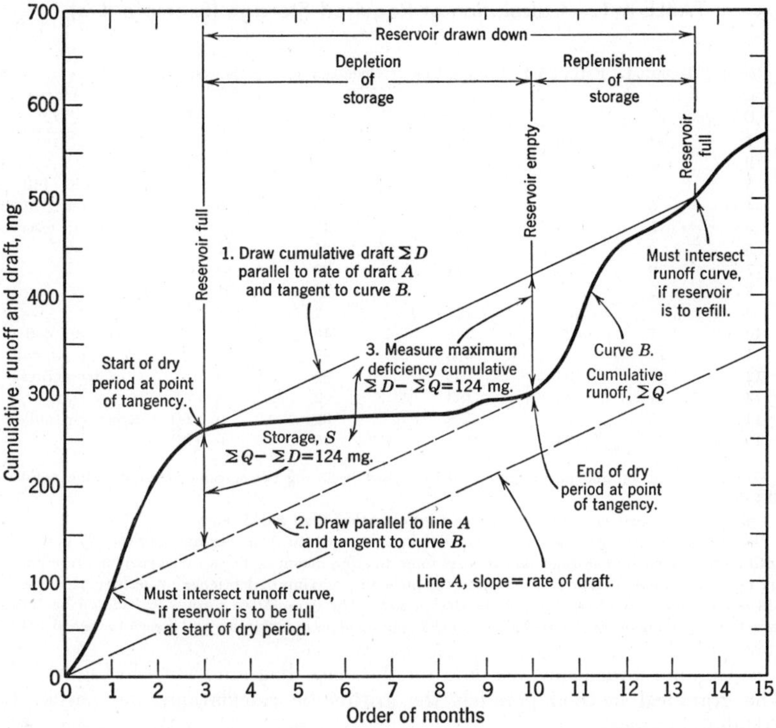

Figure 4-10. Mass-diagram or Rippl method for the determination of storage required in impounding reservoirs.

Example 4-3. Find the storage required to maintain a constant draft of 750,000 gpd per sq mile from a stream[11] with the following record of monthly mean runoff values:

Order of month	1	2	3	4	5	6	7	8	9	10	11	12	13	14	15
Observed runoff, mg per sq mile	94	122	45	5	5	2	0	2	16	7	72	92	21	55	33

a. The necessary calculations for the arithmetic and graphical solution of this problem are shown in Table 4-1, all volumes of water being stated in million gallons per square mile.

b. The schedule gives the maximum cumulative deficiency, or required storage, as 124 mg per sq mile. This equals $124/0.75 = 165$ days of draft; i.e., enough water must be stored to supply the community for 165 days (almost half a year).

[11] The Westfield Little River near Springfield, Mass., for March, 1914, to May, 1915. In New England, a yield of 750,000 gpd per sq mile can generally be assured with economical storage.

TABLE 4-1. Calculation of Required Storage (Example 4-3)

Order of Months (1)	Recorded Runoff, Q (2)	Estimated Draft, D (3)	Cumulative Runoff, ΣQ (4) = Σ(2)	Deficiency, $D - Q$ (5) = (3) − (2)	Cumulative Deficiency, $\Sigma(D - Q)$ (6) = Σ(5)	Remarks (7)
1	94	23	94	−71	0 (192)	
2	122	23	216	−99	0 (121)	
3	45	23	261	−22	0 (22)	Reservoir full at
4	5	23	266	18	18	beginning of dry
5	5	23	271	18	36	period; reservoir
6	2	23	273	21	57	empties
7	0	23	273	23	80	
8	2	23	275	21	101	
9	16	23	291	7	108	
10	7	23	298	16	124	Maximum defi-
11	72	23	370	−49	75	ciency at end
12	92	23	462	−69	6	of dry period
13	21	23	483	2	8	
14	55	23	538	−32	0 (24)	Reservoir refilled
15	33	23	571	−10	0 (34)	

Column 3: 750,000 gpd per sq mile = 0.75 × 30.4 = 23 mg per sq mile for an average month of 30.4 days.

Column 5: A negative value indicates a surplus rather than a deficiency.

Column 6: Negative values are not included in $\Sigma(D - Q)$ until the beginning of the dry period, i.e., until water is lost from storage, and there is room to store incoming flows. The surplus preceding the dry period, however, must equal or exceed the preceding maximum deficiency; otherwise, the reservoir will not be full at the beginning of the dry period. The cumulative surplus, calculated backwards from the beginning of the dry period, is shown in parentheses in Column 6 and is seen to exceed 124 mg.

c. Column 4 furnishes the data for the mass diagram shown in Figure 4-10. The graphical method parallels the arithmetic calculations and checks the calculated storage.

4-8. Design Storage. Except for occasional series of dry years, only seasonal storage is required in the well-watered regions of North America. Water is plentiful, and stream flows do not vary greatly from year to year. Under these conditions, it does not pay to go in for high or complete development of catchment areas, and reservoirs generally refill within the annual hydrologic cycle. In semiarid regions, on the other hand, water is scarce, hence more valuable, and stream flows fluctuate widely from year to year. High developments are then warranted, and the runoff of wet years must often be conserved for use during subsequent dry years. Given a series of storage values for the years of record, it is best to resort to a statistical analysis of the arrayed storage values and to select as the design storage a value of some reasonable frequency, such as the storage requirement that is equaled or exceeded but once in 20, 50, or 100 years, i.e., 5, 2, and 1% of the time. For water supply, Hazen[12] has

[12] Allen Hazen, Storage to be provided in impounding reservoirs, *Trans. Am. Soc. Civil Engrs.*, *77*, 1539 (1914).

suggested that the 5% value be employed in ordinary circumstances. In other words, design storage should be adequate to compensate for a drought of such severity that it is not expected to occur oftener than once in 20 years. In still drier years, it may be necessary to curtail the use of water by limiting, or prohibiting, lawn sprinkling, car washing, and similar practices.

As a practical matter, curtailment of use for conservation of stored water must be started well in advance of anticipated exhaustion of the impounded supply. The reserve remaining when conservation is begun generally lies between 20% and 50% of the total volume of water stored. Requiring a 25% reserve for the drought that occurs about once in 20 years is reasonable.

Estimation of the 5, 2, and 1% frequencies, or of recurrence intervals of 20, 50, and 100 years, requires extrapolation from available data. Probability plots are well adapted to this purpose. However, such plots must be prepared and used with considerable thought. Where severe droughts in the record extend over several years and require annual rather than seasonal storages, the resulting series of storage values becomes non-homogeneous and is no longer strictly subject to ordinary statistical interpretations. They can be made reasonably homogeneous by including, besides all truly seasonal storages, not only all truly annual storages but also those seasonal storages that would have been identified within the periods of annual storage if the drought of the preceding year or years had not been measured. Plots of recurrence intervals should include minor storages as well as major ones. The results of these statistical analyses are conveniently reduced to a set of draft-storage-frequency curves.

Example 4-4. Examination of the 25-year record runoff from an eastern stream[13] shows that the storages listed in Table 4-2 are needed in successive years to maintain a draft of 750,000 gpd per sq mile.

TABLE 4-2. Storage Requirements (Example 4-4)

Order of year	1	2	3	4	5	6	7	8	9	10	11	12	13
Calculated storage, mg	47	39	104	110	115	35	74	81	124	29	37	82	78
Order of year	14	15	16	17	18	19	20	21	22	23	24	25	
Calculated storage, mg	72	10	117	51	61	8	102	65	73	20	53	88	

Estimate the design storage requirement that is probably reached or exceeded but once in 20, 50, and 100 years.

[13] The Westfield Little River near Springfield, Mass., for the years 1906 to 1930.

a. The 25 calculated storage values arrayed in order of magnitude are plotted on arithmetic-probability paper in Figure 4-11. The arrayed storages are plotted at $100k/26 = 3.8\%$, 7.7%, 11.5%, etc. The straight line of best fit is identified by the arithmetic mean storage $M = 67$ mg and the standard deviation $\sigma = 33$ mg.

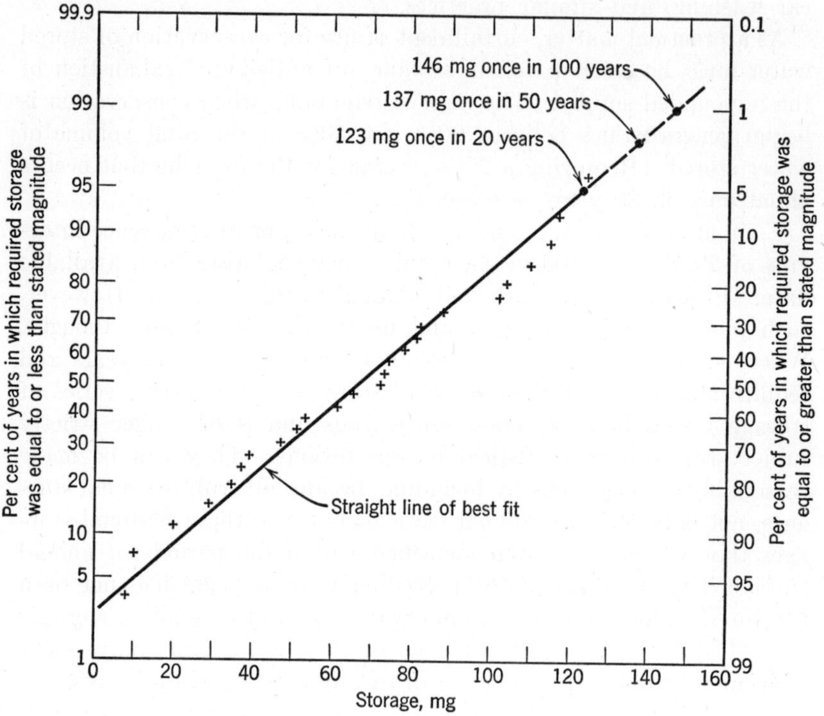

Figure 4-11. Frequency distribution of required storage plotted on arithmetic-probability paper.

b. The storage requirements that are reached or exceeded once in 20, 50, and 100 years, or 5, 2, and 1% of the time, are found to be 123, 137, and 146 mg respectively. Use is made of probability paper because it offers a rational basis for projecting the information beyond the period of experience. The once-in-20-years requirement with 25% reserve suggests a design storage of $123/0.75 = 164$ mg per sq mile of drainage area.

c. It should be noted that the coefficient of variation of the calculated storage $c_v = 100 \times 33/67 = 50\%$ is more than twice as great as the variability of runoff ($c_v = 22\%$) for closely the same period of observation (see Example 3-2).

d. For comparison with other river records, the draft and storage may be expressed in terms of the mean annual flow (MAF) and the storage also in terms of daily draft. For a mean annual flow of 26.6 in., or 26.6 × 0.0477 = 1.27 mgd per sq mile (Example 3-2):

1. Draft = 750,000 gpd per sq mile = 100 × 0.750/1.27 = 59% of MAF.
2. Storage requirement equaled or exceeded once in 20 years = 123 mg per sq mile, or (100 × 123)/(1.27 × 365) = 27% of MAF.
3. Storage requirement = 123/0.750 = 164 days of draft, or nearly half a year if 10 days are added to compensate for the use of monthly average runoffs in place of daily stream discharge.

When more than one reservoir is developed on a stream, the overflow from each impoundage becomes available to the reservoir next below together with the runoff from the intervening water shed. The amount of overflow is determined from the storage analysis for each year or for the critical year. If the reservoirs are operated jointly and those downstream are drawn on first, all reservoirs may be considered as being combined at the most-downstream location, provided that the area tributary to each reservoir is large enough to fill its reservoir during the season of heavy runoff.

4-9. Generalized Storage Values. Hazen[14] has shown that it is possible by an analysis of country-wide information to generalize regional storage requirements on the basis of the mean annual flows of streams and their coefficients of variation. A partial summary of Hazen's generalized storage values is given in Table 4-3. The use of this table is illustrated in Example 4-5.

TABLE 4-3. Generalized Storage Values for Streams East of the Mississippi River, or in Oregon and Washington

Both draft and storage are expressed in terms of the mean annual flow of the stream. The coefficient of variation in annual flows is designated c_v

	Storage for Stated Values of c_v						Deduction for 30 Days'
Draft	0.20	0.25	0.30	0.35	0.40	0.45	Ground Storage
0.9	0.85	1.05	1.31	1.60	1.88	2.20	0.074
0.8	0.54	0.64	0.78	0.97	1.19	1.39	0.066
0.7	0.39	0.43	0.50	0.62	0.76	0.92	0.058
0.6	0.31	0.32	0.34	0.40	0.49	0.60	0.049
0.5	0.23	0.23	0.24	0.26	0.32	0.39	0.041

Example 4-5. For the eastern stream dealt with in Examples 4-3 and 4-4, find the generalized storage for a draft of 750,000 gpd per sq mile on the assumption that the coefficient of variation in annual flow is 0.22 and the mean annual flow 1.27 mgd (Example 3-2).

[14] Allen Hazen, in *American Civil Engineers' Handbook,* John Wiley and Sons, New York, p. 1446, 1930.

a. The draft is 59% of MAF as shown in Example 4-4.

b. For 59% and $c_v = 0.22$, Table 4-3 gives a storage of 0.30 MAF or 0.30 × 1.27 × 365 = 139 mg per sq mile.

c. For 30 days' ground storage, deduct, according to Table 4-3, 0.048 from 0.30, making it 0.25 MAF or 0.25 × 1.27 × 365 = 116 mg per sq mile.

The agreement between the results obtained by normal analytical procedures and by the use of Hazen's generalized storage values is good.

4-10. Loss by Evaporation, Seepage, and Silting. Construction of an impounding reservoir alters the hydrology of that portion of the water shed which is inundated by the reservoir. The original land surface is replaced by a fluctuating water surface which loses water by evaporation and gains water by direct reception of rainfall. This may be called the water-surface effect. The rising water alters the pattern of ground-water flow, and seepage from the reservoir may discharge through permeable soils into neighboring catchment areas. The quiescence created by the impoundage, finally, reduces the carrying power of the stream and causes the subsidence of settleable solids or silting of the reservoir.

a. Water-surface effect. The effect of introducing a new water surface includes:

1. *Loss:* (*a*) runoff from land area flooded by the reservoir = QW (closely), where Q is the rate of runoff per unit area of original water shed, and W is the area of water surface of the reservoir; and (*b*) evaporation from the water surface = EW, where E is the rate of evaporation per unit area of reservoir.
2. *Gain:* rainfall on the water surface = RW, where R is the rate of rainfall per unit area of reservoir.

Hence the net rate of loss or gain for the portion of the water shed in question = $[R - (Q + E)]W$. A negative value records a net loss and a positive value a net gain. The mean annual water surface is normally about 90% that at spillway level.

To make for convenience in calculation, the water-surface effect is accounted for in one of the following ways:

1. *Revised runoff.* If A is the total catchment area and Q_r is the revised rate of runoff per unit area,

$$Q_r = Q - (Q + E - R)(W/A) \qquad 4\text{-}10$$

The revised values of runoff are then used in recalculating the storage requirements.

2. *Equivalent draft.* If D_e is the draft equivalent of the difference in yield between the water and land area,

$$D_e = (Q + E - R)(W/A) \qquad \text{on a unit area basis} \qquad 4\text{-}11$$

The sum of the drafts D and draft equivalents D_e, or the effective draft $(D + D_e)$, is then used in calculating the storage requirements.

3. *Equivalent land area.* The water surface is expressed in terms of the equivalent land area W_e by the relation

$$W_e = W(R - E)/Q \tag{4-12}$$

and the effective catchment area A_e is then considered to be

$$A_e = A - W + W_e = A - W[1 - (R - E)/Q] \tag{4-13}$$

This adjustment is generally based on average annual values.

4. *Adjusted flowline.* The flowline elevation of the impounding reservoir is changed by an amount equal to $Q + E - R$, all factors being stated in a unit such as inches or feet yearly. This unit, converted from the mean annual water surface to the reservoir area at spillway level, is then added to the flowline elevation. As a rough approximation, an increase in the height of the spillway level by a foot or two is sometimes employed.

Example 4-6. A mean draft of 30.0 mgd is to be developed from a catchment area of 40.0 sq miles. First calculations give a reservoir area of 1,500 acres at flowline. The mean annual rainfall is 47.0 in.; the mean annual runoff is 27.0 in.; and the mean annual evaporation is 40.0 in. Find (1) the revised mean annual runoff, (2) the equivalent mean draft, (3) the equivalent land area, and (4) the adjusted flowline.

1. By Equation 4-10: $Q_r = 27.0 - (27.0 + 40.0 - 47.0)0.9 \times 1{,}500/(640 \times 40.0) = 27.0 - 1.1 = 25.9$ in.

2. By Equation 4-11: $D_e = 1.1$ in., or 52,000 gpd per sq mile, and the effective draft is $30.0 + 40.0 \times 0.052 = 32.1$ mgd.

3. By Equation 4-13: $A_e = 40.0 - \dfrac{0.9 \times 1{,}500}{640}\left(1 - \dfrac{47.0 - 40.0}{27.0}\right) = 40.0 - 1.6 = 38.4$ sq miles.

4. $Q + E - R = 27.0 + 40.0 - 47.0 = 20$ in.
At spillway level this equals $20 \times 0.9 = 18$ in.

b. Seepage. If the valley that encloses a reservoir is underlain by porous strata, there may be considerable loss of water by seepage. Only a subsurface exploration can tell how great the expected loss will be. Seepage is not confined to the dam site proper. It occurs wherever the sides and bottom of the reservoir are sufficiently permeable to permit entrance of water and its discharge through the ground beneath the surrounding hills.

c. Silting. The silting of reservoirs is the result of soil erosion on the water shed. Both are undesirable. Erosion destroys arable lands. Silting destroys useful storage. Silt accumulated in reservoirs by sedimentation of eroded soil cannot be removed economically by any means so far devised. In favorable circumstances, however, much of the heaviest load of suspended silt can be passed through the reservoir by opening large sluices that are installed for this purpose. Flood flows are thereby selected for storage in accordance with their quality as well as their volume.

In the design of reservoirs that impound silt-bearing streams, suitable allowances must be made for loss of capacity by silting. Eroding streams carry suspended sediment in concentrations Q_s that rise with the rate of discharge Q according to the relationship $Q_s = kQ^n$ where k and n are river coefficients and n lies close to 2. The rate of silt deposition appears to be greatest for reservoirs on small catchment areas. In the southwestern United States,[15] the rate of silt deposition V_s from a given watershed A is approximated by the relationship $V_s = cA^m$ where c and m are basin coefficients and m lies close to 0.8. The similarity of this empirical relationship to a flood-flow formula is not surprising.

4-11. Area and Volume of Reservoirs. The surface areas and volumes of water associated with given flowline elevations are determined from a contour map of the site that is flooded by the reservoir. The areas enclosed by each contour line are planimetered, and volumes between contour lines are calculated ordinarily by the *average-end-area method.*

For uniform contour intervals h and successive contour areas a_0, a_1, $\cdots$ a_n, the volume V of water stored up to the nth contour is

$$V = [(a_0 + a_1) + (a_1 + a_2) + \cdots (a_{n-1} + a_n)]h/2$$

$$= \left(\frac{a_0 + a_n}{2} + \sum_1^{n-1} a\right) h \qquad 4\text{-}14$$

Surface areas and volumes that do not coincide with mapped contour lines are interpolated most satisfactorily from curves obtained by plotting the measured contour-line areas and calculated volumes against the contour elevations. Figure 4-12 shows such curves.[16]

A knowledge of surface areas and volumes of reservoirs is needed not only in the solution of hydrological problems but also in the control of algae by the addition of copper sulfate and in other questions relating to the quality of stored waters.

[15] For basic information see H. M. Eakin, Silting of reservoirs, *U. S. Dept. Agr. Tech. Bull.* 524, 1939.

[16] The vertical scale implied by elevations generally leads engineers to plot elevations as ordinates. Figure 4-12, however, is kept consistent with the injunction to plot as the ordinate the variable that is to be found.

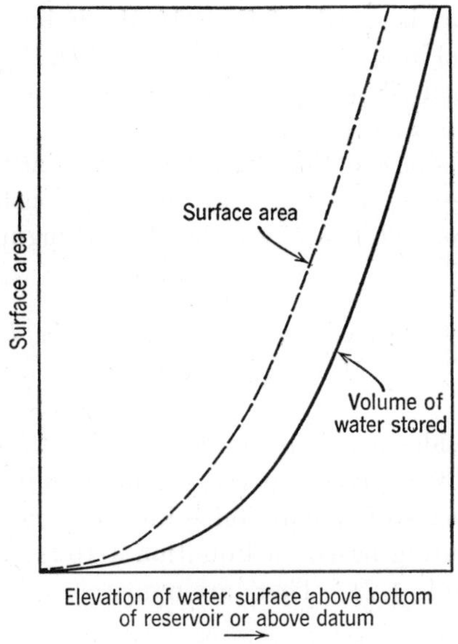

Figure 4-12. Surface area of a reservoir and volume of water stored.

4-12. Spillway Capacity and Flood Routing. Impounding reservoirs must be provided with spillways capable of discharging the maximum peak flood that the storage works are expected to pass. To be on the safe side in designing the spillway, it is assumed that the entrant flood may occur when the reservoir is full. Before the maximum head on the spillway can be developed, however, the flood waters must back up in the reservoir and fill the space between spillway level and flood level. This storage above spillway level retains some of the entering flood waters and reduces the flood peak.

The retardation of floods by storage above spillway level is a function of the rate of inflow I into the reservoir, the available storage S above spillway level, and the rate of outflow Q from the reservoir. All these factors are variable during the course of the flood and not sufficiently regular to be generalized mathematically. Analytical procedures, therefore, are usually based upon a stepwise analysis of the various hydraulic occurrences: varying inflow, changing water level, and varying outflow. For a specified interval of time, Δt,

$$Q \, \Delta t = I \, \Delta t - \Delta S \qquad \text{4-15}$$

If it is assumed that the average rates of inflow and outflow are closely equal to the arithmetic means of the rates obtaining at the beginning and the end of short intervals of time Δt, the individual steps in the proposed mechanical integration are: $Q\,\Delta t = \Delta t(Q_k + Q_{k+1})/2$; $I\,\Delta t = \Delta t(I_k + I_{k+1})/2$; and $\Delta S = (S_{k+1} - S_k)$. Here the subscripts k and $(k+1)$ denote successive intervals of time of length Δt. Substitution of these expressions in Equation 4-15 gives $\Delta t(Q_k + Q_{k+1})/2 = [\Delta t(I_k + I_{k+1})/2] - (S_{k+1} - S_k)$. In this relationship outflow and storage are both related to spillway head.[17] Bringing the associated terms together,

$$\left(\frac{S_{k+1}}{\Delta t} + \frac{Q_{k+1}}{2}\right) = \left(\frac{S_k}{\Delta t} - \frac{Q_k}{2}\right) + \left(\frac{I_k + I_{k+1}}{2}\right) \qquad 4\text{-}16$$

This equation provides a means for determining the outflow pattern that is produced by a given pattern of inflow into an impounding reservoir. The process of calculation is known as *flood routing*. The method of flood routing based on Equation 4-16 is best explained by an example (Example 4-7). There are numerous other approaches to this problem.

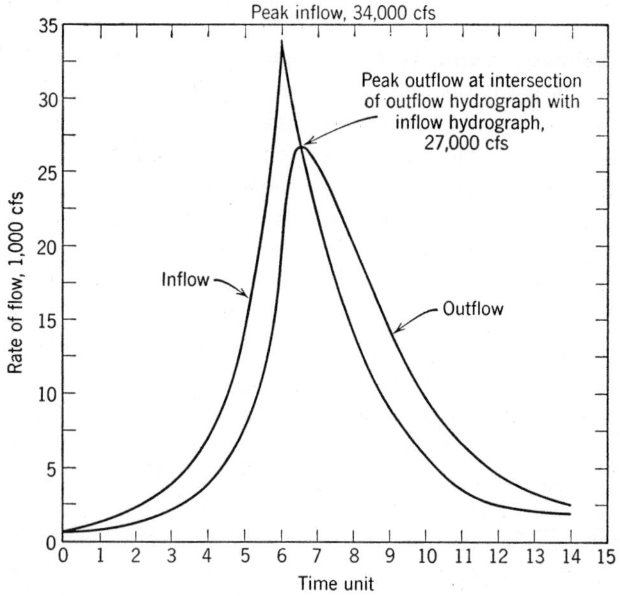

Figure 4-13. Modification of flood flow by storage.

[17] Spillway discharge $Q_1 = CL(H_1 - H_0)^{3/2}$ by the common weir formula, while storage $S_1 = V_1 - V_0 = c(H_1^m - H_0^m)$. Here H_0 is the depth of water at spillway level, $H_1 - H_0$ is the head on the spillway, L is the length of weir, and m is a coefficient not far from 3.

Example 4-7. From the predicted hydrograph of a stream in flood (Figure 4-13), construct the outflow hydrograph to be expected from a reservoir of known storage characteristics impounding the stream under the assumed conditions of runoff prevailing during the flood.

The following assumptions are made: length of spillway tentatively selected $L = 250$ ft; appropriate weir coefficient $C = 3.8$; and time interval $\Delta t = 3$ hr $= 10{,}800$ sec.

a. The first step in the solution of this problem is to determine, for increasing heads H, the outflow Q and storage S above spillway level. To do this, the surface area A of the reservoir must be found from a curve of the type shown in Figure 4-12.

b. The second step is to calculate the corresponding functional rates of storage values $\frac{S}{\Delta t}$, $\left(\frac{S}{\Delta t} - \frac{Q}{2}\right)$ and $\left(\frac{S}{\Delta t} + \frac{Q}{2}\right)$. These steps are carried out in Table 4-4.

TABLE 4-4. Calculation of Functional Rates of Storage (Example 4-7)

Head on Spillway H, ft (1)	Reservoir Area A, acres (2)	Calculated Outflow Q, cfs (3)	Calculated Storage S above Spillway Level, acre-ft (4)	Functional Rates of Storage: $\frac{S}{\Delta t}$ cfs (5)	$\left(\frac{S}{\Delta t} - \frac{Q}{2}\right)$ cfs (6)	$\left(\frac{S}{\Delta t} + \frac{Q}{2}\right)$ cfs (7)
0	670	0	0	0	0	0
1	700	950	685	2,760	2,285	3,235
2	730	2,680	1,400	5,650	4,310	6,990
3	760	4,940	2,145	8,650	6,180	11,120
4	790	7,600	2,920	11,770	7,970	15,570
5	820	10,620	3,725	15,020	9,710	20,330
6	850	13,950	4,560	18,390	11,415	25,365
7	885	17,600	5,425	21,900	13,100	30,700
8	920	21,500	6,330	25,500	14,750	36,250
9	960	25,700	7,270	29,300	16,450	42,150
10	1,000	30,100	8,250	33,300	18,300	48,400

Column 1: Assumed values; heads differing by 1 ft.
Column 2: From area curve similar to Figure 4-12.
Column 3: From $Q = CLH^{3/2} = 3.8 \times 250 \times H^{3/2}$ or straight-line plot on log-log paper (Figure 4-14).
Column 4: By Equation 4-14: $\left(\frac{A_0 + A_n}{2} + \sum_{1}^{n-1} A\right) h$.

Column 5: Column 4 × 43,560/10,800 = 4.03 × Column 4.
Column 6: Column 5 − ½ Column 3.
Column 7: Column 5 + ½ Column 3 = Column 6 + Column 3.

c. The third step is to plot the rates of discharge and storage against the heads on the spillway. This is done in Figure 4-14. The resulting curves,

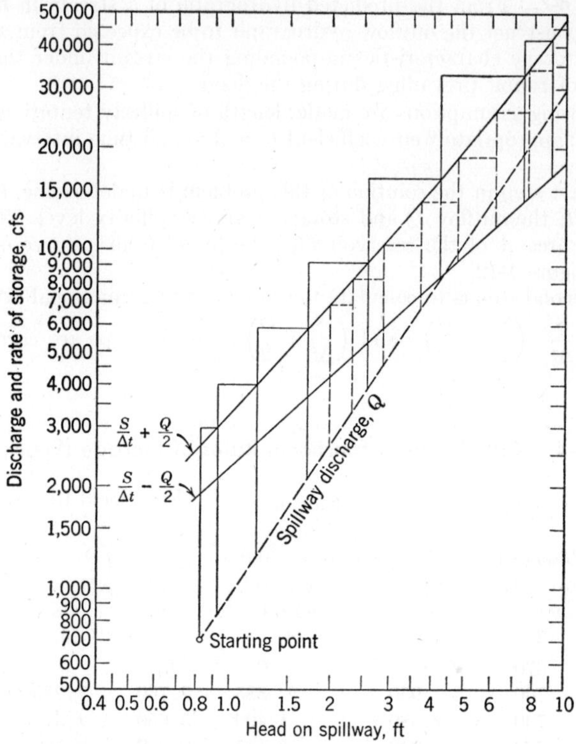

Figure 4-14. Stepwise graphical determination of head and discharge relationships in routing a flood through an impounding reservoir.

known as *routing curves* and *discharge curves*, make possible the stepwise graphical determination of spillway heads and outflows at the chosen time interval of 3 hr.

d. The fourth step is to add, in Figure 4-14, the average rate of inflow $(I_k + I_{k+1})/2$ for each specified time interval to the corresponding value of $\left(\frac{S_k}{\Delta t} - \frac{Q_k}{2}\right)$ in accordance with Equation 4-16 and to find at the resulting magnitude of $\left(\frac{S_{k+1}}{\Delta t} + \frac{Q_{k+1}}{2}\right)$ the spillway head and discharge that must obtain in order to satisfy these relationships. To establish a starting point, it is assumed that the reservoir is in equilibrium at the initial rate of inflow of 700 cfs shown in Figure 4-13, the head on the spillway being $H = \left(\frac{Q}{CL}\right)^{2/3} = \left(\frac{700}{3.8 \times 250}\right)^{2/3} = 0.82$ ft.

The necessary calculations are presented in Table 4-5.

TABLE 4-5. Calculation of Reservoir Outflows (Example 4-7)

Time Number (1)	Observed Inflow I, cfs (2)	Average Inflow cfs (3)	$\frac{S}{\Delta t} - \frac{Q}{2}$ At Beginning of Time Interval (4)	$\frac{S}{\Delta t} + \frac{Q}{2}$ At End of Time Interval (5)	Head on Spillway ft (6)	Out-flow Q cfs (7)
0	700	......	......	......	0.817	700
1	1,400	1,050	1,900	2,950	0.920	840
2	2,400	1,900	2,100	4,000	1.20	1,250
3	4,000	3,200	2,700	5,900	1.70	2,100
4	7,000	5,500	3,700	9,200	2.55	3,870
5	15,000	11,000	5,400	16,400	4.20	8,170
6	34,000	24,500	8,300	32,800	7.40	19,100
7	22,000	28,000	13,700	41,700	8.95	25,400
8	14,000	18,000	16,200	34,200	7.65	20,010
9	9,000	11,500	14,200	25,700	6.10	14,300
10	6,000	7,500	11,500	19,000	4.70	9,680
11	3,400	4,700	9,300	14,000	3.70	6,760
12	2,500	2,950	7,400	10,350	2.85	4,570
13	2,200	2,350	5,900	8,250	2.30	3,310
14	2,000	2,100	4,850	6,950	1.95	2,590

Column 1: Each time interval is 3 hours.

Column 2: The observed inflow is taken from the chosen flood hydrograph of the stream before impoundage. See Figure 4-13.

Column 3: Average of successive values in Column 2.

Column 4: Value of $\left(\frac{S}{\Delta t} - \frac{Q}{2}\right)$ at beginning of time interval read during construction of Figure 4-14.

Column 5: Value of $\left(\frac{S}{\Delta t} + \frac{Q}{2}\right)$ at end of time interval = Column 4 + Column 3 in accordance with Equation 4-16.

Columns 6 and 7: Read from Figure 4-14 with exception of the initial values: 0.82 ft and 700 cfs. These identify the starting point of the step integration.

e. The last step is to plot the calculated outflow hydrograph against the observed inflow hydrograph. This is done in Figure 4-13. It is seen that storage above spillway level lowers the peak flow from 34,000 cfs to 27,000 cfs, i.e., to 80% of its uncontrolled magnitude. The head on the spillway, therefore, is 9.2 ft (Figure 4-14).

The principles involved in this method of flood routing can be employed also in studies of the effect upon flood flows of channel storage, detention or retardation basins, and other types of storage.

A rough determination of whether calculations such as these are worth while can be had from generalized estimates suggested by

Fuller [18] (Table 4-6). If the outflow is reduced to 90% or less of the inflow, more accurate calculations are justified.

TABLE 4-6. Generalized Estimates of Reservoir Outflows

Ratio of storage above spillway level to flood flow in 24 hours, %	5	10	20	30	40	50	60	70
Ratio of peak outflow to peak inflow, %	99	97	93	86	77	65	53	40

Example 4-8. The flood flows presented in Example 4-7 will produce a maximum 24-hr flood of 27,600 acre-ft. If the maximum allowable head on the spillway is assumed to be 10 ft, the storage available above spillway level is 8,250 acre-ft. The ratio of peak outflow to peak inflow is then found as follows from Fuller's values (Table 4-6):

a. Ratio of storage above spillway level to 24-hr flood $100 \times 8{,}250/27{,}600 = 30\%$.

b. From Fuller's values, ratio of peak outflow to peak inflow = 86%.

c. The value ascertained in Example 4-7 was 80%, the maximum head on the spillway being 9.2 ft.

Since Fuller's outflow ratio is less than 90%, making the more accurate determination is warranted.

The principles presented in the preceding sections of this chapter are applicable also to the storage and regulation of storm-water runoff collected by combined municipal drainage schemes. The storm-water stand-by tanks used for this purpose may be incorporated in the collecting system itself or become auxiliary units in sewage-treatment works.

4-13. Collection of Rain Water. Rain is rarely the immediate source of municipal water supplies,[19] and the use of rain water is generally confined (1) to farms and rural settlements usually in semiarid regions devoid of satisfactory ground-water or surface-water supplies, and (2) to some hard-water communities in which, because of its softness, roof drainage is employed principally for household laundry work and general washing purposes, while the public supply satisfies all other requirements. In most hard-water communities, the installation and operation of municipal water-softening plants can ordinarily be justified economically. Their introduction is desirable and does away with the need for supplementary rain-water supplies and the associated objection of their possible cross-connection [20] with the public supply.

[18] W. E. Fuller, Flood flows, *Trans. Am. Soc. Civil Engrs.*, *70*, 564 (1914).

[19] A notable example is the water supply of the communities on the Islands of Bermuda on which streams are lacking and ground water is brackish.

[20] A *cross-connection* is a junction between water supply systems through which water from a doubtful or unsafe source may enter an otherwise safe supply.

For individual homesteads, rain water running off the roof is led through gutters and downspouts to a rain barrel or cistern situated on the ground or below it (see Figure 1-1). Barrel or cistern storage converts the intermittent rainfall into a continuous supply. For municipal service, roof water may be combined with water collected from sheds or catches on the surface of ground that is naturally impervious or rendered so by grouting, cementing, paving, or similar means.

The gross yield of rain-water supplies is proportional to the receiving area and the amount of precipitation. Some rain, however, is blown off the roof by wind, evaporated, or lost in wetting the collecting area and conduits and in filling depressions or improperly pitched gutters. Also, the first flush of water contains most of the dust and other undesirable washings from the catchment surfaces and may have to be wasted. The combined loss is particularly great during the dry season of the year. A cutoff, switch, or deflector in the downspout permits selecting the quality of water to be stored. Sand filters are successfully employed to cleanse the cistern water and prevent its deterioration (1) by the growth of undesirable organisms and (2) by the bacterial decomposition of organic materials, both of which may give rise to tastes, odors, and other changes in the attractiveness and palatability of the water.

Storage to be provided in cisterns depends upon seasonal rainfall characteristics and commonly approximates one-third to one-half the annual needs in accordance with the length of dry spells. If the water is to be filtered before storage, stand-by capacity in advance of filtration must be provided if rainfalls of high intensity are not to escape. Because of the relatively small catchment area available, roof drainage cannot be expected to yield an abundant supply of water for man and beast, and a close analysis of storm rainfalls and seasonal variations in precipitation must be made if catchment areas, stand-by tanks, filters, and cisterns are to be proportioned and developed properly.

5 Collection of Ground Water

5-1. Nature and Sources of Ground Water. Ground-water supplies have an intake or catchment area much like that of surface-water supplies, except that the catch, or recharge, is by infiltration of water into the openings of the ground rather than by runoff over its surface. The intake area may be nearby or situated at a considerable distance from the point of water collection, especially when flow is confined within a water-bearing stratum, or *aquifer,*[1] that underlies an impervious stratum, or *aquiclude*[2] (Figure 5-1). If the upper surface of the ground water is free to rise and fall with seasonal changes in recharge, flow is unconfined or free, and the water surface, or *ground-water table,* slopes downward more or less like the ground surface. Under these conditions, the ground water moves at right angles to the water-table contours. If the water-bearing stratum dips beneath an impervious layer, flow becomes confined as in a pipe that dips below the hydraulic grade line, and *artesian water*[3] will rise under pressure from the aquifer when tapped. Water caught on a lens of impervious material above the true ground-water table is called *perched* water.

Springs of ground water reach daylight (1) when the surface of the earth drops sharply below the normal ground-water table; (2) when an obstruction to flow impounds the ground water behind it and forces

[1] The word *aquifer* comes from the Latin *aqua,* water, and *ferre,* to bear.

[2] The word *aquiclude* comes from the Latin *aqua,* water, and *cludere,* to shut or close.

[3] The term *artesian water* is derived from *Artois,* the name of a province of France, where water supplies from "flowing wells" were brought in as early as the twelfth century.

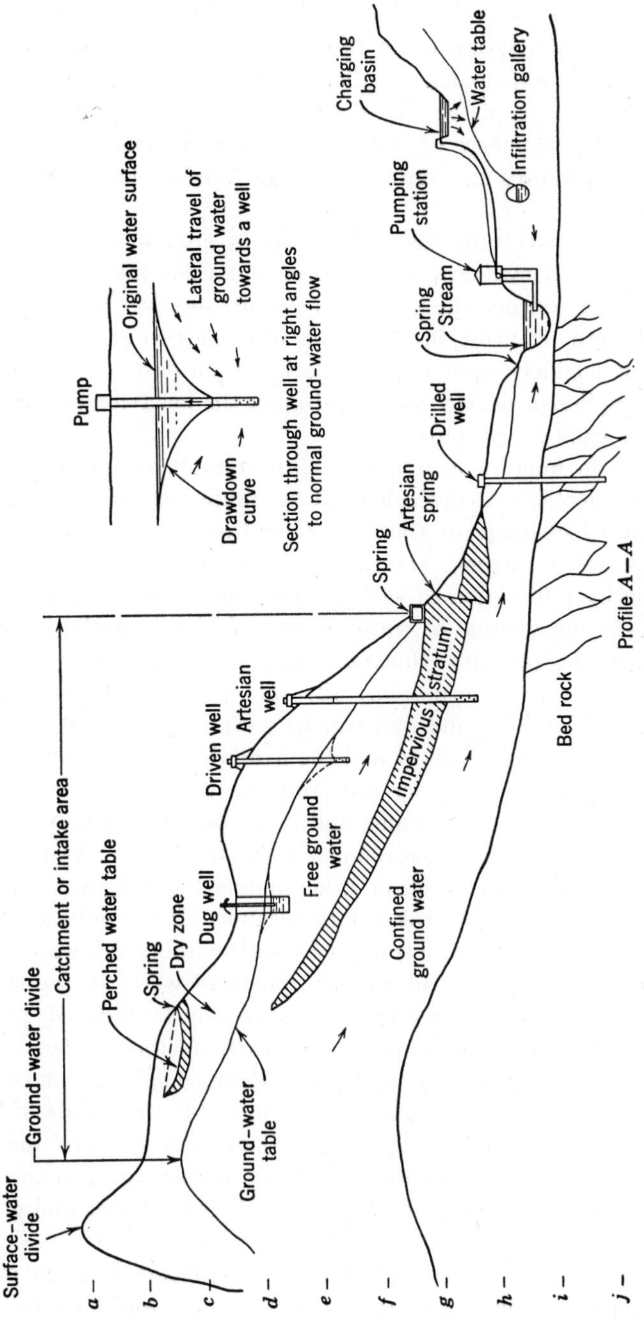

Figure 5-1. Ground water and its development as springs, wells, and infiltration galleries.

it to overflow at the surface; and (3) when a fault in an impervious stratum permits artesian water to escape from confinement. In the development of impounded supplies, a dam carried to bed rock will impound subsurface as well as surface flow behind it and so utilize the full water capacity of the catchment area, unless raising the water surface causes underground leakage from the basin around the reservoir.

The factors governing the availability of ground water, although more difficult to evaluate, are no less real than the corresponding factors that determine the yield of a surface supply. In the absence of a complete scientific investigation of a particular ground-water source, the engineer must base his decisions on past experience with similar supplies in nearby areas and upon the behavior of test wells driven for exploratory purposes.

In order to make a complete scientific study of a ground-water source, the geologic, hydrologic, and hydraulic system must first be isolated. An estimate of the safe yield then requires appreciation of the following factors: (1) the quantities of water added to the formation by infiltration of rain, melting snow and ice, and surface waters; (2) the volume of water stored within the isolated system as measured by porosity, thickness, and areal extent of the water-bearing soil or rock formation; (3) the rate at which the water moves through the ground and can be withdrawn from it, which is a function of its permeability and the available hydraulic gradients; and (4) the amount of water lost from the ground by evaporation, by effluent seepage into streams and other bodies of water, by flow from springs, and by underground routes of escape. At the same time, the effect of pumping, or other induced withdrawal of water from the ground, must be taken into account. If the natural hydrologic and hydraulic balance is upset by such withdrawal, water levels fall, directions of movement change, return of water to the surface or to the atmosphere by natural processes may be reduced, and infiltration is increased. Unfortunately, these factors cannot always be evaluated quantitatively because of their complexity or because the necessary basic data cannot be obtained. If the effects of these influencing factors are not anticipated, the supply of water may not remain adequate or its exploitation may become uneconomical in the course of time as water has to be lifted from greater and greater depths.

The history of large ground water developments is often one of great ingenuity in obtaining the supplies, accompanied by thoughtless failures to conserve them until, through overdraft, they begin to fail or are seriously damaged by encroachment of salt water. In spite of such difficulties ground water often affords a naturally purer and more economical supply than surface sources, particularly when drafts are relatively small. Hence the municipal and private ground-water supplies of North America are many times more numerous than surface-water supplies.

5-2. Geologic Aspects. The wide variation in the texture and stratigraphy of the earth's crust is reflected in the manner of occurrence of both free and confined ground water. The water table may lie at or near the earth's surface as in streams and swamps, or it may be several thousand feet down. Ground water may flow through caverns, crevices, and solution passages at velocities comparable to those of turbulent surface streams (1 or more feet per second), or it may move in laminar flow through the capillary interstices of soils and rocks at velocities of only a few feet a year. Aquifers may be thick and isotropic [4] as well as homogeneous, or they may consist of a wide variety of layers, lenses, and tortuous bands of varying materials. A detailed knowledge of the geology of ground-water areas is essential, if the capacity of water-bearing formations is to be fully established. Surface geology and exposures due to mining, quarrying, and related operations must be supplemented by *well logs.* These are records of the nature and depth of the various strata that were encountered in sinking existing wells.[5] When they are combined with measurements of capacity, the logs furnish the most important information that can be had without the aid of test wells or geophysical reconnaissance.

From a geological standpoint the earth's crust is made up of rocks and soils. The rocks are igneous, sedimentary, and metamorphic in origin. A brief description of common water-bearing formations follows.

The *intrusive* igneous rocks are dense in texture and would be barren of water, were it not for the occurrence in them of fissures and cracks. But their width is generally small (seldom more than 1 mm), and they die out with depth. The numbers of inclined joints that can be intersected by wells decreases rapidly (from about 4 per 100 ft down to the 100-ft level to less than 1 per 100 ft below the 400-ft level). Therefore, such water as can be captured is derived from depths that generally do not exceed 300 ft.

[4] Possessing the same properties in all directions.

[5] Many states require the keeping of well logs and their filing with a state authority or with the U. S. Geological Survey.

Of the intrusive rocks, basalt is a good aquifer, rhyolite a poor one. Weathering of the granites produces the silica sands and gravels that, after transportation, abrasion, and sorting by wind and water, form the most productive water-bearing soils. The *extrusive* igneous rocks may be very porous and may contain cracks, holes, and extensive caverns. As a result, some lava formations [6] yield water in abundance.

Of the four common varieties of sedimentary rocks (limestones and related calcareous rocks, shales, sandstones, and conglomerates), the *limestones* are usually dense and impervious. However, they are the most soluble of all rocks, and, where they have been subjected to the leaching action of water that contains dissolving carbon dioxide or organic acids, they are honeycombed by solution passages and caverns. Underground streams and lakes are formed in the course of time, and these may overflow at the surface to create large springs.[7] *Shales,* which result from the consolidation of clays, are generally impervious and act as aquicludes. *Sandstones,* on the other hand, may be very pervious. Their water-bearing capacity depends upon the extent to which the pores of the sand grains are filled with cementing materials. Quartzites, constituted of silica sands that are completely filled with cementing siliceous materials, are comparable to granites in density and imperviousness, whereas loosely cemented sandstones are among the most productive aquifers. The water-bearing capacity of the consolidated or cemented heterogeneous mixtures of materials that constitute *conglomerates* varies considerably. As a rule, however, they are quite tight. Good aquifers are sometimes encountered in limestone and sandstone at depths in excess of a mile. However, most ground-water developments are less than 2,000 ft deep.

None of the metamorphic rocks is an important water producer. *Marble,* like the limestone from which it is created, is soluble and may yield water from solution channels. *Slates* and *schists,* which originate in shales, are both relatively impervious, but they transmit some water along joints, cleavage cracks, and fractures. *Gneiss* resembles, in its structural and water-bearing properties, the intrusive granites from which it is generally derived.

In North America, the important water-bearing rock formations lie at considerable depths below the earth's surface and generally carry water under artesian pressure.[8] The supplies obtained from cavernous limestones near the surface are an exception.

[6] For example, in the northwestern United States and the Hawaiian Islands.

[7] Examples are numerous, particularly in Florida and in the Ozarks of Missouri and Arkansas.

[8] The great artesian systems of the United States are: (1) the extensive Paleozoic system of the east-central region, where shales confine water in sandstones and limestones, e.g., the well-known Potsdam sandstone in Wisconsin and northern Illinois; (2) the Roswell system in New Mexico, where a cavernous Permian limestone furnishes large quantities of water used for irrigation; (3) the Atlantic and Gulf coastal plain systems, in which dipping formations of pervious Cretaceous and Tertiary sands and gravels or sandstones and limestones are interbedded with clays or shales; and (4) the Cretaceous artesian systems of the Great Plains, in which water is confined under great pressure in extensive sandstones that lie

Although the water-bearing rocks of the United States are important sources of water, the areas served by them are small within the country as a whole. Greater yields of water are actually derived from the soils of the overburden in which free and artesian conditions of flow exist.

The size classification of soil particles developed by the Bureau of Chemistry and Soils of the U. S. Department of Agriculture and by the International Society of Soil Science is shown in Table 5-1.

TABLE 5-1. Size Classification of Soil Grains

	Diameter of Grain, cm	
Soil	U. S. Dept. of Agriculture	International Society of Soil Science
Fine gravel (grit)	2×10^{-1} to 10^{-1}	
Coarse sand	10^{-1} to 5×10^{-2}	2×10^{-1} to 2×10^{-2}
Medium sand	5×10^{-2} to 2.5×10^{-2}	
Fine sand	2.5×10^{-2} to 10^{-2}	2×10^{-2} to 2×10^{-3}
Very fine sand	10^{-2} to 5×10^{-3}	
Silt	5×10^{-3} to 5×10^{-4}	2×10^{-3} to 2×10^{-4}
Clay	5×10^{-4} or less	2×10^{-4} or less

Sands and *gravels* are by far the most important water-bearing materials. They have high specific yeld and permeability (Section 5-4) and are ordinarily so situated that replenishment is rapid. Uniform or well-sorted sands and gravels are the most productive, while mixed materials containing clay are least so, for example, boulder clay deposited beneath ice sheets. Transported material is generally more permeable than that in immediate contact with the mother rock. Most sand and gravel beds have been deposited in shallow, active water: (1) in seas, lakes, or river beds as alluvial deposits; (2) at the mouth of canyons as outwash cones; or (3) along the edge of retreating ice sheets as outwash plains. Since the origin of these materials and the depth and motion of the transporting water varied in time, the deposits generally include alternating layers of material of varying size and grading. Beds deposited in lakes and seas are often extensive, whereas outwash cones or river channels usually contain relatively small lenses of sand and gravel confined between layers of less pervious material.[9]

Clays and *silts,* although porous, are generally quite impervious. They are poor aquifers and are significant only (1) when they confine or interfere with the movement of water through the more pervious soils and (2) when they supply water to permeable formations by consolidation.

below thick, dense shales, e.g., the productive Dakota sandstone that underlies parts of Wyoming, Colorado, North and South Dakota, Nebraska, and Minnesota.

[9] The largest supplies of ground water in the United States come from the following sand and gravel deposits: (1) glacial outwash plains north of the Ohio and Missouri rivers and in New England; (2) valley fill in the western mountain region; (3) Tertiary and Quaternary deposits in the Quaternary terrace and lowland deposits in the Atlantic and Gulf coastal plains.

5-3. Hydrologic Aspects. Hydrological equilibrium is expressed by the following equation:

$$\Sigma R = \Sigma D + \Delta S \qquad 5\text{-}1$$

where ΣR denotes the various hydrological factors of recharge, and ΣD those of discharge, while ΔS is the associated change in storage volume. More specifically, the recharge is composed of the following:

1. Natural infiltration derived from rainfall and snow melt.
2. Infiltration from surface bodies of water.
3. Underflow.
4. Leakage through confining layers, or water displaced from them by compression.
5. Water derived from diffusion, charging, and water-spreading operations, and from recycling cooling water to the ground.

Conversely, the discharge includes:

1. Evaporation and transpiration.
2. Seepage into surface bodies of water.
3. Underflow.
4. Leakage through confining layers or absorbed by them by the reduction of compression.
5. Water withdrawn through wells and infiltration galleries or basins.

As shown by Equation 5-1, determination of the safe yield of an aquifer is quite analogous to finding the permissible draft from a surface supply. A complete hydrological inventory of a water-producing area includes, in addition to the evaluation of the three terms in Equation 5-1, a consideration of rainfall and surface runoff. The larger the area, the greater are the difficulties of obtaining accurate measurements or estimates of the components of an inventory.[10]

a. Recharge and discharge. When the bulk of the water received by an aquifer is derived by infiltration from surface streams, the progressive reduction in surface flow along the water course is the principal measure of recharge.[11] The amount of intake of rain and melting snow is much more difficult of determination, since it requires a knowledge of losses by evaporation and transpiration, and of the water needed to satisfy the field-moisture capacity or specific retention of the soil.

[10] In the United States, experimental stations for the intensive study of ground-water hydrology are maintained by the Soil Conservation Service and the Forest Service. The publications of these services hold much of interest.

[11] This is true, for example, in some parts of the western United States.

The amount of water that enters the ground from diffusion, charging, spreading, and recycling arrangements is generally a matter of record or can be made so. Discharge by evapo-transpiration of water which has reached the ground-water body is restricted to areas where the capillary fringe rises to the root zone or to the surface. Discharge by seepage sustains the dry-weather flow of streams and may be determined from the changes in dry-weather flow along a stream's course. The amount of water withdrawn through groundwater works is assessed through records of draft. Underflow and leakage may either recharge or discharge a basin, or both. The difficulty of quantitative evaluation of leakage and underflow does not lessen its importance.

b. Storage. The volume of water within a saturated formation of rock or soil equals its pore space. This is generalized in terms of the *porosity,* or ratio f of pore, void, or interstitial volume to total volume of rock or soil. The *voids ratio* or ratio of pore volume to solid volume, $e = f/(1 - f)$, is also a useful concept in ground-water hydraulics and soil mechanics. As shown in Figure 5-2, there are two limiting arrangements, or packings, of spherical particles of uniform diameter that are in contact with each other: the orthogonal, or cubic, and the rhombic, or rhombohedral. Freshly deposited silt may possess a very high porosity (up to 80%). A common porosity of natural sands and gravels is 40%. The value for sandstones is more nearly 20%. Porosity is a static quality of rocks and soils. It is not of itself a measure of perviousness or permeability. These are dynamic qualities that have no meaning in the absence of flow (Section 5-4).

Not all the water stored in a geological formation can be withdrawn by normal engineering operations. There is, therefore, a difference between total storage and useful storage. The quantity that

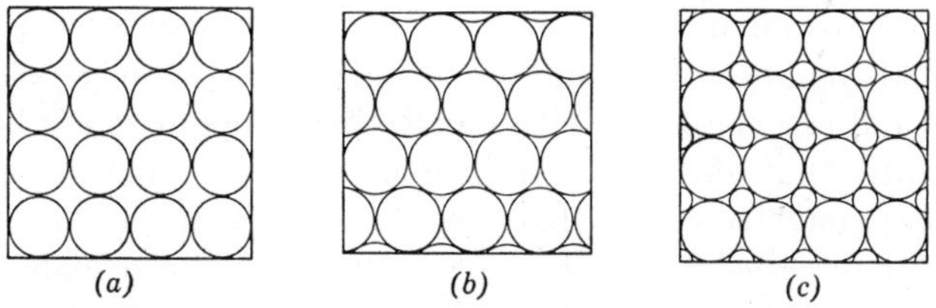

Figure 5-2. Effect of arrangement and size variation of grains upon porosity. (a) Orthogonal packing; porosity = 47.64%. (b) Rhombic packing; porosity = 25.95%. (c) Two sizes, orthogonal; porosity = 43.92%.

will drain off by gravity is called the *specific yield;* its counterpart is the *specific retention.* Specific yields vary from zero for plastic clays to values close to the magnitude of the porosity for coarse sands and gravels.

The factor of specific yield can be eliminated from an inventory of ground-water yield by starting and ending the hydrological inventory at identical values of ground-water storage. In North America, the period of accumulation of water in the ground, like that in surface reservoirs, extends from fall to spring, and the period of depletion is associated with the growing season. The U. S. Geological Survey has selected September 30 as the end of the *water year,* because it is the date at which annual depletion of ground water generally stops and recharge begins. To the extent that the storage on this date is constant from year to year, this division of time enhances the accuracy of annual inventories. Changes in storage volume are based on records of the water levels in observation wells. Volumes are calculated from contours of the water table. Ground storage is relatively large, and deficits may be extended over many years. Ultimately, of course, they must be offset by recharge if the source is not to fail.

5-4. Hydraulic Aspects. Water filtering into the ground moves downward to the zone of saturation before it percolates laterally in the direction of greatest slope of the ground-water table or piezometric surface. This slope is the hydraulic gradient of underground flow. Like the hydraulic gradient of open channels and pipes, it is a measure of the frictional resistance to flow, the energy lost being dissipated as heat. Since recharge, discharge, and storage fluctuate, flow is both unsteady and non-uniform, and the hydraulic gradient is not stationary. During replenishment, the water table rises, the gradient steepens, and flow increases. During dry spells, the opposite occurs. Ordinarily, the hydraulic gradient slopes in the direction of the ground surface, but the degree of slope is not necessarily the same. Flow may be free as in an open channel or confined as in a pipe. Flow may be laminar when pores or crevices and associated velocities or Reynolds numbers are small, or turbulent when cracks or solution passages and associated velocities or Reynolds numbers are large.

An aquifer that offers little resistance to flow is called *pervious* or *permeable;* conversely, one that offers much resistance is called *impervious* or *impermeable.* The nature of the system of pores, rather than their relative volume, determines resistance to flow at a given velocity. Hence permeability and porosity are not synonymous terms. Clays with porosities of 50%, for example, are quite impervious, whereas sandstones with porosities of 15% or less are quite pervious.

In nature, the rate of ground-water movement and slope of the ground-water table, or piezometric surface, are not large. In aquifers of high yield, velocities of 5 to 60 ft a day are associated with hydraulic gradients of 10 to 20 ft per mile. Underflow through gravel deposits may reach several hundred feet per day, but flows as low as a few feet per year may also be economically useful.

a. Darcy's law. Although Hagen [12] and Poiseuille [13] were the first to propose that the velocity of flow of water and other liquids through capillary tubes is proportional to the first power of the slope of the hydraulic gradient, credit for the verification of this observation and for its application to the flow of water through the ground, or, more specifically, its filtration through sand, must go to Henri Darcy.[14] The relationship is known as Darcy's law and may be written

$$v = Ks \tag{5-2}$$

where v is the face or approach velocity, or the quantity of water flowing per unit, gross, cross-sectional area; s is the slope of the hydraulic gradient, or the loss of head per unit length of flow path; and K is the coefficient of permeability or the proportionality constant for water of a given temperature flowing through a given material. Since s is a dimensionless ratio, K has the dimensions of velocity and is in fact the velocity of flow that is associated with a hydraulic gradient of unity. Because the value of K varies inversely as the kinematic viscosity ν of the flowing liquid (Table A-3), measurements of K are generally referred to a standard water temperature such as 60 F or 10 C. The ratio of the viscosity at the standard temperature to the observed temperature is the necessary correction factor, or

$$K_1/K_2 = \nu_2/\nu_1 \tag{5-3}$$

The upper limit of Darcy's law [15] lies at Reynolds numbers between 1 and 10. This limit is generally reached as water approaches the face of wells in coarse-grained sandy soils. In practice, no lower

[12] G. Hagen, *Über die Bewegung des Wassers in engen cylindrischen Röhren, Ann. Physik und Chemie, 46,* 423 (1839).

[13] G. L. M. Poiseuille, Recherches expérimentales sur le mouvement des liquides dans les tubes de très petit diamètre, *Roy. Acad. Sci. Inst. France Math. Phys. Sci. Mem., 9,* 433 (1846).

[14] *Les fontaines publiques de la Ville de Dijon,* Paris, 1856.

[15] As determined by the evaluation of the constituent terms proposed in Section 15-5.

limit has been observed even at vanishingly small hydraulic gradients such as a few inches a mile.

The value of K is expressed in various units, depending upon the interests of the investigator and the system of measurements employed. The U. S. Geological Survey has adopted as its *standard coefficient of permeability* the gallons per day of water at 60 F flowing through 1 sq ft of cross-section under a gradient of 1 ft per ft (100%). In the *field coefficient of permeability,* flow is related to the prevailing temperature, a cross-section 1 mile in width and 1 ft in depth, and a hydraulic gradient of 1 ft per mile. At a ground-water temperature of 60 F, the field coefficient and the standard coefficient are identical. The *coefficient of transmissibility* is obtained by multiplying the standard coefficient of permeability by the full saturated height, or depth, of the aquifer.

The range in magnitude of the coefficient of permeability for various classes of soils is shown in Figure 5-3. Individual values may be determined (1) by laboratory experiment or field test or (2), for granular deposits, by calculations that are based upon measurable characteristics of the soil and water. The second method is of particular importance in connection with the filtration of water and is discussed in Chapter 15.

Example 5-1. (*a*) Estimate the velocity of flow in feet per day and the discharge in gallons per day through an aquifer of very coarse sand 1,000 ft wide and 50 ft deep when the slope of the ground-water table is 20 ft per mile. (*b*) Find the standard coefficient of permeability and the coefficient of transmissibility on the assumption that the temperature of the ground water is 60 F.

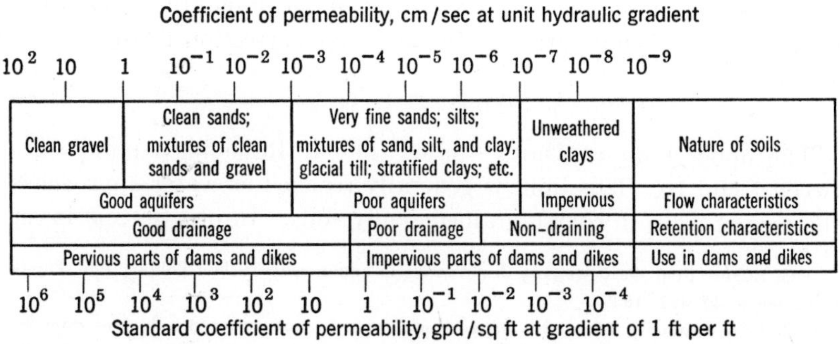
Coefficient of permeability, cm/sec at unit hydraulic gradient
10^2 10 1 10^-1 10^-2 10^-3 10^-4 10^-5 10^-6 10^-7 10^-8 10^-9
Clean gravel
Clean sands; mixtures of clean sands and gravel
Very fine sands; silts; mixtures of sand, silt, and clay; glacial till; stratified clays; etc.
Unweathered clays
Nature of soils
Good aquifers
Poor aquifers
Impervious
Flow characteristics
Good drainage
Poor drainage
Non-draining
Retention characteristics
Pervious parts of dams and dikes
Impervious parts of dams and dikes
Use in dams and dikes
10^6 10^5 10^4 10^3 10^2 10 1 10^-1 10^-2 10^-3 10^-4
Standard coefficient of permeability, gpd/sq ft at gradient of 1 ft per ft

Figure 5-3. Magnitude of the coefficient of permeability for different classes of soils. *After Arthur Casagrande.*

a. From Figure 5-3 choose a coefficient of permeability of

$$K = 1.0 \text{ cm per sec} = 2{,}835 \text{ ft per day}$$

Since $s = 20/5{,}280$, Equation 5-2 states that $v = 2{,}835 \times 20/5{,}280 = 11$ ft per day and the discharge $Q = 11 \times 1{,}000 \times 50 \times 7.5 \times 10^{-6} = 4.1$ mgd.

b. The standard coeffic ent of permeability is $2{,}835 \times 7.5 = 2.13 \times 10^4$, and the coefficient of transmissibility becomes $2.13 \times 10^4 \times 50 = 1.06 \times 10^6$.

b. Measurement of permeability. The permeability of soils is measured either in the laboratory or in the field. Laboratory determinations are more accurate, but, since the samples that can be used are relatively small and their packing is easily disturbed, the observed results are useful only when the actual texture of the aquifer is closely approximated and when it is substantially homogeneous throughout the gathering ground. If alternating layers of pervious and impervious materials or lenses of different perviousness are present, the laboratory findings are meaningless.

Laboratory measurements are made with a variety of permeameters. The *falling-head permeameter,* which is generally used for materials of moderate to low permeability and which exemplifies the principle of these instruments, is shown in Figure 5-4. The rate Q and head h decline with time as water flows through a bed of cross-section A and depth l.

For heads h_1 and h_2 at the beginning and end of a time interval t

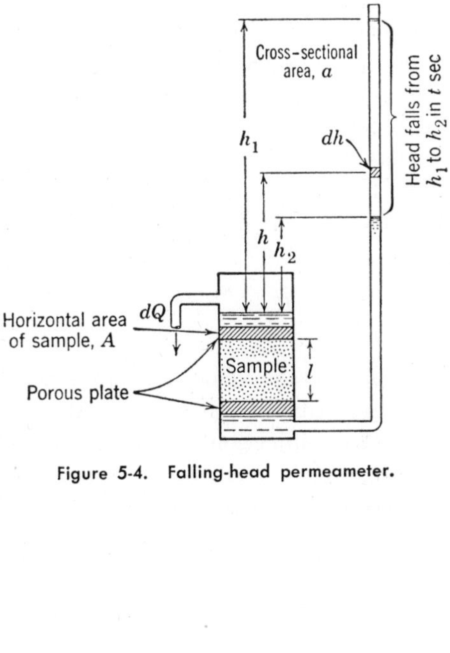

Figure 5-4. Falling-head permeameter.

and for a cross-sectional area a of the standpipe, the differential equation for the rate of flow d under a head h in the time dt is

$$dQ = -\frac{a\,dh}{dt} = K\frac{h}{l}A\frac{\nu_0}{\nu}$$

where ν is the kinematic viscosity at the observed water temperature and ν_0 that at the reference temperature. Transformation and integration give

$$\int_0^t dt = \frac{al}{KA}\frac{\nu}{\nu_0}\int_{h_1}^{h_2} -\frac{dh}{h} \quad \text{or} \quad t = \frac{al}{KA}\frac{\nu}{\nu_0}\log_e\frac{h_1}{h_2}$$

whence

$$K = \frac{al}{tA}\frac{\nu}{\nu_0}\log_e\frac{h_1}{h_2} \qquad 5\text{-}4$$

When the time of test is long, precautions may have to be taken to prevent evaporation from the liquid surface and from the sample.

Permeability is ordinarily determined in the field in one of two ways: (1) by measurement of the hydraulic gradient and velocity of water movement in the ground, or (2) by determination of the discharge and drawdown of pumped wells. The principle underlying the second method is described in Section 5-8.

The velocity observed in field measurements is the true average rate of motion through the interstices of the aquifer, whereas the velocity over the full cross-section is made part of Equation 5-2. Since not all the interstices are effective in carrying water, the average interstitial velocity v_f should be expressed as $v/(k_ff)$, where k_f is the proportion of effective pore space. The effective porosity probably lies somewhere between the gross porosity and the specific yield. Its determination has not received attention commensurate with its importance.

On the basis of effective porosity, effective velocity, and hydraulic gradient,

$$K = \frac{k_ffv_f}{s}\frac{\nu}{\nu_0} \qquad 5\text{-}5$$

The effective or true average velocity of ground-water flow can be measured in terms of the time required for a salt, dye, or radioactive substance to pass from an injection well to an observation well that lies in the direction of water movement. The time of arrival of a salt solution is determined by consecutive chemical titrations or by electrical means, that of a dye by visual observation or colorimetric methods, and that of a radioactive tracer by means of a Geiger or similar counter. The time required for half the recovered substance to have been received divided by the distance between the test wells gives the effective, or median, velocity. Similar methods can be employed in investigations of ground-water pollution. Among the dyes available for this purpose, uranin, a sodium salt of fluorescein, is visible in dilution of $1:4 \times 10^7$ without a fluoroscope and in dilution of $1:10^{10}$ with one.

Hydraulics of Collecting Works

5-5. Unconfined Steady Flow into a Gallery. If a blanked-off infiltration gallery rests on the impervious sole of an unconfined aquifer,

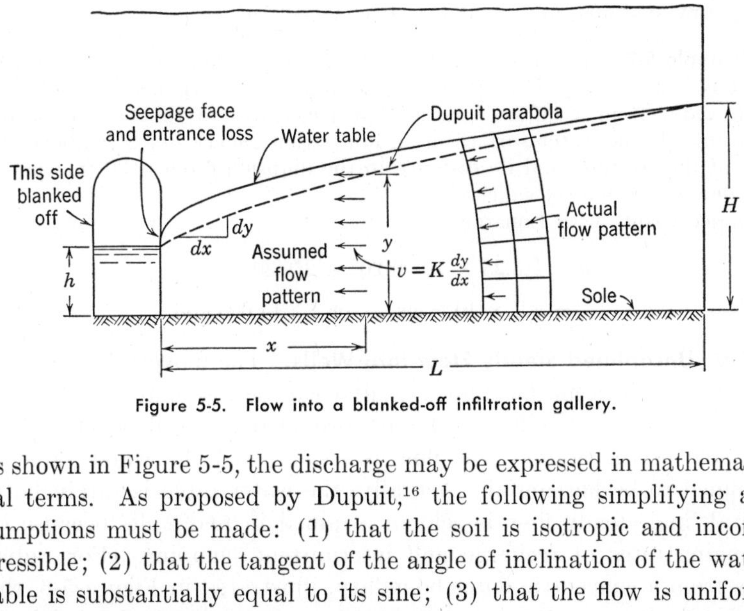

Figure 5-5. Flow into a blanked-off infiltration gallery.

as shown in Figure 5-5, the discharge may be expressed in mathematical terms. As proposed by Dupuit,[16] the following simplifying assumptions must be made: (1) that the soil is isotropic and incompressible; (2) that the tangent of the angle of inclination of the water table is substantially equal to its sine; (3) that the flow is uniform and horizontal throughout the depth of the aquifer; and (4) that the length of the gallery is sufficiently great that neglect of conditions at its two ends does not introduce a significant error.

In accordance with Darcy's law, and the notation of Figure 5-5, the discharge per unit length of gallery then becomes

[16] Jules Dupuit, *Etudes théoriques et pratiques sur le mouvement des eaux*, 2nd ed., Paris, 1863.

$$q = Ky\,dy/dx \qquad 5\text{-}6$$

where $y \times 1$ is the area of unit width through which the water flows with velocity $k\,dy/dx$. By integration

$$qx = \tfrac{1}{2}Ky^2 + c \qquad 5\text{-}7$$

If $y = H$ at $x = L$, and it is assumed that $y = h$ at $x = 0$,

$$q = \tfrac{1}{2}K(H^2 - h^2)/L \qquad 5\text{-}8$$

Equation 5-8 traces a parabolic water table that departs, often significantly, from the true water table and continues to rise beyond any finite boundary. What the line of seepage should be, in order to meet the requirements at entrance and discharge, is indicated in Figure 5-5. The capillary fringe is not taken into account. The greater the ratio of L/H, the closer is the agreement between the calculated and true flow systems, except at the discharge face.

Example 5-2. A stratum of clean sand and gravel 20 ft deep has a coefficient of permeability $K = 10^{-1}$ cm/sec (3.28×10^{-3} fps) and is supplied with water from a diffusion ditch that penetrates to the bottom of the stratum. If the water surface in an infiltration gallery lies 2 ft above the sole of the stratum, and its distance to the diffusion ditch is 30 ft, what is the flow into a foot of gallery?

In accordance with Equation 5-8,

$$q = \tfrac{1}{2}(3.28 \times 10^{-3})(20^2 - 2^2)/30$$
$$= 2.2 \times 10^{-2} \text{ cfs} \quad \text{or} \quad 14{,}000 \text{ gpd}$$

5-6. Unconfined Steady Flow into Wells. The movement of water toward a well in an unconfined aquifer can be formulated in accordance with the principles of Dupuit, provided the well penetrates to the sole of the aquifer, the flow is steady, and the water table is assumed to be horizontal. Actually, the water table is rarely horizontal, and steady flow is seldom attained in real wells because of changing rates of recharge and intermittent pumping. For radial flow from a concentric outer boundary, illustrated in Figure 5-6, the discharge through any cylindrical surface of x radius and y height is

$$Q = 2\pi Kxy\,dy/dx \qquad 5\text{-}9$$

where Q is the rate of flow into the well, and x and y are the coordinates of any point on the Dupuit cone of depression, or drawdown curve. The component factors are $2\pi xy$ the area through which flow takes place, and $K\,dy/dx$ the velocity. By integration

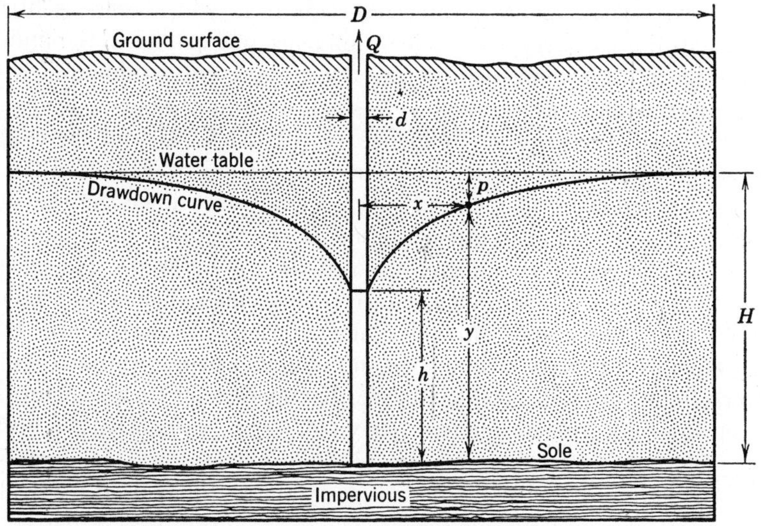

Figure 5-6. Water-table well in a ground-water reservoir.

$$Q \log_e x = \pi K y^2 + c \qquad 5\text{-}10$$

and for $y = h$ at $x = \frac{1}{2}d$ (d being the diameter of the well) and $y = H$ at $x = \frac{1}{2}D$ (D being the diameter of the circle of influence, or $\frac{1}{2}D$ being the distance of the outer boundary from the center of the well),

$$Q = \pi K \frac{H^2 - h^2}{\log_e (D/d)} = 1.36K \frac{H^2 - h^2}{\log (D/d)} \qquad 5\text{-}11$$

The significance and limitations of this equation are similar to those discussed in Section 5-5 for the Dupuit formulation of steady flow into an infiltration gallery. The order of magnitude of D can be gaged by assuming that the normal ground-water flow within the circle of influence will enter the well. If the hydraulic slope of this flow is s,

$$Q = KsDH \qquad 5\text{-}12$$

which equated to 5-11 gives

$$D = \frac{\pi(H^2 - h^2)}{sH \log_e (D/d)} = \frac{1.36(H^2 - h^2)}{sH \log (D/d)} \qquad 5\text{-}13$$

Equation 5-13 is solved for D by trial.

If a well taps a ground-water reservoir from which there is little or no natural discharge, the circle of influence will extend to the limits of the basin. Pumping then lowers the general water table and will ultimately empty the reservoir. A steep hydraulic slope s, by contrast, reduces the circle of influence (Equation 5-13) and increases the yield (Equation 5-11). Further examination of Equation 5-11 shows the following changes in yield, as the drawdown, or the diameter of the well, is varied. Since H is constant, the quantity $(H^2 - h^2)$ increases at a decreasing rate as h is reduced. Thus successive increases in drawdown reduce the specific capacity of water-table wells. For a constant value of D the logarithmic ratio of the diameters of the circle of influence and diameter of the well and their inverse relation to the yield indicate that increasing the diameter of a well does not greatly increase its yield. For example, a 2-ft well will yield only 15 to 30% more water than a 3-in. well. Diameters, therefore, are ordinarily chosen to satisfy the methods used for drilling, developing, and pumping wells.

5-7. Confined, Steady Flow into Wells. Steady flow into a well through a screen that is open to the full depth of an extensive confined aquifer of uniform thickness and permeability can be approximated mathematically by application of Dupuit's principles. Since in confined aquifers the flow is two dimensional, Dupuit's formulation can be extended by the use of potential-flow theory to cover cases in which the piezometric surface is inclined.

a. Mathematical formulation of artesian flow. For the conditions depicted in Figure 5-7.

$$Q = 2\pi Kxm \frac{dy}{dx} \qquad \text{5-14}$$

Integrating over the limits $x = \frac{1}{2}d$ for $y = h$ and $x = \frac{1}{2}D$ for $y = H$

$$Q = 2\pi Km \frac{H - h}{\log_e (D/d)} = 2.73Km \frac{H - h}{\log (D/d)} \qquad \text{5-15}$$

The discharge is seen to be proportional to the drawdown $H - h = p$. The yield per unit drawdown, or *specific capacity,* of artesian wells has been observed to remain fairly constant at all reasonable values of drawdown.

b. Flow into an artesian well with sloping piezometric surface. The paths of flow, or flow lines, around an unpumped well can be represented by a series of equally spaced parallel lines, A, B, $\cdots$ in

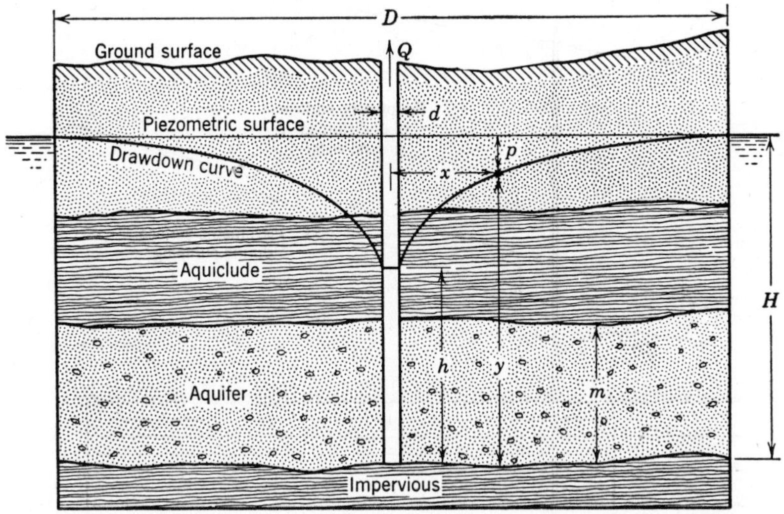

Figure 5-7. Artesian well with steady radial flow from a concentric circular boundary.

Figure 5-8. The flow lines for a pumped well with horizontal piezometric surface as formulated in Equation 5-15, may be represented by radial lines a, b, $\cdots$ in Figure 5-8. Superposition of these two systems of lines produces, by vector addition, the true paths of flow for a pumped well when the piezometric surface is inclined as shown in Figure 5-8. This vector addition is possible only when the figure is so constructed that the quantities of water flowing between adjacent parallel lines and between adjacent radial lines are equal. To attain this, the number of parallel flow paths in the width of aquifer carrying the quantity of water pumped must equal the number of radial flow paths around the pumped well (16 each in Figure 5-8). The equipotential lines cross the flowlines at right angles. If they are given the same spacing as the flowlines, they create an orthogonal flow net. The apex of the limiting flowline in Figure 5-8 establishes the point of stagnation P. The line itself demarcates the divide between water drawn into and passing by the well. The flow pattern of this outer region, incidentally, is that past a solid object of the form traced by the limiting flowline. The distance x to the point of stagnation downstream from the well is given by the equation

$$x = -q/(2\pi v_0) \qquad 5\text{-}16$$

where q is the flow through a unit depth of aquifer and v_0 is the velocity of the undisturbed ground water.

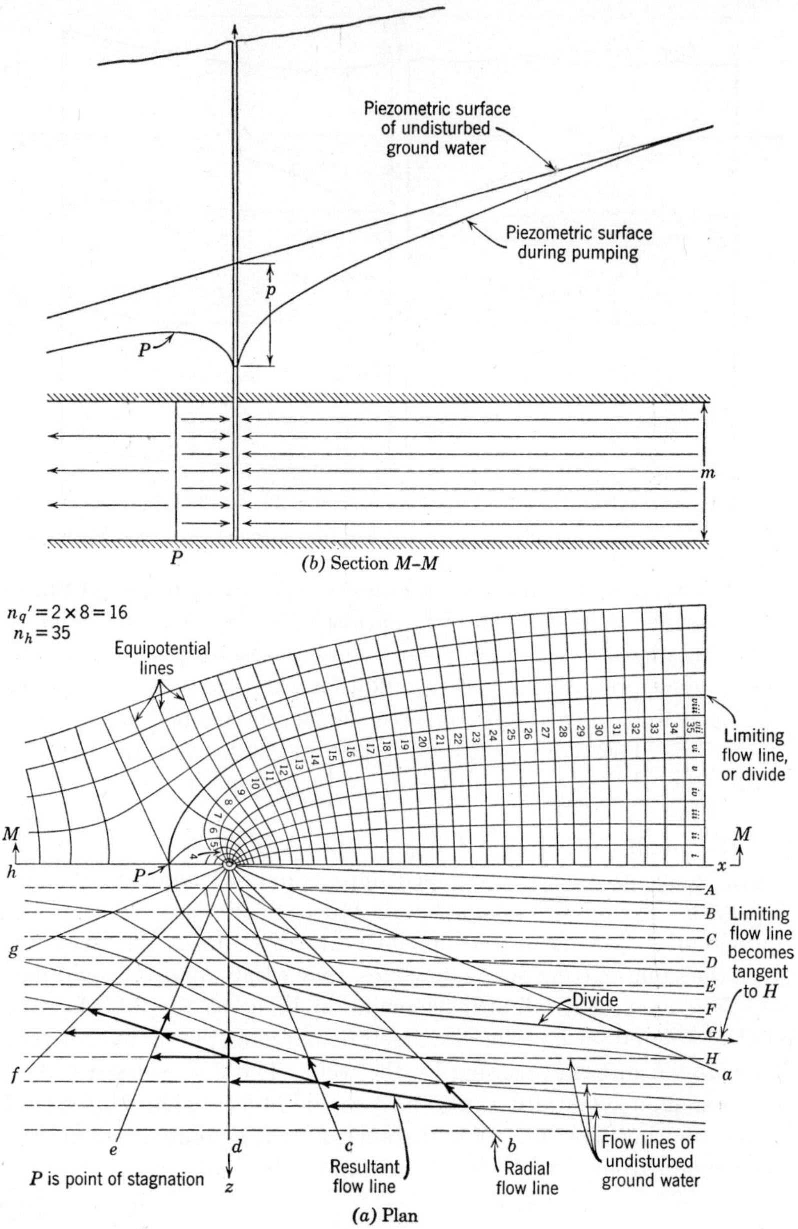

Figure 5-8. Flow net of a single artesian well.

Example 5-3. If the well shown in Figure 5-8 penetrates an aquifer 40 ft thick and draws water laterally from a distance of 56 ft, the piezometric surface being lowered significantly for a distance of 140 ft upstream from the well by a drop in head of 30 ft at the well, what is the yield of the well if the coefficient of permeability of the aquifer is 3.28×10^{-4} fps and the piezometric slope of the undisturbed ground water is 40 ft in 140 ft; also what is the distance of the point of stagnation from the well?

a. Since the yield of the well must equal the rate of flow of the tributary ground water,

$$Q = Ksa = 3.28 \times 10^{-4} \times (40/140) \times 2 \times 56 \times 40$$

$$= 0.42 \text{ cfs} \quad \text{or} \quad 272{,}000 \text{ gpd}$$

b. The point of stagnation is identified by Equation 5-16, in which $q = 0.42/40 = 1.05 \times 10^{-2}$ cfs and $v_0 = Ks = 3.28 \times 10^{-4} \times 40/140 = 9.37 \times 10^{-5}$ fps:

$$x = 1.05 \times 10^{-2}/(2\pi \times 9.37 \times 10^{-5}) = 17.8 \text{ ft}$$

5-8. Unsteady Flow into Wells. Theis [17] originated and Jacob,[18, 21] Wenzel,[19] and Cooper and Jacob [20] have further developed equational relationships for the flow of water into wells in which the time from beginning or stopping of pumping is an added variable. This important advancement of the hydraulics of wells has eliminated the difficulty arising from the long time-lag before conditions of steady flow or equilibrium assumed in earlier formulations have actually been reached.

Since the gradual approach of the cone of depression toward a steady state is due primarily to the removal of water from storage as the cone deepens, a storage factor comes into play. This factor and that of permeability are called the *formation constants* of an aquifer.

The original development of the Theis equation was based on an analogy to the flow of heat toward a *sink* or point where heat is re-

[17] C. V. Theis, The relation between the lowering of the piezometric surface and the rate and duration of discharge of a well using ground-water storage, *Trans. Am. Geophys. Union, 16,* 519–524 (1935).

[18] C. E. Jacob, On the flow of water in an elastic artesian aquifer, *Trans. Am. Geophys. Union, 21,* 574–586 (1940).

[19] L. K. Wenzel, Methods for determining permeability of water-bearing materials, *U. S. Geol. Survey Water Supply Paper* 887, facing page 89 (1942).

[20] H. H. Cooper, Jr., and C. E. Jacob, A generalized graphical method for evaluating formation constants and summarizing well-field history, *Trans. Am. Geophys. Union, 27,* 526–534 (1946).

[21] C. E. Jacob, Drawdown test to determine effective radius of artesian well, *Trans. Am. Soc. Civil Engrs., 112,* 1047 (1947).

moved at a uniform rate. The existing mathematical solution of the heat-flow problem was transferred directly to the hydraulic problem, hydraulic pressure being analogous to temperature, pressure gradient to temperature gradient, permeability to thermal conductivity, and specific yield (or coefficient of storage) to specific heat.

The equation is

$$p = \frac{Q}{4\pi Km} \int_u^\infty \frac{e^{-u}\,du}{u} = \frac{Q}{4\pi Km} F(u) \qquad \text{5-17}$$

Here u is the lower limit of the integral which is defined as

$$u = \frac{x^2 S}{4Kmt} \qquad \text{5-18}$$

S being the *storage coefficient* and t the time during which the well has been pumped. For $Km = T$ the coefficient of transmissibility in gallons per day per foot of width, Q the uniform rate of pumping in gallons per minute, x the distance from the well in feet, t the time of pumping in days, and p the drawdown in feet,

$$p = \frac{114.6Q}{T} \int_u^\infty \frac{e^{-u}\,du}{u} = \frac{114.6Q}{T} F(u) \qquad \text{5-19}$$

and

$$u = \frac{1.87}{T} S \frac{x^2}{t} \qquad \text{5-20}$$

When flow is unconfined, the storage coefficient S equals the specific yield expressed as a decimal fraction. For an artesian aquifer, S equals the volume of water released, by virtue of compression, from storage within the column of the aquifer that underlies a unit surface area during a unit drawdown of the piezometric surface.

The integral in Equation 5-19 is called the *well function of u*, $F(u)$. It can be solved by expansion into the convergent series

$$F(u) = 0.5772 - \log_e u + u - \frac{u^2}{2 \times 2!} + \frac{u^3}{3 \times 3!} - \cdots \qquad \text{5-21}$$

With a table for values of $F(u)$ (Table 5-2 [19]) and data for a pump test, an overlay plotting method [19] can be used to determine the formation constants T and S in Equations 5-19 and 5-20. Once the formation constants are evaluated, the table and equations provide the

TABLE 5-2. Values of the Well Function *F(u)* for Various Values of *u*

From *U. S. Geological Survey Water Supply Paper* 887

N	$N \times 10^{-15}$	$N \times 10^{-14}$	$N \times 10^{-13}$	$N \times 10^{-12}$	$N \times 10^{-11}$	$N \times 10^{-10}$	$N \times 10^{-9}$	$N \times 10^{-8}$
1.0	33.96	31.66	29.36	27.05	24.75	22.45	20.15	17.84
1.5	33.56	31.25	28.95	26.65	24.35	22.04	19.74	17.44
2.0	33.27	30.97	28.66	26.36	24.06	21.76	19.45	17.15
2.5	33.05	30.74	28.44	26.14	23.83	21.53	19.23	16.93
3.0	32.86	30.56	28.26	25.96	23.65	21.35	19.05	16.75
3.5	32.71	30.41	28.10	25.80	23.50	21.20	18.89	16.59
4.0	32.57	30.27	27.97	25.67	23.36	21.06	18.76	16.46
4.5	32.46	30.15	27.85	25.55	23.25	20.94	18.64	16.34
5.0	32.35	30.05	27.75	25.44	23.14	20.84	18.54	16.23
5.5	32.26	29.95	27.65	25.35	23.05	20.74	18.44	16.14
6.0	32.17	29.87	27.56	25.26	22.96	20.66	18.35	16.05
6.5	32.09	29.79	27.48	25.18	22.88	20.58	18.27	15.97
7.0	32.02	29.71	27.41	25.11	22.81	20.50	18.20	15.90
7.5	31.95	29.64	27.34	25.04	22.74	20.43	18.13	15.83
8.0	31.88	29.58	27.28	24.97	22.67	20.37	18.07	15.76
8.5	31.82	29.52	27.22	24.91	22.61	20.31	18.01	15.70
9.0	31.76	29.46	27.16	24.86	22.55	20.25	17.95	15.65
9.5	31.71	29.41	27.11	24.80	22.50	20.20	17.89	15.59

N	$N \times 10^{-7}$	$N \times 10^{-6}$	$N \times 10^{-5}$	$N \times 10^{-4}$	$N \times 10^{-3}$	$N \times 10^{-2}$	$N \times 10^{-1}$	N
1.0	15.54	13.24	10.94	8.633	6.332	4.038	1.823	2.194×10^{-1}
1.5	15.14	12.83	10.53	8.228	5.927	3.637	1.465	1.000×10^{-1}
2.0	14.85	12.55	10.24	7.940	5.639	3.355	1.223	4.890×10^{-2}
2.5	14.62	12.32	10.02	7.717	5.417	3.137	1.044	2.491×10^{-2}
3.0	14.44	12.14	9.837	7.535	5.235	2.959	0.9057	1.305×10^{-2}
3.5	14.29	11.99	9.683	7.381	5.081	2.810	0.7942	6.970×10^{-3}
4.0	14.15	11.85	9.550	7.247	4.948	2.681	0.7024	3.779×10^{-3}
4.5	14.04	11.73	9.432	7.130	4.831	2.568	0.6253	2.073×10^{-3}
5.0	13.93	11.63	9.326	7.024	4.726	2.468	0.5598	1.148×10^{-3}
5.5	13.84	11.53	9.231	6.929	4.631	2.378	0.5034	6.409×10^{-4}
6.0	13.75	11.45	9.144	6.842	4.545	2.295	0.4544	3.601×10^{-4}
6.5	13.67	11.37	9.064	6.762	4.465	2.220	0.4115	2.034×10^{-4}
7.0	13.60	11.29	8.990	6.688	4.392	2.151	0.3738	1.155×10^{-4}
7.5	13.53	11.22	8.921	6.619	4.323	2.087	0.3403	6.583×10^{-5}
8.0	13.46	11.16	8.856	6.555	4.259	2.027	0.3106	3.767×10^{-5}
8.5	13.40	11.10	8.796	6.494	4.199	1.971	0.2840	2.162×10^{-5}
9.0	13.34	11.04	8.739	6.437	4.142	1.919	0.2602	1.245×10^{-5}
9.5	13.29	10.99	8.685	6.383	4.089	1.870	0.2387	7.185×10^{-6}

means for calculating the drawdown at any distance from the well for any pumping period.

Jacob[21] developed the following rapid method for evaluating T and S. He found that for values of $u < 0.02$ the terms beyond $\log_e u$ in Equation 5-21 may be neglected without introducing a significant error. Equation 5-19 then becomes:

$$p = \frac{114.6Q}{T}\left(0.5772 - 2.3 \log \frac{1.87}{T} S \frac{x^2}{t}\right) \qquad \text{5-22}$$

If observed values of p and t are plotted on arithmetic and logarithmic scales respectively, the points for the higher values of t, those corresponding to $u < 0.02$, will fall along a straight line (Figure 5-9). Pairs of values for two points along this line can be used in Equation

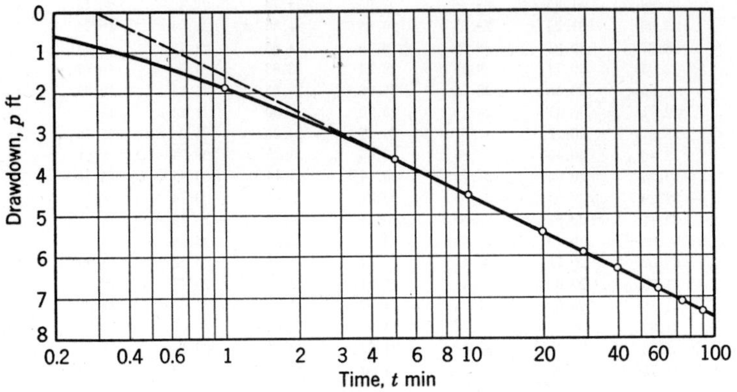

Figure 5-9. Determination of formation constants. *Data by courtesy of the U. S. Geological Survey.*

5-22 to determine the coefficient of transmissibility, T. Substitution of the point values in Equation 5-22 gives

$$p_2 - p_1 = \frac{264Q}{T} \log \frac{t_2}{t_1} \tag{5-23}$$

The storage coefficient, S, can then be calculated by reading the straight line value of t_0 at $p = 0$ and substituting in the following empirical approximation, where t_0 is in days,

$$S = \frac{0.3Tt_0}{x^2} \tag{5-24}$$

With the formation constants T and S known, Equation 5-22 gives the drawdown for any desired values of x and t, provided only that u as calculated from Equation 5-20 is less than 0.02.

Example 5-4. For purposes of illustration, Figure 5-9 shows the data for a test in which $Q = 350$ gpm and $x = 225$ ft, plotted on semilogarithmic paper, a straight line being drawn through the points for the higher values of t.

a. Selecting the points $t_1 = 1$ min, $p_1 = 1.6$ ft, and $t_2 = 10$ min, $p_2 = 4.5$ ft,

$$T = \frac{264Q}{p_2 - p_1} \log \frac{t_2}{t_1} = \frac{264 \times 350}{4.5 - 1.6} = 3.2 \times 10^4 \text{ gpd per ft}$$

and, since the straight line intersects the $p = 0$ axis at $t_0 = 0.3$ min,

$$S = \frac{0.3Tt_0}{x^2} = \frac{0.3 \times 3.2 \times 10^4 \times 0.3}{5.06 \times 10^4 \times 1440} = 3.9 \times 10^{-5}$$

b. For 10 days of pumping at a rate of 700 gpm, Equation 5-20 gives for the value of u,

$$u = \frac{1.87 \times 3.9 \times 10^{-5} \times 5.06 \times 10^4}{3.2 \times 10^4 \times 10} = 1.15 \times 10^{-5}$$

Since this is less than 0.02, p can be calculated from Equation 5-22 as

$$p = \frac{114.6 \times 700}{3.2 \times 10^4}(0.5772 - 2.3 \log 1.15 \times 10^{-5}) = 29 \text{ ft}$$

Also from Table 5-2, for $u = 1.15 \times 10^{-5}$, $F(u) = 10.82$, and, by Equation 5-19,

$$p = \frac{114.6 \times 700}{3.2 \times 10^4} 10.82 = 27 \text{ ft}$$

c. If the well is gravel-packed with an outside diameter of the gravel wall of 24 in., the drawdown at the well itself after 10 days of pumping at 700 gpm is given in a similar fashion by calculation of

$$u = \frac{1.87 \times 3.9 \times 10^{-5} \times 1}{3.2 \times 10^4 \times 10} = 2.3 \times 10^{-10}$$

and

$$p = \frac{114.6 \times 700}{3.2 \times 10^4}(0.5772 - 2.3 \log 2.3 \times 10^{-10}) = 57 \text{ ft}$$

Also from Table 5-2, for $u = 2.3 \times 10^{-10}$, $F(u) = 21.62$, and, by Equation 5-19,

$$p = \frac{11.4 \times 700}{3.2 \times 10^4} 21.62 = 54 \text{ ft}$$

The dynamic water level inside the casing is found by adding to the calculated drawdown the losses (1) through the gravel and screen and (2) in the casing up to the foot of the drop pipe.

These equations apply rigidly only when: (1) the aquifer is homogeneous; (2) the aquifer is infinite in areal extent; (3) the well penetrates the entire thickness of the aquifer; (4) the coefficients of transmissibility and storage are constant at all times and places; and

(5) water is released from storage as soon as the cone of depression develops.

Non-homogeneity of an aquifer may present difficulties. However, when the coefficient of transmissibility is determined from field tests as an average for a considerable volume of the aquifer, these difficulties are not nearly so serious as when the magnitude of the coefficient is based on laboratory tests of permeability. The coefficient of transmissibility of an unconfined aquifer changes with time because of a reduction in thickness of the saturated soil as the water table is lowered by pumping. The use of large values of x and t reduces this effect. The error due to delayed release from storage is reduced by prolonged pumping. The fact that aquifers are never infinite in extent may be accounted for by applying the method of images referred to later.

5-9. Interference of Wells. When the areas of influence of two or more pumped wells overlap, the draft of each well affects the drawdown of the other well or wells. If the wells are closely spaced, interference becomes so severe that a group of wells may behave like a single well that produces one large cone of depression. In this event, the discharge-drawdown relationships may be studied for the group as a whole rather than for the individual wells. The circle of influence of a heavily pumped well field may be many miles in diameter. Wells that lie within a circle a mile or so in diameter may then behave as a single group. Lightly pumped, shallow wells in unconfined aquifers, however, may provide no interference even when they are less than 100 ft apart.

The equations that have been developed for unsteady flow may be used to calculate for a single well the drawdown that is caused by the pumping of interfering wells. To the drawdown in the well, computed as if it were pumped by itself, is then added the drawdown due to the pumping of each of the interfering wells, one at a time.

Example 5-5. An example will illustrate the necessary calculations. If there are added to the well of Example 5-4 two other wells situated respectively 1,000 ft and 2,000 ft distant on a straight line, (*a*) what is the expected drawdown in each well when the first well is pumped at a rate of 700 gpm for 10 days, and (*b*) what are the drawdowns in each well when all three are pumped at a rate of 700 gpm for 10 days?

a. As shown in Example 5-4 the drawdown of the first well is 54 ft, while the drawdown of the well 1,000 ft away is calculated from

$$u = \frac{1.87}{3.2 \times 10^4} 3.9 \times 10^{-5} \times \frac{10^6}{10} = 2.3 \times 10^{-4}$$

and, from Table 5-2,

$$F(u) = 7.706$$

Hence

$$p = \frac{114.6 \times 700}{3.2 \times 10^4} 7.706 = 19 \text{ ft}$$

Similarly, the drawdown of the second well is given by:

$$u = \frac{1.87}{3.2 \times 10^4} 3.9 \times 10^{-5} \times \frac{4 \times 10^6}{10} = 9.2 \times 10^{-4}$$

or

$$F(u) = 6.415$$

and

$$p = \frac{114.6 \times 700}{3.2 \times 10^4} 6.415 = 16 \text{ ft}$$

b. If all three wells are pumped at a rate of 700 gpm the drawdown in the first and third wells will be their own drawdown plus the drawdown in one well 1,000 ft away and another well 2,000 ft away, or $(54 + 19 + 16) = 89$ ft, whereas the drawdown of the second or central well will be its own drawdown plus twice the drawdown in a well 1,000 ft away, or $(54 + 2 \times 19) = 92$ ft.

5-10. The Method of Images. In considering both steady and unsteady flow into wells, the aquifer was assumed to be unlimited in areal extent. Whether or not areal restriction is a matter of concern depends on the magnitude of the draft relative to the rate of replenishment. If, under conditions of equilibrium, the circle of influence does not extend to the bounds of the aquifer or to the source of replenishment, the assumption of an infinite aquifer introduces no difficulty. However, the assumption is often invalid: streams, outcrops, and topographic divides often lie within the radius of influence; formation boundaries, folds, and faults may limit the extent of the aquifer to a few miles; and water-bearing valley fills may be only 100 ft in breadth.

In order to deal with these limiting influences, the method of images developed by Lord Kelvin for analysis of electrostatic phenomena has been adapted to the solution of ground-water problems.[22,23] The method consists in imposing one or more image wells, i.e., the traces of identical wells at an equal distance beyond the boundary, in such manner that the superimposed effect of the image well produces the

[22] C. V. Theis, The effect of a well on the flow in a nearby stream, *Trans. Am. Geophys. Union*, 21, 734–737 (1940).

[23] J. G. Ferris, Ground-water hydraulics as a geophysical aid, *Michigan Dept. Conservation, Lansing, Mich., Tech. Rept.* 1 (1948).

necessary limiting conditions at the boundary. The method provides solutions for a variety of boundary conditions.

5-11. Collection of Ground Water in Contact with Salt Water. Fresh water occurs in contact with salt water most frequently (1) in islands, peninsulas, spits, or bars that are surrounded by the sea or extend into it, and (2) in artesian aquifers that outcrop under the sea. The yield of fresh water under these conditions and the encroachment of salt water upon fresh-water sources are exemplified by the dynamics of fresh water in sand, volcanic, and coral islands in the sea.

Depending upon the nature of the subsoil, rain water percolates downward to join the body of fresh water that is supported, as an underground lens, upon the denser salt water. As shown in Figure 5-10, the movement of fresh water is downward and outward within this lens. During rainy seasons, the water table rises and the bottom of the lens sinks. In the fluctuating boundary of contact between fresh and salt water, there is a gradation of water from fresh, through brackish, to salt. The thickness of the lens at any time and place is controlled by the height of the water table above sea level, because the fresh-water column must balance the salt-water pressure at the bottom of the lens. If, as shown in Figure 5-10, h_f is the thickness of the lens in any vertical plane through the lens, h_s is its depth below sea level, and s_f and s_s are respectively the specific gravity of the fresh

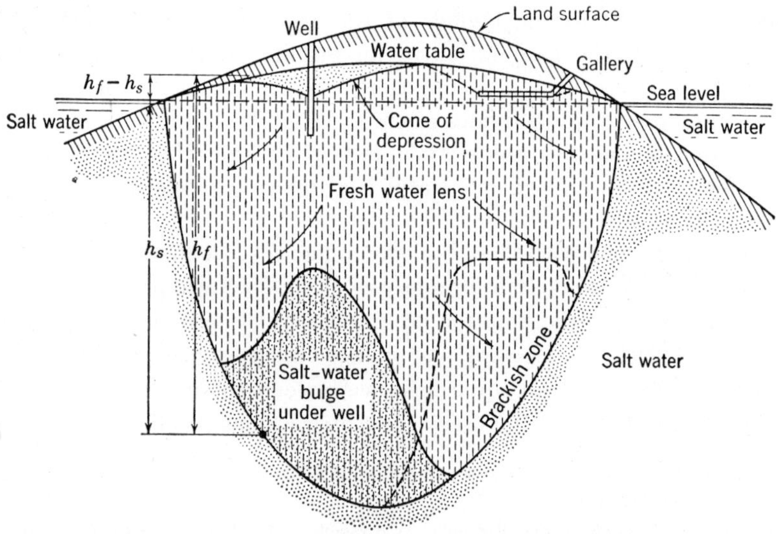

Figure 5-10. Dynamics of a fresh-water lens in contact with salt water.

water and salt water, conditions of equilibrium require that $h_f s_f = h_s s_s$ or $(h_f - h_s) s_f + h_s s_f = h_s s_s$, whence

$$h_s = \frac{s_f}{s_s - s_f} (h_f - h_s) \qquad 5\text{-}25$$

For the normal specific gravities of salt water (1.025) and fresh water (1.000), therefore,

$$h_s = 40(h_f - h_s) \qquad 5\text{-}26$$

If, for example, the water table rises 4 ft above sea level, the theoretical depth of the fresh-water lens below sea level is $40 \times 4 = 160$ ft.

Pumping, conversely, reduces the thickness of the fresh-water lens below sea level by 40 times the drawdown in the ground-water table above it. As shown in Figure 5-10 there develops, therefore, beneath the cone of depression of a well a similar, but 40 times greater, upward bulge in the zone of contact between the fresh water and salt water. The volume of fresh water that can be withdrawn, before this bulge is completely established, equals the sum of (1) the volume of water stored between the original fresh-water table and the stable cone of depression, (2) the volume of fresh water displaced by salt water in forming the bulge in the bottom of the fresh-water lens, and (3) the volume of water percolating downward into the zone of influence around the well. Since the volume of fresh water displaced in forming the bulge is often very large, the water table may fall very slowly. Some years of pumping may be required before equilibrium conditions are actually established.

Because the fresh-water lens is flat in very permeable formations, such as coral and lava, the use of galleries constructed above sea level provides a more satisfactory means than wells for the collection of fresh water in geological formations of this kind.

Construction of Collection Works

5-12. Common Features of Collection Works. Ground water must generally be raised from aquifers by pumping. To insure satisfactory performance, the suction lift including entrance and pipe losses is commonly held below 25 ft. Where the water table lies below the allowable suction depth, the collecting piping or conduit leading to the pump and the pumping unit itself must be placed below ground level, or deep-well pumps must be installed in individual wells. In favorable circumstances, air-lift pumps can be substituted for deep-well pumps. Infiltration galleries can discharge by gravity into pump wells, whence the water is lifted into force mains that lead to purification works or directly to the community. Full gravity flow, comparable to that from upland surface sources, is obtained but rarely: from springs at the base of mountains, from tunnels driven into hillsides, and from flowing artesian wells that lie sufficiently high above the community to provide the necessary head. Both suction and gravity conduits, but particularly the former, must be guarded against pollution from sources in their immediate surroundings.

Water drawn from the ground by suction or discharged by air lifts must be passed through an air-separating tank that collects the gases contributed by the air lifts or released from the water as its pressure drops below atmospheric. The collected gases are removed by a vacuum or air pump. Where sand or other soil granules are pulled into the water from the aquifer, sand separators must be employed if pumps and piping are to be protected against abrasion.

The sinking of wells is a highly specialized art that has evolved along many, more or less regional, lines. In the United States, it is common practice to allow the well driller considerable latitude in the choice of suitable methods. He undertakes to sink a well of specified minimum size at a fixed price per foot. Ordinarily, therefore, the engineer is not directly concerned with drilling operations themselves but with the adequacy, suitability, and economy of proposed developments and with the best location of the works from the standpoint of hydrology and sanitary protection. However, he is called on to select the size, number, and arrangement of wells, to specify the pumping equipment, to see that a reliable contractor is employed, to supervise the testing and development of completed wells, to see that they are properly disinfected before being placed in service, and to make certain that necessary precautions are taken to prevent contamination of the operating supply from both surface and underground sources of pollution.

Construction methods depend primarily on the nature of the ground or rock to be penetrated and on cost. In addition to size, depth, and design, the cost of construction depends on the equipment and experience of the drillers who operate in the area. Designs improve and costs decline as regional information concerning aquifers and their overlying formations accumulates. *Well logs* should, therefore, be kept. They should give an accurate description of all formations encountered, rates of drill penetration, amounts of water tapped, and other pertinent data for the various depths reached. On completion of the well, the driller's log may be supplemented by caliper, electric, and radioactivity measurements.

5-13. Construction of Wells. A brief description of the methods commonly used for sinking wells will identify the different kinds of wells.

a. Dug wells. Small dug wells are generally excavated by hand. In loose overburden, wells are cribbed with timber, lined with brick, rubble, or concrete, or cased with large-diameter vitrified tile or concrete pipe. Wells in rock are commonly left unlined. Excavation is continued until water enters more rapidly than it can be bailed out.

Large and deep dug wells are often constructed by sinking their liners as excavation proceeds. The leading ring is equipped with a steel cutting edge, and new sections are added as excavation progresses. After striking water, caisson methods may be employed.

b. Driven wells. The use of driven wells is confined to relatively shallow sand formations. As shown in Figure 5-11, a driving point

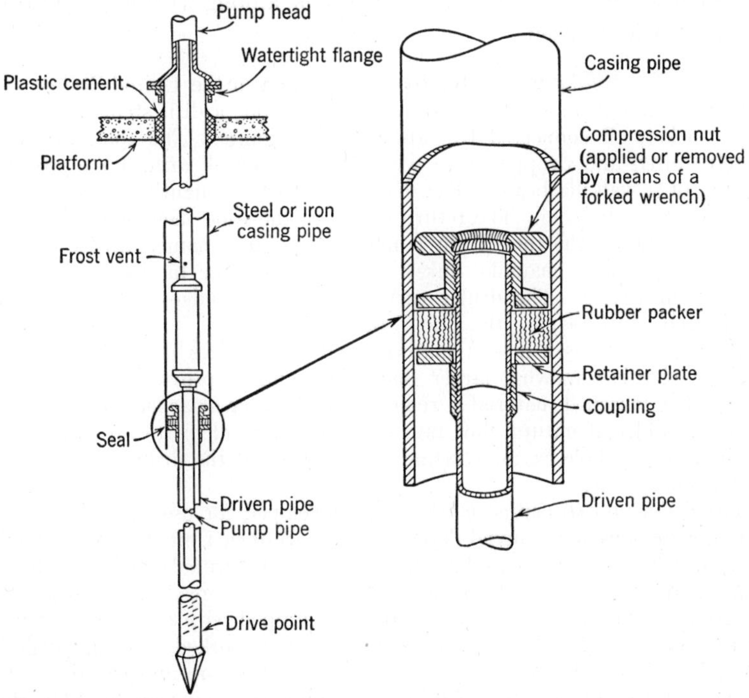

Figure 5-11. Driven well and its sanitary protection. *After Wisconsin State Board of Health.*

is attached to a strainer or perforated section of drive pipe. Driving friction is reduced by making the point somewhat larger than the casing. The driving weight is commonly suspended from a block attached to a tripod. Where the ground is hard, a cylindrical shoe equipped with water jets will loosen the soil and wash it to the surface.

c. Bored wells. In soil that is sufficiently cohesive to prevent serious caving, wells are bored with augers by hand or machinery. The soil usually remains in the auger, which is raised and cleaned periodically. Below the water table, sand may wash out of the auger and have to be removed from the bore hole by a bailer or sand pump. As boring proceeds, sections of rod are added to the auger stem. Bits up to 20 in. in diameter have been used successfully, and wells have been enlarged in diameter up to 48 in. by reaming. A well casing is inserted in the hole and cemented in place. The strainer is then installed.

d. Drilled wells. These wells are sunk either by percussion or rotary drilling. There are many methods, among which the following are most widely used.

Percussion drilling with cable tools is common in the United States. The string of tools includes a blunt or chisel-edged bit, a drill stem, jars, and a rope socket, all connected by tapered screw joints. The tools are alternately raised and dropped in a wet hole by a crank arm, a reciprocating pulley, or a walking beam. The drill rope must be slightly stretched when the bit strikes bottom. The return spring in the rope then prevents the bit from sticking or the tools from jamming. As their name implies, the *jars* (two heavy, loose, chainlike links) help to loosen the bit by jarring it on the return stroke. The driller turns the bit and judges the performance of the tools by grasping the drill rope.

Blunt bits are used in soft material and chisel edges in hard rock. The drilling edge is somewhat larger than the shank to provide working clearance. The loosened material is removed by a bailer attached to a sand line. Water is added if natural flow into the well is not adequate for drilling and bailing. If the hole caves, a casing is inserted, and the drilling is continued with a smaller bit.

The *California stovepipe method* was developed for use in the unconsolidated, water-bearing, alluvial deposits of the western United States. A mud scow which serves both as bit and bailer is substituted for the string of tools, and short joints of overlapping casing are forced down as drilling progresses. The cylindrical mud scow is equipped with a flap valve and a cutting shoe. The earth is chopped loose and worked into the drill by plunging it up and down. The filled scow is hauled up and emptied. The casing consists of sections of thin steel pipe that overlap by half their length. Joints are locked by denting the casing with a pick. The casing may be driven, a special driving head being used, or it may be forced down by hydraulic jacks anchored to timbers embedded in the soil. Slots to admit the water are cut at the level of permeable formations after the casing is in place.

Rotary drilling employs a fish-tail or similar bit, attached to a hollow drill rod, which is rotated rapidly by an engine-driven rotary table. A heavy suspension of colloidal clay is pumped into the drill pipe, flows through openings in the bit, and brings the loosened material to the surface. The drilling fluid is recirculated into the well after the suspended cuttings have been separated from it in a mud pit or settling lagoon. Rotary drilling was first used in the oil fields. Its application to water-well drilling was delayed by the fact that the thick drilling clay was forced into the aquifer and reduced the flow to the well. Development of the gravel-wall well and improvements in flushing methods have largely overcome these objections to rotary drilling.

Drilled wells should be *cemented* so as to cut off downward flow of possibly contaminated water into the well from outside, avoid erosion of the soil outside the casing, protect the casing against exterior corrosion, and prevent leakage when the casing ultimately rusts through from within. Cementing involves filling the annular space between the casing and the wall of the drill hole with dense cement grout not less than 2 in. thick. Beginning at the top of the aquifer, the grout must be forced upward until it reaches the surface of the ground. Cementing is an important conservation and health-protection measure (Figure 5-12).

e. Gravel-wall wells. As shown in Figure 5-13, an envelope of gravel placed outside the well screen creates a gravel wall which increases the effective diameter of the well. A well hole is first drilled and reamed to the desired diameter (24 in. or more). An outer casing is then cemented in, and the aquifer is cleaned before a smaller inner casing carrying the well screen is inserted. After this, pea-sized gravel is fed down between the two casings against a slowly rising mud stream. The mud prevents the settling gravel from arching to leave cavities. The mud is thinned with water as the filling proceeds, and a plunger is operated rapidly up and down inside the casing to assist in compacting the gravel. The churning action of the plunger enlarges the hole in loose material, and the thinning water washes out the mud and fine sand. Gravel-wall wells may suck in sand when they are first placed in operation, and gravel may have to be added from time to time. The gravel wall not only improves the hydraulic characteristics of the well, but it also reduces greatly difficulties with sanding and underground caving.

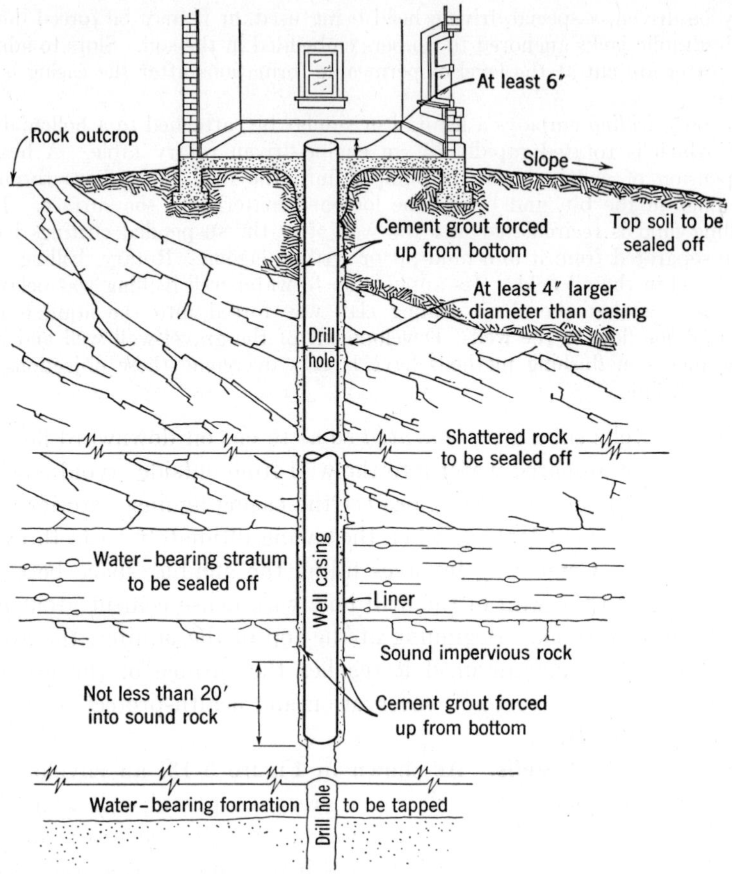

Figure 5-12. Drilled well and its sanitary protection. *After Iowa State Department of Health.*

5-14. Well Strainers. The openings in well strainers are constructed in such fashion as to keep unwanted sand out of the well while admitting water with the least possible friction. In fine, uniform material, the openings must be small enough to prevent the entrance of the constituent grains. Where the aquifer consists of particles that vary widely in size, however, the capacity of the well is improved by using strainer openings through which the finer particles are pulled into the well, while the coarser ones are left behind with increased void space. A graded filter is thereby created around the well. The finer two-thirds of the sand are generally withdrawn with the aid of backflushing operations, or by high rates of pumping.

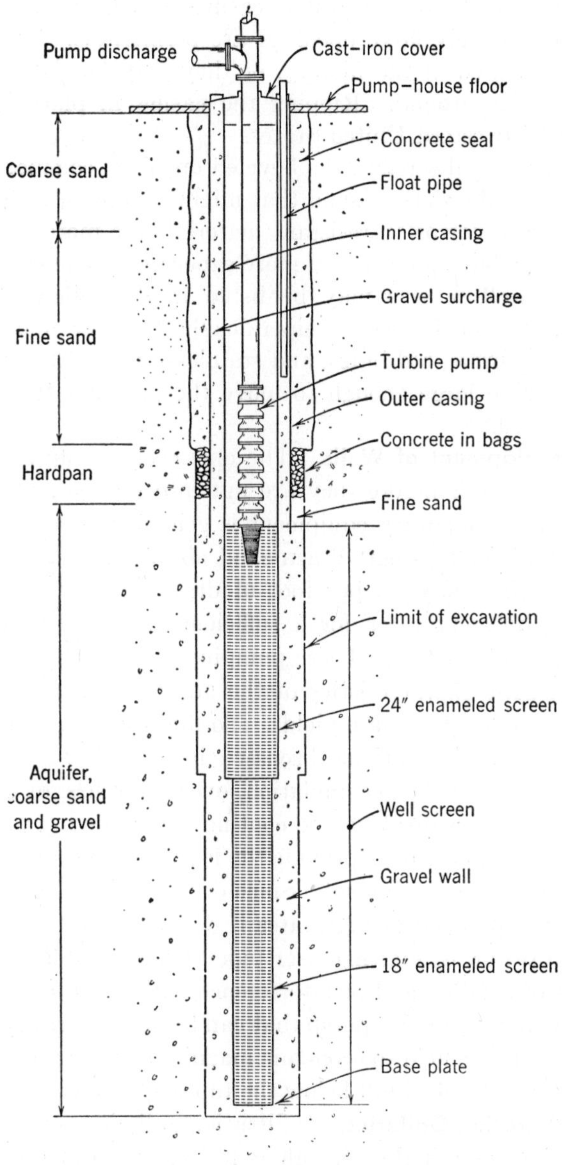

Figure 5-13. Gravel-packed well with deep-well turbine pump.

Well strainers commonly take the form of perforated casings or fabricated screens. Perforated casings are used in uncemented wells when relatively large openings are permissible. They may be machine-perforated at the factory, or they may be slotted after installation in the ground. Ripping the casing in place is common practice in the western United States.

In fabricated well screens, the beveled openings commonly enlarge inward to clear the slots of sand that might otherwise lodge in them. Screens made of corrosion-resistant materials are more durable than slotted casings, but they are also more expensive. The special metals suitable for well screens may be listed in the following order of preference:[24] Monel metal, supernickel, Everdur metal, silicon bronze, silicon brass, red brass, and stainless steel. Entrance velocities must not be large enough to move the particles that are to be left undisturbed.

5-15. Development of Wells. The operations of flushing, testing, and equipping wells before they are put into service are called *well development.* Temporary equipment is generally used for high-rate pumping and backflushing. When sand no longer enters the well its *specific capacity,* or yield per foot of drawdown, is determined by pumping at different rates for a sufficient length of time to reach fairly stable water levels. These pumping tests provide information on the hydraulic characteristics of the aquifer and the well. They do not indicate longtime safe yields. To find these, one must turn to the hydrologic considerations discussed in Section 5-3 and perhaps one must also await the accumulation, over the years, of information on the response of water levels to continued pumping.

The initial pumping tests provide the information required to select permanent pumping equipment. Since deep wells are expensive, they are commonly pumped at high rates if demands for water are large. Limiting drawdowns, limiting riser pipe velocities of 2 or 3 fps, and prevention of sanding and of interference with or by other wells determine the maximum-size pump that can be used. Drawdown, which should generally be held to economic magnitude, must not in any case cause the water level to fall below the top of the screen.

5-16. Infiltration Galleries. Infiltration galleries are suitably constructed (1) as marginal drains along hillsides; (2) at right angles to the underflow of valleys; and (3) parallel to streams toward which

[24] Tentative Standard Specifications for Deep Wells, prepared by the American Water Works Association.

upland flow is traveling, and from which water may be drawn by seepage, if this is desired. Unwanted seepage from streams is excluded by blanking off the stream side of the gallery and, if necessary, placing clay or a cutoff wall on that side.

For maximum yield, galleries should be placed at the full depth of the aquifer. Large galleries are constructed of masonry or concrete with numerous openings. They are built in open trenches or are driven by tunneling methods. Surrounding them with gravel will increase their intake, which is generally large. Tile drains laid with open joints and surrounded with gravel are used to collect smaller quantities of water. They are sometimes placed radially around springs and dug wells to increase their yield. Well points driven horizontally into the ground from a central well shaft large enough to be entered create a radial well.

The capacity of galleries that are built across a valley is increased by sinking a cutoff wall of concrete into the ground to dam up the underflow and force its entrance into the upstream collecting system.

Rural Ground-Water Supplies

5-17. Sanitary Safeguards. Rural water supplies must rely, to a considerably greater degree than their municipal counterparts, on safeguards that are inherent in their construction, since they do not receive the benefit of supervisory control or operation. To this purpose, rural water supplies should be collected, wherever possible, from sources that are certain to deliver, at all times, water that is safe and of satisfactory quality. Furthermore, the collecting system itself should be such that the water cannot be impaired in quality. Purification should be resorted to only when safe and satisfactory sources are non-existent.

No generally applicable values can be assigned to the distance that pollution may be expected to travel through the ground. As a matter of safety, it is assumed that these distances are never less than 10 ft even under the most favorable conditions: when the soil is constituted of fine-grained sand, for example, and has a high filtering effect. A minimum cover of 10 ft of fine-grained, homogeneous soil is required for the protection of ground waters against pollution by surface wash. When privies and sewage-disposal works are present, they are placed on the downward slope of the ground, the distance from the water intake being made as great as possible. Under favorable geological conditions, distances are chosen to exceed about 50 ft when pit-privies are employed, 100 ft when sewage is settled in tight septic tanks before discharge into subsurface irrigation systems, and 150 ft when bored-hole latrines or cesspools are used. In addition, all sewers and supposedly tight treatment tanks are kept at least 50 ft from the ground-water intake. Within this distance, sewers should be constructed of cast-iron pipe with lead-calked joints. Fractured ground or rock can never be considered safe.

The immediate vicinity of the ground-water intake presents the gravest dangers. For this reason, surface runoff is led away from the intake structure and the structure itself, whether it be a spring, gallery, or well, is made watertight until it has penetrated into the ground-water-bearing stratum.

5-18. Construction of Rural Water Supplies. Some of the details of construction that must be incorporated in collection works for ground water in order to prevent contamination of the water at the source are illustrated in Figures 5-14 and 5-15. They have the following features in common: (1) diversion of surface water from the intake structure; (2) drainage of overflow or spillage waters from the intake structure; (3) watertightness of the intake works for at least 10 ft below the ground surface and, if necessary, until the aquifer is reached; and (4) prevention of back-flow into the intake.

Where electric power is not available, the pumps used in rural

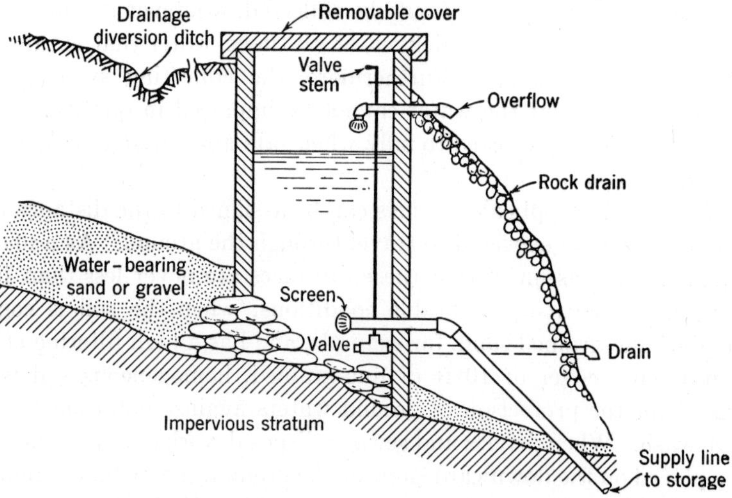

Figure 5-14. Water supply from spring. *After U. S. Public Health Service.*

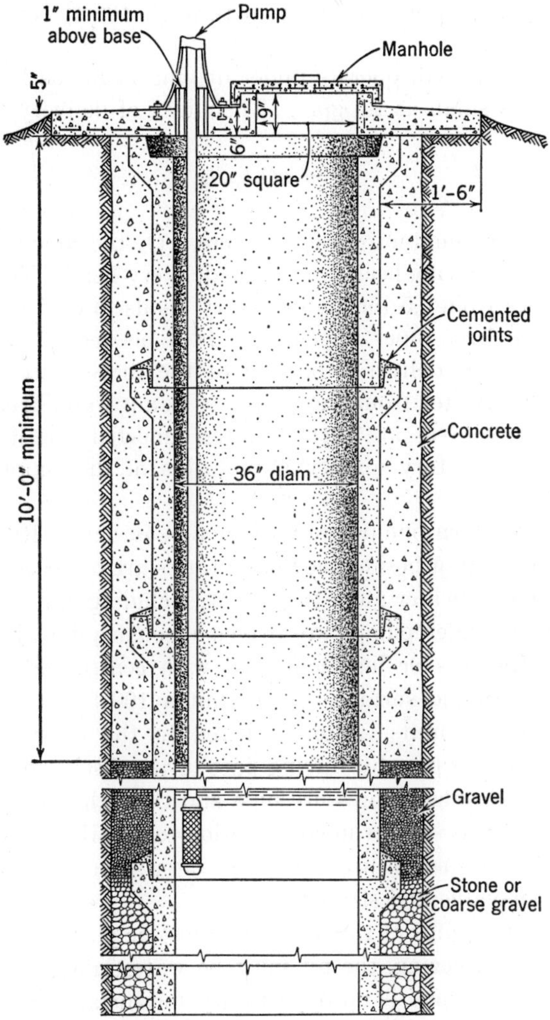

Figure 5-15. Water supply from dug well. *After U. S. Department of Agriculture.*

water supplies are operated by hand, wind, water, or gasoline engines. Windmills are generally loaded to operate in a 10- or 15-mph wind. They start to pump in winds of about half these velocities and reach their maximum output in winds of about twice these speeds. In large areas of North America, needed wind velocities do not occur during as much as two-thirds the time, and storage of water must be planned accordingly. Wheels 6 to 12 ft in diameter with 2½- to 4½-in.

cylinders will lift from 1 to 10 gpm through 100 ft when the wind speed is 15 mph.

Hydraulic rams will operate under driving heads as low as 20 in. and at flows as small as 1.5 gpm. Their rate of delivery is given by the equation

$$Q = kQ_s h_d / h \tag{5-27}$$

Here Q is the amount of water delivered, Q_s the amount of water supplied, h_d the driving head, and h the delivery head. The efficiency factor k varies from 0.5 for high delivery heads to 0.75 for low ones. The length of drive pipes is generally held between 25 and 250 ft. Single-acting rams deliver a portion of the drive water. Double-acting rams use water from one source to pump water from another. When the two sources are thereby interconnected, the drive source must be of satisfactory quality if pollution of the supply is to be avoided.

Electrically driven pumps are of numerous designs. Reciprocating pumps mounted on or beside pneumatic tanks are often used for shallow wells. To lift water more than 25 ft, including dynamic friction, rod-operated cylinder pumps are driven through pump jacks at the well head. Ejectors or jets combined with centrifugal pumps, installed at the ground surface, will permit a 100-ft suction lift. In these combination units, water is lifted to the centrifugal pump through the suction pipe by forcing part of the discharge of the centrifugal pump through a pressure pipe and through a jet in the suction lift. The jet is similar in construction to a boiler-water injector. It attaches to the suction lift below the water surface of the well but above the foot-valve and strainer.

When electric pumps at the well head must be placed below ground level to prevent freezing, the pit must be watertight and drained in such fashion that there is no opportunity for surface or other water to back into the pit and flow back into the well column.

5-19. Storage and Purification. Ground water is stored in cisterns on elevated ground, tanks in the attic of the building to be served, or elevated tanks. Pressure can also be provided by the employment of hydropneumatic tanks. These are placed either at the intake or in the cellar of the building served. The tight tank, usually constructed of steel and often galvanized, holds both air and water. The air, instead of being displaced, is compressed by the water. If the pressure in a tank of volume V is p when the tank holds its maximum volume of water V_w, the pressure p_0 when the tank is just empty is given by the isothermal relationship

$$p_0 V = p(V - V_w) \qquad \text{or} \qquad p_0 = p(1 - V_w/V) \qquad 5\text{-}28$$

The air pressure may be kept between these limits, or it may be increased for certain purposes, such as fire fighting, by adding an air compressor and air-storage tank to the system.

6 Transmission of Water

6-1. Types of Conduits. Supply conduits, or aqueducts,[1] transport water from the source of supply to the community and so form the connecting link between the collection works and the distribution system. The location of the source determines whether the conduits are short or long, and whether the water is transported by gravity or by pumping. Depending upon topography and available materials, conduits are designed to carry the water in open-channel flow or under pressure. They may follow the hydraulic grade line as (1) canals dug through the ground, (2) flumes elevated above the ground, (3) grade aqueducts laid in balanced cut and cover at the ground surface, and (4) grade tunnels penetrating hills; or they may depart from the hydraulic gradient as (5) pressure aqueducts laid in balanced cut and cover at the ground surface, (6) pressure tunnels dipping beneath valleys or hills, (7) pipelines or force mains of fabricated materials following the ground surface, if necessary over hill and through dale, sometimes rising even above the hydraulic grade line, and (8) inverted siphons or depressed pipes that connect two portions of a grade conduit (or of a pressure conduit at normal grade), when its path is crossed by a valley, stream, tidal estuary,

[1] The word *aqueduct* comes from the Latin *aqua*, water, and *ducere*, to lead or conduct. It describes all artificial channels that transport water. Use of the word is often confined by engineers to covered masonry conduits that are built in place. The great Roman aqueducts were constructed for the purpose of tapping high-lying clean sources of water and conveying it along the hydraulic gradient, because of the lack of pressure-resisting materials, to the city for distribution by gravity.

or other depression in the earth's surface, or by some other obstruction.[2] The profile of a supply conduit is shown in Figure 6-1 together with typical cross-sections of the conduit. The static pressures to which the conduits are exposed and their hydraulic grade lines are indicated.

6-2. Hydraulics of Conduits. The hydraulic design of supply conduits is concerned chiefly with the estimation of frictional resistances to flow and with the pressures that are maintained or created in the conduit. In long supply lines, changes in velocity heads and losses in transitions and appurtenances may be safely neglected. They are relatively much smaller in magnitude than the differences introduced by errors in estimating the friction or discharge coefficients of the conduit.

The most nearly rational relationship between the velocity of flow and the head loss in a conduit, also one of the earliest, is that proposed by Darcy[3] and later modified by Weisbach and others. As now used for calculating the head loss in round pipes flowing full, it has the form:

$$h_f = f \frac{l}{d} \frac{v^2}{2g} \qquad 6\text{-}1$$

where h_f is the head loss, l is the length of the pipe, d is the diameter of the pipe, v is the mean velocity of flow, g is the gravity constant, and f is a dimensionless friction factor.

Because of difficulties or inconveniences inherent in the use of this formula, engineers more commonly make use of so-called exponential equations which relate loss of head to flow. Among them the Hazen-Williams formula is most widely used to express flow relations in pressure conduits, whereas the Manning formula (Section 9-3) is favored to express flow relations in free-flow conduits.

The Hazen-Williams formula, as written by its authors, is

[2] The Colorado River Aqueduct of the Metropolitan Water District of Southern California is 242 miles long and includes 92 miles of grade tunnel, 63 miles of canal, 54 miles of grade aqueduct, 29 miles of inverted siphons, and 4 miles of force main. The Delaware Aqueduct of New York, N. Y., comprises 85 miles of pressure tunnel in three sections. Pressure tunnels 25 miles in length supply the metropolitan districts of Boston and San Francisco. The supply conduits of Springfield, Mass., are made of steel pipe and reinforced-concrete pipe; those of Albany, N. Y., of cast-iron pipe.

[3] H. Darcy, *Recherches expérimentales relatives au mouvement de l'eau dans les tuyaux*, Paris, 1857.

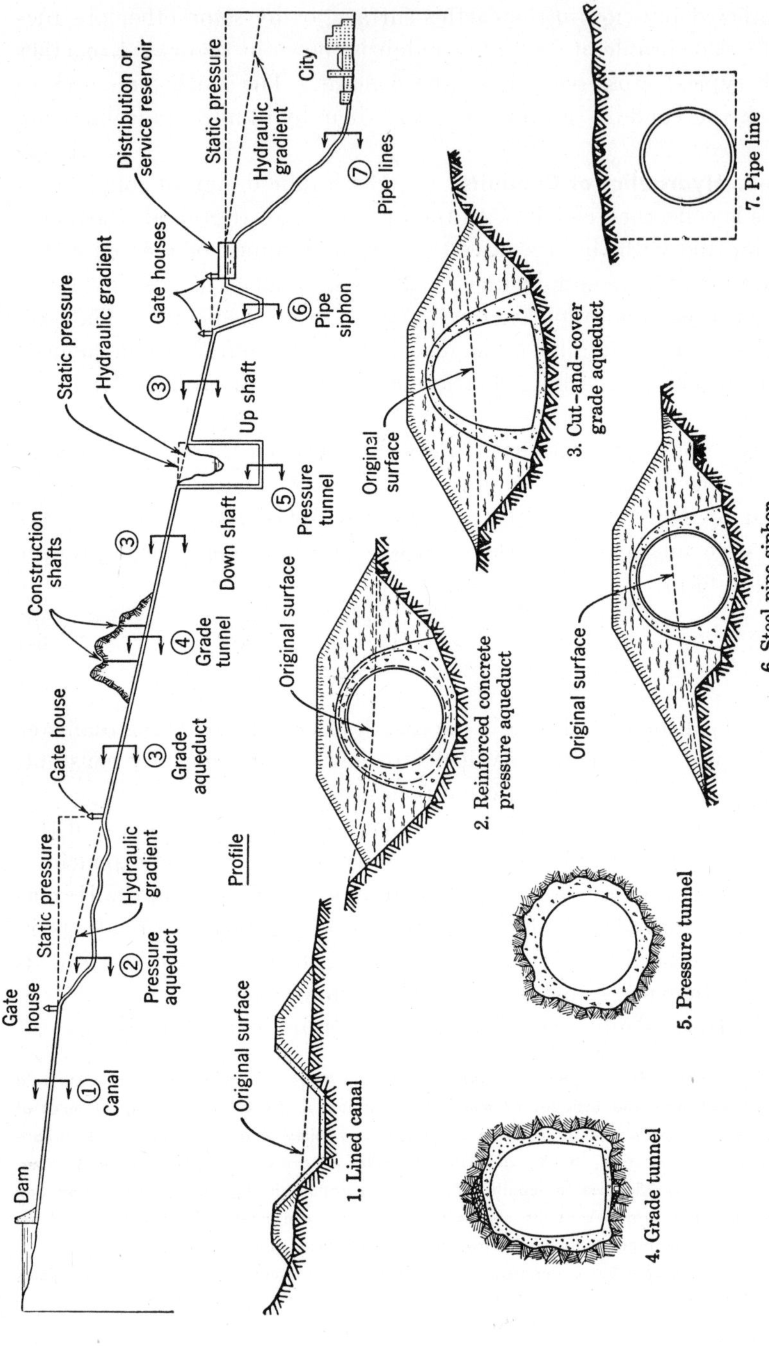

Figure 6-1. Profile and typical cross-sections of a water-supply conduit.

$$v = Cr^{0.63}s^{0.54} \times 0.001^{-0.04} \qquad 6\text{-}2$$

where v is the mean velocity of flow (fps), r is the hydraulic radius (ft), s is the hydraulic gradient, or loss of head h_f (ft) in a conduit of length l (ft), C is a coefficient, known as the Hazen-Williams coefficient, and the factor $0.001^{-0.04} = 1.318$ makes C conform in general magnitude [4] with established values of a similar coefficient in the more-than-a-century-older Chezy formula (1775).

For circular conduits:

$$v = 0.550CD^{0.63}s^{0.54} = 0.115Cd^{0.63}s^{0.54} \qquad 6\text{-}3$$

and

$$Q_{(\text{mgd})} = 0.279CD^{2.63}s^{0.54} \qquad 6\text{-}4$$

or

$$Q_{(\text{gpd})} = 405Cd^{2.63}s^{0.54} \qquad 6\text{-}5$$

Here D is the diameter of large pipes (ft), d is that of small pipes (in.), and Q is the rate of discharge as indicated. Solution of Equations 6-2 through 6-5 for Q, v, r, D, d, s, or C requires the use of logarithms, a log-log slide rule, and tables [5] or a diagram. Two types of diagrams lend themselves to this purpose: (1) a family of straight lines on logarithmic scales such as the diagram included at the end of this book, and (2) an alignment chart or nomogram.

The weakest element in the use of the Hazen-Williams formula is the estimate of the value of C when its magnitude has not been determined by actual measurements of loss of head and discharge or velocity. Values of C vary for different materials of construction and with the relative deterioration of these materials by length of service. They vary also somewhat with size and shape. The values listed in Table 6-1 reflect more or less general experience:

6-3. Capacity and Size of Conduits. With the rate of water consumption and fire demand known, the capacity of supply conduits depends upon their position in the water-works system (Section 2-7 and Figure 2-3) and upon the choice exerted by the designer between (1) a structure of full size and (2) duplicate lines that are staggered in time of construction.

Minimum workable size is one controlling factor in the design of tunnels. Otherwise, size is determined by hydraulic and economic considerations. The controlling hydraulic factors are the available

[4] Specifically for $r = 1$ ft and $s = 0.001$.

[5] Gardner S. Williams and Allen Hazen, *Hydraulic Tables*, 3rd ed., John Wiley and Sons, New York, 1933.

TABLE 6-1. Values of the Hazen-Williams Coefficient C for Different Conduit Materials and Age of Conduit

Conduit Material	Age: New	Age: Uncertain
Cast-iron pipe, coated with coal tar	130	100
Cast-iron pipe, lined with cement or bituminous enamel	130 *	130 *
Steel, riveted joints, coated with coal tar	110	90
Steel, lock-bar joints, coated with coal tar	130	100
Steel, welded joints, coated with coal tar	140	100
Steel, welded joints, lined with cement or bituminous enamel	140 *	130 *
Concrete conduits	140	130
Wood-stave pipe	130	130

* For use with the nominal diameter, i.e., diameter of unlined pipe.

heads and the allowable velocities. In finding the heads available, due allowance must be made for drawdown of reservoirs and for pressure requirements in the various parts of the community, under conditions of normal as well as fire demand. Heads greater than necessary to transport the water at normal velocities may be utilized to develop power when it is economical to do so.

Allowable velocities are determined by the characteristics of the water carried and by the need for protecting the conduit against excessive water hammer. For transportation of silt-bearing waters, there are both lower and upper limits (Section 9-2); for clear waters, only an upper limit. The minimum velocity should prevent deposition of silt; this velocity lies in the vicinity of 2 to 2.5 fps. The maximum velocity should not cause erosion or scour, nor should it endanger the conduit by creating excessive water hammer when gates are closed rapidly. Velocities of 4 to 6 fps are common, but the upper limit lies between 10 and 20 fps for most materials of which supply conduits are normally constructed and for most types of water carried.

The size of force mains and of gravity mains that include power generation is fixed by the relative cost or value of the conduit and the cost of pumping or value of power.

When aqueducts include more than one kind of conduit, the most economical distribution of the available head among the different classes of conduit is effected when the ratio of change in cost Δc to change in head Δh is the same for each component conduit, the total available head loss, H, equaling the sum of the losses in the component conduits, Σh. The proof for this statement is provided by Lagrange's method of undetermined multipliers.[6]

There is equality of the ratio $\Delta c/\Delta h$ for different relations between cost and loss of head when tangents to the cost-head curves are parallel (Figure 6-2). Hence the method is also known as the method

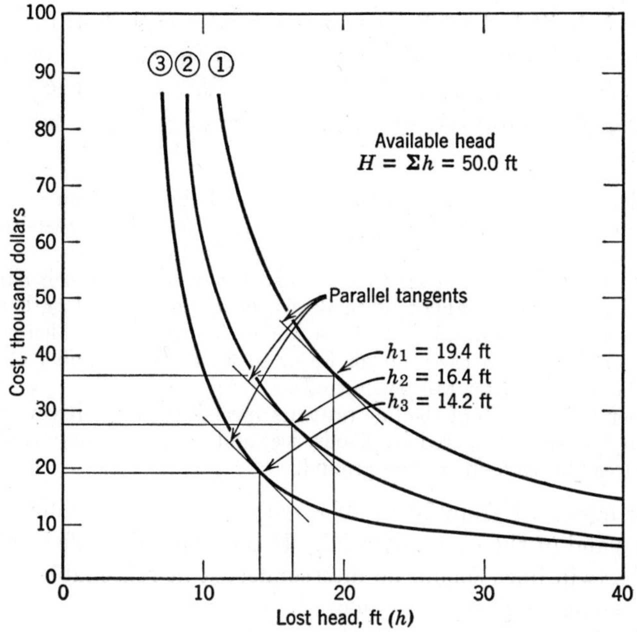

Figure 6-2. Most economical distribution of head between three different portions of a conduit.

of parallel tangents. The tangents are chosen by trial so that the sum of the heads at the points of tangency equals the available head.

Example 6-1. Given the cost and head loss relationships shown in Figure 6-2 for three sections of a conduit, find (*a*) the most economical distribution of an available head of 50 ft between the three conduits, and (*b*) the minimum cost of the conduit.

By trial draw parallel tangents to the three curves in Figure 6-2 until the sum of the heads identified by the points of tangency equals the available head of 50 ft.

a. The head losses that satisfy this constraint are $h_1 = 19.4$ ft, $h_2 = 16.4$ ft, and $h_3 = 14.2$ ft; or $h_1 + h_2 + h_3 = 50$ ft.

[6] I. S. and E. S. Sokolnikoff, *Higher Mathematics for Engineers and Physicists*, McGraw-Hill Book Co., New York, p. 127, 1934.

b. The associated costs are c_1 = \$36,500, c_2 = \$27,500, and c_3 = \$19,000; or $c_1 + c_2 + c_3$ = \$83,000.

6-4. Number of Conduits. Analysis of the cost of construction of masonry aqueducts and tunnels shows ordinarily that it is cheapest to build them to the full, projected capacity of the system. Pipelines, however, are sometimes more economical if a first line of limited capacity is built to be followed by a second line that will round out the total requirements at the time at which the capacity of the first line has been reached. Multiple supply lines may be constructed simultaneously, however, under a number of special conditions, as follows:

a. When the size of a single line would exceed the maximum size of pipe that is, or can be, manufactured satisfactorily. Centrifugal cast-iron pipe, for example, is not manufactured in sizes greater than 36 in.

b. When the pipe is known to fail in such a way that much damage is done and that repairs cannot be made within a reasonable length of time. Cast-iron pipe, for example, has been known to fracture suddenly and to open up cracks that release enough water to wash out a number of lengths of pipe before the water can be shut off.

c. When the location of the line presents special hazards. River crossings, for example, are endangered by floods, ice, and ships' anchors; conduits in mining areas by cave-ins of the ground.

Twin lines cost from 30 to 50% more than a single line of equal capacity and of the same material. If they are laid sufficiently close together, twin lines should be interconnected at reasonable intervals, and the connecting conduits should be equipped with gates so that as much of the system as possible can be kept in operation at all times. Twin lines should not be laid in the same trench if there is danger of the failure of one destroying the other. To strengthen the distribution system by having water delivered to it at two, more or less opposite, points on its periphery, dual lines may be assigned to follow widely divergent routes.

6-5. Shape of Conduits. The shape of supply conduits is varied to insure their best hydraulic performance while respecting important structural needs. Since the discharge capacity of conduits is conveniently characterized by equations, such as the Hazen-Williams formula, $Q = C'ar^{0.63}s^{0.54}$, it follows that maximum capacity Q is associated, in a conduit of given cross-sectional area a and hydraulic slope s, with the maximum attainable hydraulic radius r. Because circle and half-circle possess the largest hydraulic radius, or smallest frictional surface per unit volume of conduit, a circular cross-section is adopted for closed conduits and a semicircular one for open conduits whenever structural conditions so permit. Next best are shapes in which circle or semicircle respectively can be inscribed.

The following shapes are common:

a. For canals in earth—trapezoids approaching half a hexagon as nearly as the maintainable side slopes permit.

b. For canals in rock—rectangles twice as wide as they are deep.

c. For flumes of masonry or wood—rectangles twice as wide as they are deep.

d. For flumes of wood staves or steel—semicircles.

e. For pressure aqueducts, pressure tunnels, and pipelines—circles.

f. For grade aqueducts and grade tunnels—horseshoe sections.

Internal pressures are best resisted by circular shapes of materials that are strong in tension. External earth and rock pressures that are not opposed by internal pressures are best resisted by horseshoe sections of materials that are strong in compression. The hydraulic properties of horseshoe sections are only slightly poorer than those of the circle, and the relatively flat invert is convenient for "mucking"[7] and other construction operations. Common proportions for horseshoe sections are shown in Figure 6-3.

6-6. Strength of Conduits. Structurally, closed conduits are called upon to resist a number of different forces singly or in combination:

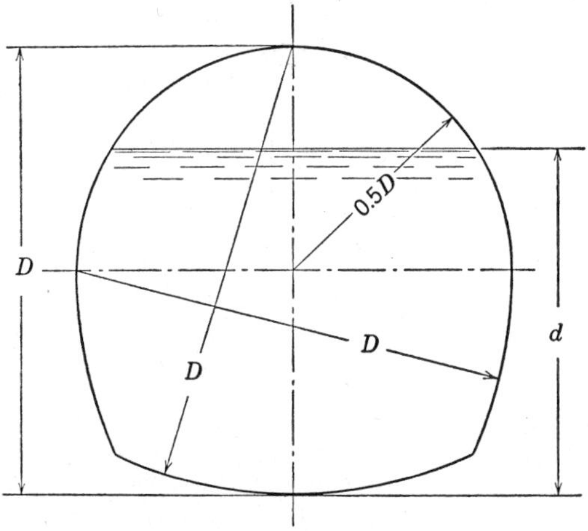

Figure 6-3. Common proportions for horseshoe sections.

[7] Mucking is the removal of debris resulting from blasting and other tunnel-driving operations.

a. Water pressure within the conduit equal to the full head of water to which the conduit can be subjected.

b. Water hammer or transient internal pressure due to sudden reduction in the velocity of the water; by the rapid closing of a gate, for example.

c. External loads in the form of backfill and traffic.

d. Expansion and contraction with changes in temperature that are normally confined to fluctuations in the temperature of the water carried in the conduit.

Internal pressure, including water hammer, creates transverse stress known as hoop tension. Bends and closures, including gates, are responsible for unbalanced pressures that produce longitudinal stress. External loads and foundation reactions (manner of support), including the weight of the conduit itself and the water it contains, as well as atmospheric pressure (when the conduit is under vacuum), result in flexural stresses. Variations in temperature, finally, produce longitudinal stresses if the conduit is not permitted to change its length.[8]

Common allowances for water hammer in cast-iron pipes are those suggested by Dexter Brackett (Table 6-2).

TABLE 6-2. Allowances for Water Hammer in Cast-Iron Pipes

Diameter, in.	4 to 10	12 and 14	16 and 18	20	24	30	36	42 to 60
Water hammer, psi	120	110	100	90	85	80	75	70

In pipes, such as cast-iron pipes with bell-and-spigot joints, the longitudinal stresses must either be resisted by the joints or relieved by motion. The magnitude of the resistance of lead and lead-substitute joints in bell-and-spigot cast-iron pipe to being pulled apart may be estimated from Prior's observational formula:[9]

$$p = \frac{3,800}{d + 6} - 40 \qquad \text{or} \qquad P = \frac{\pi d^2}{4} p = \left(\frac{3,000}{d + 6} - 31\right) d^2 \qquad \text{6-6}$$

Tables of normal thickness of cast-iron, steel, and reinforced-concrete pipe are found in professional manuals and manufacturers' publications.

[8] For the formulation of the behavior of conduits under stress, the reader is referred to standard books on hydraulics and to the following monographs: G. R. Rich, *Hydraulic Transients*, McGraw-Hill Book Co., New York, 1951; Anson Marston, The theory of external loads on closed conduits in the light of the latest experiments, *Iowa State Coll. Eng. Exp. St. Bull. 96* (1930); and W. J. Schlick, Loads on pipes in wide trenches, *Iowa State Coll. Exp. St. Bull. 108* (1932).

[9] J. C. Prior, Investigation of bell-and-spigot joints in cast-iron water pipes, *Ohio State Univ. Eng. Exp. St. Bull.* 87 (1935).

6-7. Location of Conduits. The procedure of locating a supply conduit is similar to that employed in the location of railroads or highways.

a. Line and grade. Grade aqueducts and tunnels are held rigidly to the hydraulic grade line. Cut and fill are utilized to greatest advantage in maintaining a uniform gradient. At the same time cut and cover are balanced to reduce haul. Valleys and rivers that would be bridged by railroads and highways may be bridged also by aqueducts. Such indeed was the practice of ancient Rome, but modern aqueducts no longer rise above valley, stream, and hamlet. Pressure conduits have taken the place of these lofty structures. Sometimes pressure conduits are incorporated in bridges that may be designed to serve the primary or ancillary purpose of carrying a highway; sometimes they are laid in trenches as inverted siphons, or depressed pipes, that pass beneath valleys and streams; sometimes they strike deep below the surface in pressure tunnels. For the location of such tunnels, geological exploration fixes both line and grade.

Pressure aqueducts and pipelines can move freely up and down slopes. For economy they should hug the hydraulic grade line as closely as possible while they pursue a relatively straight path between the points connected. Size and thickness of conduit and difficulty of construction must be balanced against length. The shortest route is not necessarily the cheapest.

True siphons are avoided wherever it is possible to do so. Air released from the water and trapped at high points reduces the available waterway, increases friction, and may even interrupt flow. An air ejector or vacuum pump must, therefore, be installed at summits that rise above the hydraulic grade line. If this rise is confined to less than 20 ft and the velocity is kept above 2 fps, operating troubles are held at a minimum. For best results the summit should be approached at a uniform and gradual slope and the conduit should then drop away rapidly.

b. Curves. In long supply conduits, changes in direction and changes in grade are not made sharp in the ordinary course of design. Masonry conduits that are built in place may be brought to any desired degree of curvature by proper form work, although economic utilization of forms will often circumscribe the maximum. Cast-iron pipelines are limited in curvature by the maximum bend that can be made at the juncture of standard lengths of pipe. The desired curve is then built up gradually by repeated offsets from the tangent. If the pipes are shortened by cutting or special fabrication, sharper curves can be formed. Permissible angles vary with the type of pipe. If tightness and strength of joint are to be maintained in cast-iron, bell-and-spigot pipe, the angular deflection of successive lengths of pipe should not exceed the values listed in Table 6-3. Welded-steel

TABLE 6-3. Angular Deflections in Cast-Iron, Bell-and-Spigot Pipe

Diameter, in.	4	6	8	10	12	16	18	20	24	30	36	42	48
Angle													
deg	4	3	3	3	3	2	2	2	1	1	1	1	0
min	0	30	14	7	0	41	26	9	47	26	12	2	55

pipelines less than 15 in. in diameter are sufficiently flexible to be bent after several joints have been welded together in the field. Bends in larger steel pipe are made by cutting the end of the pipe at an angle. The maximum angle depends upon the type of transverse joint employed, the thickness of the steel plate, and the size of the pipe. For riveted field joints on steel pipe larger than 30 in. in diameter, the allowable angular deflection is approximately that shown in Table 6-4. The cutting and welding of short sections make it possible to build up almost any desired angle.

TABLE 6-4. Angular Deflections in Riveted-Steel Pipes Larger than 30 in. in Diameter

Thickness, of plate, in.	$\frac{1}{4}$	$\frac{5}{16}$	$\frac{3}{8}$	$\frac{7}{16}$	$\frac{1}{2}$
Angle of bend, deg	6	5	4	$3\frac{1}{2}$	3

Long-radius curves are made in precast-concrete pipe, asbestos-cement pipe, and machine-made wood-stave pipe by offsets from the tangent. The angle that can be made varies with the type of joint employed. Values similar in magnitude to those listed for cast-iron pipe with bell-and-spigot joints are attainable. Continuous-stave pipe is built in place on curves with a minimum radius about 50 times the diameter of the pipe.

For sharp curves, transitions, and branches, special fittings are built up of the same materials as the main conduit, or special castings are employed.

c. Depth of cover. Conduits that follow the surface of the ground are generally laid below the frost line, although the thermal capacity and latent heat of water are so great that there is little danger of freezing so long as the water remains in motion. In order to reduce the external load on large conduits, only the lower half may be laid below the frost line. Along the forty-second parallel of latitude in the United States, which describes the southern boundaries of Massachusetts, upper New York, and Michigan, the frost seldom penetrates more than 5 ft beneath the surface. Along the forty-fifth parallel the depth of frost increases to 7 ft. The following equation approximates Shannon's [10] observations of the depth of the frost line:

$$d = 1.65F^{0.468} \tag{6-7}$$

where d is the depth of frozen soil in inches and F, the freezing index, is the algebraic difference between the maximum positive and negative cumulative departures, $\Sigma(T_d - 32)$, of the daily mean temperatures (T_d) from 32 F. Accumulation, as shown in Figure 6-4, begins on

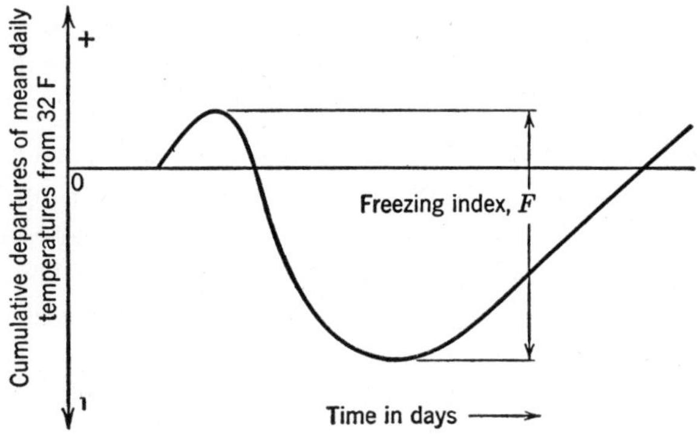

Figure 6-4. Determination of the freezing index of soils as the cumulative departure of the mean daily temperature from 32 F. *After Shannon.*

the first day on which a freezing temperature is recorded. In concept, the freezing index is analogous to the term "degree days" which describes the heat requirements of buildings during the heating season.

Protection of conduits against extremes of heat and against ordinary mechanical damage is secured at depths of 2 to 3 ft, but cover of 5 ft or more may be required in streets or roads that carry heavy vehicles.

Depth of cover, or allowable weight of backfill, is limited by the structural characteristics of the conduit. These characteristics vary for the different classes of material that are employed and may necessitate laying the conduit in open cut, i.e., cut in which the depth of backfill does not exceed the maximum allowable value.

[10] W. L. Shannon, Prediction of frost penetration, *J. New Engl. Water Works Assoc.*, *59*, 356 (1945).

6-8. Materials for Conduits. The selection of materials for pipelines and evaluation of their cost must take into consideration:

a. The initial carrying capacity of the pipe and its change with use, expressed, for example, in terms of the coefficient C in the Hazen-Williams formula (Section 6-2).

b. The strength of the pipe, i.e., its ability to resist internal pressures and external loads (Section 6-6).

c. The length of life or durability of the pipe, i.e., the resistance of cast-iron and steel pipe to corrosion; of wood-stave pipe to rotting and corrosion; and of concrete and asbestos-cement pipe to erosion and disintegration.

d. The ease or difficulty of transporting, handling, and laying the pipe under different conditions of topography and geology.

e. The safety, economy, and availability of manufactured sizes, a matter that has been mentioned in Section 6-4.

f. The availability of skilled labor for the construction of the pipeline.

g. The requirements of maintenance and repair, losses of water by leakage, and other matters of pipe behavior and suitability.

a. Carrying capacity. The initial value of the Hazen-Williams coefficient C hovers about 140 for all types of well-laid pipelines, but the coefficient tends to be somewhat higher for reinforced-concrete and asbestos-cement lines and to sink to a normal value of about 130 for unlined cast-iron pipe unless the line is laid with extraordinary care. Double-riveted steel pipe loses about 20 points in addition, but riveted longitudinal joints are seldom used today. Their place has been taken in succession by lock-bar and welded joints. The riveted transverse joint, too, has made way for the welded joint or for mechanical couplings. Unlined, welded-steel pipe has an initial coefficient of C close to 140. Cast-iron and steel pipes that are lined with cement or with bituminous enamel possess coefficients of 130 and over on the basis of their nominal diameter, because improved smoothness offsets the reduction in their cross-section.

The loss of capacity with age or, more strictly speaking, with service depends (1) upon the quality of the water carried and (2) upon the characteristics of the pipe. Modern methods of water treatment for the correction of aggressive properties (Chapter 14) give promise that the corrosion of metallic pipes as well as the disintegration of cement linings and reinforced concrete and of asbestos-cement pipe will be very largely, if not fully, controlled in the future.

Cement and bituminous-enamel linings and reinforced-concrete and asbestos-cement pipes do not, as a rule, show significant losses in capacity with service.

b. Strength. Steel pipe is best suited to resist high internal pressures, but the ability of large steel pipes to withstand external loads while empty or subjected to partial vacuum is very poor. Collapse must be guarded against by limiting the depth of cover or by surrounding the pipe with concrete. Cast-iron pipe and asbestos-cement pipe are good for moderately high water pressures and for appreciable external loads, provided that the pipes are properly laid. Reinforced-concrete pipe and wood-stave pipe are satisfactory under moderate water pressures. Reinforced-concrete pipe can carry high external loads.

c. Durability. Experience with all but tar-coated cast-iron pipe has been too short and changes in water treatment have been too numerous to permit the assigning of reliable values to the length of life of different pipe materials. In the past, engineers have employed values of the following approximate magnitude:

Cast-iron pipe, coated with coal tar	100 years or more
Steel pipe, coated with coal tar	25 to 50 years
Reinforced-concrete pipe	75 years or more
Wood-stave pipe	25 to 50 years

Wood-stave pipe must be kept under pressure if rotting of the wood is to be avoided. External corrosion (soil corrosion) and disintegration of pipe and electrolysis are important factors in the evaluation of durability. Acid soils, sea water, and cinder fills should be avoided where possible. Metal pipes and the banding of wood-stave pipe are commonly more corrodible than reinforced-concrete and asbestos-cement pipes. Metal pipes, too, are better conductors of electricity and so more exposed to destruction by electrolysis (Section 14-7). Cathodic protection is of some promise in this connection.

d. Transportation. Pipelines must frequently be constructed in rugged and normally inaccessible locations. Pipe dimensions and weights then become important. Cast-iron pipe is heavy in the larger sizes. Steel pipe is relatively much lighter though bulkier because of the longer sections ordinarily employed. The normal laying length of cast-iron pipe is 12 ft;[11] that of steel pipe is 20 to 30 ft. Wood-stave pipe is "machine made or prefabricated" in sizes up to 24 in. and lengths up to 20 ft. Pipes of greater diameter are built in place from staves and bands. This simplifies transportation. Reinforced-

[11] Lengths of 16 ft, 5 m (16.4 ft), 18 ft, and 20 ft are also available in different types of bell-and-spigot pipe.

concrete pipe is generally cast in the vicinity of the pipeline. The sections are ordinarily 12 and 16 ft long and are very heavy in the larger sizes. Sizes smaller than 24 in. are unusual. Asbestos-cement pipe comes in laying lengths of 18 ft. It weighs about one-quarter as much as cast-iron pipe of the same diameter.

e. Safety. Because of the suddenness and extensiveness of failure, breaks in cast-iron pipe are often quite destructive. Steel fails slowly, chiefly by corrosion. Perforations of the shell at scattered points create small leaks, and repairs are simple. Collapse of steel pipe under vacuum while the line is being drained is a possible but rare occurrence. Wood-stave pipe and reinforced-concrete pipe fail gradually. Asbestos-cement pipe fails much like cast-iron pipe.

f. Skilled labor. Skill is required chiefly in connection with making the joints. Mechanical joints place the smallest demands upon labor, welded and poured joints the greatest.

g. Maintenance and leakage. Large pipe that can be entered should be inspected regularly and maintained in good condition. All sizes of line must be watched for outward signs of failure, generally indicated by leakage and by loss of pressure. There is not much choice between materials in this respect. Repairs to precast concrete pipe are perhaps the most difficult to make but are seldom called for. Small cast-iron and welded-steel pipes can be cleaned by scraping machines and lined in place with cement.

All pipelines are tested for tightness during construction. The amount of leakage observed is often expressed in gallons per day per inch diameter (nominal) and mile of pipe, but gallons per day per foot of joint is a better generalization. The test pressure must naturally be stated. It is usually assumed, by reference to the behavior of orifices, that the loss varies as the square root of the pressure.

The allowable leakage of bell-and-spigot, cast-iron pipe that has been carefully laid and well tested during construction is given by the following empirical relationship:

$$Q = nd\sqrt{p}/1{,}850 \qquad \text{6-8}$$

where Q is the leakage in gallons per hour, n is the number of joints in the length of pipe tested, d is the nominal diameter of pipe in inches, and p is the average pressure during test in pounds per square inch, gage. A mile of 24-in. cast-iron pipe laid in 12-ft lengths and tested under a pressure of 64 psig, for example, may be expected to show a leakage of $Q = (5{,}280/12) \times 24 \times \sqrt{64}/1{,}850 = 46$ gal per hr. Since a 24-in. pipe has a carrying capacity of 250,000 gal per hr at a velocity of 3 fps, it is seen that leakage from joints is, relatively speaking, very small.

Steel pipe should be made tight by calking. When it is laid under water with mechanical couplings, it becomes difficult to find small leaks, and allowances as high as 6 gpd per ft of transverse joint may have to be made. The leakage to be expected from asbestos-cement pipe is of the same order of magnitude as that from cast-iron pipe, whereas that from percast-concrete pipe corresponds to the leakage from steel lines.

To make a leakage test, the pipe is isolated by closing gates and placing a temporary header or plug at the end of the section of line last completed. The pipe is then filled with water and placed under pressure, the amount of water needed to maintain the pressure being measured by an ordinary meter of the household type. In the absence of water, air may be employed. For disinfection, see Section 18-11.

6-9. Appurtenances for Conduits. In order to isolate and drain convenient sections of supply conduits for test, inspection, and repair, or for removal of silt and other deposits by scour, and in order to protect conduits in other ways, a number of appurtenances, or auxiliaries, may be needed (Figure 6-5).

a. Gates. In pressure conduits, gate valves are generally placed at the major summits, (1) because these define the sections of line that can be drained by gravity, and (2) because the pressure is least at these points, making for cheaper valves and easier operation. For the sake of economy, valves smaller in diameter than the conduit are used, where possible. They are connected to the pipe by means of reducers. Gates 8 or more inches in diameter generally include a 4-in. or 6-in. gated by-pass. When the larger gate is sealed against pressure, water can be admitted through the by-pass to the section of line behind the larger gate. The pressure on both sides is equalized, and the larger gate can then be lifted more easily.

Small gate valves are operated through gate boxes; large ones are placed in gate chambers or vaults, or they are buried in the ground. They must be protected against frost and against temperature stresses (see Part *g* of this section).

In gravity conduits, gate chambers are common. They are placed (1) at points strategic for the operation of the supply conduit, (2) at the beginning and end of depressed pipes and pressure tunnels, and

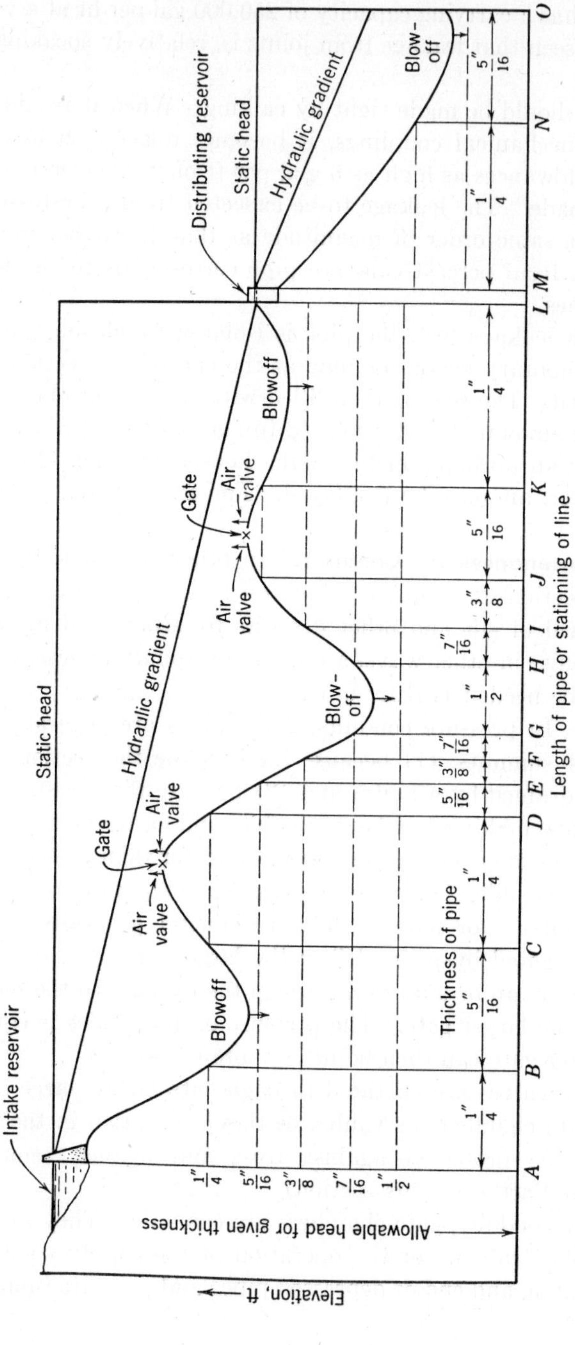

Figure 6-5. Profile of pipeline showing pipe thickness and location of gates, blowoffs, and air valves. *Not to scale, vertical scale magnified.*

(3) wherever it is convenient to drain the gravity sections. Sluice gates are normally employed on conduits that are laid at grade, especially when they are large. Needle valves for fine control of flow in supply conduits, butterfly valves for ease of operation, and cone valves for regulating the time of closure may replace gate and sluice valves in special situations.

b. Blowoff valves. In pressure conduits, small, gated take-offs are provided at low points in the line. The gates are known as blowoff or scour valves. They discharge into natural drainage channels or into a sump from which the water can be pumped to waste. There should be no direct connections to sewers. For safety in operation, two blowoff valves are normally placed in series. Their size depends upon local circumstances, especially upon the time in which the line drained by them is to be emptied. Due reference should be had to the velocities created in the conduit (see Part *c* of this section). Calculations are based upon the discharge from an orifice under a falling head. This head equals the difference in elevation of the water surface in the conduit and the blowoff, minus the friction head due to flow. Frequency of use depends upon the quality of the water carried. The gate chambers of gravity conduits include drainage gates.

c. Air valves. Cast-iron and other rigid pipes and pressure conduits require air valves at all high points for the purpose of automatically removing (1) air that is displaced during the filling of the line, and (2) air that is released from the flowing water if the pressure fluctuates appreciably and if the summit lies close to the hydraulic gradient. If the pressure at the summits is high, a manually operated cock or gate may be substituted because little, if any, air will accumulate and air removal is confined to filling operations.

Steel and other flexible conduits need air valves for the purpose of automatically admitting air to the line and preventing its collapse under vacuum. A vacuum may be created when the pipe is being drained on purpose or when water escapes accidentally from the line —as the result of a break at or near a low point, for example. Air-inlet valves must be placed on both sides of gates at summits in the line, on the downstream side of other gates, and at changes in grade to steeper slopes in sections of the line that are not otherwise protected by air valves.

The required size of valve is obviously related to the size of the conduit. The following ratios of diameter of air valve to diameter of conduit are common:

For release of air only	1:12 or 1 in. per ft
For admission as well as release of air	1:8 or 1½ in. per ft

A rough calculation [12] will show that under a vacuum of 12 in. of water, an automatic air valve, acting as an injection orifice under a head of $1/(1.3 \times 10^{-3}) = 770$ ft of air of specific gravity 1.3×10^{-3}, may be expected to admit somewhat less than $\sqrt{2g \times 770} = 220$ cfs of air per sq ft of valve. If the ratio of diameters is 1:8, the displacement velocity in the conduit can then be as high as $220/64 = 3.5$ fps without exceeding a vacuum of 12 in. of water. A similar calculation will show the rate of release of air. The amounts of air that can be dissolved by water at atmospheric pressure are about 2.9% by volume at 32 F and 1.9% at 77 F. These amounts change in direct proportion to the pressure; e.g., they are doubled at two atmospheres or 14.7 psig.

d. Manholes. To serve as access openings, manholes are spaced 1,000 to 2,000 ft apart on large conduits. They are helpful during the construction of the line and for its inspection and repair. Manholes are common on steel and concrete lines; less so on cast-iron and asbestos-cement lines.

e. Insulation joints. Use of insulation joints is naturally confined to metallic pipes. Although their primary purpose is to introduce resistance to the flow of stray electric currents along the pipeline, they may be of assistance in the control of electrolysis. They are designed in many different ways. Modern insulation joints make use, very largely, of rubber-covered sections of pipe that are sufficiently long to introduce appreciable resistance.

f. Expansion joints. Expansion joints are not needed if the pipe joints themselves will take care of pipe movements. Steel pipe that is laid with rigid transverse joints must either be permitted to expand at definite points, or motion must be restrained by anchoring the line.

g. Anchorages. Anchorages are employed for one or more of the following reasons:

1. To resist the tendency of pipes to pull apart at bends and other points of unbalanced pressure when the resistance of their joints to longitudinal (shearing) stresses is exceeded.
2. To resist the tendency of pipes to pull apart when they are laid on steep gradients and the resistance of their joints to longitudinal (shearing) stresses is inadequate.

[12] For more refined calculations, see A. W. Sweeten, Air-inlet valve design for pipelines, *Eng. News-Record*, 97, 294 (1926).

3. To restrain or direct the expansion and contraction of rigidly joined pipes under the influence of temperature changes.

Anchorages take many forms. For bends—both horizontal and vertical—they may be designed as concrete buttresses or "kick blocks" that resist the unbalanced pressure by their weight, in much the same manner as a gravity dam resists the pressure of the water that it impounds. The resistance offered by the pipe joints themselves, by the friction of the pipe exterior, and by the bearing value of the soil in which the block is buried may be taken into consideration if the cost of the block is to be held at a minimum. Steel straps attached to heavy boulders or to bedrock are used in place of buttresses where it is possible and convenient to do so. Cast-iron pipes and fittings can be cast with lugs through which tie rods are passed when it is desired to prevent movement of the pipe. In order to restrain the motion of steel pipe or force it to take place at expansion joints that have been inserted for that purpose, the pipe may be anchored in much the same way as described for bends. Due attention must be paid to the bonding of the pipe to the anchors. In the absence of expansion joints, steel pipe must be anchored at each side of gates and meters in order to prevent their destruction. Where gate chambers are used, they may be so designed of steel and concrete that they hold the two ends of the steel line rigidly in place. In the absence of anchors, flanged gates are sometimes bolted on one side to the pipe—usually the upstream side—and on the other side to a cast-iron nipple that is connected to the pipe by means of a sleeve or expansion joint.

h. Other appurtenances. These may include: air-relief towers at the first summit of the line to remove air that is mechanically entrained as water is drawn into the entrance of the pipeline; surge tanks at the end of the line to reduce water hammer that is created by rapid closing of a valve at the end of the line; pressure-relief valves or overflow towers on one or more summits to keep the pressure in the line below a given value by causing water to flow to waste when the pressure builds up beyond the design value; check valves on force mains to prevent back-flow when pumps shut down; self-acting shut-off valves that will close when the velocity in the pipe exceeds a predetermined value in case of accident to the line; altitude-control valves that will shut off the inlet to service reservoirs, elevated tanks, and standpipes when overflow levels are reached; and Venturi meters to measure the flow.

6-10. Pumping Units. Pumping stations for water and waste water are generally equipped with centrifugal pumps, driven in most cases by electric motors, occasionally by steam turbines or internal-combustion engines.[13] The direction of flow through the impeller depends on the type of pump. Radial flow occurs in volute and turbine pumps, axial flow in propeller pumps, and diagonal flow in mixed-flow pumps. Strictly speaking, a propeller pump is not a centrifugal pump.

The selection of pumping units requires a knowledge of system-head and pump characteristics. The system head, which is the sum of the static and dynamic heads against the pump, varies (1) with the flow in the system, (2) with changes in storage and suction levels, and (3) with shifts in demand when a distribution system lies between the pump and the reservoir. The pump characteristics depend on the size, speed, and design of the pump. For a given speed N in revolutions per minute, they are defined by the relationships between the rate of discharge Q, usually in gallons per minute, and the head H in feet, the efficiency E in per cent, and the power input P in horsepower. A pump of given geometrical design is also characterized by its specific speed N_s. This is the hypothetical speed of an homologous (geometrically similar) pump with an impeller diameter D such that it will discharge 1 gpm against a 1-ft head. Since discharge varies as area multiplied by velocity and since velocity must vary as $H^{1/2}$, $Q \propto D^2H^{1/2}$. But velocity varies also as $\pi DN/60$. Hence $H^{1/2} \propto DN$, or $N \propto H^{3/4}/Q^{1/2}$, and the specific speed is given by the relation

$$N_s = NQ^{1/2}/H^{3/4} \tag{6-9}$$

Generally speaking, the efficiencies of pumps increase with their size and capacity. Below specific speeds of 1,000 units, efficiencies drop off rapidly. Between specific speeds of 1,000 and 4,000 units, radial-flow pumps perform well. Mixed-flow pumps are efficient in the range of 4,000 to 7,500 units. After that axial-flow pumps have higher efficiencies. As shown by Equation 6-9, rising magnitudes of N_s at constant values of N are associated with increasing rates of discharge and decreasing heads. This explains why axial-flow pumps are often used in drainage and irrigation works, whereas radial-flow pumps are common in municipal water works. For double-suction pumps half the capacity establishes the specific speed.

[13] W. H. Sears, Pumping water—an historical review, *J. New Eng. Water Works Assoc.*, *49*, 119 (1935).

Specific speed is an important criterion, too, for determining safety against cavitation. This phenomenon occurs on impeller surfaces when conversion of potential energy to kinetic energy reduces the absolute pressure below the vapor pressure of water at the prevailing temperature. The water then vaporizes to form pockets of vapor. The sudden collapse of these pockets, when they are swept to regions of higher pressure, results in vibration, noise, and rapid destruction of the impeller. Cavitation occurs beyond certain limiting inlet pressures or when the capacity or speed of rotation is increased without a compensating rise in inlet pressure. Lowering the elevation of a pump in relation to its water source, therefore, reduces cavitation. If we replace the head H in Equation 6-9 by H_{sv}, the net inlet head or difference between the total inlet head (including the velocity head in the inlet pipe) and the head corresponding to the vapor pressure of the water pumped, we obtain the *suction specific speed*

$$S = NQ^{1/2}/H_{sv}^{3/4} \qquad \text{6-10}$$

for which certain general safe limits have been established by experiment.[14] The following are examples:

Single-suction pumps with overhung impellers	$S \leqq$ 8,000–12,000
Single-stage pumps with shaft through eye of impeller	$S \leqq$ 7,000–11,000
High-pressure, multistage pumps (single suction)	$S \leqq$ 5,500– 7,500
High-pressure, multistage pumps with special first-stage impeller (single suction)	$S \leqq$ 7,500–10,000

Interrelationships between the common performance characteristics of a centrifugal pump operating at constant speed are illustrated in Figure 6-6. Note that the shut-off head is a fixed limit and that the power consumption is minimum at shut-off. For this reason, centrifugal pumps are often started with the pump discharge valve closed. As the head falls past the point of maximum efficiency (point 1 in Figure 6-6) the power continues to rise. Care must be taken, therefore, not to operate a pump against too low a head, for this sometimes overloads the motor if it has been selected to operate the pump in a head range around maximum efficiency.

The effects of using more than one pumping unit are also shown in Figure 6-6, and a curve for the system head is drawn in. It is obvi-

[14] G. F. Wislicensus, R. M. Watson, and I. J. Karassik, Cavitation characteristics of centrifugal pumps described by similarity considerations, *Trans. Am. Soc. Mech. Engrs., 61,* 170 (1939); also G. F. Wislicensus, section on centrifugal pumps, *Mechanical Engineers' Handbook,* L. S. Marks, Editor, McGraw-Hill Book Co., New York, 1951.

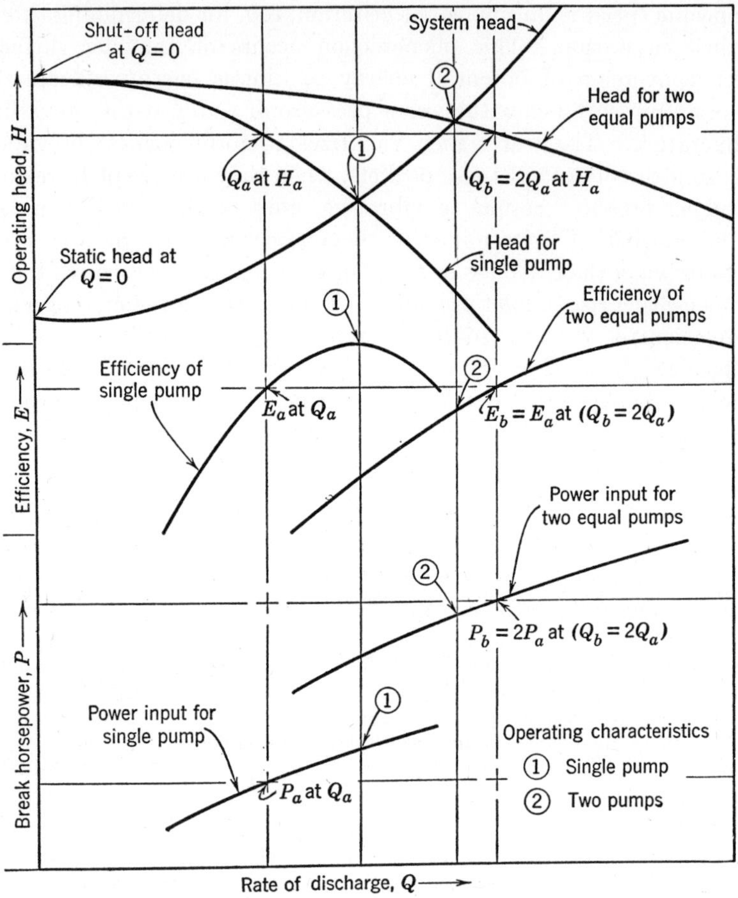

Figure 6-6. Performance characteristics of single and twin centrifugal pumps operating at constant speed.

ous that pumping units can operate only at the point of intersection of their own head curves with the head curve of the system. In practice, the system head at a given discharge varies over a considerable range (see Figure 6-7). Where a distributing reservoir is part of a system, for example, and both the reservoir and the source of water fluctuate in water-surface elevation, there is (1) a lower curve that identifies head requirements when the reservoir is empty and the water surface of the source is high and (2) an upper curve that establishes the system head for a full reservoir and a low water level at the source. How the characteristic curves for twin-unit operation

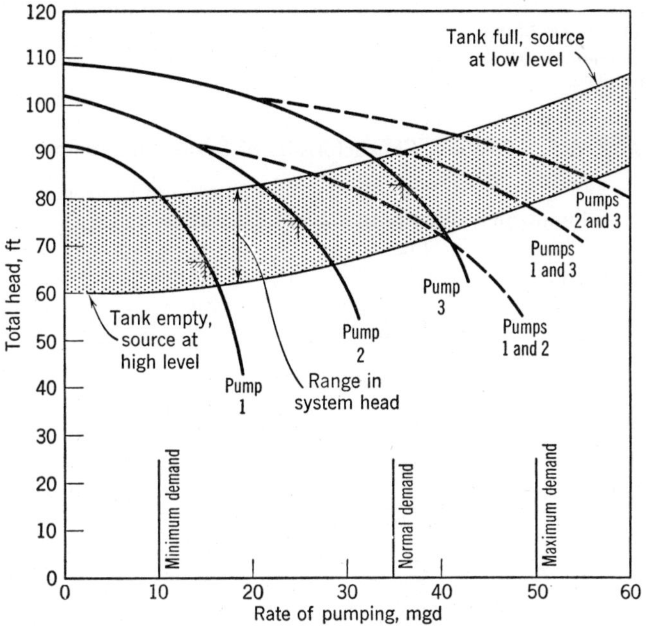

Figure 6-7. Pump selection for the water supply described in Example 6-2. *After Richard Hazen.*

are developed is indicated in Figure 6-6. It should be noted that in this illustration the two identical pumping units have not been selected with an eye to highest efficiency of operation in parallel. Development of characteristic curves for other multiple units proceeds in the same way from the known curves of the individual units.

Example 6-2. A mill supply is to draw relatively large quantities of water from a river and to deliver them at a fairly low head.[15] The minimum demand is 10 mgd, the normal demand 35 mgd, and the maximum demand 50 mgd. The river fluctuates in level by 5 ft, and the working range of a balancing tank is to be 15 ft. The vertical distance between the bottom of the tank and the surface of the river at high stage is 60 ft. The friction head in the pumping station and a 54-in. force main rises from a minimum of 1 ft at the 10-mgd rate to a maximum of nearly 20 ft at the 50-mgd rate. Make a study of suitable pumping units.

Hazen's solution of this problem is shown in Figure 6-7. Three pumps are provided: No. 1 with a capacity of 15 mgd at 66-ft head; No. 2 with

[15] See Richard Hazen, Pumps and pumping stations, *J. New Eng. Water Works Assoc., 67,* 121 (1953).

25 mgd at 78-ft head; and No. 3 with 37 mgd at 84-ft head. Each pump has an efficiency of 89% at the design point.

The efficiencies at the top and bottom of the working range are listed in Table 6-5.

TABLE 6-5. Pumping Characteristics of System in Example 6-2

Pumps in Service	Rate of Pumping, mgd.	Head, ft.	Pump Efficiency		
			No. 1	No. 2	No. 3
No. 1	10	81	80	..	..
	15	66	89	..	..
	16.5	62	88	..	..
No. 2	21	83	..	88	..
	25	78	..	89	..
	28.5	66	..	84	..
No. 3	33.5	88	..	..	88
	37	84	..	..	89
	40.5	73	..	..	86
No. 1 & No. 2	27	85	71	86	..
	34	80	82	88	..
	40	73	88	88	..
No. 1 & No. 3	36	90	35	..	87
	43.5	85	71	..	89
	49.5	79	83	..	88
No. 2 & No. 3	42	93	..	68	84
	49.5	89	..	79	87
	56.5	84	..	87	89

Centrifugal pumps are normally operated with discharge velocities of 5 to 15 fps. Therefore, the diameter (in inches) of the pump outlet, which is generally used to designate the size of the pump, is, on an average, $0.2\sqrt{Q}$, where Q is the capacity of the pump in gallons per minute.

7 Distribution of Water

7-1. Distribution Systems. The system of conduits that conveys water to the points of use from the terminus of the supply conduit is known as the distribution system (see Figure 1-2). Street plan, topography, and location of supply works and distribution storage establish the type of distribution system and the character of flow through it. From the street plan, two distribution patterns evolve: (1) a branching pattern on the outskirts of the community, in which ribbon development follows the primary arteries of roads and streets (*a* in Figure 7-1), and (2) a gridiron pattern within the built-up portions of the community in which streets crisscross and pipes are interconnected (*b* and *c* in Figure 7-1). Hydraulically, the gridiron system possesses the advantage of carrying water to any spot from

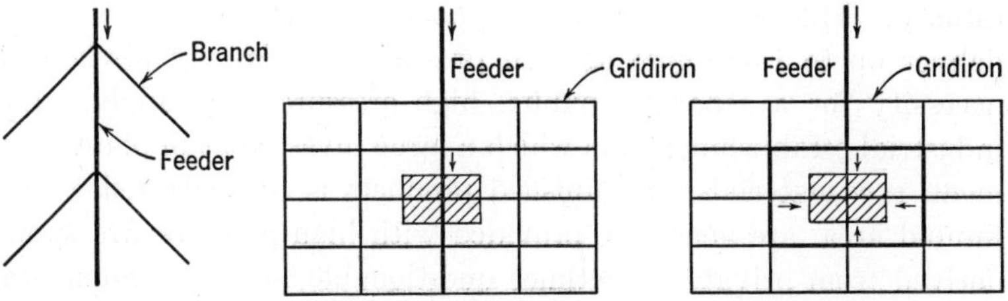

a. Branching pattern with dead ends

b. Gridiron pattern with central feeder

c. Gridiron pattern with looped feeder

High-value district is cross-hatched

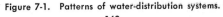

Figure 7-1. Patterns of water-distribution systems.

more than one direction; the branching system the disadvantage of dead ends. The carrying capacity of the gridiron system is strengthened by providing, in place of a central feeder, a loop or belt of feeder pipes that supplies water to the *congested,* or *high-value,* district from at least two directions, thereby more or less doubling the delivery of the grid (*c* in Figure 7-1). In large systems, feeder conduits take the form of pressure tunnels, pressure aqueducts, or steel pipes. In smaller communities, the entire distribution system is generally made up of cast-iron pipes. Cast iron is the most common material for service mains; steel and asbestos-cement pipes are less widely employed.

a. High and low services. Sections of the community that lie at too high an elevation to receive water at adequate pressure from the principal, or *low-service,* works are generally incorporated in a separate distribution system possessing independent piping and service storage. This *high-service* system is normally fed by pumps that take suction from the main supply and boost its pressure by the requisite amount. For areas of widely varying elevation, intermediate districts may be required. The different systems are commonly interconnected, for emergency use, by gated connections. Pressure-regulating valves are sometimes installed for this purpose.

b. Fire supply. The congested central portion, or high-value district, of a few large cities is protected by an independent system of pipes and hydrants that are capable of delivering large volumes of water under high pressure for fire-fighting purposes. This high-pressure fire-supply takes water from the public supply and raises its pressure by booster pumps whenever the alarm is given to do so. For use in extreme emergency, rigorously protected connections may be established to an independent source of water: river, lake, or tidal estuary. The development of the modern motor pumper, which will deliver up to 1,500 gpm at high pressure, has largely obviated the necessity for a separate, public, high-pressure fire supply. Large industrial establishments, in which a large investment in plant, equipment, raw materials, and finished products is concentrated within a limited area, are generally provided with high-pressure fire supplies derived from private, sometimes questionable, sources. Some states or communities require rigid separation of such supplies from the public system. Others permit the use of protected cross-connections that are regularly inspected, but usually only on existing and not on new installations (Section 7-9).

c. Pressures. For normal municipal uses, pressures of 60 to 75 psig in business blocks and 40 psig in residential areas are desirable. The need for higher pressures (100 psig or more) sufficient to deliver adequate amounts of water for fire fighting through hose attached directly to fire hydrants has been largely obviated by the availability of modern motor pumpers. To supply their upper stories, tall buildings must boost water to tanks on their roofs or in their towers. In large industrial complexes, the water pressure may be raised during fires by fixed installations of fire pumps.

d. Capacity. The capacity of distribution systems is dictated by domestic, industrial, and other normal water uses and by the *stand-by* or *ready-to-serve* requirements for fire fighting. Pipes should be sufficiently large to carry the maximum *coincident* draft at velocities that are not so high that pressure drops and water hammer become excessive. Velocities of 2 to 4 fps are common and establish the sizes of water mains to be employed. The minimum diameter of pipe commonly installed today in North American municipalities is 6 in.

e. One- and two-directional flow. According to type of flow, we can distinguish the four systems illustrated in Figure 7-2. The hydraulic gradients of the systems and the residual pressures within the areas served, together with the volume of distribution storage, determine the sizes of pipe within the network. It is plain that flow from opposite directions will increase the capacity of the distribution sys-

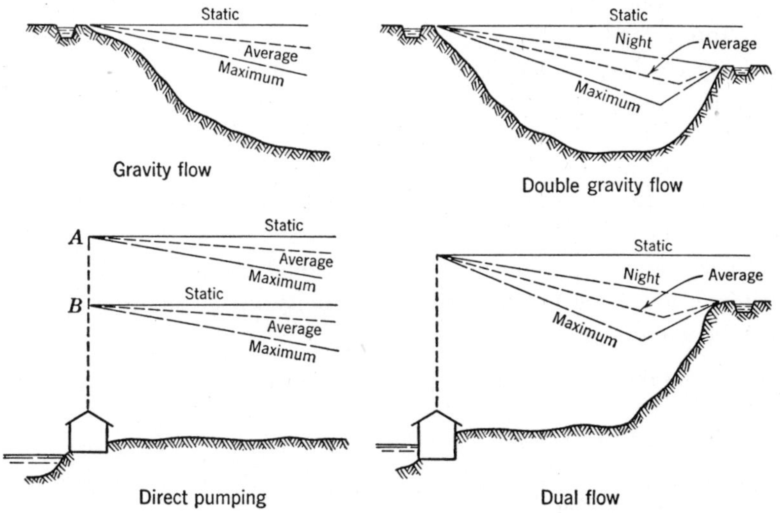

Figure 7-2. One- and two-directional flow in distribution systems.

tem. Two-directional flow in the main arteries themselves is made possible by conducting the supply from pumps, or from a gravity-supply, or service, reservoir (1) to opposite ends of the distribution system; or (2) through the system to elevated storage in a reservoir, tank, or standpipe situated toward the far end of the area of greatest water demand. Selection of volume and location of distribution storage depend upon topography and water needs (see Section 7-7).

f. Pipe grids. Within the gridiron system of pipes a choice must be made between the use of single mains and dual mains in individual streets. Single mains are customarily laid on the north and east sides of streets for protection against freezing. In a system of dual mains, *service headers* smaller in dimension than the mains parallel to them are on the south and west sides of streets. Hydraulically, the advantages of dual-main systems over single-main systems are that valves and hydrants can be so arranged that breaks in mains do not impair the usefulness of hydrants and do not dead-end mains.

7-2. Fire-Fighting Capacity of Distribution Systems. If there was no fire hazard, the hydraulic capacity of the distribution system would have to equal the maximum demand for domestic, industrial, and other general uses. For absolute safety, the fire demand would be added to this figure. Ordinarily this is not done: (1) because it would be most unusual for the maximum draft to coincide with a serious conflagration; and (2) because systems are dimensioned for the future and new construction is generally completed, in a reasonably foresighted community, before the designed capacity of the original system has been reached. In the absence of unusual hazards, such as flammable structures or storage of flammable raw or manufactured materials, a draft of 50 gpcd in excess of the average annual consumption may ordinarily be assumed to coincide with the requisite fire flow. In the presence of unusual hazards, higher allowances should be made.

The general requirements of the National Board of Fire Underwriters [1] governing the fire-fighting capacity of distribution systems may be summarized as follows:

a. Within the central, congested, or high-value district of North American communities:

1. For communities of 200,000 people or less,

[1] *Standard Schedule for Grading Cities and Towns of the United States,* National Board of Fire Underwriters, 1956.

$$Q = 1{,}020\sqrt{P}\,(1 - 0.01\sqrt{P}) \qquad 7\text{-}1$$

where Q is the fire draft in gpm and P is the population in thousands.

2. For populations in excess of 200,000, Q = 12,000 gpm with from 2,000 to 8,000 gpm in addition for a second fire.

b. For residential districts with

1. Small, low buildings—⅓ of lots in block built upon, Q = 500 gpm.
2. Larger or higher buildings, Q = 1,000 gpm.
3. Buildings approaching dimensions of hotels or high-value residences, Q = 1,500 to 3,000 gpm.
4. Three-story buildings in densely built-up sections, Q = up to 6,000 gpm.

c. Proportion or amount of the estimated flow to be concentrated, if necessary, on one block or one very large building:

1. In the high-value district, ⅔.
2. In compact residential areas, ¼ to ½.
3. For detached buildings, 500 to 750 gpm.

Table 7-1 is based upon Equation 7-1 and shows the relatively large stand-by capacity needed.

TABLE 7-1. Required Fire Flow, Fire Reserve, and Hydrant Spacing Recommended by the National Board of Fire Underwriters

	Fire Flow		Fire Reserve	Area per Hydrant, sq ft	
Population	gpm	mgd	mg	Engine Streams	Hydrant Streams
1,000	1,000	1.4	0.2	120,000	100,000
2,000	1,500	2.2	0.5	....	90,000
4,000	2,000	2.9	1.0	110,000	85,000
6,000	2,500	3.6	1.5	....	78,000
10,000	3,000	4.3	1.8	100,000	70,000
13,000	3,500	5.0	2.1	....	....
17,000	4,000	5.8	2.4	90,000	55,000
22,000	4,500	6.5	2.7	....	....
27,000	5,000	7.2	3.0	85,000	40,000 †
40,000	6,000	8.6	3.6	80,000	....
55,000	7,000	10.1	4.2	70,000	....
75,000	8,000	11.5	4.8	60,000	....
95,000	9,000	13.0	5.4	55,000	....
120,000	10,000	14.4	6.0	48,000	....
150,000	11,000	15.8	6.6	43,000	....
200,000 *	12,000	17.3	7.2	40,000	....

* For populations over 200,000 and local concentration of streams, see outline of National Board Requirements.

† For fire flows of 5,000 gpm and over.

Fire demand is commonly gaged in terms of the *standard fire stream:* 250 gpm issuing from a $1\frac{1}{8}$-in. nozzle and requiring a pressure at the base of the tip of 45 psig. When this amount of water flows through $2\frac{1}{2}$-in. rubber-lined hose, the frictional resistance is about 15 psi per 100 ft of hose. Adding to this hydraulic loss the hydrant resistance and the required nozzle pressure of 45 psig gives the pressure needs at the hydrant, or the pumper connected to it, shown in Table 7-2. A standard fire stream is effective to a height of 70 ft and has a horizontal carry of 63 ft.

TABLE 7-2. Hydrant Pressures for Different Lengths of Fire Hose [2]

Length of hose, ft	100	200	300	400	500	600
Required pressure, psig	63	77	92	106	121	135

Hydrants are normally planned to cover areas within a radius of 200 ft. Hence it is evident that, for direct attachment of fire hose to hydrants (hydrant streams), the required residual pressure at the hydrant must be about 75 psig. To maintain this pressure at times of fire, normal pressures must approach 100 psig. Disadvantages of pressures as high as this are that leakage and waste of water mount approximately in proportion to the square root of the pressure. The minimum pressure for hydrant streams is commonly set at 50 psig. Such streams, however, will not approach standard magnitudes after passing through hose as short as 50 ft.

Modern motor pumpers will deliver up to 1,500 gpm at adequate pressures, and large cities use single streams discharging as much as 1,000 gpm from a 2-in. nozzle. In order that domestic and industrial draft may be maintained and the system safeguarded against pollution by seepage and by failure under a vacuum, fire engines are not expected to pull down the pressure in the mains below 20 psig. For large hydrant outlets, this limit is sometimes lowered to 10 psig. In a sense, modern fire-fighting equipment has done away with the necessity for pressures much in excess of 60 psig except for small towns that cannot afford a full-time, well-equipped fire department. The additional pressure drop through the system made available by the use of pumpers increases the fire-fighting capacity in the ratio of $\sqrt{p - 20}/\sqrt{p - 75}$, where p is the normal dynamic pressure of the system.

[2] J. R. Freeman, Experiments relating to hydraulics of fire streams, *Trans. Am. Soc. Civil Engrs.*, *21*, 303 (1889).

7-3. Structural Components of Distributing Systems. The basic elements of the reticulation system are its pipes, gates, and hydrants. The dimensioning and spacing of these components rest upon a background of experience that is normally sufficiently precise in its minimum standards to permit roughing in all but the main arteries and feeders of most distribution systems. Common standards are given in Table 7-3.

TABLE 7-3. Common Sizes and Spacings of Pipes, Gates, and Hydrants

Pipes:	
Smallest pipes in gridiron	6-in.
Smallest branching pipes (dead ends)	8-in.
Largest spacing of 6-in. grid (8-in. pipe used beyond this value)	600 ft
Smallest pipes in high-value district	8-in.
Smallest pipes on principal streets in central district	12-in.
Largest spacing of supply mains or feeders	2,000 ft
Gates:	
Largest spacing on long branches	800 ft
Largest spacing in high-value district	500 ft
Hydrants:	
Areas protected by hydrants	(See Table 7-1.)
Largest spacing when fire flow exceeds 5,000 gpm	200 ft
Largest spacing when fire flow is as low as 1,000 gpm	300 ft

Pipe sizes in excess of the minimum are determined by the occupancy of the properties along the lines (whether residential, commercial, or industrial) and by the water uses of each, together with the fire risks involved.

The "hydrant areas" shown in Table 7-1 are based upon a single fire stream being effective within a radius of 200 ft from the hydrant. The area of the resulting circle is 120,000 sq ft. In order to attack a fire from all sides, or at least from two hydrants, a minimum of four streams (1,000 gpm) must be brought to play upon this area. As communities increase in size, buildings grow in bulk, and the area served by each hydrant must be reduced. In all these standards, experience with conflagrations underlies the recommended values.

7-4. Field Studies of Distribution Systems. The hydraulic performance of existing distribution systems is determined most directly and expeditiously by pressure surveys and hydrant-flow tests. These should cover all typical portions of the community: the high-value district, residential neighborhoods of different kinds, industrial areas, the outskirts, and high-service zones. If need be, they can be extended into every block. The results obtained will establish available pressures and flows and existing deficiencies.

a. Pressure surveys. These yield the most rudimentary information about the network. If they are conducted both at night (minimum flow) and during the day (normal demand), they will indicate the hydraulic efficiency of the system in meeting common requirements. The information presented, however, is not sufficient to establish the probable behavior of the system under conditions of stress, such as are produced by a serious conflagration.

b. Hydrant-flow tests. As commonly performed, hydrant-flow tests include (1) observation of the pressure at a centrally situated hydrant during the conduct of the test; and (2) measurement of the flow from a group of neighboring hydrants. Hydrant Pitot tubes are employed to record the velocity heads in the jets issuing from the hydrants. If the tests are to be significant, the following precautions should be observed:

1. The hydrants tested should form a group such as might be called into play in fighting a serious fire in the district under study.
2. Water should be drawn at a sufficient rate to create a drop in pressure so great that its value is not measurably affected by normal fluctuations in draft within the system.
3. The time of test should coincide with drafts (domestic, industrial, etc.) in the remainder of the system, reasonably close to expected values.

The layout of pipes and hydrants in a typical flow test is shown in Figure 7-3, and the observed values are summarized in Table 7-4.

This table is more or less self-explanatory. The initial and residual pressure was read from a Bourdon gage at hydrant 1. Hydrants 2, 3,

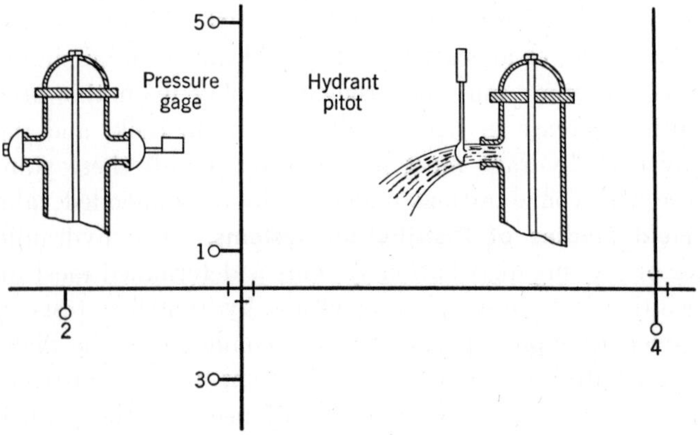

Figure 7-3. Location of pipes and hydrants in flow test and use of hydrant Pitot and pressure gage. See Table 7-4 and Figure 7-4.

TABLE 7-4. Record of a Typical Hydrant-Flow Test

All pressures are expressed in psig

Conditions of Test	Observed Pressure at Hydrant 1	Observed Discharge Pressure (p) (velocity head)	Calculated Flow (Q), gpm	Remarks
All hydrants closed	74	....	...	All hydrant outlets are
Hydrant 2 opened, 1 outlet	..	13.2	610	2½ in. in diameter.
Hydrant 3 opened, 2 outlets	..	9.6	2 × 520	Total Q = 2,980 gpm.
Hydrant 4 opened, 1 outlet	..	16.8	690	Calculated engine
Hydrant 5 opened, 1 outlet	46	14.5	640	streams = 4,200 gpm.
All hydrants closed	74	....	...	

4, and 5 were opened in quick succession, and their rates of discharge were measured simultaneously by means of hydrant Pitots. A test such as this does not consume more than 5 min, if it is conducted by a well-trained crew.

c. Hydrant-flow calculations. The necessary calculations may be outlined as follows for the flow test recorded in Table 7-4.

Example 7-1. 1. For outlets of diameter d in., the discharge Q in gpm is: $Q = 29.82cd^2\sqrt{p}$, where p is the Pitot reading in psig and c is the coefficient of hydrant discharge.[3] For smooth, well-rounded 2½-in. outlets, $c = 0.9$ and $Q = 168.2\sqrt{p}$.

2. The total discharge is 2,980 gpm for a pressure drop of $(74 - 46) = 28$ psi.

3. For engine streams the pressure drop is $(74 - 20) = 54$ psi and the approximate, expected discharge $Q_2 = Q_1\sqrt{p_2/p_1} = 2{,}980\sqrt{54/28} = 4{,}150$ gpm.

4. Since most of the loss occurs in the piping rather than the hydrant outlet, the expected discharge is calculated more closely from the Hazen-Williams formula, or $Q_2 = 2{,}980\ (54/28)^{0.54} = 4{,}250$ gpm. This value can be read directly from the Hazen-Williams diagram.

5. If the required fire flow in this district is estimated to be 6,000 gpm, the deficiency is $(6{,}000 - 4{,}200) = 1{,}800$ gpm and must be supplied by the addition of suitable piping.

The pressure-discharge relations established in this test are illustrated in Figure 7-4. If the true static pressure is known, a more exact calculation than that here proposed is possible, although the results seldom justify the additional labor involved.

[3] Since $Q = cav$ where c is the coefficient of hydrant discharge, a is the area of the hydrant outlet, and v is the velocity of discharge $(2.308p = v^2/2g)$. Here Q is measured in cfs, a in sq ft, and v in fps. The value of c varies from 0.9 for well-rounded, smooth outlets to 0.7 for sharp outlets projecting into the barrel.

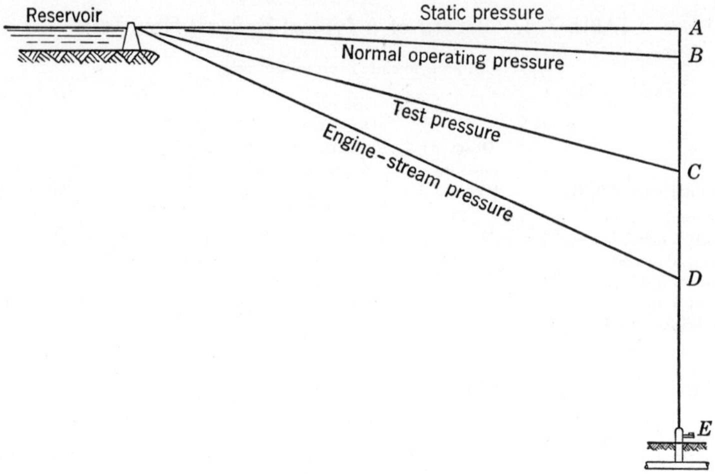

Figure 7-4. Pressure and discharge relations established by hydrant-flow test. See Figure 7-3 and Table 7-4.

A: Static water table. *B*: No hydrant discharge. Pressure = 74 psig; pressure drop p_0 due to coincident draft Q. *C*: Hydrant discharge. Pressure = 46 psig; pressure drop p_1 = (74 − 46) = 28 psi accompanies discharge of Q_1 = 2,980 gpm. *D*: Engine streams. Pressure = 20 psig; pressure drop p_2 = (74 − 20) = 54 psi accompanies discharge Q_2 = 4,200 gpm. *E*: Hydrant 1, recording residual pressure of hydrant groups shown in Figure 7-3.

7-5. Office Studies of Distribution Systems. Three methods of distribution-system analysis are particularly useful: (1) the method of sections; (2) the Hardy Cross method; and (3) the method of equivalent pipes which may be applied alone or in conjunction with the Hardy Cross method.

a. Method of sections. This is an approximate method developed by Allen Hazen as a quick check of distribution systems. Pardoe's method [4] is somewhat like it but is more involved. Of similar concept, too, is the circle method described in most textbooks on water supply but confined in its application to the cutting by a circle of the system of pipes tributary to a central fire-hydrant or group of hydrants.

Use of the method of sections is illustrated in Figure 7-5 and Example 7-2. The various steps involved may be outlined as follows:

1. Cut the network by a series of lines, not necessarily straight or regularly spaced but chosen with due regard to the varying sequence of pipe sizes and the characteristics of district. A first series of lines may well be

[4] W. S. Pardoe, *Eng. News-Record*, *93*, 516 (1924).

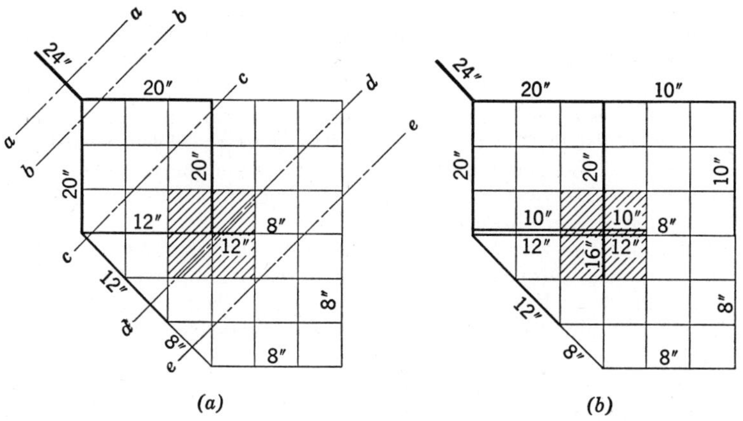

Figure 7-5. Plan of network analyzed by method of sections. See Example 7-2.

a. **Existing system.**

b. **Recommended system. When pipe size is not indicated, the pipe diameter is 6 in. The cross-hatched area is the high-value district.**

chosen so as to cut the distribution piping substantially at right angles to the general direction of flow, i.e., perpendicular to a line drawn from the supply conduit to the high-value district (see Figure 7-5). Further series may be oriented in some other critical direction; for example, horizontally and vertically in Figure 7-5. If there is more than one supply conduit, the sections may be curved to intercept the flow from each.

2. Estimate the water that must be supplied to the areas *beyond* each section. Estimates are based on a knowledge of the population density and the general characteristics of the zone: residential, commercial, and industrial. The water requirements comprise (*a*) the normal, coincident draft, here called the domestic draft; and (*b*) the fire demand (see Table 7-1). Whereas domestic use decreases progressively from section to section, as population or industry is left behind, the fire demand remains the same until the high-value district has been passed; then it drops to the figure that applies to the type of outskirt area encountered.

3. Estimate the capacity of the distribution system at each section across the piping. To do this:

a. Tabulate the number of pipes of each size cut. Count only those pipes that deliver water in the general direction of flow that is being studied.

b. Determine the average available hydraulic gradient or frictional resistance. This depends (1) upon the pressure to be maintained in the system and (2) upon the allowable pipe velocity.[5] Hydraulic gradients lie, ordinarily, between 1 and 3 ft per 1,000, and velocities range from 2 to 4 fps.

[5] To illustrate, assume a level region, a distance of 25,000 ft from the junction of the supply conduit with the network to the high-value district, a pressure of 70 psig at the junction, an available pressure drop down to 20 psig for engine streams, a requisite

4. On the basis of the available, or desirable, hydraulic gradient, determine the capacity of the existing pipes and sum them to obtain the total capacity.
5. Calculate the deficiency as the difference between the required and the existing capacity.
6. On the basis of the available, or desirable, hydraulic gradient, select the pipes to be added to the system in order to offset the deficiency. General familiarity with the community as well as studies of the network plan will aid judgment. Removal of existing small pipes to make way for larger mains must be taken into account.
7. Determine the size of pipe equivalent to the reinforced system and calculate the velocity of flow through the system. Excessive velocities, and the dangerous water hammer that may accompany them, should be avoided, if necessary, by lowering the hydraulic gradient actually called into play.
8. Check important pressure requirements against the plan developed for the network.

The method of sections is particularly useful (1) in the study of large and complicated distribution systems; (2) as a check upon other methods of hydraulic analysis; and (3) as a basis for further investigation of the system by more exact calculations.

Example 7-2. Analyze the network shown in Figure 7-5 by the method of sections. The hydraulic gradient available within the network proper is estimated to lie close to 2 ft per 1,000, and the value of C in the Hazen-Williams formula is taken to be 100. The domestic (coincident) draft is assumed to be 140 gpcd. The fire demand is taken from Table 7-1. Calculations are shown only for the first three sections.

1. Section *a-a*. Population 16,000

		mgd
a. Demands:	Domestic	= 2.2
	Fire	= 5.6
	Total	= 7.8
b. Existing pipes: 1, 24-in.	Capacity	= 6.0
c.	Deficiency	= 1.8

d. If no pipes are added, the 24-in. pipe must carry 7.8 mgd. This it will do with a loss of head of 3.2 ft per 1,000 at a velocity of 3.8 fps (see Hazen-Williams diagram).

2. Section *b-b*. Population and flow as in *a-a*.

		mgd
a.	Total demand	= 7.8
b. Existing pipes: 2, 20-in.	Capacity	= 7.4
c.	Deficiency	= 0.4

d. If no pipes are added, existing pipes will carry 7.8 mgd with a loss of head of 2.2 ft per 1,000 at a velocity of 2.8 fps.

capacity of the system of 17 mgd, and a variation in pipe sizes from 6 in. to 24 in. Since the available hydraulic gradient is $(70 - 20) \times 2.308/25 = 4.6$ ft per 1,000, the carrying capacity of the system is equivalent to that of a 30-in. pipe, and the velocities in the system lie between 1.9 fps for 6-in. pipes and 4.7 fps for 24-in. pipes. If the velocity in 24-in. pipes is to be reduced to 3 fps, the hydraulic gradient must be lowered to 2 ft per 1,000. To accomplish this, the network must be strengthened by the addition of pipes, and the reinforced network must possess a capacity equivalent to that of a 35-in. pipe.

		mgd
3. Section *c-c*. Population 14,000		
a. Demands:	Domestic	= 2.0
	Fire	= 5.6
	Total	= 7.6
b. Existing pipes: 1, 20-in.	Capacity	= 3.7
2, 12-in.	Capacity	= 2.0
5, 6-in.	Capacity	= 0.8
	Total	= 6.5
c.	Deficiency	= 1.1
d. Pipes added: 2, 10-in.	Capacity	= 1.2
Pipes removed: 1, 6-in.	Capacity	= 0.2
	Net added capacity	= 1.0
e.	Reinforced capacity	= 7.5

The reinforced system (equivalent pipe [6] 26.0 in.) will carry 7.6 mgd with a loss of head of 2.1 ft per 1,000 at a velocity of 3.2 fps.

b. Hardy Cross method.[7] This is a method of relaxation, or controlled trial and error, by which systematic corrections are applied (1) to an initial set of assumed flows, or (2) to an initial set of assumed heads, until the network is balanced hydraulically.

1. *Method of Balancing Heads by Correcting Assumed Flows.* The basic equation for the flow correction in the method of *balancing heads* by correcting assumed flows is derived as follows from a study of the flow and head relationships that must obtain in a simple network of pipes of known length, size, and condition such as that shown in (*a*) in Figure 7-6.

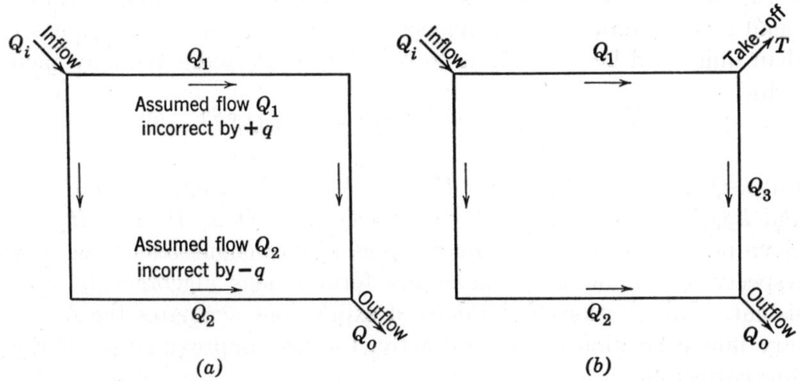

Figure 7-6. Simple network illustrating (*a*) the derivation of the Hardy Cross method and (*b*) the effect of changing flows.

[6] The equivalent pipe is one that will carry 7.5 mgd on a hydraulic gradient of 2 ft per 1,000.

[7] Hardy Cross, *Univ. Illinois Bull.* 286 (1936).

The incoming flow of water Q_i is split between the two branches so that the clockwise flow has an assumed value of Q_1 and the counterclockwise flow an assumed value of $Q_2 = Q_i - Q_1$. Calculation of the loss of head in the two branches by some convenient pipe-flow formula will then yield a loss of head H_1 due to the clockwise flow Q_1 and a loss of head H_2 due to the counterclockwise flow Q_2. In accordance with any one of the commonly used exponential formulas for the flow of water in pipes, the loss of head is $H = kQ^n$, where k is a numerical constant for a particular pipe and n is a constant for all pipes.[8] If Q_1 and Q_2 have been so chosen that the system is balanced hydraulically, $H_1 = k_1Q_1^n$ must equal $H_2 = k_2Q_2^n$, or $H_1 - H_2 = 0$. If, as may be expected, $H_1 - H_2$ is not zero, the initially assumed values of Q_1 and Q_2 are in error. For Q_1 too small by an amount q, Q_2 must be too large by the same amount q. Making the necessary corrections, the true flows become $Q_1' = (Q_1 + q)$ and $Q_2' = (Q_2 - q)$, and the associated losses of head become H_1' and H_2' respectively, where $H_1' - H_2' = 0$ because the frictional resistances through both branches are the same. It follows that:

$$H_1' - H_2' = k_1(Q_1 + q)^n - k_2(Q_2 - q)^n = 0$$

Expanding the binomials,

$$k_1(Q_1^n + nqQ_1^{n-1} + \cdots) - k_2(Q_2^n - nqQ_2^{n-1} + \cdots) = 0$$

If the first estimate of flow distribution has been reasonable, q will be small and the terms in the expansion that include powers of q greater than unity will be so small as to be safely neglected. We may then write

$$k_1Q_1^n + nk_1qQ_1^{n-1} - k_2Q_2^n + nk_2qQ_2^{n-1} = 0$$

But $k_1Q_1^n = H_1$ and $k_2Q_2^n = H_2$; also $k_1Q_1^{n-1} = k_1Q_1^n/Q_1 = H_1/Q_1$ and $k_2Q_2^{n-1} = H_2/Q_2$. Here Q_1 and Q_2 as well as H_1 and H_2 are given positive or negative signs for clockwise or counterclockwise flow respectively, in order to make the formulations algebraically consistent. Substitution of the derived expressions evaluates the necessary flow correction or, more exactly, the first approximation of the flow correction

$$q = -\frac{H_1 - H_2}{n(H_1/Q_1 + H_2/Q_2)}$$

[8] **In the Hazen-Williams formula, $Q = 405Cd^{2.63}s^{0.54}$, or (for given values of C, d, and l or $s = H/l$) $H = kQ^{1.85}$, where k is a constant for the given values.**

Since the numerator of the right-hand term in this equation represents the sum of the losses of head and its denominator is n times the sum of the head-flow ratios, we obtain as the basic equation for successive flow corrections:

$$q = -\frac{\Sigma H}{n\Sigma H/Q} = -\frac{\Sigma H}{1.85\Sigma H/Q} \qquad \text{7-2}$$

It follows from the derivation of Equation 7-2 that a network is seldom balanced by a single correction. The number of corrections that must be made depends upon the closeness of the first estimate of flow distribution.

2. *Method of Balancing Flows by Correcting Assumed Heads.* As pointed out by Cross, the method of balancing heads is directly applicable when the quantities of water entering and leaving the network are known. When the quantities are unknown and there are several inlets, the distribution of flow among them can be determined by a *method of balancing flows.* In this method, the heads at inlets and outlets must be known. Heads at junctions and associated, between-junction, friction losses are then assumed, and use is made of the fact that the sum of the flows at a junction must be zero if flows towards the junction and away from it are given opposite signs.

For any pipe, the assumed head is $H = kQ^n$ and the corrected head becomes

$$H + h = k(Q + q)^n = k(Q^n + nqQ^{n-1} + \cdots)$$

where h is the necessary head correction. Substituting H for kQ^n, H/Q for kQ^{n-1}, and neglecting the terms in the expansion that include powers of q greater than unity, we then find the head and flow corrections:

$$h = nq(H/Q) \qquad \text{and} \qquad q = (h/n)(Q/H)$$

At each junction, excepting inlet and outlet junctions at which flow to and from the junction is provided solely by the inlet or outlet respectively, the sum of the corrected flows must equal zero, i.e.,

$$\Sigma(Q + q) = 0 \qquad \text{or} \qquad \Sigma Q = -\Sigma q$$

But, since $\Sigma q = \frac{h}{n}\Sigma\frac{Q}{H}$, the unbalanced flow becomes $\Sigma Q = -\frac{h}{n}\Sigma\frac{Q}{H}$, and

$$h = -\frac{n\Sigma Q}{\Sigma Q/H} \qquad \text{7-3}$$

The systematic application of Equations 7-2 and 7-3 permits the solution of complex networks by the use of a table or diagram of the Hazen-Williams formula and by the simple arithmetic processes of addition, subtraction, multiplication, and division.

The corrections q and h are only approximate. After they have been applied once to the assumed flows, the network will be more nearly in balance than it was at the beginning. The process of correction can then be repeated as often as it is necessary to perfect the balancing operations. The work involved is straightforward, but it is greatly facilitated by a satisfactory scheme of bookkeeping such as that outlined for the method of balancing heads in Example 7-3 for the network sketched in Figure 7-7. A program of calculations can readily be devised for the solution of network problems by the Hardy Cross method with the aid of modern automatic sequence calculating machines.

In spite of the simplicity of the system used in Example 7-3, the network cannot be solved conveniently by algebraic methods, because it contains two interfering hydraulic constituents: (1) a cross-over (pipe 4) or pipe that operates in more than one circuit; and (2) a series of take-offs representing water used along the lines of pipe, fire flows drawn off through hydrants, or supplies through pipes to neighboring circuits.

Example 7-3. Balance the network shown in Figure 7-7 by applying the Hardy Cross method of balancing heads. The schedule of calculations shown in Table 7-5 includes the following:

Columns 1–4 identify the position of the pipes in the network and record their length and diameter. There are two circuits and seven pipes. Pipe 4 is shared by both circuits. To indicate this, one star is used in connection with Circuit I, and two stars in connection with Circuit II. The dual function of this pipe must not be overlooked.

Columns 5–9 deal with the assumed flows and the derived flow correction. For purposes of identification the hydraulic elements Q, s, H, and q are given a subscript zero.

Column 5 lists the assumed flows Q_0 in mgd. They are preceded by positive signs if they are clockwise in direction and by negative signs if they are counterclockwise in direction. The distribution of flows has been purposely misjudged in order to highlight the balancing operation. At each junction the total flow remaining in the system must be accounted for.

Column 6 gives the friction losses s_0 in ft per 1,000 ft when the pipe is carrying the quantities Q_0 shown in Column 5. The values of s_0 can be obtained directly from tables or diagrams of the Hazen-Williams formula.

Column 7 is obtained by multiplying the friction loss per 1,000 ft of pipe (s_0) by the length of the pipe in 1,000 ft; i.e., Column 7 = Column 6 × (Column 3 ÷ 1,000). The head losses H_0 obtained are preceded by a posi-

TABLE 7-5. Analysis of the Network of Figure 7-7, Example 7-3, by the Hardy Cross Method of Balancing Heads

Network				Assumed Conditions					First Correction				
Circuit No. (1)	Pipe No. (2)	Length, ft (3)	Diameter, in. (4)	Q_0, mgd (5)	s_0, ‰ (6)	H_0, ft (7)	H_0/Q_0 (8)	q_0, mgd (9)	Q_1, mgd (10)	s_1, ‰ (11)	H_1, ft (12)	H_1/Q_1 (13)	q_1, mgd (14)
I	1	2,000	12	+1.0	2.1	+4.2	4.2	+0.21	+1.21	3.0	+6.0	5.0	+0.03
	2	1,000	8	+0.4	2.8	+2.8	7.0	+0.21	+0.61	6.1	+6.1	10.0	+0.03
	3	1,000	8	−1.0	15.1	−15.1	15.1	+0.21	−0.79	9.8	−9.8	12.4	+0.03
	4 *	2,000	8	−0.5	4.2	−8.4	16.8	+0.21 −0.07 †	−0.36	2.3	−4.6	12.8	+0.03 −0.03 †
						−16.5 ÷	(43.1 ×	1.85) = −0.21			−2.3 ÷	(40.2 ×	1.85) = −0.03
II	4 **	2,000	8	+0.5	4.2	+8.4	16.8	+0.07 −0.21 †	+0.36	2.3	+4.6	12.8	+0.03 −0.03 †
	5	1,000	6	+0.3	6.6	+6.6	22.0	+0.07	+0.37	9.8	+9.8	26.5	+0.03
	6	1,000	6	−0.5	16.9	−16.9	33.8	+0.07	−0.43	12.9	−12.9	30.0	+0.03
	7	2,000	6	−0.3	6.6	−13.2	44.0	+0.07	−0.23	4.1	−8.2	35.6	+0.03
						−15.1 ÷	(116.6 ×	1.85) = −0.07			−6.7 ÷	(104.9 ×	1.85) = −0.03

Network				Second Correction					Result			
Circuit No. (1)	Pipe No. (2)	Length, ft (3)	Diameter, in. (4)	Q_2, mgd (15)	s_2, ‰ (16)	H_2, ft (17)	H_2/Q_2 (18)	q_2, mgd (19)	Q_3, mgd (20)	s_3, ‰ (21)	H_3, ft (22)	Loss of Head *A-E* (23)
I	1	2,000	12	+1.24	3.1	+6.2	5.0	+0.01	+1.25	3.2	+6.4	1. Via pipes 1, 2, 5, 25.0 ft
	2	1,000	8	+0.64	6.6	+6.6	10.3	+0.01	+0.65	6.8	+6.8	2. Via pipes 3, 4, 5, 25.3 ft
	3	1,000	8	−0.76	9.1	−9.1	12.0	+0.01	−0.75	8.9	−8.9	3. Via pipes 3, 6, 7, 25.5 ft
	4 *	2,000	8	−0.36	2.3	−4.6	12.8	+0.01 −0.01 †	−0.36	2.3	−4.6	
						−0.9 ÷	(40.1 ×	1.85) = −0.01			−0.3	
II	4 **	2,000	8	+0.36	2.3	+4.6	12.8	+0.01 −0.01 †	+0.36	2.6	+4.6	
	5	1,000	6	+0.40	11.3	+11.3	28.2	+0.01	+0.41	11.8	+11.8	
	6	1,000	6	−0.40	11.3	−11.3	28.2	+0.01	−0.39	10.8	−10.8	
	7	2,000	6	−0.20	3.1	−6.2	31.0	+0.01	−0.19	2.9	−5.8	
						−1.6 ÷	(100.2 ×	1.85) = −0.01			−0.2	

* Pipe serves more than one circuit; first consideration of this pipe.
** Second consideration of this pipe.
† Corrections in this column are those calculated for the same pipe in the companion circuit; they are of opposite sign.
Q = flow in mgd; s = slope of hydraulic gradient or friction loss in ft per 1,000 (‰) by the Hazen-Williams formula for $C = 100$; H = head lost in pipe (ft); q = flow correction in mgd; $q = -\frac{\Sigma H}{1.85 \Sigma H/Q}$; $Q_1 = Q_0 + q_0$; $Q_2 = Q_1 + q_1$; $Q_3 = Q_2 + q_2$.

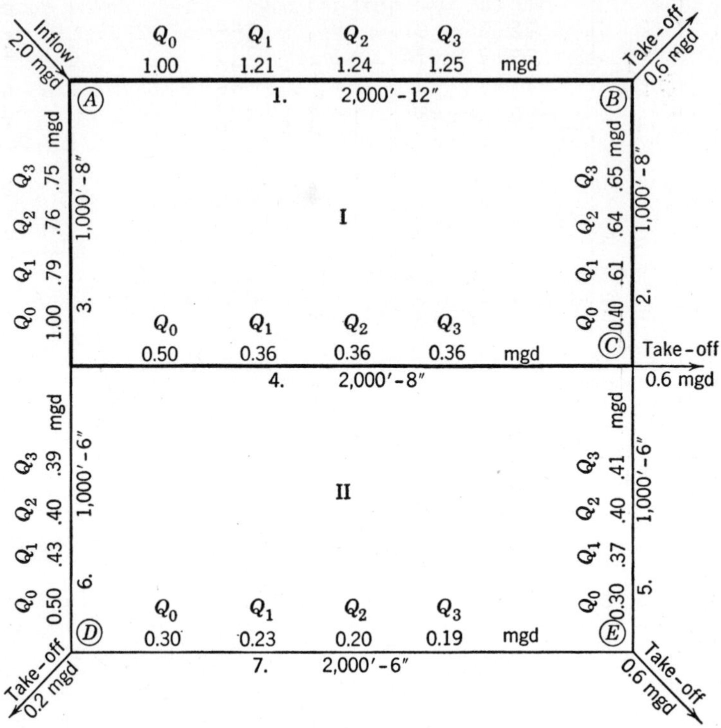

Figure 7-7. Plan of network analyzed by the Hardy Cross method of balancing heads. See Example 7-3.

tive sign if the flow is clockwise and by a negative sign if the flow is counterclockwise. The values in Column 7 are added up for each circuit, with due regard to signs, in order to obtain ΣH in the flow-correction formula.

Column 8 is found by dividing Column 7 by Column 5. Division makes all signs of H/Q positive. This column is added up for each circuit in order to obtain $\Sigma H/Q$ in the flow-correction formula.

Column 9 contains the calculated flow correction q. The computations necessary to obtain

$$q = -\Sigma H \div (1.85 \times \Sigma H/Q)$$

are performed after the two summing operations that have been described in connection with Columns 7 and 8. For example: in Circuit I, $\Sigma H = -16.5$, $\Sigma H/Q = 43.1$; and $(-16.5) \div (1.85 \times 43.1) = -0.21$; or $q = +0.21$. Since pipe 4 operates in both circuits, it draws a correction from each circuit. The second correction, however, is of opposite sign to that applied to the companion circuit. As a part of Circuit I, for example, pipe 4 receives a correction of $q = -0.07$ from Circuit II in addition to its basic correction of $q = +0.21$ from Circuit I.

Columns 10–14 cover the once-corrected flows. The hydraulic elements (Q, s, H, and q) are, therefore, given the subscript one. Column 10 is obtained by adding, with due regard to sign, Columns 5 and 9. Columns 11, 12, 13, and 14 are then found in the same manner as Columns 6, 7, 8, and 9.

Columns 15–19 record the twice-corrected flows, and the hydraulic elements (Q, s, H, and q) carry the subscript two. These columns are otherwise like Columns 10 to 14.

Columns 20–23 present the final result, Columns 20 to 22 corresponding to Columns 15 to 18 or 10 to 12. No further flow corrections are developed because the second flow corrections are of the order of 10,000 gpd for a minimum flow of 200,000 gpd, or at most 5%. To test the balance obtained, the losses of head between points A and D in Figure 7-7 via the three possible routes are given in Column 23. The losses vary from 25.0 to 25.5 ft. The average loss is 25.3 ft, and the variation is about 1%.

Example 7-4. Balance the network shown in Figure 7-8 by applying the Hardy Cross method of balancing flows. The necessary calculations are given in Table 7-6.

The schedule of calculations used in Example 7-4 includes the following:

Columns 1 to 5 identify the pipes at the three "free" junctions.

Columns 6 and 7 give the assumed head loss and the derived hydraulic gradient which determines the rate of flow shown in Column 8 and the flow-head ratio recorded in Column 9 = (Column 8 ÷ Column 6).

Column 10 contains the head correction h_0 as the negative value of 1.85 times the sum of Column 8 divided by the sum of Column 9, for each junction in accordance with Equation 7-3. A subsidiary head correction is made for "shared" pipes as in Example 7-3.

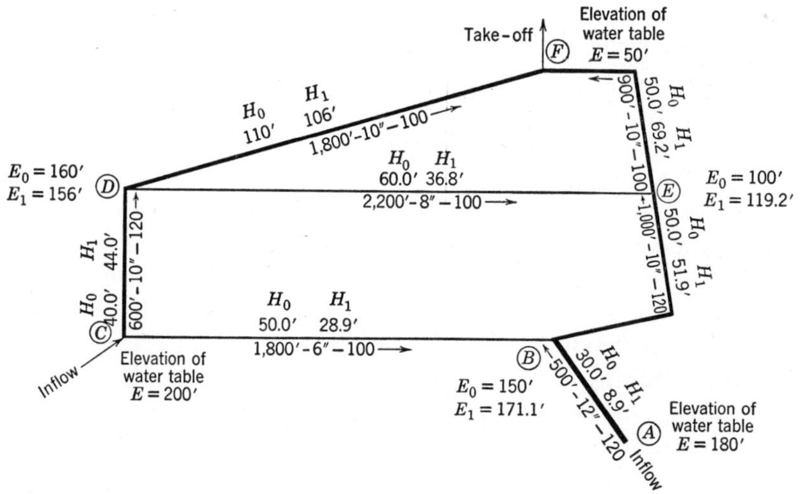

Figure 7-8. Plan of network analyzed by the Hardy Cross method of balancing flows. See Example 7-4.

TABLE 7-6. Analysis of the Network of Figure 7-8 by the Hardy Cross Method of Balancing Flows *

Only the first head correction is calculated for purposes of illustration

Junction Letter (1)	Pipe (2)	Length, ft (3)	Diameter, in. (4)	C (5)	H_0, ft (6)	s_0, ‰ (7)	Q_0, mgd (8)	Q_0/H_0 (9)	h_0, ft (10)	H_1, ft (11)
B	AB	500	12	120	+30	60.0	+7.33	0.244	−21.1	+8.9
	BE	1,000 †	10	120	−50	50.0	−4.12	0.082	−21.1 + 19.2	−51.9
	CB	1,800	6	100	+50	27.8	+0.66	0.013	−21.1	+38.9
						1.85(+3.87) ÷ 0.339 = +21.1				
D	CD	600	10	120	+40	66.7	+4.8	0.120	+4.01	+44.0
	DE	2,200 ‡	8	100	−60	27.3	−1.37	0.023	+4.01 + 19.2	−36.8
	DF	1,800	10	100	−110	61.1	−3.82	0.037	+4.01	−106.0
						1.85(−0.39) ÷ 0.180 = −4.01				
E	BE	1,000 §	10	120	+50	50.0	+4.12	0.082	−19.2 + 21.1	+51.9
	DE	2,200 ‖	8	100	+60	27.3	+1.37	0.023	−19.2 − 4.01	+36.8
	EF	900	10	100	−50	55.6	−3.64	0.073	−19.2	−69.2
						1.85(+1.85) ÷ 0.178 = +19.2				

* The basic data for this illustrative example are the same as those used by C. E. Carter and Scott Keith, *J. New Eng. Water Works Assoc.*, *59*, 273 (1945).

† First consideration of pipe BE.

‡ First consideration of pipe DE.

§ Second consideration of pipe BE.

‖ Second consideration of pipe DE.

Column 11 gives the corrected head $H_1 = H_0 + h_0$ and provides the basis for the second flow correction by determining s_1, Q_1, and Q_1/H_1 in that order.

It is not necessary to apply the Hardy Cross method to a large network as a whole. Much information can be obtained more quickly and more simply if the method is used to balance portions of the system in succession. Good judgment on the part of the analysts is an indispensable aid to network investigations such as these. The method of balancing flows would ordinarily be used in the analysis of networks that are supplied with water from two or more reservoirs.

c. Method of equivalent pipes. By this method, a complex system of pipes is replaced by a single line of equivalent capacity. The method cannot be applied directly to a system of pipes that contains cross-overs or take-offs. It is frequently possible, however, by judicious skeletonizing of the system to obtain significant information on the quantity and pressure of water available at important points in the network. In paring down the system to a workable skeleton, the analyst can be guided by the fact that the following pipes contribute little to flow: (1) small pipes, 6 in. and under in most systems and as large as 8 or 10 in. in more extensive systems; and (2) pipes at right angles to the direction of flow for which no appreciable pressure differential is established between their junctions in the system. The method of equivalent pipes is useful in simplifying networks that are to be analyzed by the Hardy Cross method. Scattered through most networks there are often combinations of pipes that can be replaced by hydraulically equivalent pipes. These reduce to advantage the number of units that must be handled in the Hardy Cross method.

The method of equivalent pipes, even as the method of Hardy Cross, makes use of two hydraulic axioms: (1) that the loss of head due to the flow of a given quantity of water through pipes in series,

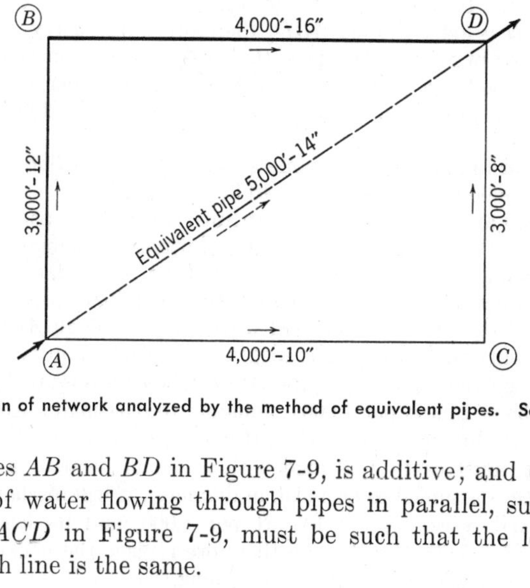

Figure 7-9. Plan of network analyzed by the method of equivalent pipes. See Example 7-5.

such as pipes *AB* and *BD* in Figure 7-9, is additive; and (2) that the quantities of water flowing through pipes in parallel, such as pipes *ABD* and *ACD* in Figure 7-9, must be such that the loss of head through each line is the same.

Example 7-5. Analyze the network of Figure 7-9 by the method of equivalent pipes. Express Q in mgd; s in ft per 1,000; H in ft; and assume a Hazen-Williams coefficient C of 100.

1. *Line ABD*. Assume $Q = 1$ mgd — ft
   a. Pipe *AB*, 3,000 ft, 12 in.; $s = 2.1$; $H = 2.1 \times 3 = 6.3$
   b. Pipe *BD*, 4,000 ft, 16 in.; $s = 0.52$; $H = 0.52 \times 4 = 2.1$
   c. Total $H = 8.4$
   d. Equivalent length of 12-in. pipe: $1{,}000 \times 8.4/2.1 = 4{,}000$ ft

2. *Line ACD*. Assume $Q = 0.5$ mgd — ft
   a. Pipe *AC*, 4,000 ft, 10 in.; $s = 1.42$; $H = 1.42 \times 4 = 5.7$
   b. Pipe *CD*, 3,000 ft, 8 in.; $s = 4.2$; $H = 4.2 \times 3 = 12.6$
   c. Total $H = 18.3$
   d. Equivalent length of 8-in. pipe: $1{,}000 \times 18.3/4.2 = 4{,}360$ ft

3. *Equivalent line AD*. Assume $H = 8.4$ ft mgd
   a. Line *ABD*, 4,000 ft, 12 in.; $s = 8.4/4.00 = 2.1$; $Q = 1.00$
   b. Line *ACD*, 4,360 ft, 8 in.; $s = 8.4/4.36 = 1.92$; $Q = 0.33$
   c. Total $Q = 1.33$
   d. Equivalent length of 14-in. pipe: $Q = 1.33$, $s = 1.68$, $1{,}000 \times 8.4/1.68 = 5{,}000$ ft.
   e. Result: 5,000 ft of 14-in. pipe.

The calculations involved in Example 7-5 may be outlined as follows:

1. Since line *ABD* consists of two pipes in series, the losses of head created by a given flow of water are additive. Find, therefore, from the Hazen-Williams diagram the frictional resistance *s* for some reasonable flow (1 mgd), (*a*) in pipe *AB* and (*b*) in pipe *BD*. Multiply these resistances by the length of pipe to obtain the loss of head *H*. Add the two losses to find the total loss $H = 8.4$ ft. Line *ABD*, therefore, must carry 1 mgd with a total loss of head of 8.4 ft. Any pipe that will do this is an equivalent pipe. Since a 12-in. pipe has a resistance $s = 2.1$ ft per 1,000 when it carries 1 mgd of water, a 12-in. pipe, to be an equivalent pipe, must be $1{,}000 \times 8.4/2.1 = 4{,}000$ ft long.

2. Proceed for line *ACD* in the same general way as for line *ABD* and find the length of the equivalent 8-in. pipe to be 4,360 ft.

3. Since *ABD* and *ACD* together constitute two lines in parallel, the flows through them for a given loss of head are additive. If some convenient loss is assumed, such as the loss already calculated for one of the lines, the missing, companion flow can be found from the Hazen-Williams diagram. Assuming a loss of 8.4 ft, which is associated with a flow through *ABD* of 1 mgd,[9] it is only necessary to find from the diagram that the quantity of water that will flow through the equivalent pipe *ACD*, when the loss of head is 8.4 ft (or $s = 8.4/4.36 = 1.92$ ft per 1,000), amounts to 0.33 mgd. Add this quantity to the flow through line *ABD* (1.0 mgd) and obtain 1.33 mgd. Line *AD*, therefore, must carry 1.33 mgd with a loss of head of 8.4 ft. If the equivalent pipe is assumed to be 14 in. in diameter, it will discharge 1.33 mgd with a frictional resistance $s = 1.68$ ft per 1,000, and its length must be $1{,}000 \times 8.4/1.68 = 5{,}000$ ft. We can therefore replace the network shown in Figure 7-9 by a single 14-in. pipe 5,000 ft long.

No matter what the original assumptions for quantity, diameter, and loss of head may be, the calculated equivalent pipe will always perform hydraulically in the same way as the network that it replaces.

d. Other methods of analysis. There are a number of other methods for studying the hydraulics of networks. Among them should be mentioned in particular Freeman's graphical method as expanded by Howland [10] and the use of electric analyzers. Camp and

[9] It was, therefore, really unnecessary to specify the length and diameter of the equivalent pipe *ABD*.

[10] W. E. Howland, Expansion of the Freeman method for the solution of pipe flow problems, *J. New Eng. Water Works Assoc.*, *48*, 408 (1934).

Hazen[11] built the first electric analyzer designed specifically for the hydraulic analysis of water distribution systems. McIlroy[12] continued this approach to network analysis and developed an analyzer that is manufactured commercially. Electric analyzers use non-linear resistors to simulate the resistance of pipes. For each branch of the system, the pipe equation, $H = kQ^{1.85}$, is thus replaced by an electrical equation, $V = K_e I^{1.85}$, where V is the voltage drop in the branch, I is the current, and K_e is the non-linear-resistor coefficient whose value is suited to the pipe coefficient k for the selected voltage-head loss and the amperage-water flow scale ratios. If the current inputs and take-offs are made proportional to the water flowing into and out of the system, the head losses will be proportional to the measured voltage drops.

The conversion factors $B = V/H$, $G = I/Q$ and $\theta = K_e/k$ are related by the equation $\theta = 1.81B/G^{1.85}$ for Q in mgd, H in ft, I in amperes, and V in volts. B is chosen so that the average voltage drop per resistor in series will be roughly 2.5 and G is selected to give currents suitable for the load devices. The resistor coefficients are then $K_e = \theta k$.

The pipe coefficient k, according to the Hazen-Williams formula, is

$$k/l = 5830d^{-4.87}C^{-1.85} \tag{7-4}$$

where the line length, l, is in thousands of ft and the diameter, d, is in in. A log-log graph of this equation provides a convenient means for finding k. The Hazen-Williams formula, written $k/l = 0.553 Q^{-1.85}(H/l)$, may be plotted on the same sheet of graph paper to facilitate checking.

Once a network has been simulated in the analyzer, the hydraulic merits of numerous alternate methods of strengthening it may readily be compared. Because of the rapidity with which solutions are obtained, the analyzer provides also a means for taking into account pumping-station characteristics and for predicting the fluctuations of water levels in service reservoirs.

7-6. Distributing Reservoirs. Where topography and geology permit, the water stored for distribution is held in reservoirs that are formed by impoundage, by balanced excavation and embankment, or

[11] T. R. Camp and H. L. Hazen, Hydraulic analysis of water distribution systems by means of an electric network analyzer, *J. New Eng. Water Works Assoc.*, *48*, 383 (1934).

[12] M. S. McIlroy, Direct-reading electric analyzer for pipeline networks, *J. Am. Water Works Assoc.*, *42*, 347 (1950).

by masonry construction (Figure 7-10). In order to protect the water against chance contamination and against deterioration, particularly by the growth of algae under the influence of sunlight, distributing reservoirs should be covered. Roofs need not be watertight if the reservoir is properly fenced. Open reservoirs should always be fenced, and, where they are so placed that surface runoff can be carried into

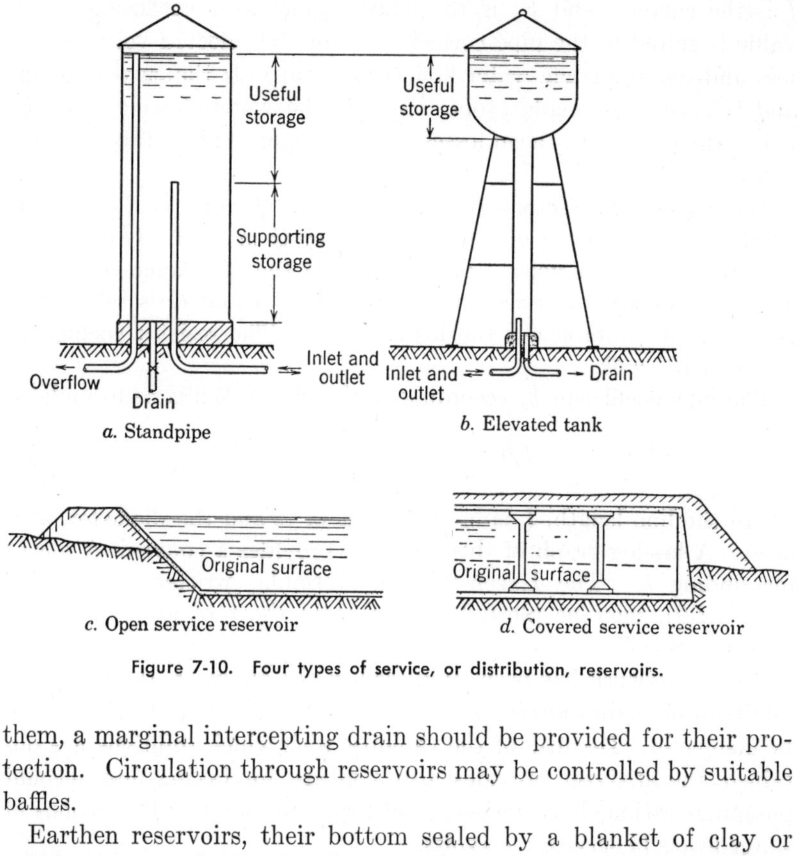

Figure 7-10. Four types of service, or distribution, reservoirs.

them, a marginal intercepting drain should be provided for their protection. Circulation through reservoirs may be controlled by suitable baffles.

Earthen reservoirs, their bottom sealed by a blanket of clay or rubble masonry and their sides by core walls, were widely employed at one time. Lining with concrete slabs is more common today. Wood roofs and concrete roofs of beam and girder, flat-slab, arch, and groined-arch construction are used. Concrete roofs are commonly covered with earth for the protection of roof and water against extremes of temperature. Gunite, a sand-cement-water mixture, discharged from a nozzle or gun through and onto a mat of reinforcing steel, has been employed to line or reline the invert and sides of reservoirs.

Inlets, outlets, and overflows are suitably placed in a gate house. Circulation (1) to insure more or less continuous displacement of the water, or (2) to provide proper detention of water after chlorination, may be controlled by baffles or subdivisions. The capacity of the overflow should equal the maximum rate of inflow. Altitude-control valves on reservoir inlets will automatically shut off inflow when maximum water level is reached. An arrangement that does not interfere with draft from the reservoir includes a by-pass with a swing check valve seating against the inflow.

Where natural elevation is inadequate, elevated storage is obtained in standpipes and elevated tanks that are constructed of wood, concrete, or steel. In cold climates, steel is found most suitable. Unless the steel is prestressed in reinforced-concrete tanks, vertical cracks are formed, and leakage and freezing cause rapid deterioration of the structure. Wood has been employed almost wholly for railroad and industrial supplies.

The useful capacity of standpipes and elevated tanks is confined to the volume of water stored above the elevation at which adequate pressure is created in the connected distribution system. In elevated tanks this elevation generally coincides with the bottom of the water tank proper; in standpipes it may lie much higher. For steel tanks, both welded and riveted construction are employed. Structural design and erection of steel tanks has become the specialized activity of a number of manufacturers.

7-7. Service Storage. The three major components of service storage are: (1) equalizing, or operating, storage; (2) fire reserve; and (3) emergency reserve.

a. Equalizing, or operating, storage. If the planned rate of supply and the fluctuation in the rate of demand are known, the equalizing, or operating, storage that should be provided may be ascertained from a rate curve or, more satisfactorily, from a mass diagram similar to the Rippl diagram (Section 4-7). As shown in Figure 7-11 for the simple conditions of steady inflow, during 12 and 24 hr respectively, the amount of equalizing, or operating, storage is the sum of the maximum ordinates between the demand and supply lines. To construct a mass diagram proceed as follows:

1. From past measurements of flow, determine the draft during each hour of the day and night for typical days (maximum, average, and minimum).

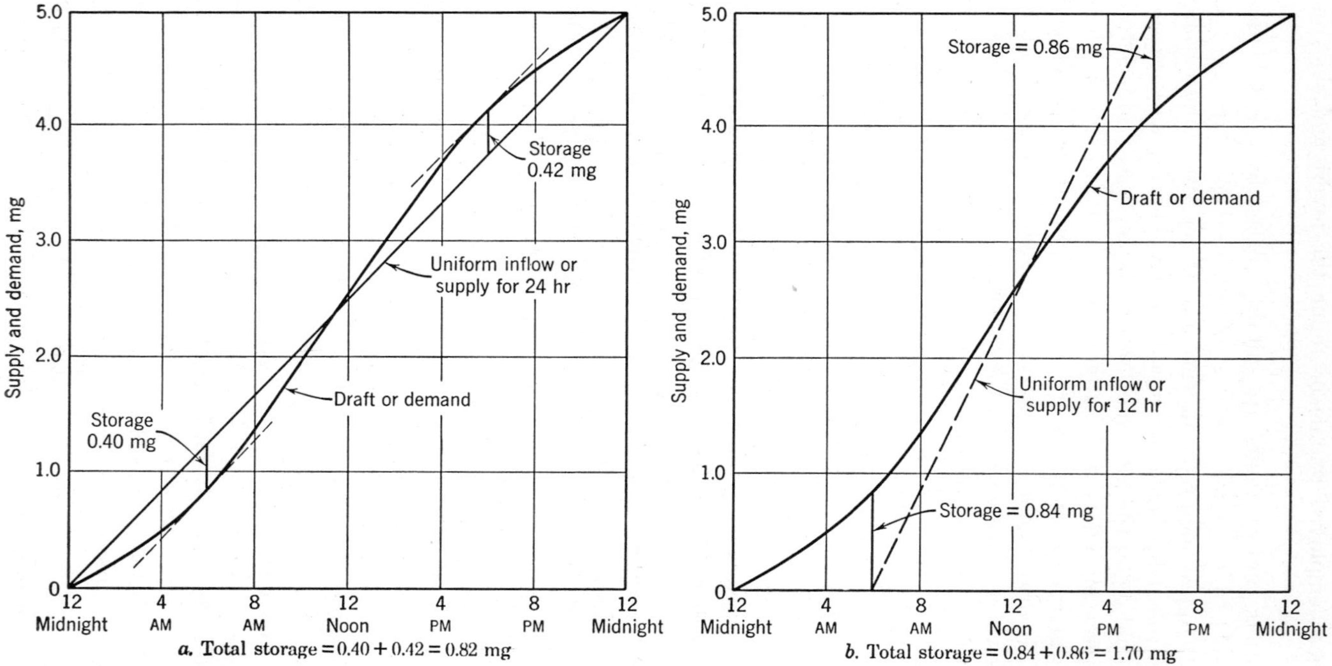

Figure 7-11. Determination of equalizing, or operating, storage by mass diagram. See Example 7-6.

a. Uniform inflow, or supply, extending over 24 hr.
b. Uniform inflow, or supply, confined to 12 hr.

2. Calculate the amounts of water that are drawn up to certain times, i.e., the cumulative draft.
3. Plot the cumulative draft against time, as shown in Figure 7-11.
4. For steady supply during 24 hr, draw a straight line diagonally across the diagram, as in Figure 7-11*a*. The ordinates between the draft and the supply line measure the difference between demand and supply.
5. For steady supply during 12 hr, by pumping, for example, draw a straight line diagonally from the beginning of the pumping period to its end (from 6 A.M. to 6 P.M. in Figure 7-11*b*).

Steady supply at the rate of maximum daily use will ordinarily require an equalizing storage close to 15% of the average day's consumption. Limitation of supply to 12 hr may be expected to raise the operating storage to 50% of the average day's consumption.

Example 7-6. Determine the equalizing, or operating, storage for the drafts of water shown in Table 7-7 (*a*) when inflow is uniform during 24 hr; (*b*) when flow is confined to the 12 hr from 6 A.M. to 6 P.M.

TABLE 7-7. Observed Drafts (Example 7-6)

	4-hr Periods Lapsing at					
a. Time	4 A.M.	8 A.M.	noon	4 P.M.	8 P.M.	midnight
b. Draft, mg	0.484	0.874	1.216	1.102	0.818	0.506
c. Cumulative draft, mg	0.484	1.358	2.574	3.676	4.494	5.000

a. For steady supply during 24 hr, the draft plotted in Figure 7-11*a* exceeds the demand by 0.40 mg by 6 A.M. If this excess is stored, it is used up by 11 A.M. In the afternoon, the demand exceeds the supply by 0.42 mg by 6 P.M. and must be drawn from storage that is replenished by midnight. Hence the required storage is the sum of the morning excess and afternoon deficiency, or 0.82 mg. This equals 16.4% of the daily draft.

b. For steady supply during the 12-hr period from 6 A.M. to 6 P.M., the draft plotted in Figure 7-11*b* exceeds the supply by 0.84 mg between midnight and 6 A.M. and must be drawn from storage. In the afternoon, the supply exceeds the demand by 0.86 mg by 6 P.M., but this excess is required to furnish water from storage between 6 P.M. and midnight. Total storage, therefore, is 1.70 mg, or 34% of the day's consumption.

b. Fire reserve. Based upon the durations of serious conflagrations that have been experienced in the past, the recommendations of the National Board of Fire Underwriters are that distributing reservoirs be made large enough to supply water for fighting a serious conflagration for 10 hr in communities of 6,000 people or more and for 4–8 hr in smaller ones. The resulting fire reserve is shown in Table 7-1.

c. Emergency reserve. The magnitude of this component of storage depends (1) upon the danger of interruption of reservoir inflow by failure of supply works; and (2) upon the time needed to make repairs. If the shutdown of the supply is confined to the time necessary for routine inspections and these are relegated to the hours of minimum draft, the emergency reserve is sometimes taken as equal to 25% of the total storage capacity, i.e., the reservoir is assumed to be drawn down by ¼ its average depth. If supply lines or equipment are expected to be out of operation for longer periods of time, suitable allowances must be made. The National Board of Fire Underwriters bases its rating system on an emergency storage of 5 days at maximum flow.

d. Total storage. The total amount of storage is desirably equal to the sum of the component requirements. In each instance, economic considerations determine the final choice. In pumped supplies, cost of storage must be balanced against cost of pumping. Particular attention must be paid to the economies that can be effected by more uniform operation of pumps and by restricting pumping to a portion of the day. In all supplies, cost of storage must be balanced against cost of supply lines, increased fire protection, and more uniform pressures in the distribution system.

Example 7-7. For a steady gravity supply equal to the maximum daily demand, a 10-hr fire supply, and no particular hazard to the supply works, find the storage to be provided for a city of 50,000 people using an average of 5 mgd of water.

	mg
Equalizing storage = 15% of 5 mg	0.75
Fire reserve (Table 7-1)	4.00
Subtotal	4.75
Emergency reserve = ¼ of total storage. Therefore subtotal is ¾ of total storage, and total storage = 4.75/0.75	6.33

If we assume that the maximum daily use is 150% of the average, the emergency storage suggested by the National Board would approximate $5 \times 5 \times 1.5 = 38$ mg, instead of $6.33 - 4.75 = 1.58$ mg.

e. Location of storage. As shown in Section 7-1 and Figure 7-2, location as well as capacity of service storage is an important factor in the control of distribution systems. A million gallons of elevated fire reserve, suitably situated with reference to the area that is to be protected, is equivalent, for example, to the addition of a 12-in. supply main. If this volume of water is drawn in a 10-hr fire, flow would be provided at a rate of $(24/10) \times 1 = 2.4$ mgd. This is the amount of water that a 12-in. pipe can carry at a velocity of less than 5 fps.

That this must be neighborhood storage is evidenced by the high frictional resistance of more than 10 ft per 1,000 that accompanies such use.

7-8. Water Supply of Buildings. That portion of the water supply of a building which lies between the public main and the take-offs to the various plumbing fixtures or other points of use of water is illustrated in Figure 7-12. It includes the service pipe, its fittings, and accessories. It begins with the corporation[13] cock and ends with the

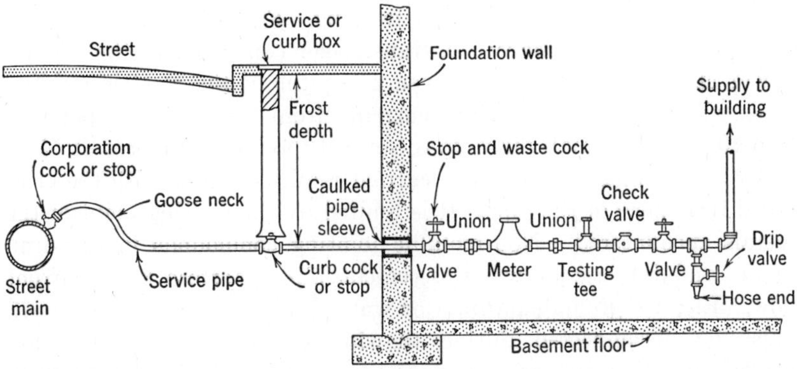

Figure 7-12. Service pipe, fittings, and accessories. There are many possible modifications, both inside and outside the building. In moderate climates, the meter is often placed in a vault outside the building.

stop-and-waste cock or with the water meter inside the building. The remainder of the system consists of vertical risers, horizontal runs, and necessary fittings.

a. Service pipes. The service pipe is either connected rigidly to the street main, or a flexible *gooseneck* is interposed in order to avoid breakage of the service pipe by settlement of the street main or by traffic shock. The materials that have been used in small services include lead, galvanized iron, or steel, lead-lined or cement-lined iron or steel, brass[14] of varying copper content, admiralty metal,[15] and copper. Lead and lead-lined pipes are seldom installed today because corrosion renders their use dangerous. The use of lead pipe for the construction of goosenecks has persisted for the longest time. The introduction of flexible copper tubing has made even this use

[13] So named after the body politic, or corporate, that owns the water-supply system.

[14] Brass is an alloy of copper and zinc. It may contain as little as 60% copper and is then known as Muntz metal.

[15] Admiralty metal contains about 71% copper, 28% zinc, and 1% tin.

of lead unnecessary. Large services are commonly constructed of coated or lined cast-iron pipe. For dwellings and similar buildings, the minimum desirable size of service is ¾ in. Special tapping machines make it possible to connect services to the main without shutting off the water. Similar machines are also used in making larger connections within water-distribution systems. Plastic pipes are coming into use.

b. Thawing frozen pipes. Services are more liable to freeze than are water mains. There is little or no flow through them at night, unless water is wasted to prevent freezing. Frozen pipes are thawed most readily by electricity. A transformer connected to the electric power circuit, or a gasoline-driven generator of the electric-welding type, will supply the necessary current: from 100 to 200 amperes at 3 to 10 volts for small pipes up to several thousand amperes at 55 or 110 volts for large mains. The current required varies with the electrical resistance of the pipe. It is limited by the melting point of the metals encountered. Non-metallic jointing compounds in cast-iron mains and the use of asbestos-cement pipe interfere with current flow. Electric grounds on interior water piping, or the piping itself, must be disconnected during thawing operations. Grounds are needed, but they are an annoyance to water-works operators when the ground carries sufficient current into the pipes to shock workmen who must disconnect piping or meters. In the absence of electricity, steam from a portable boiler may be blown into frozen pipes through flexible block-tin tubing. Frozen hydrants may also be thawed by these means.

c. Service meters. In well-regulated communities, meters are installed to measure the amount of water drawn by the consumer and to charge for it. Their use encourages the avoidance of waste. Operating requirements and costs have introduced types of meters not otherwise encountered in hydraulic measurements. Small service, or house, meters are most commonly of the displacement type. They measure the quantity of water flowing by recording the number of times a space of known volume within the meter is filled and emptied. A rotating, or mutating, disk generally controls the filling and emptying operations. In North American practice, inlet and outlet connections to disk meters have diameters varying from ⅝ in. to 6 in. for flows rated normally at 10 to 500 gpm. For heavy flows and high pressures, current or velocity meters are employed. In these a calibrated propeller or water wheel constitutes the measuring element. Displacement and velocity meters are used singly and in various combinations with themselves or with a free waterway, in which a friction ring creates proportional flow through the by-pass on which the meter is mounted. Such combinations are known as proportional-flow, compound, and fire-flow meters.

d. Distributing pipes. The pipe materials employed to distribute water through buildings are the same as for service pipes. In poorly proportioned distributing systems or systems in which iron rust or other products of corrosion have restricted the water way, the pressure may become so low that water will not reach fixtures in upper stories when water is being drawn at one or more fixtures in lower stories. A vacuum may then be created in parts of the system and cause contaminated or polluted water to enter the water-supply system from fixtures that are not protected against back-flow (Figure 7-13). A vacuum may be produced also when a street main breaks or is emptied for inspection and repairs, or when water is pumped at too high a rate from the main during a fire. To prevent this type of vacuum, which may also collapse hot-water boilers, the distribution system of buildings is sometimes provided with a check valve at or near the terminus of the service pipe on the house side of the water meter (Figure 7-12). If a check valve is used, the hot-water system must be equipped with a reliable pressure-relief valve.

To protect the water supply against pollution by back-flow, one of the following conditions must obtain: (1) a sufficient air gap must intervene between the water-supply outlet and the maximum possible water or liquid level; or (2) the supply pipe must be equipped with a suitable vacuum breaker, or back-siphonage preventer. Water will not back-siphon across an air gap that is three times the diameter of the smallest waterway in the fitting.

Vacuum breakers or back-siphonage preventers admit air to the supply pipe whenever a vacuum is created within it. To offer adequate protection, these devices must function satisfactorily under a vacuum as high as 15 in. of mercury.

7-9. Supplementary Water Supplies. In addition to a supply of water from the public distribution system, some (usually industrial) buildings and yard areas secure water from a supplementary source for one or more of the following reasons: (1) to obtain softer, cooler, more palatable, or otherwise more suitable water for washing, drinking, air conditioning, industrial processing, and other uses; (2) to secure cheaper water for air conditioning and industrial purposes; and (3) to provide additional quantities of water for fire-fighting purposes, particularly in large industrial establishments with high

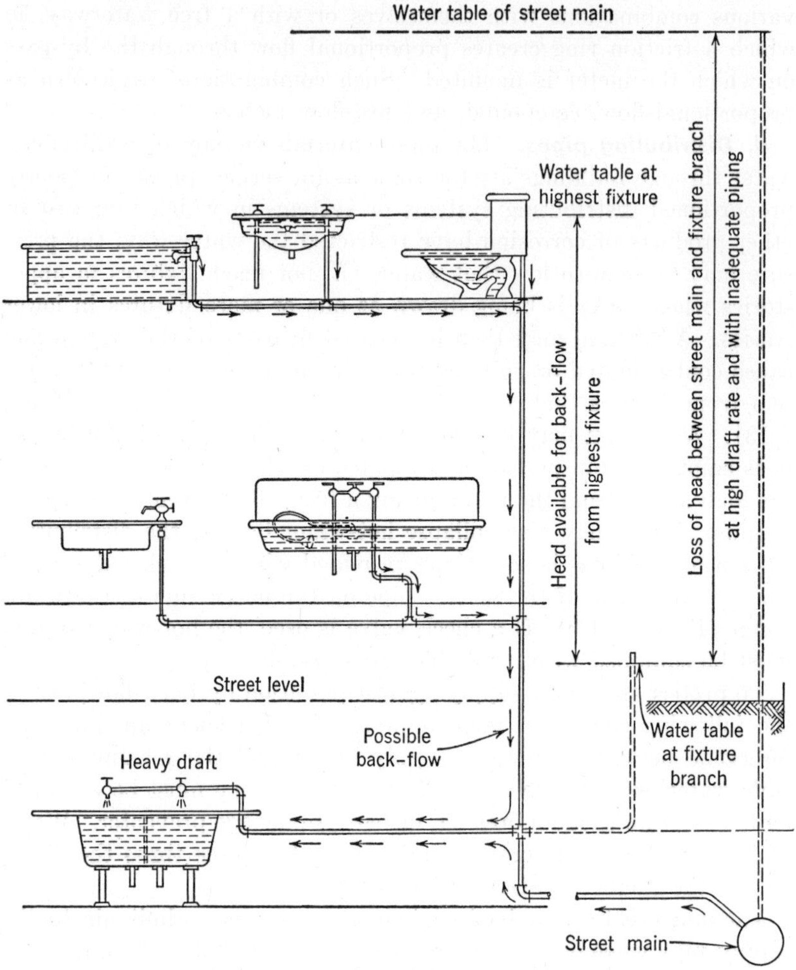

Figure 7-13. Hydraulics of back-flow, and common back-flow hazards in dwellings.

fire risks. The supplementary sources may be: (*a*) rain-water cisterns that store soft water; (*b*) wells that, in comparison with the public supply, yield colder water in summer, more palatable water, or cheaper water; and (*c*) streams or ponds from which are drawn independent supplies of water for use in manufacturing processes or to quench fires.

a. Cross-connections. Unless the quality of supplementary water supplies is equal or superior to that of the public supply and unless it is so maintained at all times, a direct cross-connection between the two should not be tolerated. How the two sources can be divorced without losing altogether the protective benefit of a dual supply is illustrated in Figure 7-14. Ground-level storage may be substituted but is less advantageous for fire protection.

Existing cross-connections that it is not expedient to remove should be equipped with approved double check-valves installed in vaults

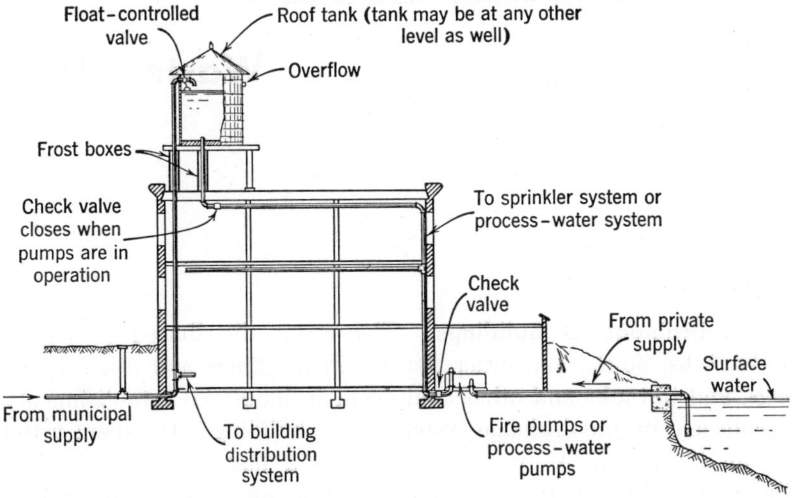

Figure 7-14. Use of private water supply without cross-connection. ***After Minnesota State Board of Health.***

accessible for inspection and provided with the necessary valves, gages, and bleeders. The connection should be tested at regular intervals by water and health authorities. There is no record of water-borne disease traceable to an approved and properly supervised, protected cross-connection. Such installations can be further safeguarded by automatic chlorination of the auxiliary supply.

b. Interconnections. The term cross-connection is generally applied to a physical connection between a public and private source of water. The term interconnection applies to any physical connection or arrangement of pipes between two otherwise separate water-piping systems whereby water can flow from one to the other. The use of interconnections should be avoided except where the water is of the same origin or of equally good quality.

8 Collection of Waste Water

8-1. Drainage of Buildings. The water distributed to basins, sinks, tubs, bowls, and other fixtures in dwellings and other buildings, and to tanks and other equipment in industrial establishments, is collected by the drainage system of the building if the spent water is run to waste. A drainage system of a building is outlined in Figure 8-1. The fixtures, it is seen, are arranged singly or in batteries. They discharge their waste waters into substantially horizontal *branches* or *drains* that must not flow full or under pressure. Otherwise, tributary fixtures would not discharge freely, and their protecting *traps* might become unsealed. The horizontal drains empty into substantially vertical *stacks*. These, too, must not flow full, if waste waters are not to back up into fixtures on the lower floors. The drainage stacks discharge into the *building drain* which, 5 ft outside of the building, becomes the *building sewer* (or *house sewer*) and empties into the street sewer (Figures 8-2 and 8-3).

Traps form part of the drainage piping or are built into fixtures, such as water closets. The traps hold a water seal that obstructs, and essentially prevents, the passage of foul odors and noxious gases, as well as insects and other vermin, from the drainage pipes and sewers into the building. Discharge of fixtures sends water rushing into the drains and tumbling down the stacks. Air is dragged along by the water, and air pressures above or below atmospheric would be created within the system and might unseal the traps were it not for the provision of *vents*. These lead from the traps to the atmos-

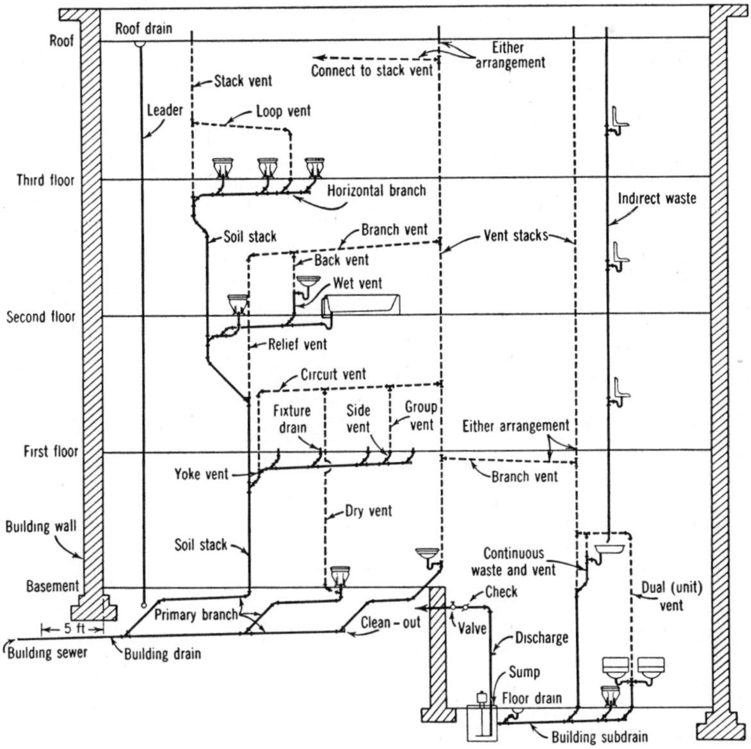

Figure 8-1. Building drainage system.

phere and allow the air pressures in the drainage pipes to become equalized.

The waste water from fixtures and floor drains that lie below the level of the public sewer must be lifted by ejectors or pumps (Figure 8-1). Sumps or receiving tanks facilitate automatic operation. Sand and other solids from cellars or yards are kept out of the drainage system by *sand intercepters,* grease by *grease intercepters,* and oil by *oil intercepters.* These devices are also called separators or traps. They take the form of small settling, skimming, or holding tanks.

Cast iron, galvanized steel or wrought iron, lead, brass, and copper piping are employed for drains and vents above ground. Building drains laid below ground are made of cast iron. For the building sewer, vitrified-clay, concrete, or cast-iron pipe is used.

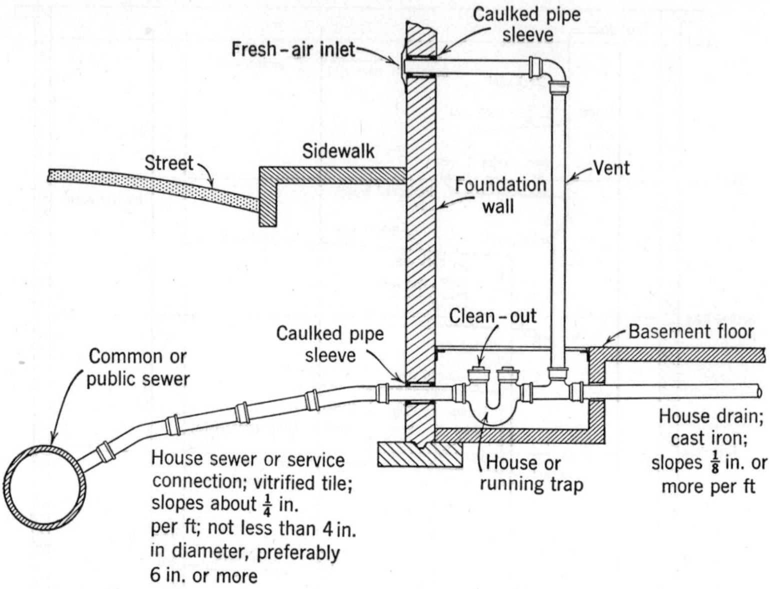

Figure 8-2. Connecting building drainage system to sewer. House, or running, trap may be installed or omitted.

If there is a separate system of sanitary sewers, the storm water that falls upon roofs and paved areas is carried away through separate storm drains into the public storm-drainage system or into the public gutter. Where the combined system of sewerage is used, roof and yard drains may be led into the building drain or building sewer through a Y-fitting at least 10 ft downstream from any primary branch. Separation of the two systems, however, is preferable.

8-2. Collection of Sanitary Sewage. A system of sanitary sewers is shown in Figure 1-3. Since about 70% of the water led into a community must be removed by its sewers, the average flow in sanitary sewers is about 100 gpcd. Daily and hourly variations in water use multiply this value about threefold. Illicit storm water and ground water further add to the required capacity, and a design value of about 400 gpcd is not unusual.

In order to hold in check the fouling of sanitary sewers by the deposition of waste matters, self-cleaning velocities (2 to 2.5 fps) are necessary. Except in unusually flat country, sewer grades are chosen so as to secure these velocities when the sewers are running reason-

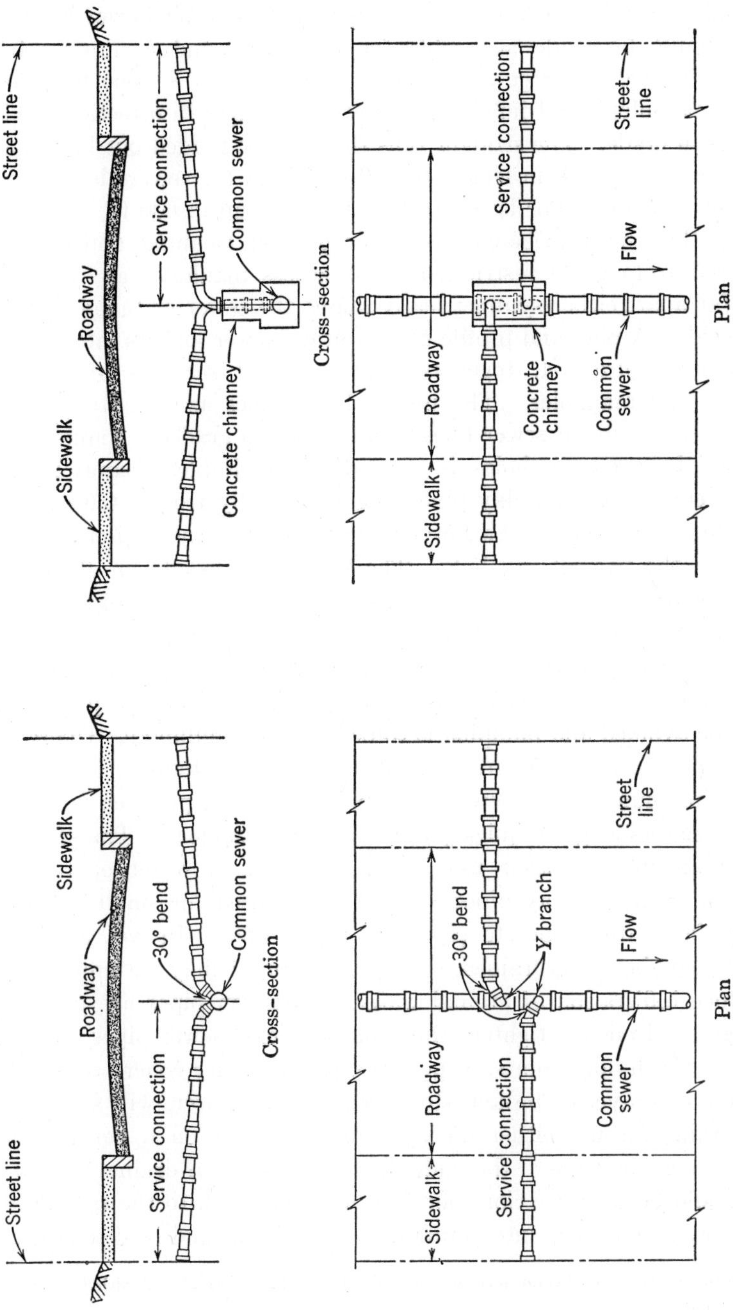

a. **Sewer at normal depth**

b. **Sewer in deep trench**

Figure 8-3. Service connections to public sewer.

ably full.[1] Some deposition of solids is bound to occur, however, and sewers must be made accessible for inspection and cleaning. In sewers that are not large enough to be entered, this is done by providing manholes at all junctions of sewers, changes in direction, and changes in grade. The straight runs that can be rodded out between manholes are limited in length to 300 or 400 ft for sewers less than 24 in. in diameter. For larger sewers, they are up to 600 ft. Sewers so large that they can be entered for inspection, cleaning, and repair are freed from these restrictions, and access manholes are placed quite far apart either symmetrically above the sewer or tangentially to one side. A plan and profile of a sanitary sewer and its laterals is shown in Figure 8-4, together with enlarged sections of sewer trenches and manholes. The use of lamp holes as substitutes for manholes on stubs of sewer lines or at breaks in grade or changes in direction between manholes is generally undesirable. Lamp holes usually consist of 8-in. clay pipes rising vertically from a tee in the sewer line. A light can be lowered into them for inspection of the run from the nearest manhole. The use of clean-outs on stubs is slightly more favorable. The clean-outs consist of 8-in. pipes that slope to the street surface from a Y in the sewer; this makes it possible to rod out the run. In very flat country and in other unusual circumstances, sewers must be laid on flat grades if very deep sewers are to be avoided and pumping is to be held to a minimum. Operating difficulties, however, are multiplied in such systems.

The minimum size of sewers in North American practice is 8 in. Smaller sewers clog too quickly and are harder to clean. The saving in cost effected by their use is not sufficient to offset operating troubles. Vitrified-clay pipes are commonly used for small sewers, and prefabricated concrete pipes for larger ones. In wet ground, sewers may be underdrained, or cast-iron pipes may be employed to reduce infiltration of ground water. Cast-iron pipes are greater in length and possess tighter joints than common sewer pipes. Clay pipes laid with open joints, or porous pipes of cinder concrete placed in a bed of gravel or broken stone beneath the sewer, will serve as underdrains for use either during construction or on a permanent basis. Free discharge of the underdrains into natural drainage channels should be sought. Consideration must be given to the fact that some sewage may seep into permanent underdrains and be discharged

[1] Half full or more in circular sections, since the hydraulic radius of a semicircle equals that of a circle.

by them after the system has been placed in service. If the sewage contains grit or other abrading materials and the scouring of concrete is to be prevented, velocities in sewers must be held below 8 to 10 fps. Very large sewers are built in place, sometimes by tunneling operations. Hydraulically and structurally, they have much in common with the grade aqueducts used in water supplies and are given similar shapes.

Sewers are commonly laid at sufficient depth (1) to protect them against breakage or traffic shock, (2) to keep them from freezing, and (3) to permit them to drain the lowest fixture on the premises served by them. In fixing the depth of street sewers, due allowance must be made for the slope of the building sewer (Figures 8-2 and 8-3). Slopes of ¼ in. per ft or more are common.[2] In the northern United States, cellar depths generally range from 6 to 8 ft and frost depths from 4 to 6 ft. An earth cover of 2 ft will cushion most shocks. Sewage from deep basements may have to be ejected or pumped into the street sewer.

As shown in Figure 8-4, manholes are channeled so as to cause as little disturbance to flow as is possible in the circumstances. Drop manholes are used for a like purpose in connection with the entrance of high-lying laterals. Otherwise these laterals would have to be lowered over the length of their last run—a wasteful arrangement. The upper reaches of lateral sewers ordinarily receive so little sewage that self-cleaning velocities cannot be attained in 8-in. sewers. Such runs must be flushed out from time to time. This can be done (1) by damming up the flow at a lower manhole and releasing the stored waters after the sewer is almost full; (2) by suddenly discharging a large amount of water into a manhole; (3) by providing at the end of the line a *flushing manhole* that can be filled with water through fire hose attached to a nearby fire hydrant before a flap valve, shear gate, or similar quick-opening device leading to the sewer is opened; and (4) by installing an automatic flush tank that fills slowly and discharges suddenly. Possible back-flow from the sewer to the water supply is a bad feature of automatic flush tanks, in addition to cost and to maintenance difficulties.

8-3. Collection of Storm Water. In separate sewerage systems, much of the suspended load of solids carried by storm sewers or drains is heavy mineral matter that will settle out unless the velocity of

[2] At this slope a 6-in. sewer flowing full will carry about 300 gpm or 40 cfm at a velocity of 3.5 fps.

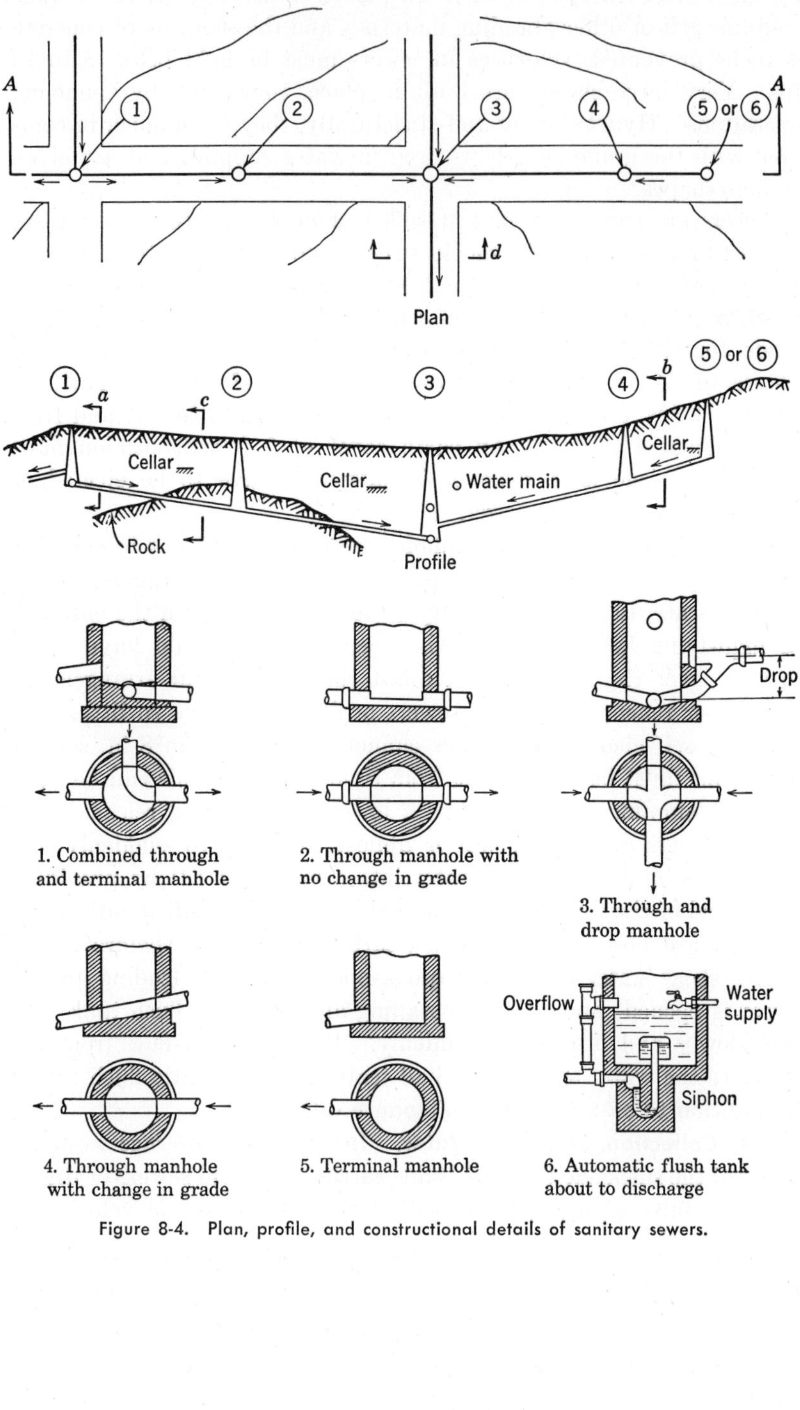

Figure 8-4. Plan, profile, and constructional details of sanitary sewers.

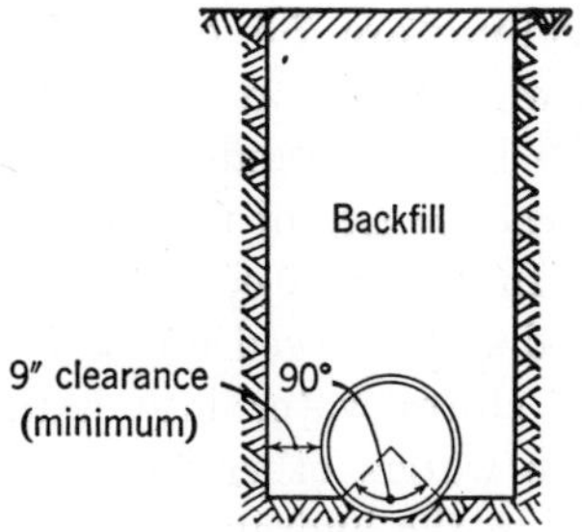

a. Pipe in earth trench

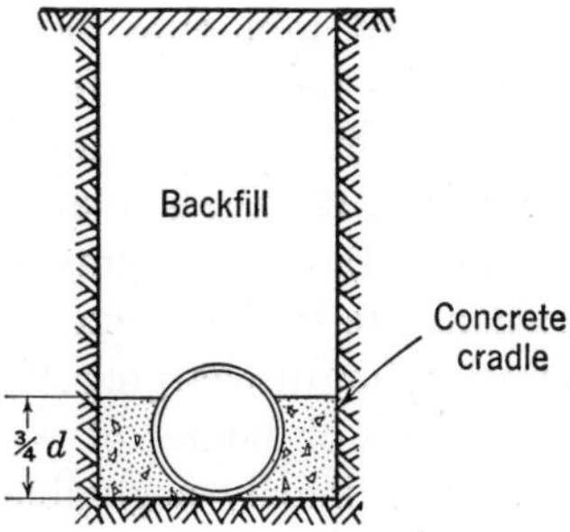

b. Pipe in cradle

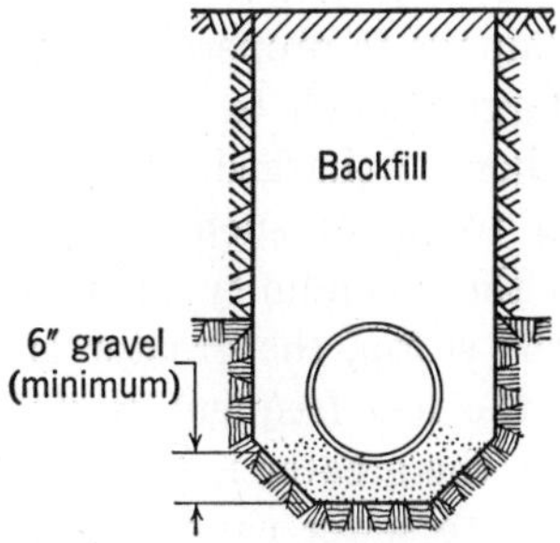

c. Pipe in rock trench

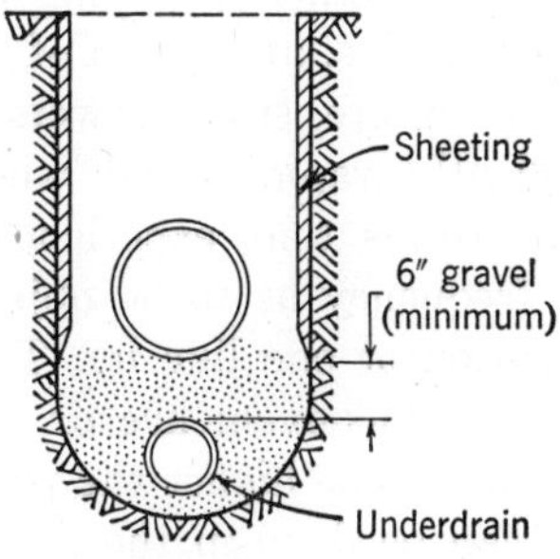

d. Pipe with underdrain

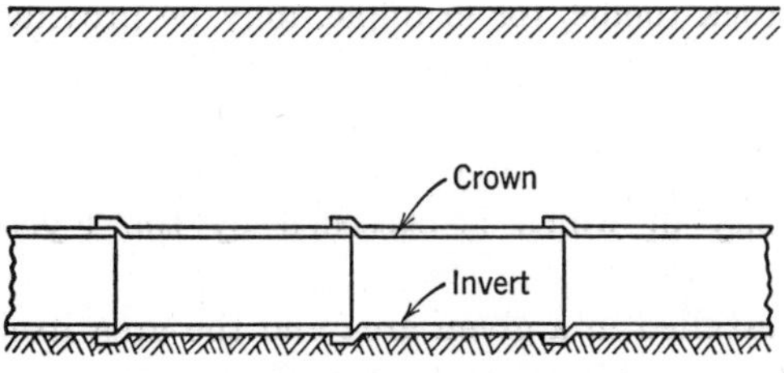

Pipe in earth trench

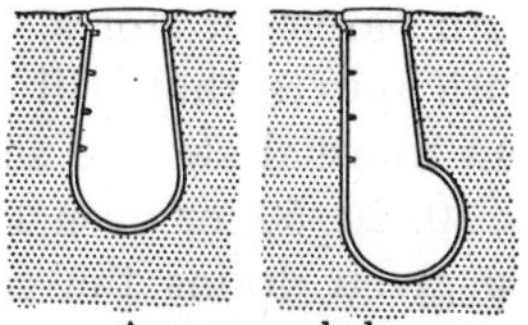

Access manholes for large sewers

Figure 8-4 (*continued*).

flow is kept sufficiently high. Fine sand is ordinarily transported by water at velocities of 1 fps or more and gravel at 2 fps or more. Recommended minimum velocities, therefore, are 2.5 to 3 fps, or about 0.5 fps more than for sanitary sewers. Factors determining the capacity of storm drains are: (1) the intensity and duration of local rainfall, (2) the size and runoff characteristics of the tributary areas, and (3) the economy of design. Included in economic considerations are the characteristics of the district served and the opportunities for discharging the collected storm water into natural water courses or bodies of water. Waste waters other than storm runoff are ordinarily negligible quantities in the hydraulic design of storm drains, the primary function of which is to prevent the inundation of streets, walks, and yard areas, and the flooding of basements and other low-lying structures, together with the attendant inconvenience, disruption of traffic, and damage to property. In general, therefore, storm sewers are made large enough to drain away, sufficiently rapidly and without becoming surcharged, the runoff from storms that experience has shown to be of such magnitude and frequency as to be objectionable in the community under consideration or one like it. The heavier the storm, the greater is the potential inconvenience or damage, but the less frequent is its occurrence. The higher the property values, the greater is the damage that can be done in the absence of adequate sewer capacity. In a well-balanced system of storm drains, all these factors will have received recognition for each kind of area served: residential, mercantile, industrial, or mixed. The high-value mercantile district with basement stores, or stock rooms, for example, may be provided with sewers that will carry away surface runoff resulting from all but unusual storms, such as those estimated to occur only once in 5, 10, 20, 50, or even 100 years. Suburban residential districts may be given drains the capacity of which is exceeded by the 1-year or 2-year storm.

Until storm drains are installed in a given area and the area itself is fully developed, it is not possible to make runoff measurements. Normally, therefore, the design of storm sewers must proceed not through the analysis of recorded runoff but through: (1) the analysis of records of storm rainfalls—their intensity or rate of precipitation, duration, and frequency of occurrence; and (2) the estimation of runoff resulting from these rainfalls.

Although storm sewers are occasionally surcharged and subjected to pressures equal to their depth below street level, they are designed for open-channel flow and equipped with manholes in much the same manner as sanitary sewers. The minimum size of storm sewers commonly employed in North American practice, however, is 12 in. The greater size will help to prevent clogging of the drains by trash of one kind or another. The minimum depth is determined by structural requirements rather than the elevation of basement floors. Surface runoff is led into storm drains from street gutters through *street inlets* or *catch basins* (Figure 8-5) and through *property drains.* Street inlets are made large enough in size and number to prevent undue flooding of the traffic way. Their location and number are determined in part also by the desirability of keeping pedestrian crossings reasonably dry. Inlet pipes discharge preferably into manholes in order to permit inspection and cleaning of the pipes. Inlets that are enlarged and trapped constitute settling chambers in which the entering storm water will deposit some of the debris and heavy solids carried by it. They are then called catch basins. Historically, they antedate street inlets and were devised in connection with combined sewerage systems at a time when streets were largely unpaved and much sand and gravel was washed away by storm runoff. In those days, furthermore, the air in sewers, called "sewer gas," was erroneously considered dangerous to health. To prevent the escape of sewer air through catch basins, they were provided with a water-sealed trap. Catch basins need a good deal of maintenance. They should be cleaned after every major storm, particularly in the fall of the year when they become filled with leaves. During the mosquito-breeding season, they must be oiled to prevent the production of large crops of mosquitoes. On the whole, catch basins find little use in modern sewerage systems.

8-4. Collection of Combined Sewage. In combined sewerage systems, a single set of sewers collects both surface runoff and sanitary sewage (Figure 1-3). The quantity of storm water is often 50 to 100 times that of the sanitary sewage. Since the accuracy with which surface runoff can be estimated is generally of a lower order of magnitude than the difference between storm and combined sewage, combined sewers are designed essentially as storm drains. However, they are laid as deep as sanitary sewers since they must carry away the flows from building drains as well as street inlets or catch basins. Needless to say, the surcharging and overflowing of combined sewers is more objectionable than the backing-up of drains that carry only storm water.

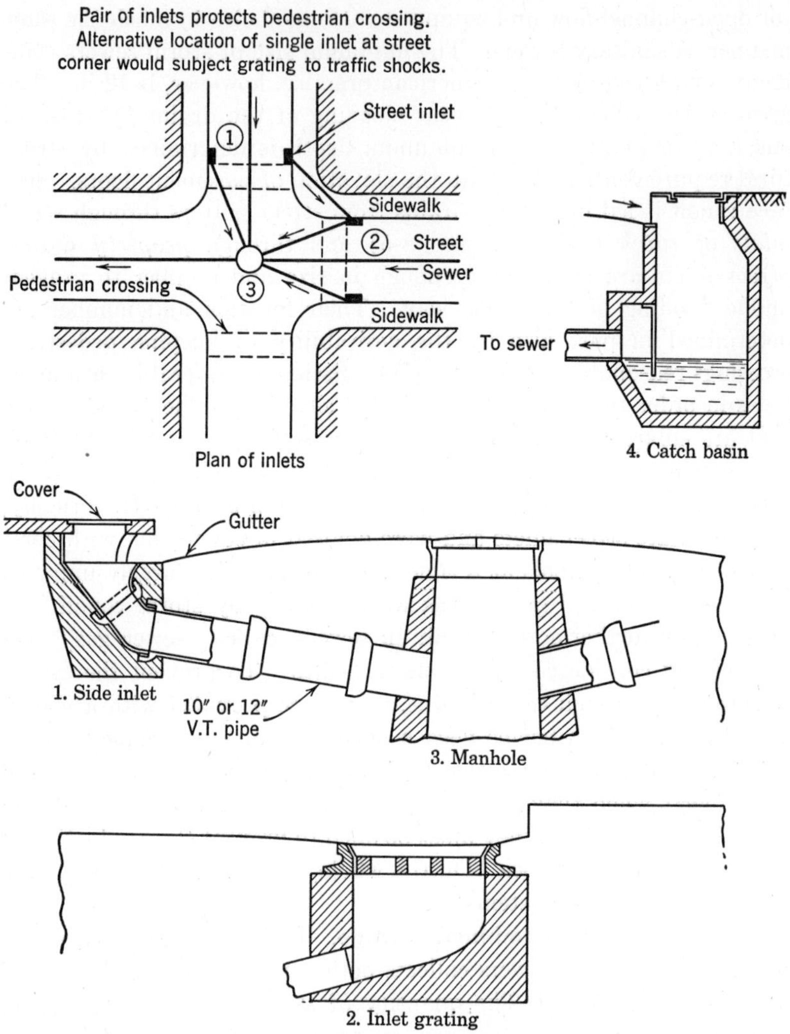

Figure 8-5. Street inlets and their connection to a manhole.

The wide range of flows in combined sewers creates certain special problems. Among them are:

a. The choice of cross-section for the purpose of insuring self-cleaning velocities for the dry-weather flows of sanitary sewage.

b. The design of inverted siphons or depressed sewers which dip below the hydraulic grade line in order to carry sewage across a depression or below an obstruction, such as a stream or subway. Depressed sewers flow full and under pressure. If a single conduit were retained, variations in velocity would be much greater than those in open-channel flow. For this reason the flow is generally distributed between two or more parallel depressed sewers.

c. Provision of storm-water overflows in connection with the intercepters that will generally have to be introduced in the course of time if receiving waters are to be given reasonable protection against pollution.

a. Sections. Departures from circular cross-sections are generally prompted by structural or economic rather than hydraulic considerations. To secure reasonably good hydraulic performance at dry-weather flows, however, some combined sewers have been given special shapes. Examples are the *egg-shaped* sewer and the *cunette* illustrated in Figure 8-6. The egg-shaped section is, in essence, an integration of two circular sewers: an underlying sanitary sewer and an overlying storm drain. An attempt is made to keep the hydraulic radius constant at all depths. The cunette [3] forms a trough dimensioned to carry the dry-weather flow, or sanitary sewage. The

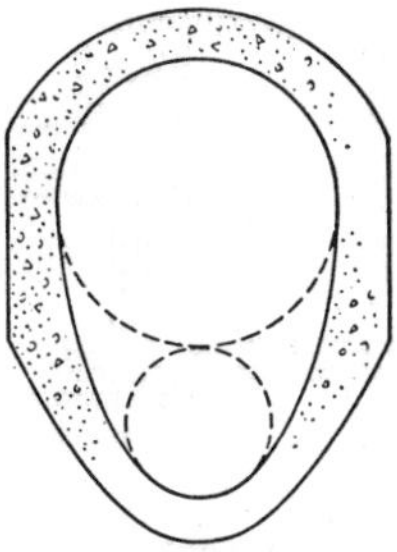

a. Egg-shaped or oval

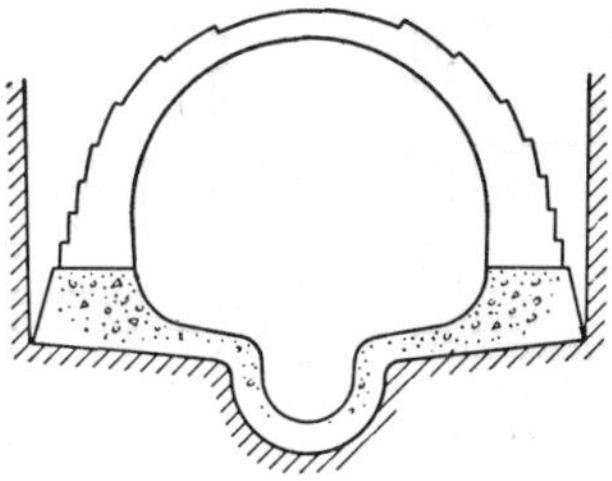

b. Semicircular section with cunette

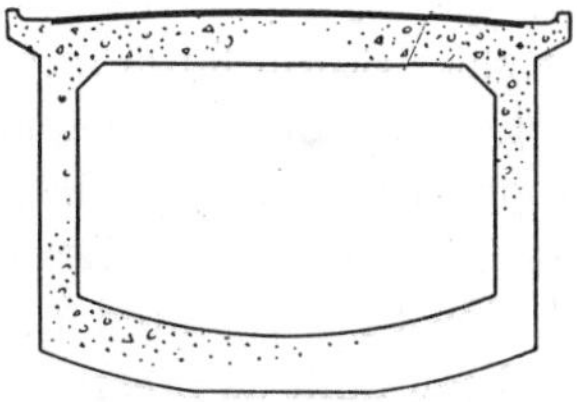

c. Rectangular section

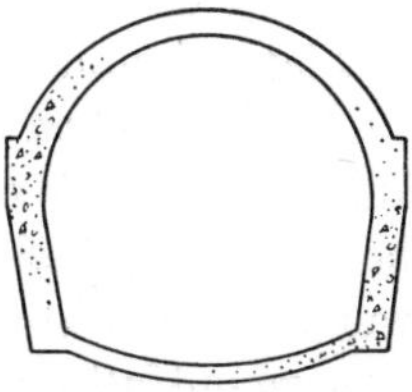

d. Horseshoe section

Figure 8-6. Sections of storm and combined sewers.

[3] The main drains of Paris, France, made famous by Victor Hugo's references to them in *Les Misérables,* were constructed from 1833 onward. They were made sufficiently large (6 ft high and at least 2 ft 6 in. wide) to permit laborers to work in comfort. Their conversion from 1880 onward into combined sewers necessitated the addition of *cunettes.*

rectangular section is easy to construct and makes for an economical trench with low head-room requirements. The *horseshoe section* is structurally very satisfactory (see also Figure 6-3).

b. Inverted siphons. The spread between dry-weather flows and storm flows through inverted siphons, or depressed sewers, is cared for by installing a sufficient number of pipes to carry characteristic flows through the siphon at self-cleaning velocities. A simple example

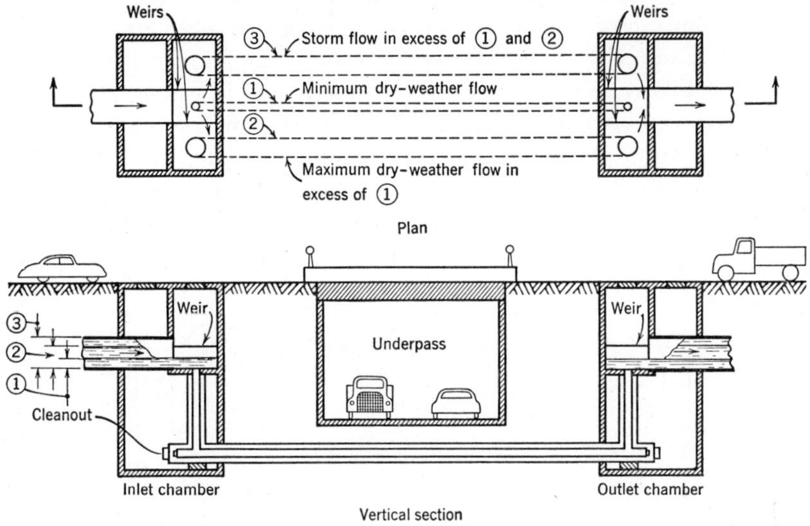

Figure 8-7. Inverted siphon or depressed sewer for combined sewage.

is shown in Figure 8-7. Low dry-weather flows of sanitary sewage are carried by the central siphon. High dry-weather flows spill over a weir into a lateral siphon to the right. Storm flows discharge over a weir into a lateral siphon to the left. The combined capacity of the three siphons equals that of the approach sewer. Weir heights are fixed by the depth to which the three characteristic flows fill the approach sewer and inlet structure. Flows are reunited in the outlet chamber. Large outfall sewers have been built as pressure tunnels.

c. Intercepters. Intercepting sewers (Figure 1-3) are generally intended to carry the maximum dry-weather flow or, since maximum dry-weather flow and storms do not necessarily coincide, to bleed off as much combined sewage as is warranted by hygienic, esthetic, and economic considerations. Where rainfalls are intense and of short duration, as in most parts of the North American continent, it is not possible to discharge a substantial amount of storm water through intercepters that are reasonably proportioned, and intercepters are commonly designed to carry only 2 to 3 times the average dry-weather flow, or from 250 to 600 gpcd. A more informative measure of the capacity of intercepters in excess of the average dry-weather flow is the amount of rainfall or runoff that they can carry, expressed, for example, in inches per hour. Since the first flush of storm water is likely to move most of the accumulated sewer deposits, its interception is particularly important. Most of the storm water carried by the collector tributary to the intercepter must be allowed to overflow into the body of water that the intercepter is designed to protect. This overflow contains a proportionate share of the sanitary sewage that enters the combined system during the period of storm runoff. As a result, the total amount of polluting material reaching the "protected" body of water in the course of a year is usually a significant though small fraction of the total annual volume of sanitary sewage. For this reason, health authorities generally frown upon the installation or extension of sewerage systems that are built on the combined plan. Just how much sewage goes overboard is a function of the intensity and duration of rainfall and the relation of resulting storm runoff to the capacity of the intercepter. The amount can be calculated for a given locality. Relative losses equaling 1% or more of the annual volume of sanitary sewage are not unusual.

d. Storm stand-by tanks. Interception is improved by installing storm-water stand-by tanks at the junction of the submain with the intercepter. These tanks, until they arc filled, store the flows in excess of intercepter capacity; after that, they continue to function as settling basins and remove much of the gross and unsightly settleable matter from the overflowing storm water, even when the detention period becomes as short as 15 minutes. The tank contents, together with the settled solids, are eventually flushed into the intercepter after the storm subsides. The operating range of tanks lies between the dry-weather flowline of the intercepter and the crown of the combined sewer. Where appreciable quantities of storm water are carried as far as the treatment works, the location of storm-water stand-by tanks may be shifted to the treatment plant.

e. Overflows. The amount of water entering the intercepter at the junctions of the submains of the combined system with it must be controlled by admitting only as much water to the intercepter as the capacity of its various reaches permits. All water in excess of this value must be diverted into storm-water overflows. Admission and diversion can be regulated hydraulically or mechanically, as shown in Figure 8-8.

Hydraulic separation of excess flows from dry-weather flows is accomplished by the following devices:

1. Diverting weirs in the form of side spillways. The crest level and length are chosen to spill excess flows, which, figuratively speaking, override the

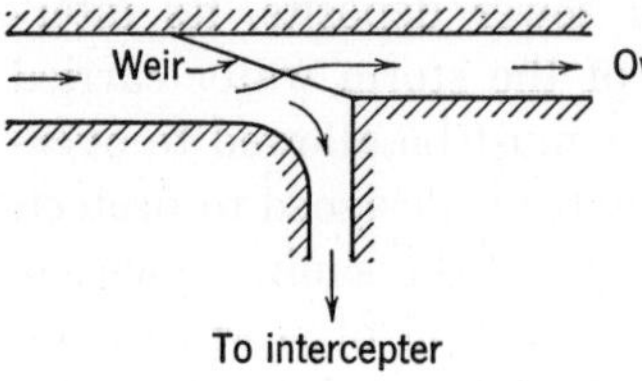

a. Diverting weir—plan

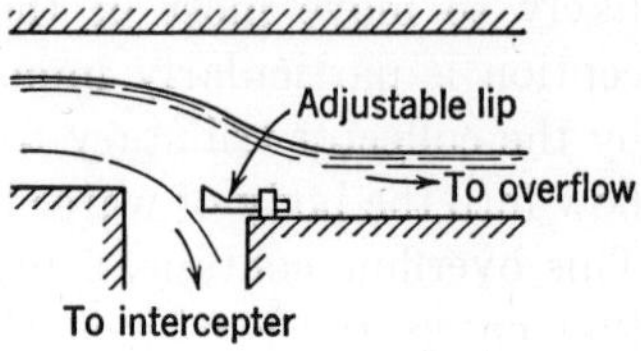

b. Leaping weir—vertical section

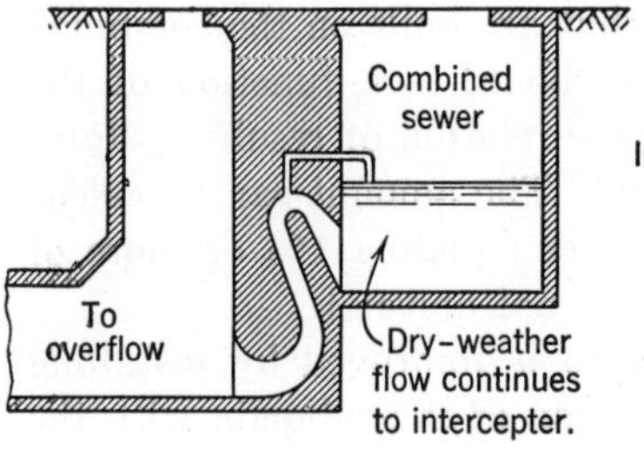

c. Siphon spillway—vertical section

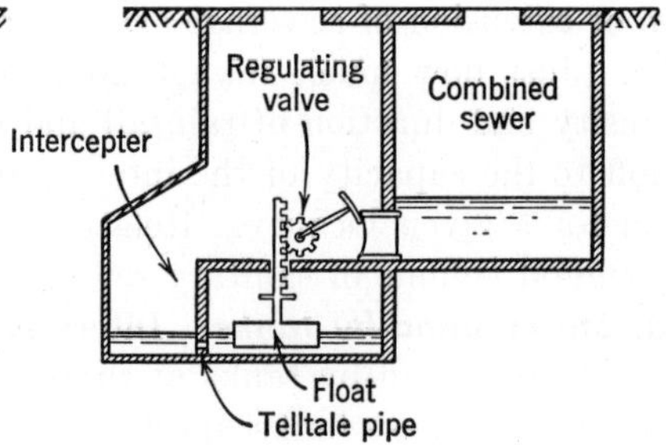

d. Mechanical diverter, or regulator—vertical section; actual mechanisms are more complicated.

Figure 8-8. Regulation of storm-water overflow.

dry-weather flows, into the overflow. Dry-weather flows continue along their normal path to the intercepter. (*a* in Figure 8-8.)

2. Leaping weirs consisting essentially of gaps in the floor of the channel. Excess flows leap over these gaps under their own momentum. Dry-weather flows tumble through the gap into the intercepter. (*b* in Figure 8-8.)

3. Siphon spillways. Flows in excess of intercepter capacity are siphoned off into the overflow channel. (*c* in Figure 8-8.)

Mechanical diversion of storm-water flows is generally regulated by a float-operated valve which controls the admission of water to the intercepter. (*d* in Figure 8-8.)

8-5. Choice of Collecting System. The combined system of sewerage, apart from questions of economy, is at best a compromise between the two wholly different functions that it attempts to perform: namely, water carriage of wastes, and removal of flooding runoff. In the life of growing communities, economies that are initially effected by the use of combined sewers will generally be offset in the long run (1) by undesirable pollution of natural water courses through necessary storm-water spills and consequent nuisance or, at least, ineffective utilization of the esthetic and recreational values of these bodies of water; (2) by increased cost of eventual sewage treatment or pumping associated with disposal of intercepted sewage; and (3) by greater nuisance caused by the occasional overflowing or backing-up of combined sewage rather than storm water. Many small streams, around which parks and other recreational areas could have been developed, have been forced into combined sewerage systems that, in the course of their evolution, degraded these streams into open sewers. A separate system of sewerage can utilize natural water courses hydraulically to the fullest possible extent by discharging storm water into them through short runs of storm drains. This will not pollute them, but it may necessitate their being channelized in order to improve their carrying capacity and control their flooding.

9 Flow in Sewers and Their Appurtenances

9-1. General Considerations. Hydraulically, a waste-water disposal system differs from a water-supply system in three essentials: (1) the conduits employed are almost exclusively of the free-flow type; (2) the flow of waste water is almost without exception unsteady and non-uniform; and (3) relatively large amounts of floating and suspended matter are impressed upon the flowing waters. Sewers accordingly are designed (1) for open-channel flow; (2) to satisfy the requirements of unsteady and non-uniform flow; and (3) to transport the waste materials in such fashion that their deposition and decomposition will be avoided or kept within reason.

As shown in Section 2-2, the design period for the main collectors, outfalls, and intercepters of a sewerage system, because of the cost and difficulty of enlargement or supplementation, is as much as 50 yr. Rates of flow, therefore, are subject not merely to the seasonal, daily, and hourly fluctuations that are normal to any one year but also to the changes imposed by expansion of the system and growth of population from the time when the system is first placed in operation to the end of the design period. Systems that include storm drainage are subject, furthermore, to the chance variations of runoff from rainfall and melting snow and ice. Although sanitary sewerage systems share their changing capacity requirements with water-distribution systems, the hydraulic balance of the latter is less delicate. They do not need to maintain self-cleansing velocities but can, with relative impunity, vary their velocities over a wide range of values and adjust their hydraulic gradients to the passage of time. The hydraulic gradients of sewers, by contrast, are, in essence, set once and for all when the sewers are built.

9-2. Limiting Velocities of Flow. Fecal solids, kitchen refuse, and other household wastes are flushed into sanitary sewers. Sand, gravel, and the debris of streets enter storm sewers through curb inlets. Combined sewers carry the gross solids received from both of these sources. The heaviest materials are swept along the sewer invert and constitute the "bed load" of the channel. The lightest materials float along the water surface. If the velocity of flow is too low, the heaviest solids are deposited on the bottom and the lightest are left stranded at the water's edge. If the velocity is too high, the invert is eroded. Both deposition and erosion are functions of the tractive force of the moving stream of sewage or storm water.

The average intensity of tractive force exerted by flowing water on its channel or on deposits within it equals the weight of water per unit surface area of channel (or deposit) times the loss of head per unit length.[1] Since the volume of water per unit surface area of channel equals the hydraulic radius of the channel, we may write

$$\tau = \gamma rs \qquad 9\text{-}1$$

where τ is the intensity of tractive force, γ is the specific weight of water at the temperature of the sewage or storm water; r is the hydraulic radius of the filled section; and s is the slope of the invert or loss of head per unit length of channel when flow is uniform and the water surface parallels the invert.

a. Damaging velocities. Since the velocity of flow in a sewer is a function of r and s, we may replace these terms in Equation 9-1 by a velocity term. Using the Chezy formula, $v = c\sqrt{rs}$, for example,

$$\tau = \gamma(v/c)^2 \qquad 9\text{-}2$$

Here v is the velocity and c is the Chezy coefficient. The intensity of tractive force is seen to vary as the square of the velocity. In order to avoid erosion of the sewer invert, an effort is generally made to hold velocities below 12 fps for tile sewers and 8 fps for concrete drains.

Of the ceramic materials used in sewer construction, vitrified tile and glazed brick are very resistant to wear. Building brick, on the other hand, is easily eroded. Concrete, too, is subject to abrasion.

[1] This tractive force is analogous, in a sense, to the friction of a body sliding down an inclined plane, the sine of small angles being equal to their tangents.

The inverts of large concrete or brick sewers are, therefore, often protected by vitrified-tile liners, glazed or paving brick, or granite blocks.

b. Transporting velocities. If sewers and their appurtenances are to be self-cleansing, they must flow at velocities that will transport the solid matter discharged into them. The required velocities can be derived from Equation 9-1 as follows:

If A is the surface area of the sediment layer (Figure 9-1), h is its depth, and f is its porosity ratio, and if T is the drag force of the water acting on the top of the sediment and R is the friction on the bottom

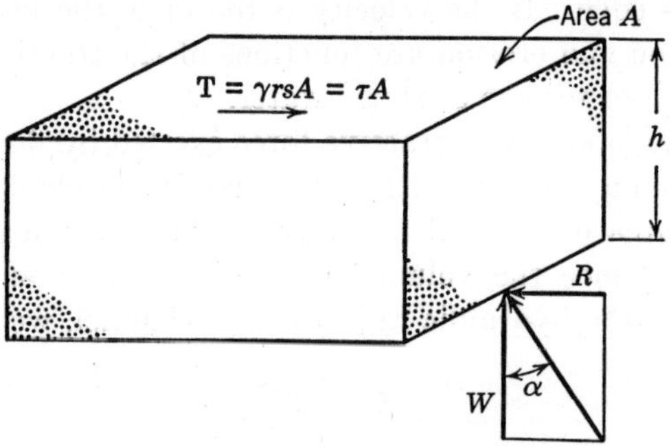

Figure 9-1. Forces acting on sediment.

or the resistance to motion, then $T = R = W \tan \alpha$ where W is the weight of the sediment and α is the friction angle. Since $W = Ah(\gamma_s - \gamma)(1 - f)$, where γ_s is the unit weight of the particles composing the sediment, and $T = \gamma r s A$,

$$\gamma r s A = Ah(\gamma_s - \gamma)(1 - f) \tan \alpha$$

or

$$\gamma r s = k(\gamma_s - \gamma)h \qquad 9\text{-}3$$

where $k = (1 - f) \tan \alpha$. For single grains of diameter d, A may be considered the surface area of the grain exposed to drag.

It follows that the invert slope at which a sewer will be self-cleansing is

$$s = \frac{k}{r} \frac{\gamma_s - \gamma}{\gamma} d \qquad 9\text{-}4$$

In accordance with the Chezy formula, furthermore, the velocity v of a stream that will transport the particles is given by the equation

$$v = c\sqrt{k\,\frac{\gamma_s - \gamma}{\gamma}\,d} \qquad 9\text{-}5$$

Here, the value of c for the conduit or stream must be chosen with due regard to the presence of deposited solids. If the Kutter coefficient of roughness n is to be introduced into Equation 9-5, the pertinent expressions for c in the Kutter or Manning formulas (Equations 9-7 and 9-8) are substituted. Substitution of the Darcy-Weisbach friction factor f, on the basis of $c = \sqrt{8g/f}$, yields a formula derived by Camp from studies by Shields:

$$v = \sqrt{\frac{8k}{f}\,g\,\frac{\gamma_s - \gamma}{\gamma}\,d} = \sqrt{\frac{8k}{f}\,g(s_s - 1)d} \qquad 9\text{-}6$$

Here s_s is the specific gravity of the particles and $(s_s - 1) = (\gamma_s - \gamma)/\gamma$ closely.

The magnitude of the sediment characteristic k must be determined by experiment. Values reported by Shields range from 0.04 for the initiation of scour to 0.8 or more for adequate cleansing.

Example 9-1. Find the minimum velocity and gradient required to transport coarse sand through a sewer 12 in. in diameter.

Coarse sand has a diameter of 0.1 cm (0.1/30.48 ft) and a specific gravity of 2.65.

Neglecting changes in the density of water with temperature and assuming values of $k = 0.04$ and $n = 0.012$:

By Equations 9-5 and 9-8:

$$v = \frac{1.486}{0.012}\left(\frac{1}{4}\right)^{1/6}\sqrt{0.04\,\frac{(2.65 - 1.00)}{1.00}\,\frac{0.1}{30.48}} = 1.45 \text{ fps}$$

By Equation 9-4:

$$s = \frac{0.04}{0.25}\,\frac{2.65 - 1.00}{1.00}\,\frac{0.1}{30.48} = 0.00087$$

9-3. Flow in Filled Sewers. In the absence of precise information on the roughness factors that attach to theoretical formulations of the flow in open channels, engineers continue to base the hydraulic design of sewers, like that of water conduits flowing under pressure (Section 6-2), upon suitable empirical formulas. Two such formulas are in common use in North America: the Kutter formula which dates back to 1869 and the Manning formula of 1890. Both of them evaluate the velocity or discharge coefficient c in the Chezy formula and include a coefficient of roughness n which is of identical magnitude.

Using the same notation that was employed for the Hazen-Williams formula (Section 6-2), the two expressions for c may be written as follows:

According to Kutter,

$$c = \frac{41.65 + \dfrac{0.00281}{s} + \dfrac{1.811}{n}}{1 + \left(41.65 + \dfrac{0.00281}{s}\right)\dfrac{n}{\sqrt{r}}} \qquad 9\text{-}7$$

and according to Manning,

$$c = \frac{1.486}{n} r^{1/6} \qquad 9\text{-}8$$

Manning's value satisfies experimental findings just as well as the clumsier formulation of Kutter and Ganguillet, and it lends itself more satisfactorily to mathematical manipulation, arithmetic computations, and graphic representation. Manning's formula is, therefore, used by preference within these pages in all matters relating to open-channel flow. An example of this use has already been given in the preceding section of this chapter.

In its complete form, Manning's formula reads as follows:

$$v = \frac{1.486}{n} r^{2/3} s^{1/2} \qquad 9\text{-}9$$

It is seen to be akin to the Hazen-Williams formula in concept and, similarly, is readily adapted to flow in circular conduits and evaluation of rates of discharge.

Calculation of the velocity of flow and rate of discharge of standard circular sewers by the Manning formula is simplified by using the values for $1.486R^{2/3}$ and $1.486AR^{2/3}$ shown in Table 9-1.[2]

Like the selection of C in the Hazen-Williams formula, the choice of a suitable value of the roughness factor N is of utmost importance but must usually be left to the judgment of the designer. Of assistance in this connection can be the values in Table 9-2 which are taken from a list compiled by Horton [3] from reliable experimental data.

[2] Capital letters are employed in this book to identify the hydraulic elements of sewers that flow full; lower-case letters for partially filled sewers.

[3] R. E. Horton, Some better Kutter's formula coefficients, *Eng. News*, 75, 373 (1916).

TABLE 9-1. Velocity and Discharge of Circular Sewers Flowing Full $S^{1/2}/N = 1$ in the Manning Formula

Diameter, D, in.	Area, A, sq ft	Velocity, V_0, fps	Discharge, Q_0, cfs
6	0.1963	0.3715	0.07293
8	0.3491	0.4500	0.1571
10	0.5455	0.5222	0.2848
12	0.7854	0.5897	0.4632
15	1.2272	0.6843	0.8398
18	1.7671	0.7728	1.366
21	2.4053	0.8564	2.060
24	3.1416	0.9361	2.941
27	3.9761	1.0116	4.026
30	4.9087	1.0863	5.332
36	7.0686	1.2267	8.671
42	9.6211	1.3594	13.08
48	12.5664	1.4860	18.67
54	15.9043	1.6074	25.56
60	19.6350	1.7244	33.86

For given values of S and N multiply velocity V_0 and discharge Q_0 by $S^{1/2}/N$ in order to obtain V and Q respectively.

TABLE 9-2. Values of the Kutter Coefficient of Friction N for Different Conduit Materials (*after Horton*)

	Condition of Interior Surface			
Conduit Material	Best	Good	Fair	Bad
Tile pipe, vitrified (glazed)	0.010	0.012	0.014	0.017
unglazed	0.011	0.013	0.015	0.017
Concrete pipe	0.012	0.013	0.015	0.016
Cast-iron pipe, coated	0.011	0.012	0.013	.....
Brick sewers, glazed	0.011	0.012	0.013	0.015
unglazed	0.012	0.013	0.015	0.017
Steel pipe, welded	0.010	0.011	0.013	.....
riveted	0.013	0.015	0.017	.....
Concrete-lined channels	0.012	0.014	0.016	0.018

The values listed for fair conditions of the interior surface are widely employed as the basis of design for sewers flowing partially full as well as full. Studies by Wilcox [4] on 8-in. sewer pipe and by Yarnell and Woodward [5] on clay and concrete drain tile 4 to 12 in. in diameter have recorded values of $N = 0.0095$ to 0.011 in Man-

[4] E. R. Wilcox, *Univ. Wash. Eng. Exp. Sta. Ser. Bull.* 27 (1924).

[5] D. L. Yarnell and S. M. Woodward, *U. S. Dept. Agr. Bull.* 854 (1920).

ning's formula when the pipes were clean and flowing full. For partially filled sections, however, n was observed to increase by as much as 25% when the depth of flow dropped to 0.4 of the full depth. In the absence of actual measurements of discharge of substantially identical pipes, a design value [6] of $N = 0.012$ is suggested for the filled sections of tile and concrete sewers 6 to 24 in. in diameter. For larger sizes, the value of N may be dropped to 0.011.

The minimum grades S and capacities Q of sewers up to 24 in. in diameter flowing full at velocities V of 2.0, 2.5, and 3.0 fps are shown in Table 9-3 for a coefficient of roughness of 0.012.

TABLE 9-3. Minimum Grades and Capacities of Circular Sewers Flowing Full

$N = 0.012$ in the Manning Formula

Diameter, in.	6	8	10	12	15	18	21	24
				$V = 2.0$ fps				
$S \times 10^3$	4.18	2.85	2.12	1.66	1.23	0.969	0.788	0.657
Q, cfs	0.393	0.698	1.09	1.57	2.45	3.53	4.81	6.28
				$V = 2.5$ fps				
$S \times 10^3$	6.51	4.44	3.30	2.58	1.93	1.51	1.23	1.02
Q, cfs	0.491	0.873	1.36	1.96	3.07	4.42	6.01	7.85
				$V = 3.0$ fps				
$S \times 10^3$	9.20	6.27	4.77	3.73	2.78	2.17	1.78	1.48
Q, cfs	0.589	1.05	1.64	2.36	3.68	5.30	7.22	9.42

9-4. Flow in Partially Filled Sewers. The upper reaches of sanitary sewers generally flow at shallow depths, because the pipe size employed is relatively large whereas the number of houses served is relatively small. Other portions of the system are planned to flow full only toward the end of their design period and then but spasmodically at times of maximum flow. Discharge ratios varying from 4:1 to as high as 18:1 are thereby established for sanitary sewers. For this reason, the upper reaches of sanitary sewers are often designed on a basis of flowing full at a velocity of 3.0 fps rather than 2.5 or 2.0 fps. Even greater variations in requisite capacity are registered by combined and storm sewers. The design of sewerage systems, therefore, is concerned with the hydraulic performance of partially filled as well as filled sections and with the maintenance, insofar as

[6] Report of committee to study limiting velocities of flow in sewers, *J. Boston Soc. Civil Engrs.*, 29, 286 (1942).

practicable, of self-cleansing velocities throughout the range of expected flows.

A flow formula such as Manning's has within it the following variables: Q or v, r or a/p (p = wetted perimeter), s or h/l, and n. Together these variables constitute the hydraulic elements of a conduit of given shape. For any one shape and for a fixed coefficient of roughness and invert slope, these elements vary in individual magnitude with the depth d of the filled section. For purposes of generalization, this variation is conveniently expressed in terms of the ratio of each element of the filled section (indicated by a lower-case letter) to the corresponding element of the full section (indicated by a capital letter). This is done for a sewer of circular cross-section in Figure 9-2, the variation of n with depth suggested by Camp [7] being plotted as the reciprocal of n/N for convenience of calculation.

Of the elements shown in Figure 9-2, those of area and hydraulic radius are static, or elements of shape, and those of roughness, velocity, and discharge are dynamic, or elements of flow. The basis for

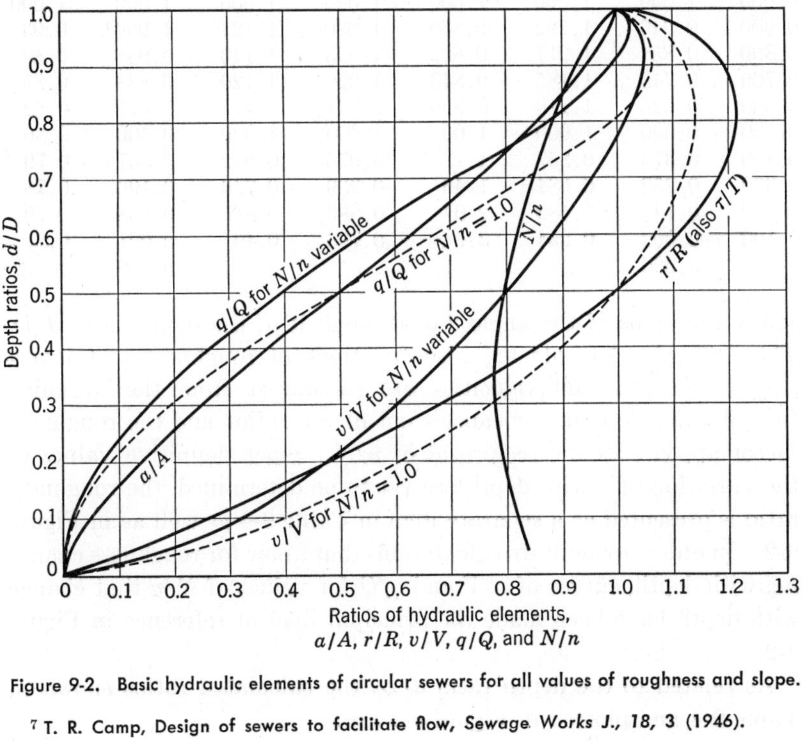

Figure 9-2. Basic hydraulic elements of circular sewers for all values of roughness and slope.

[7] T. R. Camp, Design of sewers to facilitate flow, *Sewage Works J.*, 18, 3 (1946).

the computation of both groups of elements, with the exception of n, is shown in Table 9-4. The geometric elements of circular sewers are

TABLE 9-4. Hydraulic Elements of a Sewer of Circular Cross-Section

(Uncorrected for variations in roughness with depth.)

Central angle: $\cos \frac{1}{2}\theta = 1 - 2d/D$

Area: $\frac{D^2}{4}\left(\frac{\pi\theta}{360} - \frac{\sin\theta}{2}\right)$

Wetted perimeter: $\pi D\theta/360$

Hydraulic radius: $\frac{D}{4}\left(1 - \frac{360 \sin\theta}{2\pi\theta}\right)$

Velocity: $\frac{1.486}{n} r^{2/3} s^{1/2}$

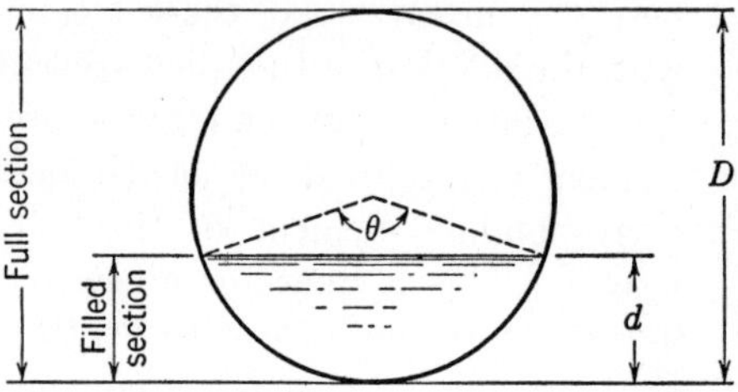

Depth d/D (1)	Area a/A (2)	Hydraulic Radius r/R (3)	Hydraulic Radius R/r (4)	Hydraulic Radius $(r/R)^{1/6}$ (5)	Velocity v/V for $N/n = 1.0$ (6)	Discharge q/Q for $N/n = 1.0$ (7)	Roughness N/n (8)
1.000	1.000	1.000	1.000	1.000	1.000	1.000	1.000
0.900	0.949	1.192	0.839	1.030	1.124	1.066	0.93
0.800	0.858	1.217	0.822	1.033	1.140	0.988	0.89
0.700	0.748	1.185	0.843	1.029	1.120	0.838	0.85
0.600	0.626	1.110	0.900	1.018	1.072	0.671	0.82
0.500	0.500	1.000	1.00	1.000	1.000	0.500	0.80
0.400	0.373	0.857	1.17	0.975	0.902	0.337	0.79
0.300	0.252	0.684	1.46	0.939	0.776	0.196	0.78
0.200	0.143	0.482	2.07	0.886	0.615	0.088	0.79
0.100	0.052	0.254	3.94	0.796	0.401	0.021	0.81
0.000	0.000	.....	.....	.....	.....	0.000	.....

solely functions of the angle θ or through it of the depth ratio d/D. The dynamic elements are also functions of roughness and invert slope. If flows and velocities are calculated from the Manning formula, the slope factor cancels out of the ratios and the roughness factor appears as the reciprocal of n/N. Since definitive values of the variation of n with depth are yet to be determined, the roughness ratio is presented as a separate item in Table 9-4 as well as in Figure 9-2. In order to facilitate calculations that allow for roughness changing with depth, curves of v/V and q/Q for values of N/n that change with depth have been made the principal lines of reference in Figure 9-2.

As related to the depth ratio d/D, the calculated ratios shown in Table 9-4 and plotted in Figure 9-2 are:

Column 2: $\dfrac{a}{A} = \dfrac{\theta}{360} - \dfrac{\sin\theta}{2\pi}$.

Column 3: $\dfrac{r}{R} = 1 - \dfrac{360 \sin\theta}{2\pi\theta}$.

Column 6: $\dfrac{v}{V} = \dfrac{N}{n}\left(\dfrac{r}{R}\right)^{2/3}\left(\dfrac{s}{S}\right)^{1/2}$, or $\left(\dfrac{r}{R}\right)^{2/3}$ for $n = N$ and $s = S$.

Column 7: $\dfrac{q}{Q} = \dfrac{N}{n}\dfrac{a}{A}\left(\dfrac{r}{R}\right)^{2/3}\left(\dfrac{s}{S}\right)^{1/2}$, or $\dfrac{a}{A}\left(\dfrac{r}{R}\right)^{2/3}$ for $n = N$ and $s = S$.

As shown in Table 9-4 and Figure 9-2, the velocity of flow in the partially filled, circular section will equal or exceed that in the full section whenever the sewer flows more than half full provided that there is no increase in roughness at lowered depth. Where there is such an increase, velocities equal to, or greater than, the velocity at full depth are restricted, in accordance with Camp's values of n, to the upper 20% of the depth only. This does not imply that sewers flowing at depths between 0.5 and 0.8 full must be placed on steeper grades if they are to be as self-cleaning as sewers flowing full. The grade actually required and the associated velocity and discharge are functions of the intensity of the tractive force. This involves the coefficient of friction as well as the velocity of flow. The needed hydraulic elements can be computed from Equation 9-1 on the assumption that sewers flowing at partial depth will remain as self-cleaning as sewers flowing full if the intensity of the tractive force on sewer deposits remains the same at all depths of flow, or

$$\tau = \mathrm{T} = \gamma r s = \gamma R S$$

Hence

$$\frac{s}{S} = \frac{R}{r} \quad \text{or} \quad s = \frac{R}{r}S \qquad 9\text{-}10$$

and the induced self-cleaning velocity v_s and rate of flow q_s are determined by the Manning formula as:

$$\frac{v_s}{V} = \frac{N}{n}\left(\frac{r}{R}\right)^{2/3}\left(\frac{s}{S}\right)^{1/2} \qquad 9\text{-}11$$

or from Equation 9-10:

$$\frac{v_s}{V} = \frac{N}{n}\left(\frac{r}{R}\right)^{1/6} \qquad 9\text{-}12$$

and

$$\frac{q_s}{Q} = \frac{N}{n}\frac{a}{A}\left(\frac{r}{R}\right)^{1/6} \qquad 9\text{-}13$$

The significance of these equations is shown in the following example.

Example 9-2. An 8-in. sewer is to flow at 0.3 depth on a grade that will insure a degree of self-cleaning equivalent to that obtaining at full depth for a velocity of 2.5 fps. Find the required grades and associated velocities and rates of discharge at full depth and 0.3 depth. Assume $N = 0.012$ at full depth.

a. From Table 9-3, find for full depth of flow and $V = 2.5$ fps, $Q = 0.873$ cfs and $S = 4.44$ ft per 1,000.

b. From Figure 9-2 or Table 9-4, find for 0.3 depth, $a/A = 0.252$, $r/R = 0.684$ (or $R/r = 1.46$), $v/V = 0.776$, $q/Q = 0.196$, and $N/n = 0.78$; and from Table 9-4, find $(r/R)^{1/6} = 0.939$.

Hence at 0.3 depth and a grade of 4.44 ft per 1,000, $v = 0.776 \times 2.5 = 1.94$ fps for $n = N$, or 1.51 fps for $N/n = 0.78$, and $q = 0.196 \times 0.873 = 0.171$ cfs for $n = N$, or 0.133 cfs for $N/n = 0.78$.

c. For self-cleaning flow, however, $s = 1.46 \times 4.44 = 6.5$ ft per 1,000, by Equation 9-10; $v_s = 0.939 \times 2.5 = 2.35$ for $n = N$, or $0.78 \times 2.35 = 1.83$ fps for $N/n = 0.78$, by Equation 9-12; and $q_s = 0.252 \times 0.939 \times 0.873 = 0.207$ cfs for $n = N$, or $0.78 \times 0.207 = 0.161$ cfs for $N/n = 0.78$, by Equation 9-13.

To facilitate findings such as these, the implications of the variation of n with depth and of Equations 9-10 to 9-13 can be incorporated in a diagram of the hydraulic elements that are associated with a sewer that will flow, at all depths, at velocities equal in self-cleaning action to the velocity of the full section. This has been done in Figure 9-3 which shows, among other matters, that no change in slope need be made when a sewer flows more than half full but that the slope must be doubled when the depth of flow drops to 0.2 full and quadrupled at 0.1 depth.

Example 9-3. An 8-in. sewer is to discharge 0.161 cfs at a velocity equivalent in self-cleaning action to that of a sewer flowing full at 2.5 fps. Find the depth and velocity of flow and the required slope.

a. From Example 9-2, $Q = 0.873$ cfs and $S = 4.44$ ft per 1,000. Hence $q_s/Q = 0.161/0.873 = 0.185$.

b. From Figure 9-3, for $N = n$ and $q_s/Q = 0.185$, $d_s/D = 0.25$, $v_s/V = 0.91$, and $s/S = 1.70$. Hence $v_s = 0.91 \times 2.5 = 2.28$ fps, and $s = 1.70 \times 4.44 = 7.5$ ft per 1,000.

c. From Figure 9-3, for N/n variable and $q_s/Q = 0.185$, $d_s/D = 0.30$, $v_s/V = 0.732$, and $s/S = 1.46$. Hence $v_s = 0.732 \times 2.5 = 1.83$ fps, and $s = 1.46 \times 4.44 = 6.5$ ft per 1,000.

The increase in the coefficient of roughness is seen to be an aid to the cleansing action of flow and to allow lower velocities and slopes.

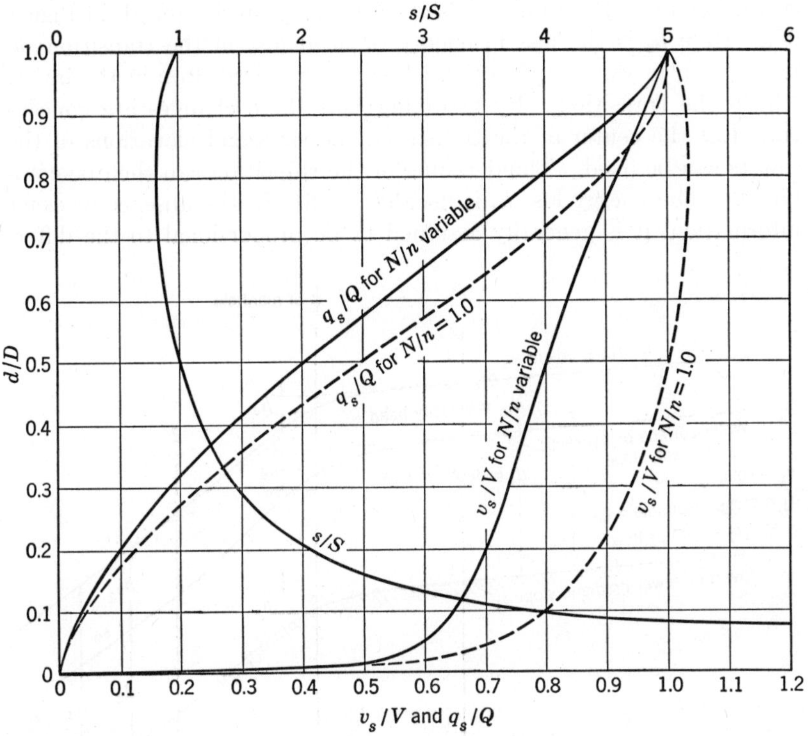

Figure 9-3. Hydraulic elements of circular sewers that possess equal self-cleansing properties at all depths.

9-5. Flow in Sewer Transitions. The flow in sewers, as has been stated, is both unsteady (changing in rate of discharge) and nonuniform (changing in velocity and depth). Since it is not practicable to identify with needed accuracy the variation in flow with time for all reaches of the sewerage system and since the system is designed for the maximum expected flow, the design flow is assumed to be steady except in unusual circumstances. In sewer transitions, however, nonuniformity of the flow must be taken into account if a rational and economical design of the system is to be attained.

Sewer transitions include (1) changes in size, grade, and volume of flow; (2) free and submerged discharge at the end of the line; (3) passage through measuring and diversion devices; and (4) junctions. The most common form of sewer transition occurs at a change in size or grade. The influence of such a change upon the shape of the water surface and energy gradient is shown, greatly foreshortened, in Figure 9-4. Here h_e is the loss in energy or head lost in the transition; h_s is the drop in water surface; and h_i is the required drop in the invert within the transition. By assuming that these changes are concentrated at the center of the transition, the sizes and elevations of the sewers can be fixed. The detailing of the transition can then be completed. The energy loss h_e is usually small. In the absence of exact information, it is generally assumed to be proportional to the differ-

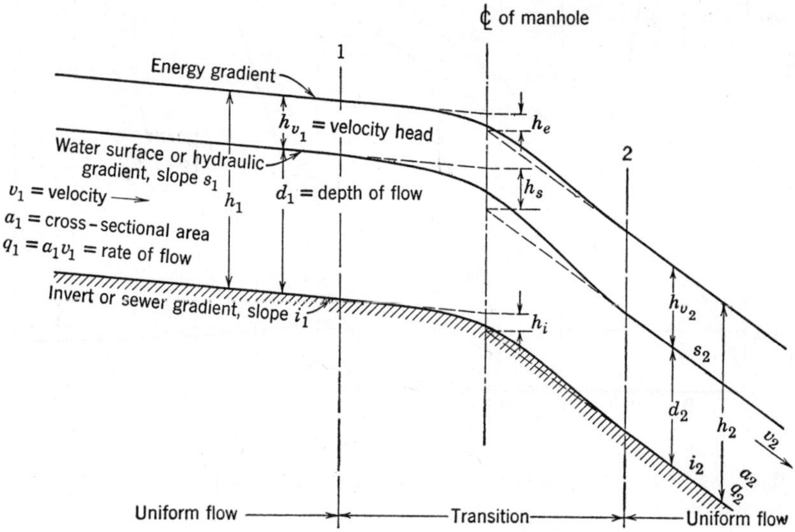

Figure 9-4. Changes in hydraulic and energy gradients at a transition in size or grade of sewer.

ence, or change, in velocity heads, i.e., $h_e = k(h_{v_2} - h_{v_1})$. According to Hinds,[8] the proportionality factor k may have a value as low as 0.1 for increasing velocities and as low as 0.2 for decreasing velocities, provided that flow is in the "upper alternate stage." For flow in the "lower alternate stage," the value of k may be expected to increase approximately as the square of the velocity ratios. Camp [7] has suggested allowing a minimum value of 0.02 ft for the loss of head in a transition of this kind. If a curve is included in the transition, the loss of head will be greater.

[8] Julian Hinds, The hydraulic design of flume and siphon transitions, *Trans. Am. Soc. Civil Engrs.*, 92, 1423 (1928).

With the energy loss placed at a reasonable value, the requisite drop h_i in the invert of the sewer follows from the relationships demonstrated in Figure 9-4, where

$$h_2 + h_e = h_1 + h_i$$

or

$$h_i = (h_2 - h_1) + h_e = \Delta(d + h_v) + k\Delta h_v \qquad 9\text{-}14$$

The value of h_i may be positive or negative, negative values being associated with sharply decreasing gradients. A positive value calls for a drop in the invert, a negative value for a rise. A rise, however, is never introduced; instead, the invert is made continuous. The elevation of the water surface in the downstream sewer is thereby lowered, and the waters in the run of sewer entering the transition are drawn down towards it.

Rules of thumb are sometimes used by engineers in place of the computations called for by Equation 9-14. However, employment of these rules is often not justified by circumstances. The following rules for drops in manholes at changes in size are examples:

a. $h_i = \frac{1}{2}(d_2 - d_1)$ for sewers smaller than 24 in. $h_i = \frac{3}{4}(d_2 - d_1)$ for 24-in. sewers and larger.

b. Keeping the $0.8d$ line continuous on the principle that it represents the line of maximum velocity.

c. Basing flow calculations on a roughness factor greater than that obtaining in straight runs; $N = 0.015$, for example, instead of $N = 0.012$.

d. Allowing a drop of 0.1 ft in a through manhole; 0.2 ft in the presence of one lateral or bend; and 0.3 ft for two laterals.

Example 9-4. Two 8-in. sanitary sewers, each flowing full and carrying 0.7 cfs at a velocity of 2 fps on minimum grade, discharge into a steeper sewer that is to pick up 0.01 cfs in the course of its next run. The lower sewer can be laid on a grade as low as 10 per 1,000 and as high as 13 per 1,000. Find the required slope of the lower sewer and the invert drop in the transition.

a. From Table 9-1, an 8-in. sewer flowing full will carry 1.41 cfs on a slope of 11.6 per 1,000 with a velocity of 4.05 fps if $N = 0.012$. Pertinent information is, therefore, as follows:

$$d_1 = 0.67 \text{ ft}, \quad v_1 = 2.00 \text{ fps}, \quad h_{v_1} = 0.062 \text{ ft}, \quad d_1 + h_{v_1} = 0.73 \text{ ft}$$

$$d_2 = 0.67 \text{ ft}, \quad v_2 = 4.05 \text{ fps}, \quad h_{v_2} = 0.255 \text{ ft}, \quad d_2 + h_{v_2} = 0.92 \text{ ft}$$

$$\Delta h_v = 0.19 \text{ ft}, \quad \Delta(d + h_v) = 0.19 \text{ ft}$$

Assuming a loss of head of $h_e = 0.2\Delta h_v = 0.038$ ft, Equation 9-14 gives the required drop in invert,

$$h_i = 0.19 + 0.04 = 0.23 \text{ ft}$$

b. A 10-in. sewer laid on a grade of 10 per 1,000 has a capacity of 2.37 cfs and velocity of 4.35 fps when flowing full. From Figure 9-2, for $N/n \times q/Q = 0.595$, $d/D = 0.63$, and $N/n \times v/V = 0.905$, or $d = 6.3$ in., and $v = 3.94$ fps. Hence, the upper sewers remaining unchanged,

$$d_2 = 0.525 \text{ ft}, \quad v_2 = 3.94 \text{ fps}, \quad h_{v_2} = 0.24 \text{ ft}, \quad d_2 + h_{v_2} = 0.77 \text{ ft}$$

$$\Delta h_v = 0.18 \text{ ft}, \quad \Delta(d + h_v) = 0.04 \text{ ft}$$

Assuming a loss of head $h_e = 0.2\Delta h_v = 0.036$ ft, we find

$$h_i = 0.04 + 0.04 = 0.08 \text{ ft}$$

9-6. Alternate Stages and Critical Depth of Flow. For a full analysis of transitions, the designer must be able to identify the alternate stages of open-channel flow and the special case of flow at critical depth. Taking the elevation of the sewer invert as the datum, the energy gradient, as shown in Figure 9-4, is situated at a height

$$h = d + h_v = d + v^2/2g = d + q^2/(2ga^2) \qquad 9\text{-}15$$

above this datum.[9] Since the cross-sectional area of the conduit is a function of its depth, Equation 9-15 is a cubic equation in terms of the depth. Two roots of this equation are positive and represent the two alternate stages at which a given rate of discharge q will be maintained for a given energy head h. The two stages fuse into a single "critical stage" for conditions of maximum discharge. Critical flow is unstable and should be avoided in design if uncertainties and fluctuations in depth of flow are not to be introduced. Depths of flow within 10% of the critical depth are also likely to be unstable.

Equation 9-15 may be generalized by expressing its three terms as dimensionless ratios. A family of curves or a nomogram can then be prepared to facilitate the determination of the alternate stages and critical depth of flow in a conduit of given cross-section. Bringing the term containing the rate of discharge q to one side of the equation and multiplying both sides of the resulting equation by $\dfrac{1}{D}\left(\dfrac{a}{A}\right)^2$, we

[9] If v is the mean velocity of flow, the kinetic energy head is actually greater than $v^2/2g$ by 10 to 20%, depending upon the shape and roughness of the channel. But this fact is not ordinarily taken into account in hydraulic computations.[7]

obtain the following straight-line relationship:

$$\left(\frac{q}{A\sqrt{gD}}\right)^2 = 2\left(\frac{a}{A}\right)^2\left(\frac{h}{D} - \frac{d}{D}\right) \qquad \text{9-16}$$

Again, the capital letters in this equation denote the hydraulic elements of the full section, and the lower-case letters those of the partially filled section of the conduit.

A plot of Equation 9-16 for circular conduits is shown in Figure 9-5. It will be noted that the family of straight lines for particular values of d/D spontaneously generates a curve for the critical depth.

Maximum rate of discharge obtains at the critical depth d_c. Hence this element is determined analytically [10] by differentiating Equation 9-16 with respect to d and equating the result to 0.

The following relation is obtained for a circular cross-section:

$$\frac{h}{D} = \frac{1}{8}\left[\left(10\frac{d_c}{D} - 1\right) + \frac{\frac{1}{4}\pi + \frac{1}{2}\sin^{-1}\left(2\frac{d_c}{D} - 1\right)}{\sqrt{\frac{d_c}{D}\left(1 - \frac{d_c}{D}\right)}}\right] \qquad \text{9-17}$$

Substitution into Equation 9-17 of values of d_c/D varying by tenths from 0.1 to 0.9 yields the numerical results for h/D, $\frac{v_c}{\sqrt{gD}}$, and $\left(\frac{q}{A\sqrt{gD}}\right)^2$, shown in Table 9-5.

[10] For a circular cross-section the area a of the partially filled section is related to the depth as follows:

$$a = \frac{1}{2}\pi\frac{D^2}{4} + 2\int_{y=0}^{y=y} x\,dy$$

where x and y are the coordinates of a point on the circle referred to axes passing through the center of the circle. Expressed in terms of y and of D and d,

$$2\int_{y=0}^{y=y} x\,dy = 2\int_{y=0}^{y=y}\sqrt{(D^2/4 - y^2)}\,dy = 2\int_{d=D/2}^{d=d}\sqrt{d(D-d)}\,dd$$

$$= \left(d - \frac{D}{2}\right)\sqrt{d(D-d)} + \frac{D^2}{4}\sin^{-1}\left(2\frac{d}{D} - 1\right)$$

Introduction of these quantities into Equation 9-16 and differentiation yield Equation 9-17.

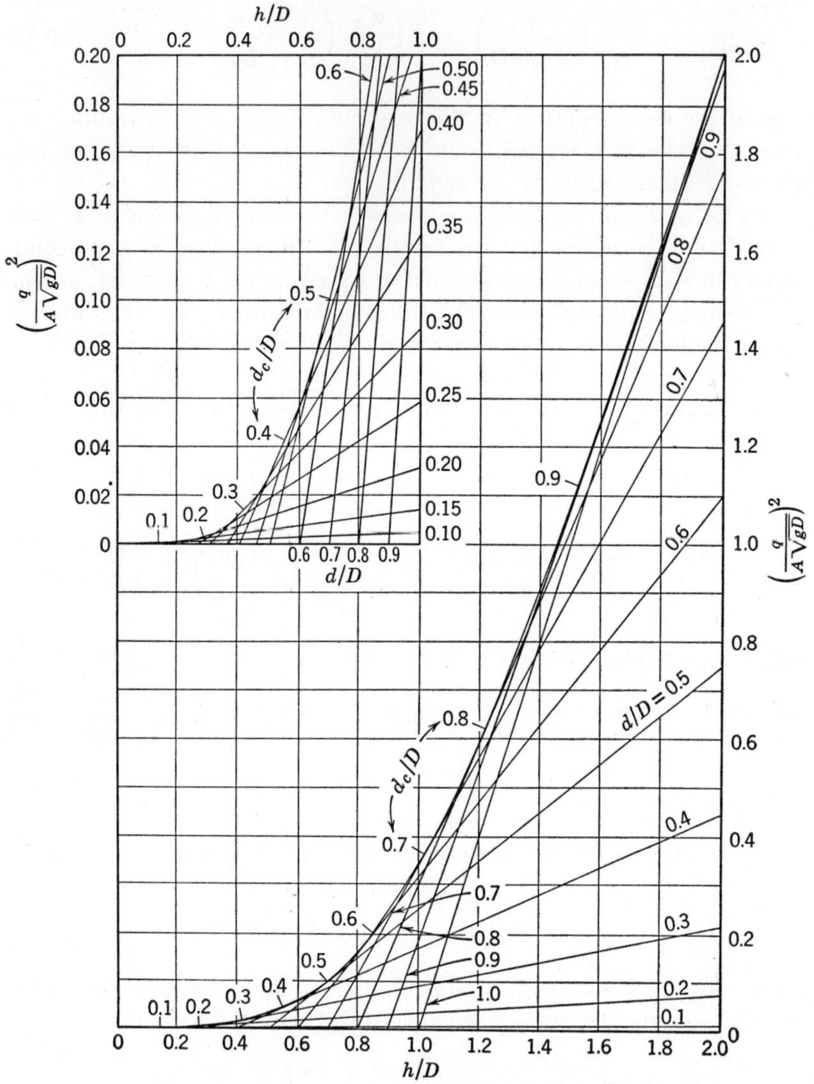

Figure 9-5. Alternate stages and critical depths of flow in circular conduits.

TABLE 9-5. Values of h/D, $v_c/\sqrt{gD}$, and $(q/A\sqrt{gD})^2$ for Varying Values of d_c/D in a Circular Conduit

d_c/D	h/D	$v_c/\sqrt{gD}$	$(q/A\sqrt{gD})^2$
0.1	0.134	0.261	1.184×10^{-4}
0.2	0.270	0.378	2.86×10^{-3}
0.3	0.408	0.465	1.37×10^{-2}
0.4	0.550	0.553	4.18×10^{-2}
0.5	0.696	0.626	9.80×10^{-2}
0.6	0.851	0.709	1.97×10^{-1}
0.7	1.020	0.800	3.58×10^{-1}
0.8	1.222	0.919	6.23×10^{-1}
0.9	1.521	1.11	1.12

For a trapezoidal channel (Section 4-6) of bottom width b and with side slopes of z (horizontal to vertical)

$$\frac{h}{D} = \frac{d_c}{D} + \frac{d_c}{2D}\left(\frac{b + zd_c}{b + 2zd_c}\right) \qquad 9\text{-}18$$

This equation contains the well-known relationship for a rectangular channel for the special case of $z = 0$,

$$\frac{h}{D} = \frac{3}{2}\frac{d_c}{D} \quad \text{or} \quad h = \frac{3}{2} d_c \qquad 9\text{-}19$$

whence

$$v_c^2/2g = h - d_c \quad \text{or} \quad v_c = \sqrt{gd_c} \qquad 9\text{-}20$$

In a closed conduit, the critical depth line, as shown in Figure 9-5, is asymptotic to the line $d/D = 1.0$. There is, therefore, neither a critical nor an alternate stage for an enclosed conduit that is flowing full.

Example 9-5. The use of Figure 9-5, construction of which is simple and straightforward, can be exemplified as follows:

Given a discharge of 60 cfs in a 4-ft sewer, find (*a*) the critical depth, (*b*) the alternate stages for an energy head of 4 ft, (*c*) the alternate stage for an energy head of 6 ft, and (*d*) the lower alternate stage associated with an upper alternate stage at 0.8 depth.

a. For $q = 60$ cfs and $D = 4$ ft, $\left(\frac{q}{A\sqrt{gD}}\right)^2 = \left(\frac{60 \times 4}{\pi \times 16\sqrt{4g}}\right)^2 = 0.177.$ From Figure 9-5, read $d_c/D = 0.59$. Hence $d_c = 0.59 \times 4 = 2.36$ ft.

b. For $h = 4.0$, $h/D = 1.0$, and $\left(\frac{q}{A\sqrt{gD}}\right)^2 = 0.177$ as in (*a*), read, from Figure 9-5, $d/D = 0.42$ and 0.90, or $d_l = 0.42 \times 4 = 1.7$ ft, and $d_u = 0.90 \times 4 = 3.6$ ft.

c. For $h = 6.0$, $h/D = 1.5$, and $\left(\frac{q}{A\sqrt{gD}}\right)^2 = 0.177$ as in (*a*), read, from Figure 9-5, $d/D = 0.32$, whence $d_l = 0.32 \times 4 = 1.3$ ft. There is no upper stage since the conduit flows full when h/D equals or exceeds 1.09 (at intersection of $d/D = 1.0$ and ordinate of 0.177). Hence the conduit is placed under a pressure of $(1.5 - 1.09 = 0.41) \times 4 = 1.6$ ft.

d. For $\left(\frac{q}{A\sqrt{gD}}\right)^2 = 0.177$ as in (*a*) and $d_u/D = 0.8$, or $d_u = 3.2$ ft, read, from Figure 9-5, $d_l/D = 0.45$, or $d_l = 1.8$ ft.

9-7. Length of Transitions. Transition from one to the other alternate stage carries the flow through the critical depth. Passage from the upper alternate stage d_u to the critical depth d_c, or through it, to the lower alternate stage d_l or to free fall produces non-uniform (accelerating) flow and a drawdown curve in the water surface. Passage from the lower to the subsequent stage creates the hydraulic jump. Reduction in velocity of flow, (1) by discharge into relatively quiet water or (2) by weirs and other obstructions to flow, dams up the water and induces non-uniform (decelerating) flow and a backwater curve in the water surface. Economy of design requires that the size of conduit be adapted to the conditions of flow within the range of changing depths associated with non-uniformity in flow. If the depths of flow at both ends of the transition are known, the energy and hydraulic gradients of transition can be traced by stepwise calculations or by integration (graphical [11] or analytical [12]).

As shown in Figure 9-6, both methods are based upon the consideration that

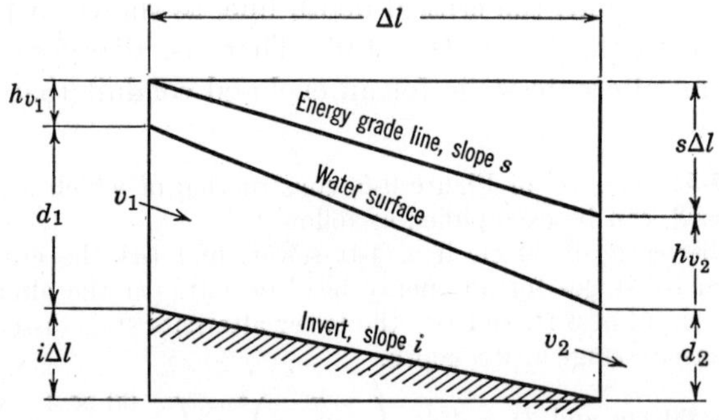

Figure 9-6. Changes in conditions of flow with changing (increasing) velocity of flow in a hydraulic transition.

[11] H. A. Thomas, *Hydraulics of Flood Movement*, Carnegie Institute of Technology, 1934.

[12] M. E. von Seggern, Integrating the equation of non-uniform flow, *Proc. Am. Soc. Civil Engrs.*, *75*, 105 (1949).

$$i\,\Delta l + d_1 + h_{v_1} = s\,\Delta l + d_2 + h_{v_2}$$

or

$$\Delta l = \Delta(d + h_v)/(s - i) \qquad 9\text{-}21$$

and that, closely, the slope of the energy grade line is given by the Manning formula as

$$s = \left\{\frac{n(v_1 + v_2)/2}{1.486[(r_1 + r_2)/2]^{2/3}}\right\}^2 \qquad 9\text{-}22$$

where $(v_1 + v_2)/2$ and $(r_1 + r_2)/2$ are, respectively, average (arithmetic mean) values of the velocities at the beginning and end of the section of channel under consideration and of its hydraulic radii. Flow being steady, the rate of discharge is constant, and the velocity of flow at any depth is fully determined. The invert slope i is likewise known. In place of the arithmetic mean values of v and r, their geometric mean or the harmonic mean values can be used with equal justification. The necessary calculations are shown in Example 9-6 for a backwater curve and in Example 9-7 for a drawdown curve.

Example 9-6. A 10-ft circular sewer laid on a gradient of 0.5 ft per 1,000 discharges 106 cfs into a pump well. The water level in this well rises, at times, 10 ft above the invert elevation of the incoming sewer. Trace the profile of the water surface in the sewer. Assume a coefficient of roughness of 0.012 for the full sewer.

a. A 10-ft sewer on a grade of 5×10^{-4} has a capacity of 400 cfs by Manning's formula. The value of q/Q, therefore, equals $106/400 = 0.265$, and d/D from Figure 9-2 equals 0.40 for variable N/n. Hence the initial depth of flow is $0.40 \times 10 = 4.0$ ft, and the terminal depth 10 ft.

b. The length of reach in which the depth changes by a chosen amount is given by Equation 9-21. The calculations are shown in Table 9-6. The length of run in which the transition from a depth of 4.0 to 10.0 ft takes place is 14,440 ft, or slightly under 3 miles.

The calculations involve no difficulties. The values shown in the successive columns of Table 9-6 are found as follows:

Column 1: Assumed depths between initial depth of 4 ft and terminal depth of 10 ft.
Column 2: Column 1 ÷ 10 (the diameter of the sewer).
Columns 3, 4, and 5: a/A, r/R, and N/n read from Figure 9-2.
Column 6: Column 3 × 78.5 (the area of the sewer).
Column 7: Column 1 × 2.50 (the hydraulic radius of the sewer).
Column 8: 106 (the rate of flow) ÷ Column 6.
Column 9: $v^2/2g$ for Column 8.
Column 10: Column 9 + Column 1.
Column 11: 0.012 (Manning's N for the sewer) ÷ (Column 5).
Column 12: Column 11 × Column 8.

TABLE 9-6. Calculation of Backwater Curve (Example 9-6)

d (1)	d/D (2)	a/A (3)	r/R (4)	N/n (5)	a (6)	r (7)	v (8)	$h_v \times 10^2$ (9)	$d + h_v$ (10)
10.0	1.00	1.000	1.000	1.00	78.5	2.50	1.35	2.83	10.028
8.0	0.80	0.858	1.217	0.89	67.5	3.04	1.57	3.83	8.038
6.0	0.60	0.626	1.110	0.82	49.1	2.78	2.16	7.23	6.072
4.0	0.40	0.373	0.857	0.79	29.3	2.14	3.62	20.3	4.203

$n \times 10^2$	$nv \times 10^2$	Average			$s \times 10^5$	$(s - i) \times 10^5$	$\Delta(d + h_v)$	Δl	$\Sigma \Delta l$
		r	$r^{2/3}$	$nv \times 10^2$					
(11)	(12)	(13)	(14)	(15)	(16)	(17)	(18)	(19)	(20)
1.20	1.62								0
		2.77	1.97	1.87	4.07	−45.9	−1.990	4,330	
1.35	2.12								4,330
		2.91	2.04	2.63	7.53	−42.5	−1.966	4,620	
1.46	3.15								8,950
		2.46	1.82	4.32	15.97	−34.0	−1.869	5,490	
1.52	5.50								14,440

Column 13: Arithmetic mean of successive pairs of values in Column 7.
Column 14: (Column 13)$^{2/3}$.
Column 15: Arithmetic mean of successive pairs of values in Column 12.
Column 16: (Column 15 ÷ 1.486 × Column 14)^2, Equation 9-22.
Column 17: Column 16 − 50.
Column 18: Difference between successive pairs of values in Column 10.
Column 19: Column 18 ÷ Column 17 × 10^{-5}, Equation 9-21.
Column 20: Cumulative values of Column 19.

Example 9-7. A 10-ft circular sewer laid on a gradient of 0.5 ft per 1,000 discharges freely into a water course. Trace the profile of the water surface in the sewer when it is flowing at maximum capacity without surcharge.

a. The maximum capacity of this sewer, as shown in Example 9-6, is 400 cfs for $N = 0.012$.

b. To discharge in free fall, the flow must pass through the critical depth. Since

$$\left(\frac{Q}{A\sqrt{gD}}\right)^2 = \left(\frac{400}{78.5\sqrt{10g}}\right)^2 = 0.0807$$

$d_c = 0.47 \times 10 = 4.7$ ft, from Figure 9-5.

c. The length of reach in which the depth changes from 10 ft to 4.7 ft is calculated in Table 9-7 in accordance with Equation 9-21 and as in Example 9-6.

The drawdown, therefore, extends over a length of 23,600 ft, or over 4 miles, between the full depth of the sewer and a critical depth of 4.7 ft. There is a

TABLE 9-7. Calculation of Drawdown Curve (Example 9-7)

d (1)	d/D (2)	a/A (3)	r/R (4)	N/n (5)	a (6)	r (7)	v (8)	h_v (9)	$d + h_v$ (10)
4.7	0.47	0.463	0.960	0.79	36.4	2.40	11.0	1.88	6.58
6.0	0.60	0.626	1.110	0.82	49.1	2.78	8.15	1.02	7.02
8.0	0.80	0.858	1.217	0.89	67.5	3.04	5.93	0.54	8.54
10.0	1.00	1.000	1.000	1.00	78.5	2.50	5.10	0.40	10.40

$n \times 10^2$	$nv \times 10^2$	Average			$s \times 10^4$	$(s - i) \times 10^4$	$\Delta(d + h_v)$	Δl	$\Sigma \Delta l$
		r	$r^{2/3}$	$nv \times 10^2$					
(11)	(12)	(13)	(14)	(15)	(16)	(17)	(18)	(19)	(20)
1.52	16.8								0
		2.59	1.88	14.3	26.2	21.2	0.44	210	
1.46	11.9								209
		2.91	2.04	9.9	10.65	5.65	1.52	2,690	
1.35	7.99								2,900
		2.77	1.97	7.1	5.90	0.90	1.86	20,700	
1.20	6.12								23,600

further short stretch of flow between the point of critical depth and the end of the sewer. This additional distance, however, is small and seldom in excess of $5d_c$, or 23.5 ft in the example chosen.

9-8. Length of Overfalls or Side Weirs. The length of weir required to carry away storm flows in excess of intercepter capacity varies with the general dimensions and hydraulic characteristics of the sewer and with the nature and orientation of the weir employed. True side weirs parallel the direction of flow and have capacities that are but a small fraction of weirs that are placed at right angles to the direction of flow.

For the conditions of flow outlined in Figure 9-7, application of

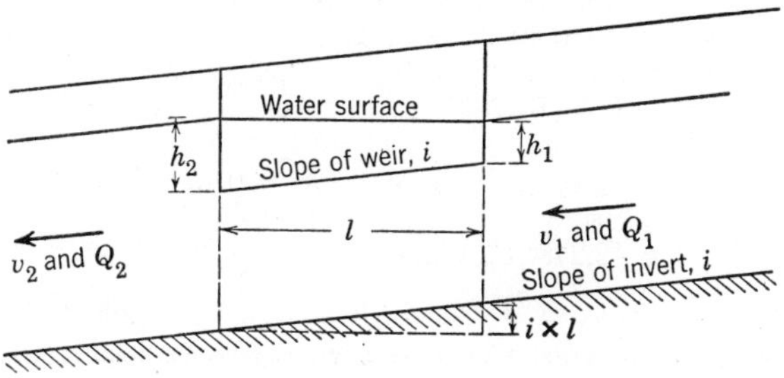

Figure 9-7. Flow over a side weir.

Bernoulli's theorem gives the following relationship if we include a loss of head factor based upon Manning's formula.

$$\frac{v_1^2}{2g} + il + h_1 = \frac{v_2^2}{2g} + h_2 + l\left(\frac{nv}{1.486r^{2/3}}\right)^2$$

Hence

$$h_2 - h_1 = \frac{Q_1^2 - Q_2^2}{2ga^2} + il - l\left[\frac{n(Q_1 + Q_2)}{2 \times 1.486ar^{2/3}}\right]^2 \qquad \text{9-23}$$

Here the parameters a and r are chosen for the average dimensions of the filled channel, i.e., at the center of the weir for example. Taking the flow over the weir Q, as approximated by $clh^{3/2}$,

$$Q = cl\left(\frac{h_1 + h_2}{2}\right)^{3/2} \quad \text{and} \quad h_2 + h_1 = 2\left(\frac{Q_1 - Q_2}{cl}\right)^{2/3} \qquad \text{9-24}$$

Given Q_1, Q_2, a, r, i, n, and h_2, values of l and h_1 are readily determined by trial, as shown in Example 9-8. This approach to the problem of side-weir flow was first suggested by Forchheimer.[13] Other formulations have been presented by Engels [14] for uniform and for contracted channels as follows:

For uniform channels,

$$Q = 3.32l^{0.83}h_2^{1.67} \qquad \text{9-25}$$

and for contracted channels,

$$Q = 3.32l^{0.9}h_2^{1.6} \qquad \text{9-26}$$

In the contracted section, the weir occupies either the contracting side of the channel or the straight side in juxtaposition to the contracting side.

Example 9-8. Given $Q_1 = 30$ cfs; $Q_2 = 16$ cfs; $a = 32$ sq ft; $r = 1.6$ ft; $i = 10^{-4}$; $n = 1.25 \times 10^{-2}$; and $h_2 = 0.50$ ft.

Find l and h, by Forchheimer's method; assume $c = 3.33$.

By Equation 9-23: $h_1 = 0.49022 - 8.04 \times 10^{-5}l$.

By Equation 9-24: $h_1 = 5.20l^{-2/3} - 0.5$. Hence $(0.99022 - 8.04 \times 10^{-5}l)l^{2/3} = 5.20$, or $(12{,}320 - l)l^{2/3} = 64{,}700$.

By trial

$l = 12$ ft and $h_1 = 0.49$ ft *Answer,*

or

$l = 12{,}248$ ft and $h_1 = -0.49$ ft

[13] Philip Forchheimer, *Hydraulik,* B. Teubner, Leipzig, p. 406, 1930.

[14] Hubert Engels, *Handbuch des Wasserbaues,* W. Engelmann, Leipzig, Vol. 1, p. 501, 1921.

9-9. Capacity of Street Inlets. As stated in Section 8-3, the street inlets that admit runoff from rainfall to storm-drainage systems are placed and designed to concentrate and remove the flow in gutters at minimum cost with minimum interference to traffic, both pedestrian and vehicular. Some features of design that improve hydraulic capacity are costly and interfere with traffic. The wide variety of designs encountered represents different compromises between these factors (Figure 8-5). There are three general types of inlets: curb inlets, gutter inlets, and combination curb and gutter inlets. Where traffic speed is low, the gutter surface and gutter inlets may be depressed in order to increase their intake capacity. Flow in gutters can be expressed by a formulation such as Manning's. The value of the coefficient of roughness is quite high (0.015 or more).

The intake capacity of inlets, particularly that of curb inlets, increases with decreasing street slope and with increasing crown slope. However, curb inlets with diagonal deflectors placed in the gutter along the opening become more efficient as the street grade increases. Gutter inlets are more efficient in capturing gutter flow than are curb inlets, but clogging by debris is a problem. Combination inlets are better still, especially if the grating is placed downstream from the curb opening. Debris accumulating on the grating will then deflect water into the curb inlet. The most efficient grating for gutter inlets is one in which the bars lie parallel to the curb. If cross bars are added for structural reasons, they should be depressed to near the bottom of the longitudinal bars. Depression of the inlet enhances its capacity. The capacity of curb inlets is increased most thereby. Long shallow depressions are as effective as short deep ones. If a small amount of flow is allowed to pass by the inlet, the relative intake of water is greatly increased. Significant economies can be effected, therefore, by permitting a small carry-over flow and arranging for its acceptance by a down-grade inlet.

On the basis of model studies and street tests empirical formulas have been developed for the flow into gutter inlets and curb inlets with and without depressions.[15] The relationship for curb openings without depressions is

$$Q/l = 4.82 \times 10^{-3} d\sqrt{gd} = 2.73 \times 10^{-2} d^{3/2} \qquad 9\text{-}27$$

or

$$d = 11.05(Q/l)^{2/3} \qquad 9\text{-}28$$

[15] *The Design of Storm-Water Inlets,* Department of Sanitary Engineering and Water Resources, Johns Hopkins University, Baltimore, June 1956.

Here Q is the discharge into the inlet in cubic feet per second, l is the length of the opening in feet, g is the gravitational acceleration in feet per second squared, and d is the depth of gutter flow at the curb in inches. The value of d may be calculated from Manning's formula. The equation for a gutter that is wedge shaped in cross-section is

$$d = 0.1105 \frac{(1 + \sec\theta)^{1/4}}{\tan^{5/8}\theta} \left(\frac{Q_0}{\sqrt{s}/n}\right)^{3/8} \tag{9-29}$$

where Q_0 is the flow in the gutter in cubic feet per second, θ is the angle between the vertical curb and the mean crosswise slope of the gutter within the width of flow, n is the coefficient of roughness of the gutter, and s is the slope of the hydraulic gradient. This slope is assumed to be parallel to the longitudinal slope of the street surface.

Combining Equation 9-29 with Equation 9-28 and solving for Q/l,

$$\frac{Q}{l} = 1.74 \frac{(1 + \sec\theta)^{3/8}}{\tan^{15/16}\theta} \left(\frac{Q_0}{\sqrt{s}/n}\right)^{9/16} \tag{9-30}$$

For cross-sectional street slopes of 10^{-3} to 10^{-1}, Equation 9-30 is closely approximated by

$$\frac{Q}{l} = 1.87 i^{0.579} \left(\frac{Q_0}{\sqrt{s}/n}\right)^{0.563} \tag{9-31}$$

Here i is the mean crosswise slope of the gutter within the width of flow.

Example 9-9. For a flow of 1.0 cfs, a longitudinal street grade of 2.0%, a mean crosswise street grade of 5.6%, and a Kutter coefficient of roughness of 0.015, find (*a*) the length of an undepressed curb inlet required to capture 90% of the flow, and (*b*) the maximum depth of flow in the gutter.

a. By Equation 9-31: $Q/l = 1.87 \times 0.056^{0.579}[1/(\sqrt{0.02}/0.015)]^{0.563} = 0.10$, or $l = 10Q = 10 \times 0.9 \times Q_0 = 10 \times 0.9 \times 1.0 = 9$ ft.

b. By Equation 9-28: $d = 11.05 \times 0.10^{2/3} = 2.4$ in.

9-10. Flow in Depressed Sewers and Appurtenant Structures. The purpose and method of performance of depressed sewers or inverted siphons have been discussed in Section 8-4. The design of the siphon pipes presents no special problems. They flow full, and the velocity of flow varies directly with the rate of discharge. In order to prevent deposition of solids in pipes in which the flow fluctuates, relatively high velocities are assigned to these pipes: namely, 3 fps when they carry sanitary sewage and 5 fps when they contain storm or combined sewage. The smallest diameter of pipe employed is 6 in., and the choice of pipe material is adjusted to the hydrostatic head under which it must operate.

Inlet chambers, as suggested in Figure 8-7, generally include lateral weirs which are submerged when they receive their full flow. Losses of head are incurred in passing over these weirs and in entering the pipes to which they lead. Outlet chambers are streamlined to reduce hydraulic losses and to keep eddy currents from sweeping sewage solids into idle pipes. A by-pass over the obstruction that is circumvented by the siphon or a relief outlet to a receiving water may be provided to avoid flooding overflows when the siphon clogs or its capacity is exceeded.

10 Design of Drainage Systems

10-1. Basic Information. The elements of capacity, hydraulic, and hydrological design of sewers and drains have been discussed in Chapters 2, 8, and 9. It remains for this chapter to show how individual sewers are integrated into a comprehensive drainage scheme.

Surveys will provide the needed topographic information—both surface and underground—in the form of: (1) plans and profiles of the streets to be sewered; (2) plans and contour lines of the properties to be drained; (3) sill or cellar elevations of buildings to be connected; (4) location and elevation of existing or projected building drains; (5) location of existing or planned surface and subsurface utilities; (6) character and location of soils and rock through which sewers must be laid; (7) depth of ground-water table; (8) location of divides of drainage areas; (9) nature of street paving; (10) projected changes in street grades; (11) location and availability of sites for pumping stations and treatment works; and (12) character of receiving bodies of water or other disposal facilities.

Much of the topographic information needed is assembled for illustrative purposes in Figure 10-1 for a single sanitary sewer in a street that also contains a storm drain.

The variations in flow that must be handled by sanitary sewers are determined (1) by the anticipated growth in population and water use during the design period and (2) by the fluctuations in flow that spring from normal water use. The design period itself remains a function of population increase and interest rates (Section 2-2). By contrast the design period for storm drains and combined sewers is of importance only in estimating the effect of future development of drainage areas on the runoff coefficient and on the magnitude of damage caused by flooding. The required capacity of storm drains is determined primarily by the variations in time, or recurrence interval, of flooding rainstorms of different intensities. Since storms of high intensity occur at random, the design values adopted for these systems may be reached and even exceeded as soon as the sewers and drains are laid.

a. Sanitary sewers. Critical rates of flow in sanitary sewers are encountered at the beginning as well as at the end of the design period. They must be taken into consideration if the system is to function properly. Critical rates are outlined in the following schedule.

Beginning of design period: (*a*) Extreme minimum flows = ½ of minimum daily flows. Critical for velocities of flow and cleanliness of sewers. (*b*) Minimum daily flows = ⅔ of average daily flows. Critical for subdivision of units in treatment works.

Beginning and end of design period: (*c*) Average daily flows at beginning of design period = ½ average daily flows at end of period. Critical for velocities of flow in force mains.

End of design period: (*d*) Maximum daily flows = 2 × average daily flows. Critical for capacity of treatment works. (*e*) Extreme maximum flows = 1½ × maximum daily flows. Critical for capacity of sewers and pumps.

The flow ratios included in this outline are suggestive of small sewers and relatively rapidly growing areas, the over-all ratio of the extremes being $(2 \times 1.5 \times 2 \times 2 \times 1.5 = 18):1$. For large sewers and stationary populations the over-all ratio is more nearly 4:1.

b. Storm drains and combined sewers. Storm drains are dry much of the time. When the rainfall is gentle, the runoff is relatively clear, and low flows present no serious problem. Flooding runoffs, however, wash a heavy load of solids into the systems. But the drains then flow full or nearly full and thereby tend to keep themselves clean.

The situation is not as favorable when storm and sanitary flows are combined. If a combined sewer is designed for a runoff of 1 in. per hr, for example, the storm flow from a single acre will be at the rate of 1 cfs or 646,000 gpd as against an average daily dry-weather contribution of about 10,000 gpd from an area that is very densely populated. The resulting ratio of $q/Q = 0.016$ is associated with a depth ratio of but 0.07 and a velocity ratio of 0.3. The need for a high design velocity, such as 3.5 fps at full depth, for combined sewers is apparent if putrescible solids are not to accumulate during dry

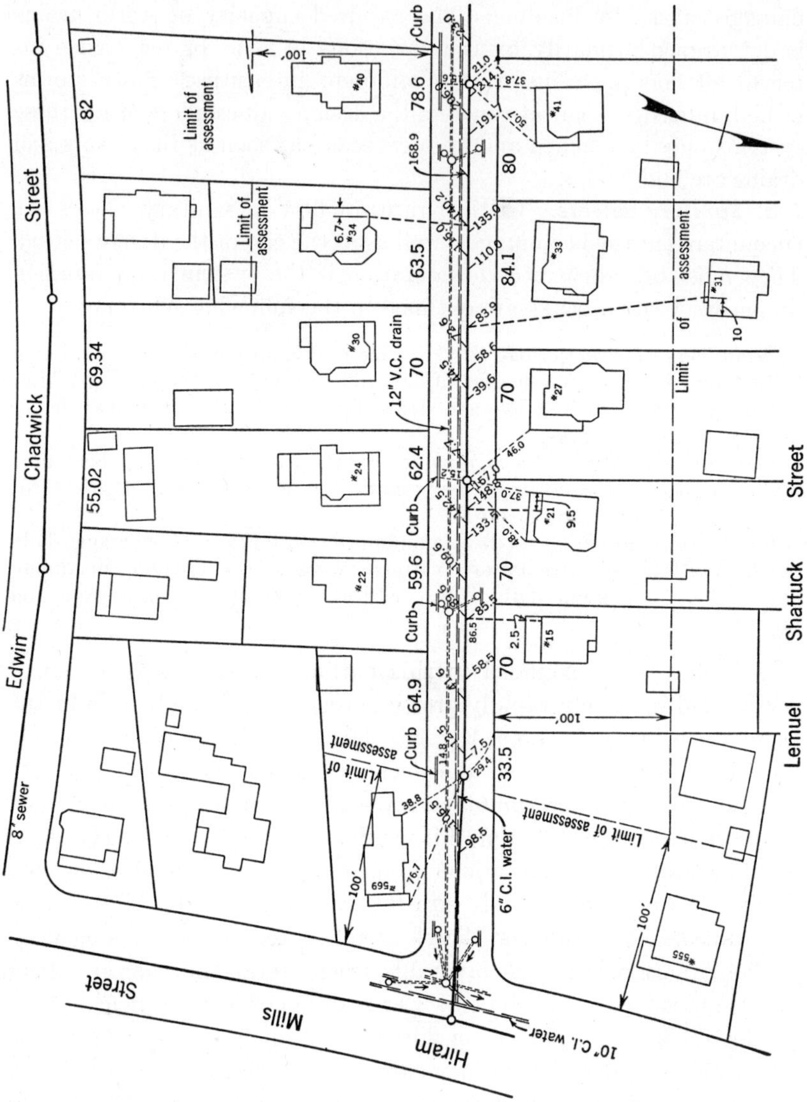

Edwin Chadwick Street
8" sewer
Limit of assessment
12" V.C. drain
Curb
6" C.I. water
10" C.I. water
Hiram Mills Street
Lemuel Shattuck Street
100'

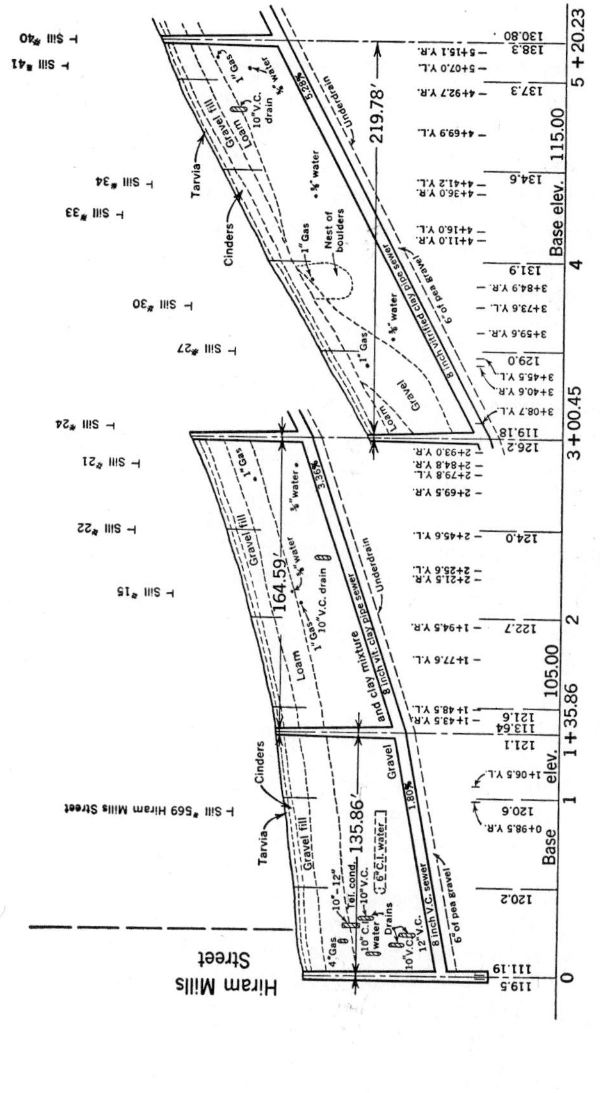

Figure 10-1. Plan and profile of a sanitary sewer.

weather. These solids give rise not only to septic conditions and offensive odors; they also increase the amounts of sewage solids that escape through storm overflows when the accumulated deposits are dislodged by sudden high flows.

10-2. Common Elements of Sewer Design. For specified conditions of minimum velocity, minimum depth of sewer, and maximum distance between manholes, a number of situations repeat themselves in general schemes of sewerage wherein street gradient, sewer gradient, size of sewer, and depth of sewer become interrelated elements of design. Some of these recurrent situations are illustrated in Figure 10-2 and involve, beside a flow formulation such as Manning's, the following simple equational relationship:

$$h_1 - h_2 = l(g - s) \tag{10-1}$$

where h_1 and h_2 are sewer depths *in excess of minimum requirements*, l is the distance between manholes, and g and s are respectively the street and sewer grades. Conditions of flow are stated below Figure 10-2.

Case a is encountered whenever the required sewer grade is greater than the grade of the street. Arriving at a depth equal to or greater than the minimum requirement, 7.0 ft, the depth of the sewer becomes greater and greater until it is more economical to lift the sewage by placing a pumping station in the line. Specifically for Case a in Figure 10-2, the sewer grade is held at minimum (0.33%), and

$$h_2 = h_1 - l(g - s) = 0.9 - 3(0.033 - 0.33) = 1.8 \text{ ft}$$

i.e., the depth increases by $(1.8 - 0.9) = 0.9$ ft.

Case b is unusual in that the required sewer grade is the same as the street grade. The depth of the sewer, therefore, remains unchanged.

Case c introduces a street grade that is steep enough to provide, in a sewer paralleling it, the required capacity in an 8-in. rather than a 10-in. conduit. Arriving at minimum depth, there is no possibility of utilizing the available fall in part or as a whole to recover minimum depth as will be indicated in Cases d and e. The reduced size of pipe becomes the sole means of profiting from the steep street grade, provided, of course, that the upstream sewer is also no greater than 8 in.

Case d aims at maximum reduction of excess depth by placing a 10-in. sewer on minimum grade, or, in accordance with Equation 10-1, $s = g - (h_1 - h_2)/l$. For $h_2 = 0$, $s = 1.00 - (0.9 - 0.0)/3 = 0.70\%$ which is more than the required minimum of 0.33%. Hence the sewer can be brought back to minimum depth, or $h_2 = 0$.

Case e is like Case d, but full reduction to minimum depth is not attainable, because $s = 0.70 - (1.9 - 0)/3 = 0.07\%$. This is less than the

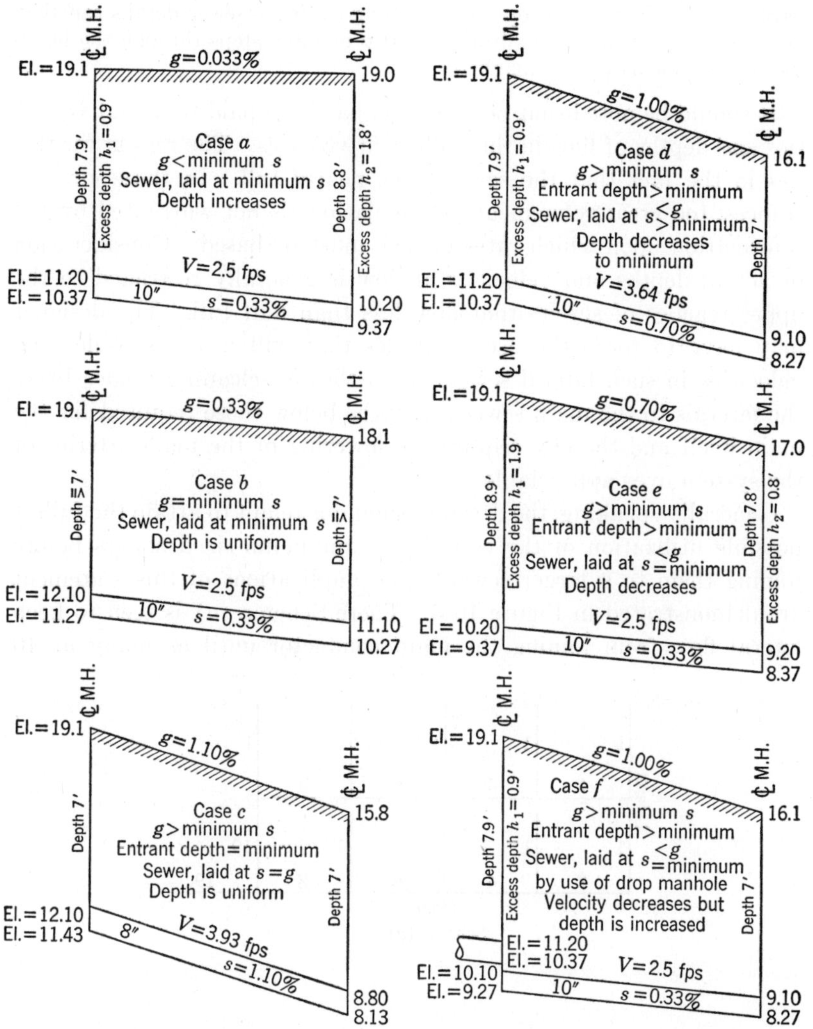

Figure 10-2. Common elements of sewer design. Required $q = 1.2$ cfs ($Q = 1.2$ cfs), $V = 2.5$ fps, $N = 0.012$, $l = 300$ ft, minimum depth to crown = 7.0 ft; 8-in. sewer $Q = 1.2$ cfs, $S = 0.84\%$, $V = 3.4$ fps; 10-in. sewer $V = 2.5$ fps, $S = 0.33\%$, $Q = 1.36$ cfs.

required minimum of 0.33%. Hence the minimum grade must be used, and $h_2 = 1.9 - 3(0.70 - 0.33) = 0.8$ ft.

Case *f* illustrates how high velocities can be avoided by the use of drop manholes on steep slopes. Case *f* parallels Case *d* but introduces a drop of 1.1 ft to place the sewer on minimum grade and give it minimum velocity. This arrangement is normally considered only when grades are extraordinarily steep. Excessive drops and resulting excessive sewer depths can then be avoided by breaking the drops into two or more steps through the insertion of intermediate drop manholes.

It should be noted that no attention has been paid to actual velocities and depths of flow in these illustrative cases. The reason for this lies in the fact that the sewers flow nearly full. In these circumstances, too great refinement in calculations is not warranted by the information upon which rates of flow must be based. Consideration of actual depths and velocities of flow is generally restricted to the upper reaches of sewers that flow less than half full. The designer may have to forgo the use of grades that will insure self-cleaning velocities in such lateral sewers when the self-cleaning grades bring the laterals to the main sewer at depths below those required for the main itself and thereby require the lowering of the main arteries of the system over appreciable distances.

Generally speaking, the designer should attempt to attain the fullest possible utilization of the capacity of minimum-sized sewers before joining them to a larger sewer. The implications of this statement are demonstrated in Figure 10-3. There Scheme (*a*) is seen to keep lateral flow from joining the main conductor until as many as 10

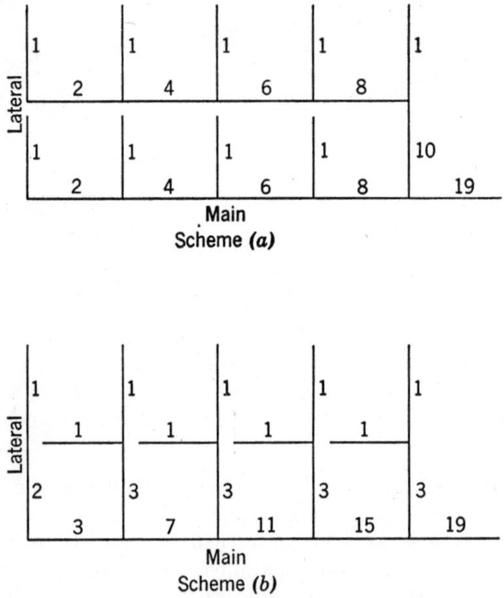

Figure 10-3. Relative utilization of the capacity of lateral sewers.

units of flow have accumulated, whereas no lateral carries more than 3 units in Scheme (*b*). As a result, the main in Scheme (*b*) exceeds 10 units in two sections in which the required capacities of the mains in Scheme (*a*) are still 6 and 8 units respectively.

10-3. Capacity Design of Sanitary Sewerage Systems. Systems of sanitary sewers carry the water-borne wastes from households, from mercantile and industrial establishments, and from public buildings and institutions. In addition they receive more or less ground water by infiltration from the soil and sometimes, too, illicit storm drainage or surface runoff. The requisite capacity of sanitary sewers, therefore, is determined by the tributary domestic and institutional population, commercial water use, industrial activity, height of groundwater table, and enforcement of rain-water separation. To translate all these matters into working figures for individual runs and for a complex of sewers is a responsibility that cannot be taken lightly.

It is generally found convenient to arrive at unit values of domestic sewage on the basis of the population density and area served; but it would also be possible to develop figures for the number of people per front foot in districts of varying occupancy and make sewer length rather than area served the criterion of capacity design. Length (sometimes coupled with diameter) of sewer, indeed, offers the more rational basis for the estimation of ground-water infiltration. Unit values for flow from commercial districts are generally expressed in terms of the area served. The quantities of waste waters produced by industrial operations are more logically evaluated in terms of the units of daily production, e.g., gallons per: barrel of beer, 100 cases of canned goods, 1,000 bushels of grain mashed, 100 lb of live weight of animals slaughtered, or 1,000 lb of raw milk. Common values are suggested in Section 20-7.

Peak domestic and commercial flows may be assumed to originate at about the same hour of the day but must travel varying distances through the collecting systems before they can reach a given point in the sewerage system. Hence a reduction in, or damping of, the peak of the cumulative flows is generally assumed to obtain. In a fashion similar to the reduction in flood flows with time of concentration (as represented by the size of drainage area), the lowering of peak flows in sanitary sewers is conveniently related to the volume of flows or to the number of people served, and unit values of design are generally not accumulated in direct proportion to the rate of discharge or to the tributary population.

10-4. Layout and Hydraulic Design of Sanitary Sewerage Systems. Before entering upon the design of individual sewer runs, a preliminary layout is made of the entire system. Sanitary sewers are so placed in streets, or alleys (where they exist), that a connection can be provided to each building served. Terminal manholes of lateral sewers are generally placed within the service frontage of the last lot that is to be sewered, with due regard to the location of the building sewer.

In general, sewers should slope with the ground surface and should conduct the sewage to the point of discharge by as direct a route as topography and street layout will permit. Thus the flow in a well-designed system will follow approximately the same path as the surface runoff.

Where alleys are part of the community plan, local considerations of the relative advantages of placing the sewers in the alleys rather than the streets will govern the choice of location. Alley location offers important advantages, particularly, in business districts.

After lines representing all the sewers have been drawn on the preliminary layout and arrows have been inserted to show the direction of flow, manholes are indicated at changes in direction, at sewer junctions, and at intermediate points that will hold their spacing to the allowable maximum or less. The manholes are then numbered for identification, and the hydraulic design of the system can begin. Alternate layouts will determine the final design.

The hydraulic design of a system of sanitary sewers is straightforward and is readily carried to completion by a series of systematic computations such as those outlined in Example 10-1.[1]

Example 10-1. Determine the required capacity and find the slope, size, and hydraulic characteristics of the system of sanitary sewers shown in the accompanying tabulation (Table 10-1) of their location, the areas and population served, and the expected sewage flows.

Capacity requirements are based upon the following assumptions:

a. Water consumption: Average day, 95 gpcd; maximum day, 175% of average; maximum hour, 140% of maximum day.

b. Domestic sewage: 70% of water consumption; maximum 285 gpcd for 5 acres decreasing to 245 gpcd for 100 acres or more.

c. Ground water: 30,000 to 50,000 gpd per mile of sewer for low land and 20,000 to 35,000 gpd per mile of sewer for high land; or 0.0014 to 0.0015 cfs

[1] The numerical values shown in this example are taken from computations for the sewerage system of Cranston, R. I., by the firm of Fay, Spofford, and Thorndike as reported in *Eng. News-Record, 123,* 419 (1939). Some of the values given do not agree in detail with values suggested in this book.

TABLE 10-1. Illustrative Computations for a System of Sanitary Sewers * (Example 10-1)

Section	Location of Sewer			Adjacent Area						Total Tributary Area				
	Street	Stations or Limits		Total Acres	Indus-trial Acres	Com-mercial Acres	Domestic Acres	Population		Indus-trial Acres	Com-mercial Acres	Domestic Acres	Population	
		From	To					Per Acre	Total				Per Acre	Total
(1)	(2)	(3)	(4)	(5)	(6)	(7)	(8)	(9)	(10)	(11)	(12)	(13)	(14)	(15)
a	A Ave.	B Ave.	C St.	49	5	4	40	27	1,080	5	4	40	27.0	1,080
b	D Ave.	C St.	E St.	37	3	7	27	19	513	8	11	67	23.8	1,593
c	F St.	G St.	H St.	29	8	1	20	25	500	16	12	87	24.1	2,093
d	I St.	J St.	K St.	63	. .	10	53	21	1,113	16	22	140	22.9	3,206

Section	Maximum Volume of Sewage, cfs					Design Profile											
	Indus-trial	Com-mer-cial	Domes-tic	Infiltra-tion	Total	Size, in.	Slope	Capac-ity, cfs	Velocity, fps		Depth of Flow, in,	Length, ft	Invert Elevation		Cut		
									Full	Actual			Upper End	Lower End	Upper End	Lower End	Aver-age
(1)	(16)	(17)	(18)	(19)	(20)	(21)	(22)	(23)	(24)	(25)	(26)	(27)	(28)	(29)	(30)	(31)	(32)
a	.156	.155	.440	.044	.795	8	.008	0.82	2.35	2.72	6.37	850	120.00	113.20	7.50	11.50	9.50
b	.248	.429	.650	.086	1.413	10	.007	1.42	2.22	3.02	8.1	1,260	113.03	104.21	11.67	8.50	10.08
c	.496	.468	.852	.115	1.931	12	.0045	2.23	2.45	2.84	9.7	1,880	104.04	95.58	8.67	12.00	10.33
d	.496	.858	1.300	.178	2.832	15	.003	3.35	2.35	2.72	12.0	1,760	95.33	90.05	12.25	11.00	11.63

* **Note:** Sections of sewers rather than runs between manholes are shown in this example in order to include major changes in required capacity and consequent size.

per acre for 8-in. to 15-in. sewers in low land and 0.0009 to 0.0011 cfs per acre in high land.

d. Commercial sewage: 25,000 gpd per acre = 0.0388 cfs per acre.

e. Industrial sewage: Flow in accordance with industry.

Hydraulic requirements are as follows:

a. Minimum velocity in sewers: 2.5 fps (actual).

b. Kutter's coefficient of roughness $N = 0.015$ includes allowances for change in direction and related losses in manholes except for (*c*) below.

c. Crown of sewers is made continuous to prevent surcharge of upstream sewer.

Columns 1–4 identify the location of the sewer run. The sections are continuous.

Columns 5–8 list the acreage immediately adjacent to the sewer.

Column 9 gives the density of the population per domestic acre.

Column 10 = Column 9 × Column 8.

Columns 11–13 list the accumulated acreage drained by the sewer. For example, in Section *b*, Column 13 is the sum of Column 8 in Sections *a* and *b*, or $(40 + 27) = 67$.

Column 14 gives the average density of the population for the total tributary area. For example, in Section *b*,

$$\text{Column (14)} = \frac{40 \times 27 + 27 \times 19}{40 + 27} = 23.8$$

Column 15 = Column 14 × Column 13.

Column 16 lists values obtained in a survey of industries in the areas served.

Column 17 = Column 12 × 0.0388.

Column 18 = Column 15 × (245 to 285) × (1.547×10^{-6}). For example, in Section *a*, $1{,}080 \times 264 \times (1.547 \times 10^{-6}) = 0.440$ cfs.

Column 19 = Sum of Columns 11–13 × rate of infiltration. For example, in Section *a*, $(5 + 4 + 40) \times 0.0009 = 0.044$ cfs.

Column 20 = Sum of Columns 16–19.

Columns 21–29 record the size of sewer for required capacity and available, or required, grade together with depth and velocity of flow. For example in Section *a*, an 8-in. sewer laid on a grade of $6.8/850 = 0.008$ will discharge $Q = 0.82$ cfs at a velocity of 2.35 cfs when it flows full. Hence for $q/Q = 0.795/0.82 = 0.971$: $d/D = 0.796$, $v/V = 1.16$, or $d = 8 \times 0.796 = 6.37$ in.; $v = 2.35 \times 1.16 = 2.72$ fps.

Columns 28–31 are taken from profile of street and sewer.

Column 28, Section *b*, shows a drop in the manhole of $(113.20 - 113.03) = 0.17$ ft compared with Column 28, Section *a*. This allows for a full drop of $0.17 \times 12 = 2$ in. to offset the increase in the diameter of the sewer from 8 in. to 10 in.

Column 32 = arithmetic mean of Columns 30 and 31.

10-5. Capacity Design of Storm-Drainage Systems. The concepts of the rational method of estimating runoff from rainfall which generally provide the hydrological basis for the capacity design of storm-drainage systems have been discussed in Section 3-15. If in accordance with this method Equation 3-7, $Q = cia$, is made the axiom of design, it becomes the responsibility of the designer to arrive at the best possible estimates of c, the runoff-rainfall ratio, and i, the rainfall intensity, the determination of the value of a being a simple matter of measurement. Both c and i are variable in time. Hence the storm flows reaching a given point in a drainage system are compounded of the waters that have fallen within the stretch of time, or time of concentration, during which the runoff from the farthest portions of the tributary area travels to the point in question.

a. Time of concentration. The time of concentration is composed of two parts: (1) the inlet time, or time required for runoff to gain entrance into a sewer, and (2) the time of flow in the sewerage system.

There is no ready rule for the determination of the inlet time, which is a function of (1) the roughness of the surfaces offering resistance to flow and storage of water in depressions, (2) the steepness of the slope, (3) the size of block or distance from the periphery of the area to the sewer inlet, and (4) the method of roof and surface drainage including the spacing of street inlets. In large communities in which roofs shed their water directly to the sewers and the runoff from paved yards and streets enters the sewer through closely spaced street inlets, the inlet time will be less than 5 min. In commercial districts with relatively flat slopes and greater inlet spacing, the inlet time lengthens to 10 to 15 min. In relatively flat residential areas in which street inlets are minimal, inlet times of 20 to 30 min are observed. For steeper slopes, these values must be reduced in magnitude.

The time of flow in the system is accumulated in passage to the point of concentration from the most distant sewer. Elapsed time is calculated as the sum of the quotients of the length of the individual sewers and their velocity when flowing full. Neither the increase in time which results from the filling of the sewers nor the decrease in time which is produced by the flood waves created by the rapid discharge of lateral sewers is ordinarily taken into account in calculating the time of flow in the system.

b. Runoff coefficients. Runoff from storm rainfall is reduced by evaporation, storage in depressions, required wetting of surfaces before they will shed water, and percolation of rain into the ground. All these losses decrease in magnitude with the duration of storms. As a result, the value of the runoff-rainfall ratio, or shedding characteristic of the area c, increases proportionately. The value of c may exceed unity. It may do so, for example, when melting ice and snow contribute to runoff. Ordinarily c approaches unity, in the absence of melting ice and snow, only when the area drained is essentially impervious and storms are of long duration. Generalized values for the runoff coefficient in its relation to duration of rainfall and type of area drained are plotted in Figure 10-4. Choice of a suitable runoff coefficient is seen to present some difficulty. The matter is further complicated by the possibility that a flooding rainstorm

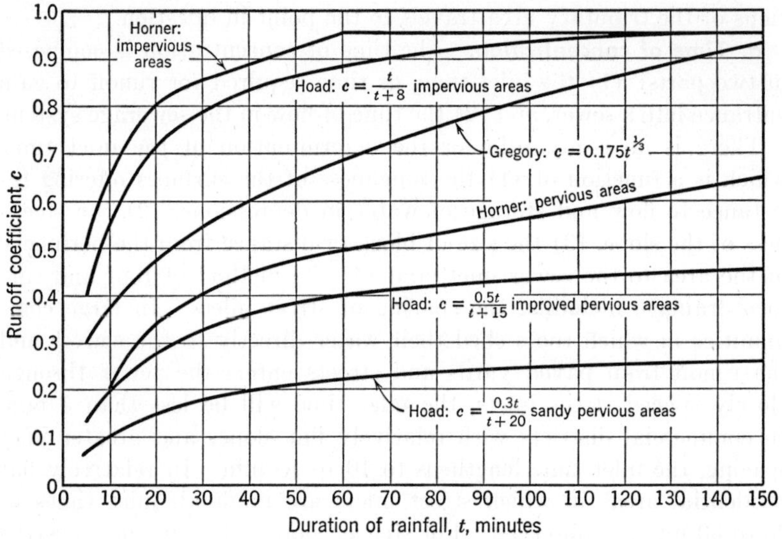

Figure 10-4. **Variation in runoff coefficients with duration of rainfall and nature of area drained.**

may set in after the area to be drained has been wetted by light showers.

The basic coefficients plotted in Figure 10-4 apply to areas that shed their waters in a relatively short time. As shown in Figure 10-5, the runoff coefficient that applies for a particular time of concentration should logically be averaged in accordance with the geometric configuration of the area draining to the point of concentration. A weighted average can then be calculated as $c = \Sigma ca/\Sigma a$; but the fundamental evaluation of c as well as i is generally not sufficiently exact to warrant this refinement. Up to 60 min, the weighted average coefficient of runoff is approximately 80% of the basic coefficient for the pertinent time of concentration in a sector-shaped area; for a rectangular area 4 times as long as wide, the

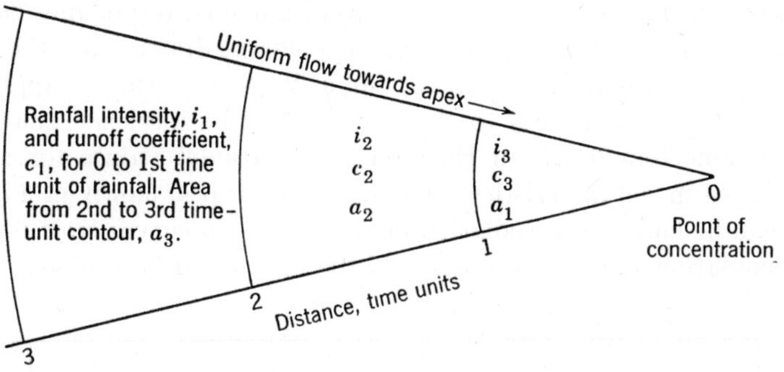

Figure 10-5. Composition of runoff reaching a point of concentration at the apex of a sector-shaped area. $Q = c_3 i_3 a_1 + c_2 i_2 a_2 + c_1 i_1 a_3 = \Sigma cia$. **For** i **averaged in the rainfall analysis,** $Q = i\Sigma ca$ **and weighted average** $c = \Sigma ca/\Sigma a$.

corresponding value is about 85%. For pervious areas these percentages decrease to 60% for sector-shaped areas and 75% for rectangular areas.

The probable future proportion of impervious and pervious areas in the district to be drained can be gaged from surveys of typical zones of the community. The percentage range of impervious surfaces in North American cities is about as shown in Table 10-2.

Because of the uncertainties involved in the estimates of rainfall intensities and inlet times, a constant value of the runoff coefficient, or shedding coefficient, is assumed by some engineers. The reported range in magnitude of the coefficient is shown in Table 10-2.

TABLE 10-2. Range of Impervious Surfaces and Runoff Coefficients in North American Cities

	Per Cent Impervious	Runoff Coefficient
Mercantile districts	70–90	0.70–0.95
Commercial districts	40–50	0.60–0.85
Industrial districts	35–60	0.55–0.80
Residential districts		
Apartment houses	40–80	0.5 –0.7
Single- and two-family dwellings	20–50	0.25–0.6
Parks	.....	0.25
Undeveloped areas	.....	0.05–0.25

c. Intensity of rainfall and runoff. The analysis of storm rainfalls has been discussed in Sections 3-11 to 3-13. After the rainfall-intensity curve has been selected in accordance with the principles there outlined, it is often convenient to combine corresponding values of c and i, as shown in Figure 10-6. The curves drawn trace the rate of runoff, or product of c and i, for a 10-year storm by applying Hoad's runoff coefficients to the storm-rainfall experience analyzed in the same manner as in Example 3-4.[2] Runoff values for areas that differ in characteristics from the three types shown in Figure 10-6 can be had by interpolation between the two curves most nearly approximating the characteristics of the district to be drained.

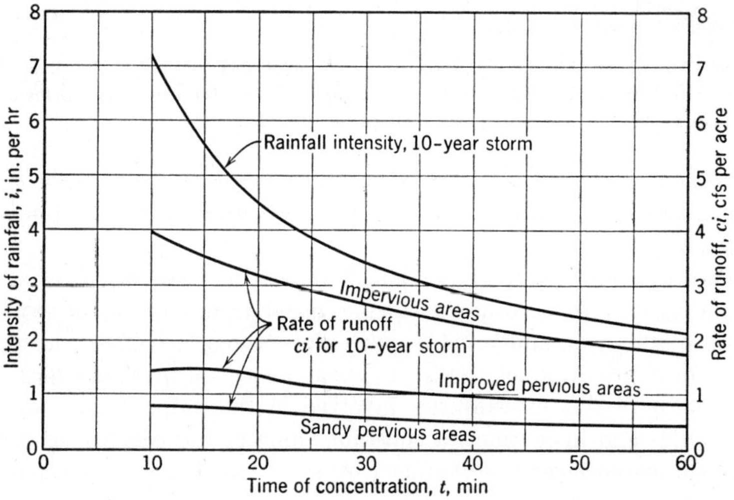

Figure 10-6. Time intensities of rainfall and related runoff for areas of varying imperviousness.

10-6. Capacity Design by Other Methods. As discussed in Section 3-16, the variations of c and i with time, when time is expressed in terms of the size of the water shed, produce over-all runoff formulations for a given locality. An example is the relationship devised by McMath for the design of sewers in St. Louis, Mo. Such formulations antedate the rational method. However, they were not derived from a study of the individual elements entering into the problem but from correlations of the magnitude of runoff from rainfall of flooding proportions with areas of given magnitude. Hence their use in sewer design has been called the empirical, in contrast to the rational, method. The McMath formula $Q = cia^{4/5}s^{1/5}$ introduces a

[2] The product ci records runoff in cubic feet per second per acre because of the close numerical equivalence of inches per hour per acre and cubic feet per second per acre.

slope factor s as a modifier of the time of concentration and the runoff coefficient. The values of c and i themselves are constants for a given locality and drainage area. With more complete knowledge of the variations of rainfall and runoff, it is possible to devise overall formulas that will yield results for the capacity design of storm sewers comparable to those obtained by the rational method.

Where storm drains are in existence in a community, the capacity design of a drainage system for adjacent unsewered areas, or the capacity design of relief sewers, can receive aid from gagings of sewers in time of heavy rainfall or from surcharge experience in its relation to storms of varying magnitude. Surcharge must be linked to sewer capacity on the basis of size and slope, care being taken to identify possible downstream influences upon the section of sewer in which surcharge occurs. Gagings and observations of surcharge provide values for the runoff for areas of given magnitudes, and these values, together with a consideration of the type of district drained, can then be used in the capacity design of the drains that are to be added to the community.

New approaches to the capacity design of storm drains, somewhat akin to those underlying the unit hydrograph method, are being investigated but as yet lack adequate numerical information to be applied in general practice.[3]

10-7. Layout and Hydraulic Design of Storm-Drainage Systems. The layout of a storm-drainage system has much in common with that of a system of sanitary sewers. Ordinarily the layout is related, however, to the location of street inlets instead of the buildings to be served. When roof and areaway drains are to be connected directly to the storm sewer rather than discharging into the street gutters, however, the location of the buildings must also receive consideration. Street inlets are placed at the intersections of streets to keep the crossings for pedestrians passable. They are also inserted at intermediate points as need be to prevent the flooding of gutters and to hold the flow in the gutters within the capacity of the inlets. The area that can be drained through a street inlet is determined by the capacity of the inlet (Section 9-9) in relation to the product of the runoff coefficient and the rainfall intensity for a given inlet time.

Example 10-2. A street inlet has a capacity of 3 cfs. What is the maximum area that can be drained to the inlet if runoff conditions are reflected by the curve for improved pervious areas in Figure 10-6 and the inlet time

[3] W. W. Horner and F. L. Flynt, *Trans. Am. Soc. Civil Engrs.*, *101*, 140 (1936); W. W. Horner and S. W. Jens, *Trans. Am. Soc. Civil Engrs.*, *107*, 1039 (1942).

is 20 min? From Figure 10-6, $ci = 1.3$ cfs per acre. Hence $a = Q/(ci) = 3.0/1.3 = 2.3$ acres.

After the probable location of the street inlets has been identified, the sewer lines are laid out to collect the water (1) from the inlets and (2) from the buildings or areaways draining directly to the sewers. The lines should proceed by the most direct route to outlets that empty into natural drainage channels. Easements or rights of way across private property may shorten the path of the drains. Manholes are placed as for sanitary sewers but with due reference to the need for emptying street inlets directly into them.

Surface topography determines the area tributary to each inlet. For the sake of simplicity, however, it is often assumed that lots drain to adjacent street gutters. Direct drainage of roofs and areaways to storm drains reduces the inlet time and thereby places a greater intensity of load upon the drainage system. Necessary computations are illustrated in Table 10-3 which accompanies Example 10-3.

TABLE 10-3. Illustrative Computations for a System of Storm Drains (Example 10-3)

Line Number	Location of Drain			Tributary Area, Acres, a		Time of Flow, min		Runoff, cfs, Q	
	Street	Manhole from	Number to	Increment	Total	To Upper End	In Drain	Per Acre ci	Total
(1)	(2)	(3)	(4)	(5)	(6)	(7)	(8)	(9)	(10)
1	A	1	2	2.19	2.19	20.0	1.5	1.30	2.85
2	A	2	3	1.97	4.16	21.5	1.9	1.27	5.28
3	B	3	4	3.05	7.21	23.4	1.3	1.25	9.02

Line Number	Design				Profile			Invert Elevation	
	Diameter, in.	Slope, ft/1,000	Capacity, cfs	Velocity, fps	Length, ft	Fall, ft	Drop in M.H., ft	Upper End	Lower End
(1)	(11)	(12)	(13)	(14)	(15)	(16)	(17)	(18)	(19)
1	12	6.42	3.09	3.94	340	2.18	0.00	86.46	84.28
2	18	2.71	5.93	3.35	340	0.92	0.42	83.86	82.94
3	24	1.50	9.48	3.02	440	0.66	0.46	82.48	81.82

Example 10-3. Determine the required capacity and find the slope, size, and hydraulic characteristics of the system of storm drains shown in the accompanying tabulation of location, tributary area, and expected storm runoff.

Capacity requirements are based upon the rainfall and runoff curves included in Figure 10-6. The area is assumed to be an improved pervious one, and the inlet time is assumed to be 20 min. Hydraulic requirements include a value of $N = 0.012$ in Manning's formula and drops in manholes equal to $\Delta(d + h_v) + 0.2\,\Delta h_v$ (Equation 9-14) for the sewers flowing full.

Columns 1–4 identify the location of the drains. The runs are continuous.

Column 5 records the area tributary to the street inlets that discharge into the manhole at the upper end of the line.

Column 6 gives the cumulative area tributary to a line. For example, in Line 2, Column 6 is the sum of Column 6, Line 1 and Column 5, Line 2, or $(2.19 + 1.97) = 4.16$.

Columns 7 and 8 record the times of flow to the upper end of the drain and in the drain. For example, the inlet time to Manhole 1 is estimated to be 20 min, and the time of flow in Line 1 is calculated to be $340/(60 \times 3.94) = 1.5$ min from Column 15/(60 × Column 14). Hence the time of flow to the upper end of Line 2 is $(20 + 1.5) = 21.5$ min.

Column 9 is the *ci* value read from Figure 10-6 for the time of flow to the upper end of the line.

Column 10 = Column 9 × Column 6. For example, the runoff entering Line 1 is $1.30 \times 2.19 = 2.85$ cfs.

Columns 11–14 record the chosen size and resulting capacity and velocity of flow of the drains for the tributary runoff and available or required grade. For example, in Line 1, a grade of 6.42 ft per 1,000 and a flow of 2.85 cfs call for a 12-in. drain. This drain will have a capacity of 3.09 cfs and flow at a velocity of 3.94 fps.

Columns 15–19 identify the profile of the drain. Column 15 is taken from the plan or profile of the street; Column 16 = Column 15 × Column 12; Column 17 is obtained from Equation 9-14, the required drop in Manhole 2 being $\Delta(d + h_v) + 0.2\,\Delta h_v = \{[(1.5 + 0.17) - (1.0 + 0.24)] + 0.2(0.17 - 0.24)\} = 0.42$ ft; and Column 19 = Column 18 − Column 16, Column 18 furthermore being Column 19 for the entrant line − Column 17. For example, for Line 2, $(84.28 - 0.42) = 83.86$ and subsequently $(83.86 - 0.92) = 82.94$.

10-8. Design of Combined Sewerage Systems. The capacity design of combined sewers makes allowance for the maximum rate of sewage flow in addition to the storm-water runoff. If the rain water entering the system is confined to the discharge of roof water, the flow of sanitary sewage is a considerable item in required sewer capacity, and the system is sometimes called a roof-water system rather than a combined system. If the runoff from storms of unusual intensity is carried away by the system, the flow of sanitary sewage, on the other hand, becomes relatively insignificant as an item of required sewer capacity.

The hydraulic design of combined sewerage systems is essentially the same as that for storm sewerage systems. Combined sewerage systems, however, often include structures not ordinarily associated with separate systems. Among these, intercepters, overflows, regulators, and storm-water stand-by tanks are discussed in Sections 8-4 and 9-8.

10-9. Outfalls. The outfall pipes that carry sewage into receiving waters should terminate well below the low-water mark and there disperse the sewage or effluent as quickly and uniformly as possible. Dispersal is aided by providing a number of different outlets (1) spaced sufficiently far apart to prevent interference and (2) situated at or near the bottom of the receiving water in order to keep the generally warmer and lighter [4] sewage from overriding the dilution water in a thin layer (Figure 10-7).

Outfalls must be located with due regard to prevailing currents and their bearing upon water-works intakes, bathing places, shellfish layings, and the like. No matter what the relative dilution, the forces of natural purification, or self-purification, inherent in natural bodies

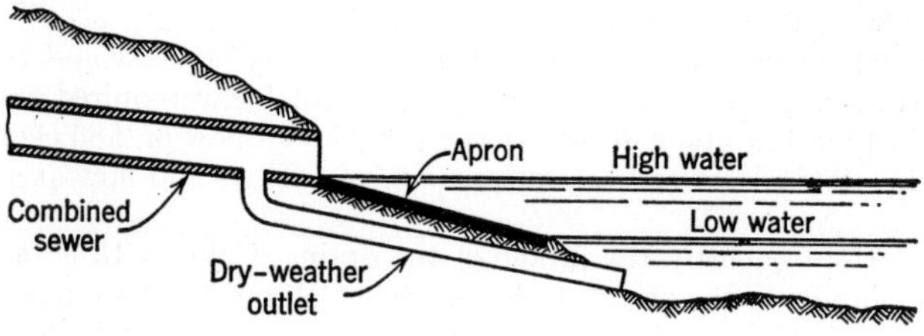

a. **Outfall of combined sewer into a stream.**

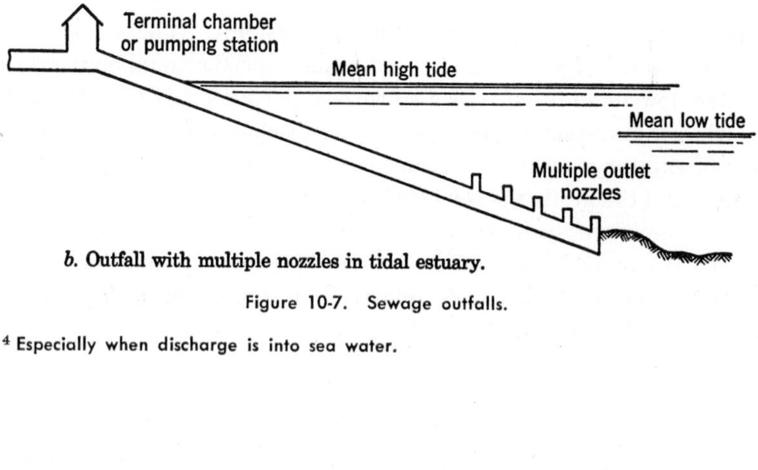

b. **Outfall with multiple nozzles in tidal estuary.**

Figure 10-7. Sewage outfalls.

[4] Especially when discharge is into sea water.

of water will, in the course of time and associated distance, return the receiving water to its original state of cleanliness. These forces are essentially similar to those called upon in the controlled treatment of sewage by most of the methods presently in use. If dilution is sufficient, natural purification will be accomplished without nuisance, because conditions relatively close to those prevailing in clean waters will obtain and the complicated physical, chemical, and biological balance of the receiving water will not be disturbed. If dilution is insufficient, decomposition of putrescible matter may proceed at such a pace as to upset the normal balance of the receiving water and create, for a time at least, a black, unsightly, and malodorous body of water whose normal flora and fauna are completely destroyed.

A rule of thumb formulated by engineers for large American streams and giving a rough estimate of the required dilution is that untreated, combined sewage may be discharged safely (1) into swift streams that carry 2.5 cfs of water per 1,000 persons contributing sewage and (2) into sluggish streams that carry 10 cfs per 1,000 persons contributing sewage. The average value is 6 cfs per 1,000 persons. For domestic sewage, treated sewage, and industrial wastes, these figures can be apportioned to the relative amount of putrescible matter present.[5] Where the emphasis is on water supply, recreational use of water, and preservation of fish and other useful aquatic life, rather than on the avoidance of nuisance, dilution requirements become very much larger. If available dilution is inadequate, the sewage must be treated before disposal by dilution.

[5] Combined sewage containing a normal amount of industrial waste water is about 40% stronger than domestic sewage.

11 Examination of Water and Waste Water

11-1. Methods of Examination. The examination of water and waste water involves (1) surveys of the conditions under which the water or waste water exists or is produced; (2) observations and examinations of certain attributes or properties of the water or waste water in the field; and (3) laboratory determinations of specific qualities or properties of the water or waste water.

Field surveys are called (1) sanitary surveys when they identify the conditions that affect the sanitary quality of water for water-supply purposes; (2) pollutional surveys when they determine the effect of waste waters upon receiving bodies of water; and (3) industrial-waste surveys when they deal with the amounts and characteristics of the waste waters discharged by industrial establishments.

A knowledge of the conditions under which the water or waste water is found and of the conditions of sampling is essential to the interpretation of laboratory analyses. The analysis of a single sample of water establishes but a single cross-sectional pattern of the quality of the water at the time of collection. Multiple samplings and analyses are needed to delineate the profile of the water either in terms of the variation of its essential qualities or properties in time, or in terms of the progressive changes that take place as water moves about in nature and is collected, stored, purified, used, and becomes waste water which, in turn, is collected, treated, and discharged into natural bodies of water or onto land.

The methods of collection and analysis must be standardized if the results obtained by different laboratories are to be comparable and if they are to have legal validity. In the United States, *Standard Methods for the Examination of Water and Sewage*[1] has been prepared, approved, and published jointly by the American Public Health Association, the American Water Works Association, and the Federation of Sewage and Industrial Wastes Associations.

Based upon standardized methods of analysis are (1) standards of water quality for the various purposes that the water is to serve, and (2) standards of the quality of sewage effluents and industrial waste waters as criteria for the maintenance of acceptable conditions in water courses or on land areas that are to receive the effluents.

It is not possible within the covers of this book to describe or explain the methods of analysis themselves. It will suit our purposes better to discuss the reasons for the different examinations and the significance of the needed tests.

11-2. Standard Tests. As shown in the following lists, many of the tests employed in the examination of samples of water and sewage are identical.

a. Examination of water. *"Standard Methods"* includes the following tests. Tests that are not routinely part of a sanitary analysis are printed in italics.

PHYSICAL AND CHEMICAL EXAMINATION:

Temperature, turbidity, color, and odor (cold and hot).

Residue: solids after evaporation (total, *dissolved, suspended;* for each the fixed portion and the loss on ignition). *Solids by electrolytic conductivity.*

Hardness by Schwarzenbach (Versenate or EDTA) method and by calculation from mineral analysis.

Acidity, including mineral acids, alkalinity (phenolphthalein and total), pH value, carbon dioxide (free and *total*), *bicarbonate ion, carbonate ion,* and *hydroxide.*

Oil. Silica. Copper, lead, aluminum, iron, *chromium, manganese,* and *zinc. Magnesium, calcium, sodium,* and *potassium.*

Nitrogen: ammonia, albuminoid, *organic,* nitrite, and nitrate.

Chloride, *iodide,* and *fluoride.*

Phosphate: orthophosphate, pyrophosphate, and *metaphosphate.*

Sulfate, sulfite, and *sulfide. Arsenic, boron, cyanide,* and *selenium. Tannin* and *lignin. Phenols.*

Active chlorine (free available and combined available chlorine) and chlorine demand.

Dissolved oxygen (DO), hydrogen sulfide, and *methane.*

BIOLOGICAL EXAMINATION:

Examination and enumeration of microscopic organisms and amorphous matter.

[1] 10th Ed., New York, 1955.

Tests for the presence of members of the coliform group.

Plate counts (normally only for swimming pools and bathing places).

b. Examination of sewage. *"Standard Methods"* includes the following tests. Tests that are not routinely performed are again printed in italics.

PHYSICAL AND CHEMICAL EXAMINATION:

Temperature, *turbidity, color,* and *odor,* the color determination not being on a quantitative basis.

Residue, or solids by evaporation: total, dissolved, suspended, settleable; for each the volatile and fixed portions.

Acidity, alkalinity, and *p*H value.

Nitrogen: ammonia, organic (Kjeldahl), *nitrite,* and *nitrate.*

Oxygen consumed from dichromate (COD).

Dissolved oxygen (DO), biochemical oxygen demand (5-day, 20 C, BOD) and relative stability.

Chloride and *sulfide.*

Active chlorine and chlorine demand.

Grease.

BIOLOGICAL EXAMINATION:

Bacteriological examination is not specified but can be conducted as for water.

Microscopic examination of sewage sludges and river muds, but not of sewage, is specified.

11-3. Expression of Test Results. In the immediate past, the results of chemical analyses have been expressed in parts per million by weight (ppm); they are now recorded more precisely in milligrams per liter (mg/l). The results of tests for color and turbidity were formerly forced into line by placing the comparative color and turbidity simulants (platinum in potassium chloroplatinate for color and silica in diatomaceous or fuller's earth for turbidity) on a ppm basis. Results of these tests are now recorded as units of color and turbidity. Mineral analyses are preferably reported in terms of the concentration of the ions. Odor intensity is given by the reciprocal of the dilution ratio with odor-free water that will reduce the odor to a point at which it is just noticeable. If, for example, 5 ml of sample are diluted to 200 ml to reduce the odor to its just noticeable, or threshold, intensity, the threshold odor number is $200/5 = 40$. Hydrogen-ion concentration is expressed in terms of the *p*H value or negative logarithm of the concentration in mols/l. Bacteriological results are stated in terms of the plate count per milliliter or the most probable number of coliform bacteria per 100 ml (Section 11-16). Algae and related plankton are counted, or their bulk is measured and expressed in terms of standard units per milliliter. A volumetric standard unit contains 20^3 cubic microns. Settleable solids are sometimes determined volumetrically (ml/l) instead of gravimetrically.

Nature and Significance of Common Tests

11-4. Physical Tests. The physical tests included in *"Standard Methods"* need little explanation. They each evaluate a readily understood property or quality of water and sewage.

Temperature measurements are important not only for their own sake, but also because they identify the magnitude of the density, viscosity, vapor pressure, and surface tension of the fluid, the saturation values of solids and gases that are dissolved in it, and the rates of chemical, biochemical, and biological activity such as corrosion, BOD, and growth and death of microorganisms.

Turbidity in water consists of clay, silt, finely divided organic matter, microscopic organisms, and similar substances. Soil erosion is responsible for most of the turbidity in natural waters.

Color is imparted to natural waters by dissolved or colloidal substances extracted from leaves, peaty matter, and the like. It is quite as harmless as tea and consists of tannins, glucosides, and their derivatives as well as iron compounds and other substances. Natural color is most intense in water draining from swamps. It is reduced by storage or ageing of the water and by the bleaching action of sunlight. Industrial wastes may contain dyes and other coloring substances of varying hues that are not measured by the standard test for color. The color of sewage reflects its strength and condition. Fresh sewage is gray; septic sewage is black.

The Public Health Service Drinking Water Standards [2] set upper limits of 10 units of turbidity (silica scale) and 20 units of color (platinum-cobalt scale).

Odors in water are caused by volatile substances associated with organic matter, living organisms, principally algae and related organisms, and gases such as hydrogen sulfide. The odors produced by plankton growths are listed for specific genera in Section 18-13. Some of the causative organisms are illustrated in Figure 11-5. The chlorination of water may produce odors of its own or intensify those of odor-producing agents. Since the keenness of odor perception varies with individual observers, and with fatigue of the olfactory

[2] *Public Health Repts.* *61*, 371 (1946).

nerves in the same observer, odor measurements are by no means absolute. Heating the water generally intensifies the odor. The nature of the odor is commonly noted. Often this gives a clue to the nature of the substances or living organisms responsible for the odor.

Observation of the odor of sewage provides a superficial but valuable indication of its condition. It tells, in particular, whether the sewage is fresh, stale, or septic; it may also suggest the presence of specific trade wastes.

Tastes in water are generally due to the presence of dissolved salts. Iron salts and sulfates are particular offenders. True tastes may be produced also by algae that contain a taste principle and by industrial wastes. The intensity of such tastes is often magnified by chlorine either through the destruction of the responsible organism and liberation of its taste principle or through the formation of reaction products with this principle or with substances that are contained in industrial wastes. Examples are the bitter, cucumber-like taste produced by the golden-brown alga *Synura* (Figure 11-5), and the iodoform or medicinal taste that has its source in phenoloid or comparable substances. The phenolic tastes are very disagreeable and cause widespread consumer complaints. Minute concentrations of the offending substance [1 μg/l $= 10^{-3}$ mg/l, or 1 ppb $= 10^{-3}$ ppm, the upper limit for phenolic compounds (as phenol) set by the Public Health Service Drinking Water Standards] may be responsible. Phenols, cresols, and allied substances find their way into water from industrial works, such as coke by-product plants and gas works.

Taste intensity can be measured in the same manner as odor intensity. Sodium chloride is detected in concentrations from 300 to 900 mg/l of NaCl and becomes objectionable enough to curtail water consumption when its concentration reaches 1,000 to 1,500 mg/l. There is reason to assume that the sulfates of sodium as well as the chlorides and sulfates of potassium, calcium, and magnesium possess thresholds of detection and refusal of like order of magnitude (Section 11-11).

11-5. Residue or Solid Matter (Water and Sewage). The tests for residue or solid matter are measures of the concentration and physical state of the principal constituents of water and, more especially, of sewage. Evaporation of water or sewage to dryness and weighing of the residue gives the *total residue* (water) or *total solids* (sewage) content of the sample. Ignition of the residue and reweighing establishes the *fixed residue* or *solids* and by difference the *volatile residue* or *solids.* Since organic matter burns, the *loss on ignition* is a measure of the amount of organic matter present, but ignition volatilizes also some mineral matter.

Filtration of the sample measures the *suspended residue* or *solids,* the volatile component again being found by ignition. Settling of the sample for a given period before making the solids determinations evaluates the *settleable solids.* The results of this separation as well as of suspended matter are generally more important in sewage analyses than water analyses. In the control of sewage treatment works, the volumetric determination of *settleable solids* in an Imhoff cone (Figure 11-1) is often convenient.

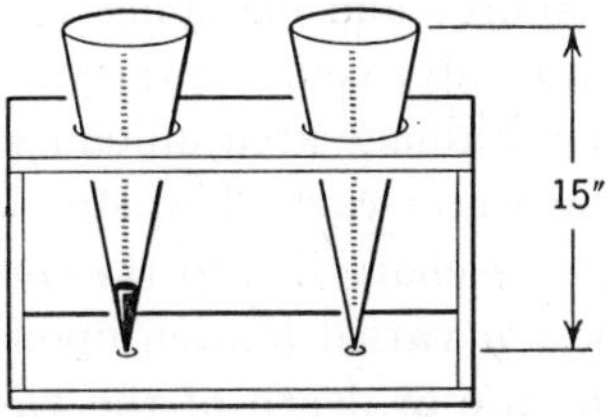

Figure 11-1. Imhoff settling cones for the volumetric determination of settleable sewage solids. *After Imhoff.*

The lower limit of the size range of suspended solids lies between 0.1 and 1 micron (1 micron or $\mu = 10^{-4}$ cm), varying somewhat with the shape and density of the particles. This is about the common size of bacteria and the wave length of visible light (0.4–0.8 μ) and so represents also about the lower limit of microscopic visibility.

In the *dissolved* state the divided material or *solute* is homogeneously and molecularly (or ionically) dispersed in the *solvent* to form a *true solution.* Particle diameters range from those of single atoms, 2×10^{-8} to 3×10^{-8} cm, up to about 1 mμ (10^{-7} cm), approximately the resolution limit of the electron microscope. Materials in true solution cannot be separated from the solvent by any form of filtration.

Between the upper limit of true solutions and the lower limit of suspensions lies the *colloidal* range. In colloidal dispersions, the particles (1) cannot be removed from the water by means of ordinary filtration but can be separated by processes of *ultrafiltration* or of *dialysis* through the pores of animal or artificial membranes, (2) are not microscopically visible, but can be visualized as specks of light in the *ultramicroscope* and can be photographed by the electron microscope, and (3) will not settle under the action of gravity because of their "Brownian motion," but can be caused to settle in a centrifuge or, better, in an ultracentrifuge. Colloidal particles may either be aggregates or single large molecules, such as those of proteins or starches.

Many substances of interest to the field of sanitary engineering occur as colloidal dispersions; the stain or color of natural waters, the proteins of sewage, and highly dispersed forms of the hydrated oxides of iron, aluminum, and silicon are examples of such materials.

The determination of total dissolved solids by electrolytic-conductivity measurements is common in industrial operations, especially steam generation.

11-6. Decomposition or Decay. Waste organic substances find their way into water in many ways: trees along the banks of a stream shed their leaves into it; the runoff from agricultural lands carries manures and decaying vegetation into drainage ditches that empty into water courses; the washings from streets and roads that traverse the drainage area unload suspended matter into sewers and streams; the water-carried wastes of human habitations and industries that are discharged into the natural drainage channels of the region impose a varied burden upon them; and the substances contributed by the life or death of the varied organisms that make the water itself their habitat constitute an inherent source of waste matter. The organic matter and some of the inorganic substances liberated from it are utilized as sources of energy by a succession of living things. A series of biochemical reactions is thereby set in motion, and polluted waters are eventually returned to a normal state of purity. The mechanisms by which substances are synthesized into living cells and analyzed to provide needed energy are complex. They proceed through the agency of protein catalysts called enzymes, which are themselves produced by the living cells. A host of specific enzymatic reactions intervenes before complex organic substances are simplified and eventually converted to stable products.

Engineers are concerned with the reactions that characterize the decomposition or decay of waste organic substances and, in particular, with the rates at which these reactions proceed in nature and can be made to proceed in treatment works by providing environments in which the processes of decomposition can operate at maximal rates. For the purposes of the engineer, identification of the cyclical changes that take place is generally restricted (1) to measurement of characteristic compounds of the elements that constitute organic and other nutritional matters, notably nitrogen, carbon, and sulfur, and (2) to measurement of the oxygen used up in accomplishing the changes or of the gases released in the course of decomposition.

a. Aerobic Decomposition. Figure 11-2 idealizes the cycles of nitrogen, carbon, and sulfur in aerobic decomposition. Organic nitrogen is seen to be converted successively by living things to ammonia, nitrite, and nitrate. Nitrate is then assimilated by plants, with the aid of sunlight (photosyn-

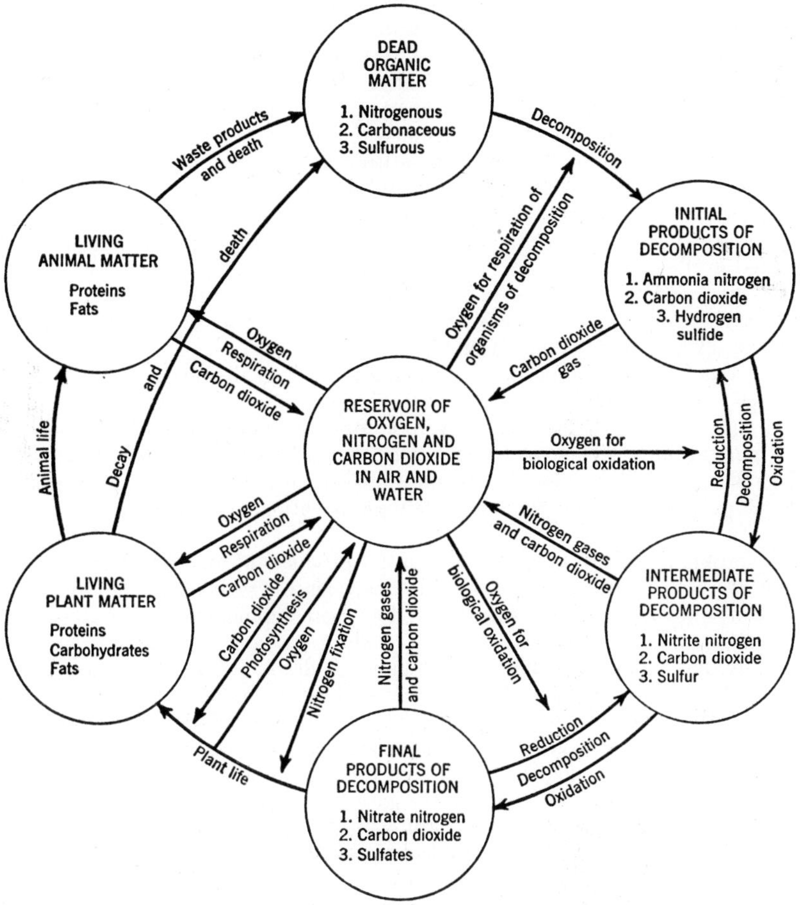

Figure 11-2. Cycle of nitrogen, carbon, and sulfur in aerobic decomposition.

thesis), to build living plant matter which is used in turn by animals to construct animal tissue. The progress of decomposition can be determined chemically in terms of the organic nitrogen, ammonia, nitrite, and nitrate that are present in water into which waste organic substances have been discharged. The cyclical changes in the form of combined nitrogen, therefore, underlie the nitrogen determinations of a sanitary water analysis. Changes similar to those of nitrogen obtain for carbon and sulfur.

Figure 11-2 shows, furthermore, that oxygen is needed for the respiration of the organisms that are responsible for the decomposition represented in the descending arc of the circle as well as for the respiration of the plants and animals that resynthesize organic matter in the ascending arc of the circle. Gaseous oxygen furnishes the normal needs in aerobic decomposition. Terrestrial organisms draw upon the oxygen of the atmosphere, aquatic organisms on the oxygen dissolved in water. The atmosphere contains about 21% of oxygen by volume, whereas water holds but 0.8% by volume in solution at normal temperatures (50 F). For this reason, the aquatic environment is critically sensitive to the oxygen demands of the organisms that populate it. It follows that determinations of the amount of oxygen dissolved in water (DO) relative to its saturation value and of the amount and rate of oxygen utilization, called the biochemical oxygen demand (BOD), furnish excellent means for identifying the pollutional status of water and by indirection also the amount of decomposable, or organic, matter contained in it.

Plants, as seen in Figure 11-2, release oxygen during photosynthesis and use carbon dioxide. This must be taken into account in striking oxygen balances where plants flourish in water.

b. Anaerobic Decomposition. When the oxygen dissolved in water becomes exhausted by living organisms that are busily engaged in the destruction of nutrient matter, the *aerobic* organisms, which require dissolved oxygen, succumb. Their place is taken by *anaerobic* or *facultatively anaerobic* organisms, which can live and grow in the absence of free oxygen. Anaerobic decomposition then supplants aerobic decomposition, and the cycles of nitrogen, carbon, and sulfur, which are idealized in Figure 11-3 for purposes of illustration, are set in motion. The initial products of anaerobic decomposition are seen to be organic acids, acid carbonates, carbon dioxide, and hydrogen sulfide; the intermediate products are ammonia, acid carbonates, carbon dioxide, and sulfides; the final products are ammonia, humus, carbon dioxide, methane, and sulfides. The gases of decomposition are released to the water and escape from it to the atmosphere in contact with the water as soon as the water has become saturated. The characteristic and identifiable gases are carbon dioxide and methane (or marsh gas). Methane is combustible and of high calorific power. In the anaerobic decomposition of sewage sludge, called sludge digestion, the gases produced are generally captured and utilized as an important source of energy.

The end products of anaerobic decomposition are plant foods. They are utilized by plants and through them by animals in the reconstruction of the substances from which these products were derived.

Suitable measures of the amount of decomposable, or organic, matter undergoing anaerobic decomposition in a given time are (1) the volume and rate of gas production and (2) the reduction in weight of volatile (organic) material and its rate of loss.

11-7. Tests for Organic Matter. Organic matter in water and sewage includes so great a variety of compounds in such varied and individually minute amounts that no attempt is made to isolate them. Tests are generally confined to the determination of gross

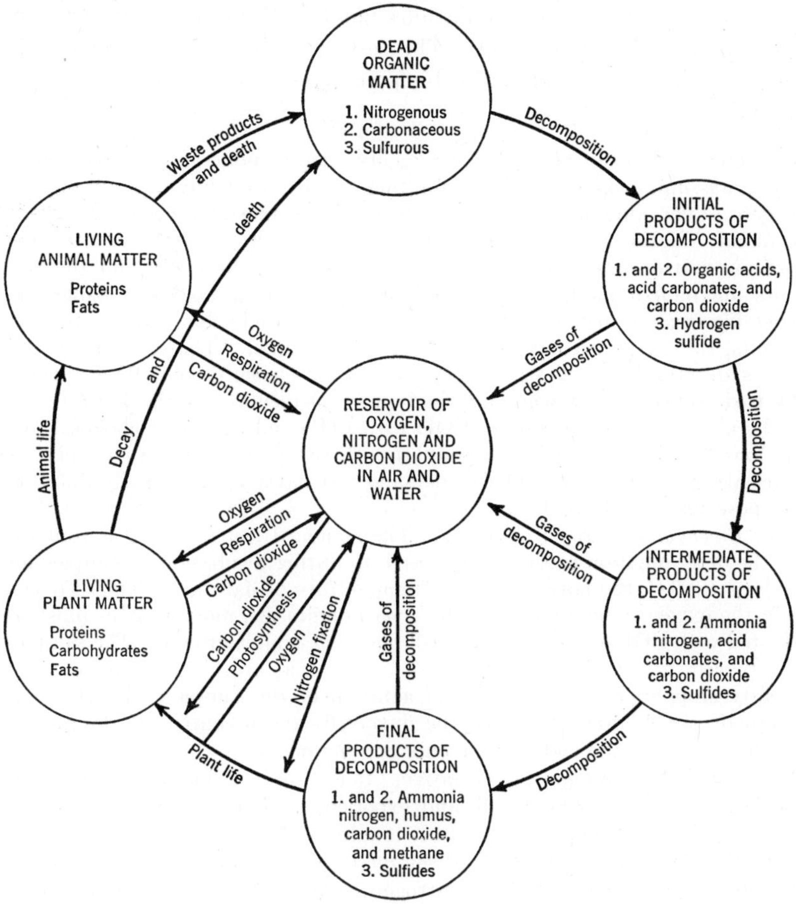

Figure 11-3. Cycle of nitrogen, carbon, and sulfur in anaerobic decomposition.

organic matter and its subdivisions into nitrogenous and carbonaceous matter; suspended, filtrable, and settleable organic matter; putrescible organic matter and relative stability; and living organic matter.

In addition to loss on ignition, the nitrogen determinations are useful in both water and sewage analysis; the test for oxygen consumed from chemical oxidants (COD) gives information on chemically oxidizable carbonaceous matter (more particularly of sewage and industrial wastes); the biochemical oxygen demand (BOD) identifies the biologically decomposable substances; the test for relative stability is a rough measure of the stability of a sample; and the tests for bacterial and plankton populations identify some of the living portions of the organic content. The tests for nitrogen compounds are discussed in Section 11-8, the biological tests in Sections 11-16 and 11-17.

a. Oxygen Consumed. Oxidizing agents, such as potassium permanganate and potassium dichromate in acid solution, will oxidize many types of organic matter. The amount of oxidizing chemical consumed or chemical oxygen demand (COD) is expressed as equivalent oxygen. Only a part of the organic matter reacts with the permanganate or dichromate, and the test does not offer a predictable differentiation between biologically stable and unstable organic matter. In order to obtain reproducible and comparable results, the test procedure must be rigidly regulated. The dichromate test offers an estimate of the strength of waste waters when their BOD is affected by toxic substances or when information supplementary to the BOD test is to be obtained. Correlation of COD with BOD and of similar chemical oxidations (chlorine demand for example) with BOD has not been fruitful. As normally performed, the chlorine-demand test has a fundamentally different purpose (Section 18-5).

b. Biochemical Oxygen Demand. The standard test for BOD is confined to the determination of the oxygen used up during incubation of samples for 5 days at 20 C, the normal summer temperature of natural waters. To satisfy the oxygen requirements of the active organisms, most samples must be diluted with BOD-free water that will not itself inhibit growth. The samples are placed in standardized incubation bottles that are filled completely and tightly stoppered in order to avoid aeration of the samples. The BOD is given by the difference between the dissolved-oxygen content of the sample at the beginning and end of the incubation period.

The BOD test is highly informative. It is also very delicate. Its correct performance requires both skill and experience, its correct interpretation a thorough acquaintance with its nature and limitations.

In the operation and control of sewage disposal works, the BOD test has largely superseded the tests for nitrogen compounds and oxygen consumed from permanganate. The BOD test possesses an important advantage over these tests, as well as the test for loss on ignition, in that it records the decomposability or putrescibility of the organic matter. It is a measure of the potential nuisance level of the sewage or industrial waste, effluent, or polluted water. In 5 days and up to 10 days at 20 C, however, it is practically only the carbon of the organic matter that has been oxidized. This is called the first-stage BOD. A full picture of probable decomposition can be had only by long-term BOD tests (Section 19-6).

c. Relative Stability. Relative stability may be defined as the percentage ratio of the oxygen available as dissolved oxygen, nitrite oxygen, and nitrate oxygen to the oxygen required to satisfy the first-stage BOD. However, this percentage ratio is obtainable only if the rate constants and limiting values of the first-stage BOD of the sample are known (Section 19-6). Calculations are then based on the number of days required to exhaust the available oxygen in the sample. The discoloration of methylene blue, which occurs when the last trace of oxygen has been removed, is used as the point of timing.

Because the basic rates of deoxygenation are not constant, this determination has lost favor. When the laboratory facilities of small treatment plants are poor, the relative stability may still perform a stop-gap function. However, the severe limitations of the test must be recognized.

11-8. Tests for Nitrogen Compounds. These include tests for organic nitrogen and for ammonia, nitrite, and nitrate.

Organic materials containing nitrogen are found in living cells, in the waste products of these cells, and in cell extracts or residues. This *organic nitrogen* is determined by effecting the complete destruction of organic matter by concentrated sulfuric acid (the Kjeldahl method) and the conversion of all organic nitrogen in the sample to ammonia. Since animal tissue is richer in protein than plant tissue, high concentrations of organic nitrogen point to pollution of animal origin. In accordance with the nitrogen cycle, high values are also characteristic of fresh or recent pollution.

Albuminoid nitrogen is that portion of the organic nitrogen that can be liberated as ammonia by the action of alkaline permanganate upon the nitrogenous matter. Large numbers of algae produce high albuminoid values as does sewage pollution.

Ammonia can be separated from other nitrogenous materials by boiling or distilling the sample after alkalinizing. Ammonia is the initial product in the decomposition of nitrogenous organic matter. It is formed less often when nitrates and nitrites are reduced to ammonia either biologically or chemically; the latter occurs, possibly, by the reducing action of ferrous salts sometimes encountered in deep well waters and bottom waters of deep lakes or reservoirs. Some ammonia may be swept out of the atmosphere by rain water.

Nitrite is usually an oxidation product of ammonia. The significance of nitrites, therefore, varies with their amount, source, and relation to other constituents of the sample, notably the relative magnitude of ammonia and nitrate present. Since nitrite is rapidly and easily converted to nitrate, its presence in concentrations greater than a few thousandths of a milligram per liter is generally indicative of active biological processes in the water.

Nitrate is the end product of decomposition of nitrogenous matter, and its presence carries this significance. Nitrate concentration is of particular interest in relation to the other forms of nitrogen that may be present in the sample. Nitrates occur in the crust of the earth in many places and are a source of its fertility. The presence in water of nitrate nitrogen in excess of about 10 mg/l has been responsible for the occurrence of methemoglobinemia or cyanosis in bottle-fed infants.

11-9. Alkalinity and Related Quantities. The *alkalinity* of water, which may be defined as its capacity for neutralizing acid, is usually due to the presence of bicarbonate and carbonate ions. In treated waters, and occasionally in natural waters, hydroxide, borate, silicate, or phosphate ions may also contribute to it. Determinations of alkalinity and its forms, along with the interrelated determinations of pH, acidity, carbon dioxide, and hardness are of interest in water softening, coagulation, and corrosion control.

Alkalinity in some form is essential for the formation of floc in coagulation with aluminum and iron salts, carbonate alkalinity is necessary for the removal of calcium hardness in softening, and hydroxide alkalinity is required for the removal of magnesium hardness. See Chapters 14 and 20.

a. Forms of alkalinity. The three common forms of alkalinity are related to the total alkalinity as follows:

$$[HCO_3^-] + 2[CO_3^=] + [OH^-] = A/(50 \times 10^3) + [H^+] \qquad 11\text{-}1$$

Here $[HCO_3^-]$ is the bicarbonate, $[CO_3^=]$ the carbonate, and $[OH^-]$ the hydroxide alkalinity, all in mols/l, A is the total alkalinity in mg/l as $CaCO_3$, and $[H^+]$ is the hydrogen ion concentration in mols/l. Milligrams per liter are converted to mols/l in accordance with the general equation

$$\text{mols/l} = (\text{mg/l})/[(\text{gram-molecular wt}) \times 10^3] \qquad 11\text{-}2$$

The equivalent weight of alkalinity as $CaCO_3$ is $\frac{1}{2} \times 100 = 50$.

The distribution of the individual components can be calculated with the help of the following equations [3] of chemical equilibrium:

$$[H^+][HCO_3^-] = K_1[H_2CO_3] \qquad 11\text{-}3$$

$$[H^+][CO_3^=] = K_2[HCO_3^-] \qquad 11\text{-}4$$

$$[H^+][OH^-] = K_w[H^+] \qquad 11\text{-}5$$

Here $K_1 = 4.45 \times 10^{-7}$ at 25 C and $K_2 = 4.69 \times 10^{-11}$ at 25 C are the equilibrium, acid dissociation, or ionization constants of carbonic acid, and $K_w = 10^{-14}$ at 25 C is the ion product of water. Combining Equations 11-4 and 11-5 with Equations 11-1 and 11-2 establishes the working relationships for the three forms of alkalinity in mg/l:

$$HCO_3^- = 50 \times 10^3\{A/(50 \times 10^3) + [H^+] - K_w/[H^+]\}/\{1 + 2K_2/[H^+]\} \qquad 11\text{-}6$$

$$CO_3^= = 2K_2(HCO_3^-)/[H^+] \qquad 11\text{-}7$$

$$OH^- = \tfrac{1}{2} \times 10^5 K_w/[H^+] \qquad 11\text{-}8$$

[3] Equation 11-3 is inserted here for completeness of statement. It will be used in connection with the determination of carbon dioxide.

K_2, K_1, and K_w vary with temperature and the ionic strength, activity, or salinity of the water. This complicates calculations.[4]

Example 11-1. The total alkalinity of a sample of water with a *p*H of 10.0 is 50.0 mg/l. Find the distribution of the alkalinity as (*a*) bicarbonate, (*b*) carbonate, and (*c*) hydroxide alkalinity in mg/l as $CaCO_3$. The temperature of the water is 25 C, and it is assumed that the effect of salinity can be neglected.

a. By Equation 11-6:

$$HCO_3^- = (50.0 + 50 \times 10^3 \times 10^{-10} - 50 \times 10^3 \times 10^{-14}/10^{-10})/(1 + 2 \times 4.69 \times 10^{-11}/10^{-10})$$

$$= 45.0/1.94 = 23.2 \text{ mg/l as } CaCO_3$$

b. By Equation 11-7:

$$CO_3^{=} = 2 \times 4.69 \times 10^{-11} \times 23.2/10^{-10} = 21.8 \text{ mg/l as } CaCO_3$$

c. By Equation 11-8:

$$OH^- = 50 \times 10^3 \times 10^{-14}/10^{-10} = 5.0 \text{ mg/l as } CaCO_3$$

As a check 23.2 + 21.8 + 5.0 = 50 mg/l.

b. Acidity. Acidity, like alkalinity, is a capacity factor and may be defined as the capacity for neutralizing base. In contrast, *p*H is an intensity factor which expresses the existing concentration of hydrogen ions. Acidity is normally associated with the presence of carbon dioxide, mineral and organic acids, and salts of strong acids and weak bases, like $Al_2(SO_4)_3$, that are acid by hydrolysis. To facilitate comparison with alkalinity and hardness results, acidity determinations, too, are expressed as mg/l of equivalent calcium carbonate.

c. Carbon dioxide. Frequently, dissolved carbon dioxide is the sole source of acidity in water. Then the titration for acidity is also a determination of the *carbon dioxide* present and may be conventionally expressed as mg/l of carbon dioxide. Alternatively, the amount of carbon dioxide in mg/l as CO_2 (molecular weight 44.0) can be calculated from the *p*H value and total alkalinity by means of Equation 11-9 derived from Equations 11-1, 11-2, and 11-3:

$$CO_2 = 44 \times 10^3\{[H^+]/K_1\}\{A/(50 \times 10^3) + [H^+] - K_w/[H^+]\}/\{1 + 2K_2/H^+\} \qquad 11\text{-}9$$

[4] For aids to calculation, see J. F. Dye, Calculation of the effect of temperature on pH, free carbon dioxide, and the three forms of alkalinity, *J. Am. Water Works Assn., 44,* 356 (1952).

Example 11-2. The total alkalinity of a sample of water with pH 7.0 is 15 mg/l. Find the concentration of CO_2 in mg/l. The temperature of the water is 25 C, and it is assumed that the effect of salinity can be neglected.

By Equation 11-9:

$$CO_2 = 44 \times 10^3(10^{-7}/4.45 \times 10^{-7})(2 \times 10^{-5} \times 15 + 10^{-7} - 10^{-14}/10^{-7})/$$
$$(1 + 2 \times 4.69 \times 10^{-11}/10^{-7})$$
$$= 3.0 \text{ mg/l}$$

The concentration of carbon dioxide in water in equilibrium with a normal atmosphere at 32 F is approximately 1 mg/l. Larger amounts may be absorbed from ground air that is enriched in CO_2 by the decomposition of organic matter. They may also be formed by oxidation of organic matter in water or sewage, or they may result from a lowering of pH for some reason in water containing reserve alkalinity.

Since the amount of dissolved carbon dioxide in equilibrium with the atmosphere is small, great care must be exercised in the collection and titration of samples containing much CO_2 in order to avoid loss to the air. Loss of CO_2 also leads to erroneous pH determinations. The alkalinity determination is not affected, however.

11-10. Hardness. Hardness is of special concern in water supply. Hard water requires much soap before a lather is formed, and hard water deposits sludges or incrustations on surfaces with which it comes into contact and in vessels and boilers in which it is heated. The responsible substances are calcium and magnesium ions and to a lesser extent (because of their normally smaller concentration) those of iron, manganese, strontium, and aluminum. The pseudohardness of brines is related to the prevention of solution of sodium soaps by sodium ion. Water is normally considered hard when it contains in excess of 100 mg/l of hardness, soft when the value is less than 50 mg/l.

When the total hardness has a value greater than the sum of the carbonate and bicarbonate alkalinity (see Section 11-9), the amount of hardness equivalent to the alkalinity is called carbonate hardness and the amount in excess of this is called non-carbonate hardness. When the total hardness has a value equal to or smaller than the sum of the carbonate and bicarbonate alkalinity, there is no non-carbonate hardness.

The differentiation between carbonate and non-carbonate hardness is important (Figure 14-3). Carbonate hardness is thrown down when water is boiled. A soft deposit is usually formed, which is readily removed from boilers by blowing them down. Non-carbonate hardness includes in particular chlorides and sulfates, but possibly also nitrates, of calcium and magnesium. Evaporation of waters containing these ions renders the water highly corrosive ($CaCl_2$, $MgCl_2$, and $MgSO_4$) and creates a hard and brittle scale ($CaSO_4$) that opposes heat transfer in boilers in the approximate ratios of 17:1 for $CaCO_3$ and 48:1 for $CaSO_4$, both relative to wrought iron. The sudden production of large volumes of steam when thick scales crack and water comes into contact with overheated metal surfaces may cause explosions. Local overheating causes the "bagging" of boiler tubes and shells.

Determinations of calcium, magnesium, sodium, and potassium, as well as of bicarbonate ion, carbonate ion, hydroxide, chloride, sulfate, nitrate, and silica, are part of a more complete analysis of water. They are of significance in connection with the softening of water, the coagulation of water, the interpretation and control of corrosion, and the preparation of boiler feed-waters (Chapter 14 and Section 20-5).

11-11. Chloride, Sulfate, and Sulfide. *Chlorides* are widely distributed in nature. They are present in mineral deposits, in sea and brackish water, in ocean vapors and spray carried inland by the wind, in human excreta (more particularly urine), in other water-carried wastes from households, and in industrial wastes. Sea water contains about 18,000 mg/l of chloride, brackish water in tidal estuaries proportionately less. Some inland "salt lakes," such as the Dead Sea and Great Salt Lake, contain about 150,000 mg/l of chloride. The human body wastes from 8 to 15 grams of sodium chloride (5 to 9 grams of chloride) a day. In the absence of pollution and mineral deposits, the "normal chloride" of most surface and ground waters is small, varying with the distance from the ocean or other bodies of salt water and the prevailing winds. The chloride content of water is not affected by normal passage over the ground or through it. Hence an increase in chloride above the "normal" is a pollution index that does not change with time. Hence, also, chlorides can be added to water to trace flow, especially underground flow. However, there are more sensitive tracers, such as fluorescein. In general, there are more direct and informative tests of pollution than chloride determinations. Examples are those for coliform bacteria, BOD, and the forms of combined nitrogen.

In water supply, the chloride determination is of importance principally in connection with salty tastes produced by high chloride content and in identifying the nature of non-carbonate hardness. The upper limit set by the Public Health Service Drinking Water Standards for chloride ion is 250 ppm Cl. When sewage is disposed of in tidal estuaries or salt water, the chloride content must be known, because it affects the solubility of dissolved oxygen (Section 11-13).

As shown in the cycle of sulfur in nature (Figures 11-2 and 11-3), *sulfate* and *sulfide* are common decomposition products of organic matter. In both water and sewage, the reduction of compounds of sulfur to sulfide and the anaerobic destruction of other sulfur-containing matters produce objectionable odors. Hydrogen sulfide is responsible for the destruction of cement and concrete as well as the corrosion of metals.

More than half of the people who are dependent on supplies of saline water report laxative effects [5] when the sulfate content of the water, or its magnesium and sulfate content taken together, exceeds 1,000 mg/l and when the total dissolved solids exceed 2,000 mg/l.

The upper limits set by the Public Health Service are 125 ppm magnesium (Mg), 250 ppm sulfate (SO_4), and 500 ppm total solids.[6]

In water, sulfate, like chloride, is of significance in identifying the nature of non-carbonate hardness. *"Standard Methods,"* therefore, includes tests for sulfate in the analysis of water and for sulfide in the analysis of both water and sewage.

11-12. Iron and Other Metals. The presence in water of the ions of iron, manganese, lead, copper, zinc, and other metals is of special concern in water supply. *Iron* compounds are generously distributed in nature. They occur in soil and rocks and are common constituents of plant matter. Iron is normally the favored metal for water pipes, and iron compounds are also widely used as coagulants. Growths of filamentous iron bacteria are dependent on the presence of iron in water. Ferrous iron occurs in true solution in water. Dissolved oxygen oxidizes dissolved ferrous iron and precipitates it as flocculent ferric hydroxide. This imparts a rusty color or turbidity to the water. Heavy corrosion of iron in distribution systems, including the piping of buildings, is spoken of as "red water trouble" (Section 14-7). In nature, the release of iron from organic matter and the reduction of iron in the soil in the presence of organic matter are responsible for the solution of iron in water. This statement applies

[5] Communication from the North Dakota State Department of Health analyzed by E. W. Moore.

[6] 1,000 ppm when water of better quality is not obtainable.

particularly to ground water and water from the stagnant portions of deep lakes and reservoirs. Iron may also occur in water as the result of the solution of ferrous carbonate in the presence of CO_2. Most of the previous remarks are applicable to *manganese*, except that this metal is less common in occurrence. When oxidized to hydrous manganic oxides, it forms black precipitates that may accumulate in distribution systems to be released in occasional large shocks. These cause "black water trouble."

The *lead, copper,* and *zinc* ions found in water are normally taken into solution from pipes that contain the metals, but they may have their origin in industrial wastes along with many other substances, such as arsenic, chromium, and cyanide. Copper may be present when it is used for the control of algae.

The Public Health Service has set the following upper limits for these and related categories of impurities in drinking water: 3.0 ppm copper (Cu), 0.3 ppm iron (Fe) and manganese (Mn) together, 0.1 ppm lead (Pb), and 15 ppm zinc (Zn); and 1.5 ppm fluorine (F), 0.05 ppm arsenic (As), 0.05 ppm selenium (Se), and 0.05 ppm hexavalent chromium (Cr).

Where much copper is used in industry, the industrial wastes and sewage with which they are mixed may contain sufficient amounts to interfere with biological treatment processes and even to render them ineffective. Arsenic and cyanides may be similarly implicated.

The laboratory tests for these substances are specific analytical procedures chosen for their sensitiveness to what are often microquantities.

11-13. Dissolved Oxygen. The role of oxygen in the biological economy of water, its relation to processes of aerobic decomposition, and its part in the solution of metals and precipitation of iron and manganese make its determination in water and sewage extremely important. Because of the rapid absorption of oxygen from the atmosphere, suitable precautions must be taken in the collection of samples for analysis. Special sampling equipment may have to be employed.

Dissolved oxygen concentration is frequently reported as the percentage saturation with dissolved oxygen. Calculation of this value requires a knowledge of the dissolved-oxygen saturation value (Table 6 in the Appendix).

11-14. Water-borne Infections. The water-borne infective diseases fall into five categories according to the nature of the organisms that cause disease: bacteria, protozoa, worms, viruses, and fungi.

Water itself would not become the means of spreading disease, however, were it not for its pollution by the excreta (1) of persons acutely ill with an intestinal or related infection or (2) of apparently healthy carriers of the responsible organisms.

The enteric, water-borne, bacterial infections include typhoid fever, paratyphoid fever (salmonellosis), bacillary dysentery (shigellosis), and cholera. Typhoid fever, at the beginning of the present century a scourge of many communities, has been placed under control by proper methods of water supply and by other sanitary safeguards. The fact that civilized communities have been relatively free from attack for a generation, however, has left them more vulnerable to infection than before, because their inhabitants have not had an opportunity to acquire immunity to this disease. This warning applies to other water-borne infections as well. It is one that should spur the responsible agencies to continual vigilance.

Water-borne paratyphoid fever (salmonellosis) and bacillary dysentery (shigellosis) are probably of more frequent occurrence than our statistics indicate. The groups of diseases vary widely in severity and individual response. Mild outbreaks are probably never reported.

Cholera, which was pandemic during the nineteenth century, is confined, at present, to the Asiatic continent. The rapid communication with other parts of the world by air transport has renewed interest in the potential hazard of new epidemics.

Although it is estimated that between 5 and 10% of the American people are carriers of amebic cysts, the reported incidence of water-borne amebic dysentery (amebiasis) has been small. The probable reason for this is (1) the number of cysts excreted by carriers, which is relatively much lower than the number of typhoid organisms excreted by carriers of that disease, and (2) the effective removal of the cysts from water by natural purification and by filtration because of their large size (15 microns) relative to that of bacteria (1 to 2 microns).

The eggs of some intestinal worms and the larvae of others undoubtedly find their way from human and animal carriers (either directly or from the soil) into water courses and so possibly into water supplies. The numbers in which these organisms are discharged from the alimentary tract are relatively so small, however, and the organisms themselves are relatively so large that no widespread infections from this source have been reported.

About water-borne virus infections we know little. However, we do have knowledge of at least one virus—that of infectious hepatitis or epidemic jaundice—being spread by drinking water. We also know that other viruses—among them those of infantile paralysis and of coxsackie disease—occur in the stools of patients suffering from specific virus diseases. Epidemiological evidence, however, is overwhelmingly against the hypothesis that poliomyelitis is a water-borne disease. Whether some of the gastrointestinal upsets commonly experienced are water-borne virus infections remains to be demonstrated.

The only fungus that may be suspected of being allied to water in its spread is that associated with histoplasmosis. So little is known about the epidemiology of this disease at the present time that judgment as to the possibility of water-borne infection must be reserved.

11-15. Bacteriological Indicators of Contamination and Pollution. By *contamination* of water we understand the introduction into it of pathogenic organisms that render the water unfit for human consumption or domestic purposes. A similar definition applies to contaminants that are pathogenic to animals. Strictly speaking, *pollution* of a body of water is the introduction into it of substances of such characteristics and in such quantity as to render it offensive to the senses of sight, smell, or taste. The term pollution is more generally used, however, to include also potential contamination.

The otherwise fortunate circumstance that the number of pathogens in natural waters is small, together with the fact that they occur in wide variety, forces us to resort to indirect quantitative evidence of the presence of bacterial contaminants. *Indicator* organisms provide the substitute. As their name implies, their determination points to pollution and to the possible presence of contaminating organisms. Therefore they are, in essence, measures of guilt by association. In the United States, the standard indicator organisms constitute the coliform group of bacteria. This group has as one of its primary habitats the intestinal tract of human beings. Hence its presence is an indication of the possible presence of other organisms that originate in the human intestinal tract and, in particular, in the tract of individuals who are ill with an enteric disease such as typhoid fever or who are carriers of a pathogen such as the typhoid bacillus.

a. The coliform group of organisms. The coliform group of organisms is a satisfactory bacteriological indicator of contamination or pollution for the following reasons:

1. As a statistical average, about half the tests for the presence of coliform organisms in sewage are found to represent organisms that originate in fecal matter. Since human feces are the primary source of pathogenic enteric organisms, the presence in water of coliforms offers significant evidence of

the potential presence of such pathogens. The rate of destruction or death of the coliforms and the rate of their removal from water and sewage, furthermore, is substantially parallel to that of the pathogenic enteric bacteria, and the coliform group is, if anything, more resistant to disinfection than are the pathogenic enteric bacteria.

2. The number of coliform organisms in human feces and in sewage is very great. The daily per capita excretion of this group varies from 125 to 150 billion in winter and is close to 400 billion in summer. Parenthetically, the *total* number of bacteria in fecal matter that can be counted by simple bacteriological techniques is approximately a thousand times greater still. The number of coliforms that may enter bodies of water used as a source of drinking water is decreased: (1) by death, in time, of these organisms because they do not generally maintain themselves in sewage or in cleaner water; (2) by the removal and destruction of these organisms in sewage treatment works before discharge into receiving waters; and (3) by their removal and destruction in water-supply and water-purification works before the water is used for domestic purposes. The expected effects of time and treatment in reducing the coliform load are discussed in other chapters of this book.

The generalized U. S. Public Health Service standard of approximately 1 coliform organism in 100 ml of water is, in a sense, a standard of expediency: it does not exclude entirely the possibility of acquiring an intestinal infection. The standard is one that can be attained (1) by the economic development of available water supplies, their disinfection and, if need be, treatment in purification works by economically feasible methods and (2) by the economic development of waste-water disposal systems including the necessary degree of treatment of the waste waters in suitable works by economically feasible processes. The exposure to typhoid fever by the consumption of water that meets the current bacteriological standard of the U. S. Public Health Service can be gaged from statistical studies by Kehr and Butterfield [7] of the ratio of *Salmonella typhosa* to coliforms in sewage and polluted streams. In accordance with the results of these workers the number y of *S. typhosa* per million coliforms varies, as is to be expected, with the incidence of typhoid in the community, as expressed, for example, by the annual case rate r from typhoid fever per 100,000 population. A plot of available data suggests the following relationship:

$$y = ar^n = 3r^{0.461} \qquad 11\text{-}10$$

For a case rate of 14 per 100,000 per annum, for example, $y = 10$ typhoid organisms per million coliforms.

3. The test for organisms of the coliform group is sufficiently simple of performance to place it in the hands of the kind of personnel that is currently recruited for the supervision of the quality of public water supplies.

4. As discussed in Section 11-16, numerical evaluation of the density of coliform organisms in samples of water and sewage is readily accomplished by dilution methods or filtration methods.

[7] R. H. Kehr and C. T. Butterfield, Some notes on the relation between coliforms and enteric pathogens, *Public Health Repts. 58,* 589 (1943).

A matter of concern in evaluating the relative danger of spread of enteric infections is the large number of pathogenic organisms included in the excreta of carriers and patients. A carrier of typhoid fever, for example, may excrete up to 200 billion *S. typhosa* per day; a carrier of amebic dysentery up to 10 million cysts of *Endameba histolytica* per day. The smaller the quantities of water exposed to the excreta of a patient or carrier, therefore, the greater becomes their concentration of viable organisms and the greater, too, becomes the chance of infecting a person who consumes the water. Although the minimum infective dose of water-borne infections has not been established, there is statistical evidence that typhoid fever will be produced in 1 to 2% of the persons who ingest a single viable cell of *S. typhosa.* Massive doses are known to break down the immunity acquired by inoculation.

b. Other bacterial indicators. Much thought has been given to the use of bacterial indicator organisms of sewage pollution other than the coliform group; among them, in particular, of the so-called sewage streptococci. Houston,[8] for example, interested himself in their identification as indicating dangerous pollution since they were "readily demonstrable in waters recently polluted and seemingly altogether absent from waters above suspicion of contamination."

In the sanitary control of indoor swimming pools, there is need for an indicator organism or group of organisms that will reflect the contamination of the pool water by pathogenic organisms that have their habitat in the eyes, nose, mouth, and throat as well as on other mucous surfaces of the body and on the skin. Numerous streptococci and staphylococci are implicated in infections of these organs and body areas. In the absence of a simple test for significant organisms of this kind, the 37-C plate count is generally employed in gaging the bacterial contamination of indoor pools.

11-16. Bacteriological Tests. *"Standard Methods"* suggests three bacteriological tests:

1. The test for the coliform group of bacteria. Requisite techniques involve either (*a*) the inoculation of multiple, geometrically (normally decimal) serial quantities of the sample into a liquid nutrient medium for the identification of the group and confirmatory testing of the results obtained, or (*b*) the filtration of a measured amount of water through a filter membrane that will retain the bacteria in the sample of water and permit identification

[8] Houston, A. C., Supplements to the 28th and 29th Annual Reports of the Local Government Board Containing the Report of the Medical Officer of Health for 1889–99 (p. 439) and 1899–1900 (p. 467) repectively, London, England.

and counting of the coliforms when the membrane is placed on absorbent pads containing, as a first step, an enrichment medium and, as a second step, a differential medium.

2. The 24-hr agar plate count at 35 C. This test is a measure of a heterogeneous group of bacteria, developing under the conditions of cultivation and having their natural habitat and optimum environment in the bodies of man and other warm-blooded animals. Serial dilution in the culture medium is employed when the number of developing colonies is large.

3. The 48-hr agar plate count at 20 C. This test is a measure of another heterogeneous group of bacteria, developing under the conditions of cultivation and having their natural habitat and optimum environment in nature within the usual range of water temperatures.

When the dilution technique is employed, a rough estimate of the density of coliform organisms is obtained by calculation of the "indicated number" (IN); a statistically more informative estimate is derived from the calculation of the "most probable number" (MPN).

a. The Indicated Number of Coliform Organisms. In calculating the indicated number, it is assumed that a positive result for the smallest portion of multiple, geometrically serial quantities is produced by the presence of a single organism. Hence the indicated number is obtained by taking the reciprocal, or in multiple tests the averaged reciprocal, of the smallest positive portion or dilution in a decimal series. If a negative result is reached for a portion larger than the smallest portion giving a positive result, it is converted by convention to a positive result in exchange for a negative result in the smallest positive portion.

Calculation of the indicated number for single series is illustrated in Table 11-1, using a plus sign (+) to record the presence and a negative sign (−)

TABLE 11-1. Calculation of Indicated Number of Coliform Organisms

Series	Portion of Sample Tested and Result: 10 ml	1.0 ml	0.1 ml	0.01 ml	Indicated Number per 100 ml
1	+	−	−		100/10 = 10
2	+	+	−	−	100/1 = 100
3	+	+	−	+	100/0.1 = 1,000
4	+	+	+	−	100/0.1 = 1,000
5	+	+	+	+	100/0.01 ⋝ 10,000

the absence of coliform bacteria in the various portions tested. All these series with the exception of the second are lacking in full support. The second has two positive as well as two negative decimal portions. The fifth series, reported as ⋝ 10,000, is inconclusive. The indicated number is often made the basis of reporting results for sewage and polluted waters and, sometimes also, for raw and partially finished water.

b. The Most Probable Number of Coliform Organisms. The most probable number in a sample of water is the density most likely to produce a particular analytical result.

If, as shown by Greenwood and Yule,[9] the distribution of n organisms in V ml of water from which 1-ml portions of water are drawn for analysis is assumed to be random, the probable numbers of 1-ml portions containing 0, 1, 2, 3, etc., organisms in each 1-ml portion are given by the expansion of the fundamental binomial relationship,

$$\left(\frac{V-1}{V}+\frac{1}{V}\right)^n \qquad 11\text{-}11$$

Since both n and V are numerically large, it is possible, according to Poisson, to transform this expression into

$$e^{-\lambda}+\lambda e^{-\lambda}+\frac{\lambda^2}{2!}e^{-\lambda}+\frac{\lambda^3}{3!}e^{-\lambda}+\cdots \qquad 11\text{-}12$$

where $\lambda = n/V$ (or the average density of coliform bacteria), e is the base of the Napierian system of logarithms, and the successive terms in the series represent respectively the probability of the 1-ml portion containing exactly 0, 1, 2, 3, etc., coliform bacteria. Hence the probability of a 1-ml portion of sample being found negative is $e^{-\lambda}$ and that of its being positive $(1 - e^{-\lambda})$. For portions containing N ml of the sample, similarly, the probability of a negative result is $e^{-N\lambda}$ and of a positive result $(1 - e^{-N\lambda})$.

Further development of the most probable number may be had by examples such as the following:

Assume a decimal series in which the 100-ml and 10-ml portions of the sample are positive for coliform bacteria, and the 1-ml, 0.1-ml, and 0.01-ml portions negative. The probability P that these results will occur at the same time and that the density of coliform bacteria falls between $\lambda = 0$ and $\lambda = \lambda$, is then

$$P=\frac{\int_0^{\lambda}(1-e^{-100\lambda})(1-e^{-10\lambda})e^{-\lambda}e^{-0.1\lambda}e^{-0.01\lambda}d\lambda}{\int_0^{\infty}(1-e^{-100\lambda})(1-e^{-10\lambda})e^{-\lambda}e^{-0.1\lambda}e^{-0.01\lambda}d\lambda} \qquad 11\text{-}13$$

Since the denominator is a definite integral with a numerical value, in this instance of $a = 0.8100018$, the equation of the probability curve of densities is

$$y = 1.234565(e^{-1.11\lambda} - e^{-11.11\lambda} - e^{-101.11\lambda} + e^{-111.11\lambda}) \qquad 11\text{-}14$$

and y, as shown in Figure 11-4, has a maximum or modal value when $\lambda = n/V = 0.230$, or 23 coliform organisms per 100 ml. Similar equations, curves, and maximal values can be derived for other combinations of results. If multiple plantings are made of decimal portions, the results from only three are significant. How these are chosen and what adjustment must be made in apparently anomalous cases is explained in "*Standard Methods.*" Reference should be made to this source for useful tables of the most probable numbers associated with different test results. A single numerical value is obtained for a series of analytical results by finding the MPN for each result and calculating the median MPN.

[9] M. Greenwood and G. Udny Yule, On the statistical interpretation of some bacteriological methods employed in water analysis, *J. Hygiene*, *16* (1917).

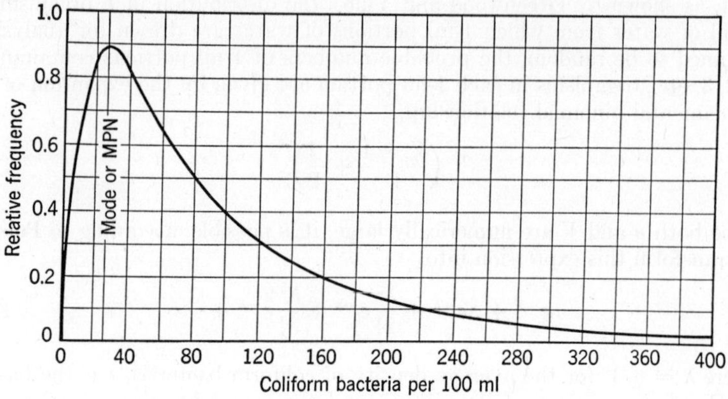

Figure 11-4. Probability curve of coliform organisms in a sample for which the 100-ml and 10-ml portions are positive, and the 1-ml, 0.1-ml, and 0.01-ml portions, negative.

The general form of the probability curve of coliform densities for the three significant results is

$$y = \frac{1}{a}[(1 - e^{-N_1\lambda})^p(e^{-N_1\lambda})^q][(1 - e^{-N_2\lambda})^r(e^{-N_2\lambda})^s][(1 - e^{-N_3\lambda})^t(e^{-N_3\lambda})^u] \quad 11\text{-}15$$

where y, a, and e have the significance previously indicated; p, r, and t are the numbers of positive portions of size N_1, N_2, and N_3 ml respectively in the decimal series; and q, s, and u are the numbers of negative portions of size N_1, N_2, and N_3 ml respectively in the decimal series.[10]

As previously suggested, the most probable numbers are normally calculated for finished waters for which four or less of five 10-ml plantings are positive. The possible results and the equations of the corresponding frequency curves are shown together with the mode, most probable number, and indicated number in Table 11-2.

c. Bacteriological Quality. Samples for bacteriological examination must be collected from representative points in the distribution system with sufficient frequency to establish the safety of the water in all parts of the system. The larger the system, the greater must be the number of collections. The minimum number of samples prescribed is shown in Table 11-3 on a population basis.

[10] For no positive tubes in 5 10-ml portions, for example,

$$y = [(1 - e^{-10\lambda})^0(e^{-10\lambda})^5]/\int_0^\infty (1 - e^{-10\lambda})^0(e^{-10\lambda})^5 = 50e^{-50\lambda}$$

because

$$\int_0^\infty e^{-50\lambda} = 1/50$$

TABLE 11-2. Equations of Probability Curves and Magnitudes of Modes and Most Probable Numbers and Indicated Numbers of Coliform Bacteria for Different Results Obtained in the Planting of Five 10-ml Portions of a Sample of Water

Test Series	Number of 10-ml Portions: Positive	Number of 10-ml Portions: Negative	Equation of Probability Curve	Mode	MPN per 100 ml	IN per 100 ml
1	0	5	$y = 50e^{-50\lambda}$	0.000	<2.2	<2
2	1	4	$y = 200e^{-40\lambda}(1 - e^{-10\lambda})$	0.022	2.2	2
3	2	3	$y = 300e^{-30\lambda}(1 - e^{-10\lambda})^2$	0.051	5.1	4
4	3	2	$y = 200e^{-20\lambda}(1 - e^{-10\lambda})^3$	0.092	9.2	6
5	4	1	$y = 50e^{-10\lambda}(1 - e^{-10\lambda})^4$	0.160	16.0	8

When five 100-ml portions are examined, the MPN values are <0.22, 0.22, 0.51, 0.92, and 1.60 respectively.

TABLE 11-3. Frequency of Collection of Samples, Public Health Service Standards

Population Served	Minimum Number of Samples per Month
2,500 or less	1
10,000	7
20,000	25
100,000	100
1,000,000	300
2,000,000	390
5,000,000	500

Certain rules are laid down as to the collection and consideration of special samples after discovery that any part of the system is dispensing water of unsatisfactory quality.

The Public Health Service bacteriological standards delimit the density of coliform bacteria present in the water as determined by the examination of five 10-ml (or 100-ml) portions of each sample. The results must satisfy the following statistical criteria:

1. Not more than 10% of all the 10-ml portions (or 60% of all the 100-ml portions) examined per month may be positive for organisms of the coliform group.
2. Occasionally three or more of the five 10-ml portions (or all of the 100-ml portions) of a single sample may be positive, provided that this does not occur (*a*) in consecutive samples, (*b*) in more than 5% of 20 or more samples per month when 10-ml portions are examined (or 20% of 5 or more samples per month when 100-ml portions are examined), or (*c*) in one sample among 20 or less samples per month when 10-ml portions are examined (or among 5 or less samples per month when 100-ml portions are examined).
3. When three or more of the five 10-ml portions (or all of the 100-ml portions) of a single sample are positive, daily samples must be collected

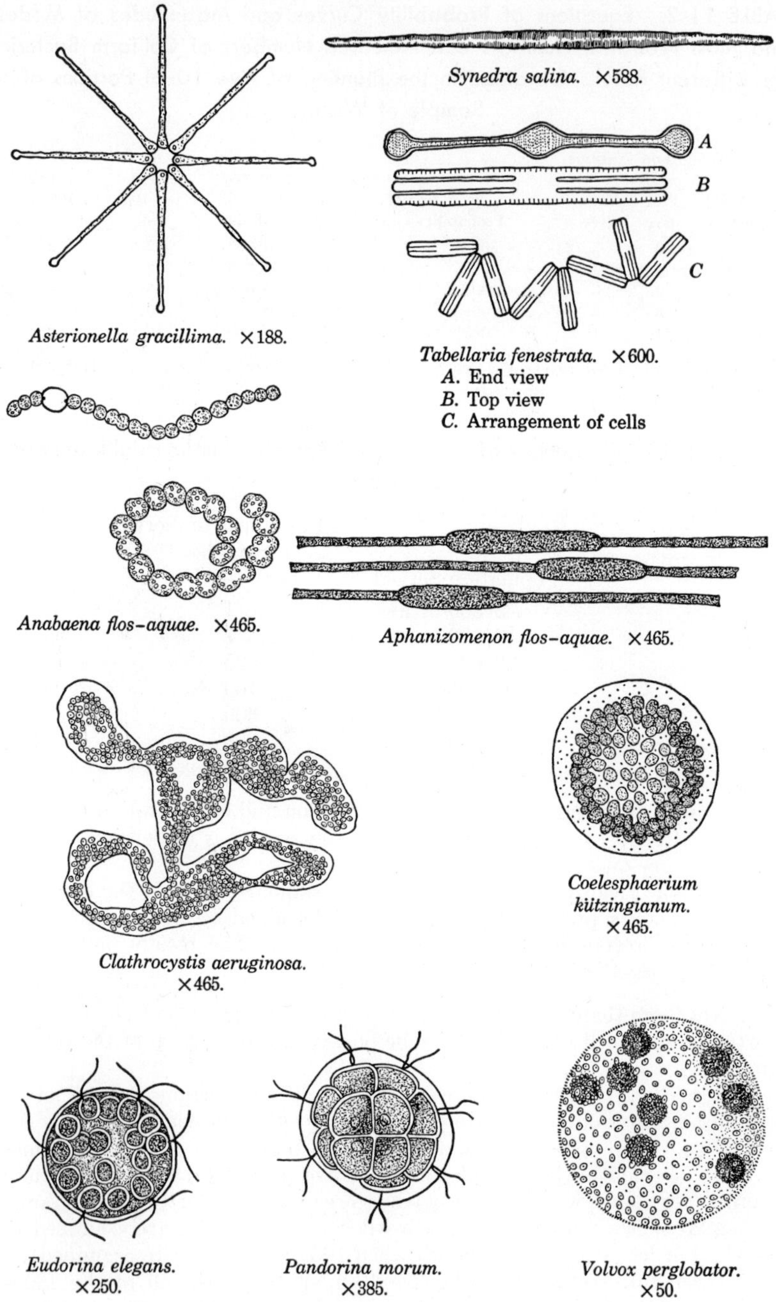

Figure 11-5. Common taste- and odor-producing algae.

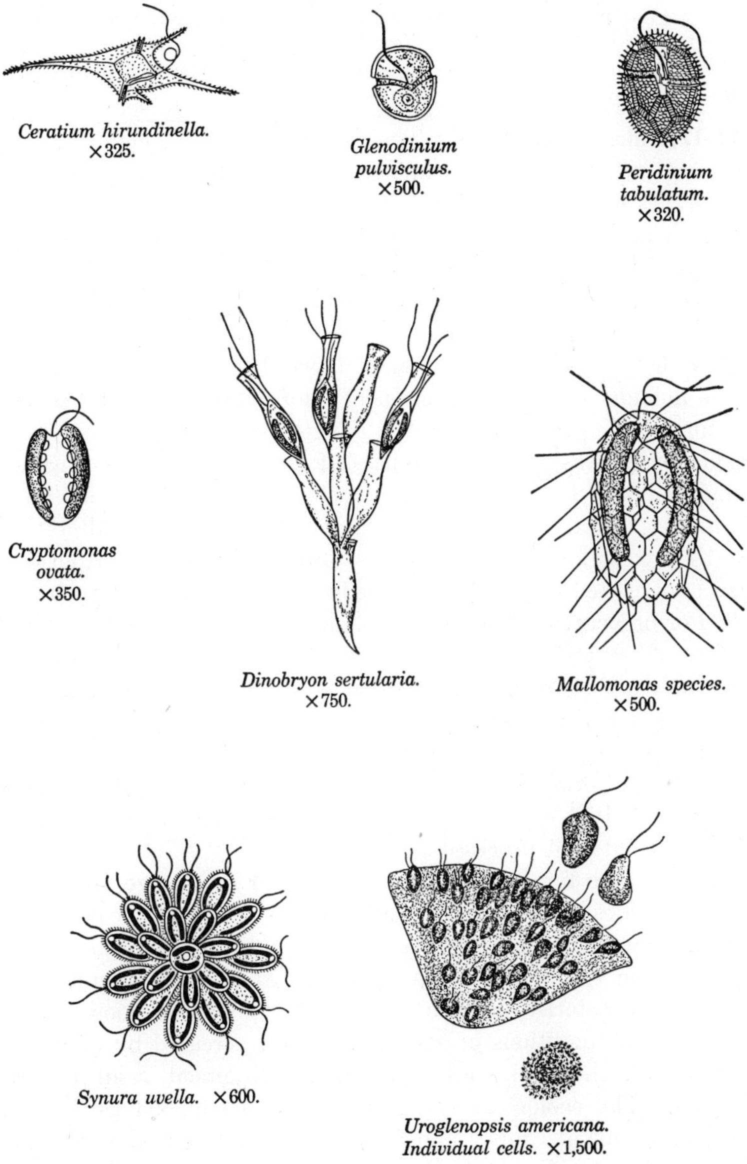

Figure 11-5 (*continued*). From H. B. Ward and G. C. Whipple, *Fresh-water Biology*, John Wiley and Sons, New York, 1918.

from the offending point or points and tested in multiple portions of a decimal series ranging to 0.1 ml or less, until two consecutive samples show that the water is again of satisfactory quality. Multiple portions of a decimal series yielding significant results must be used also when the quality of the water examined is unknown.

11-17. Microscopic Tests. The identification and enumeration of algae and other, principally microscopic, organisms other than bacteria serves a useful function both in water supply and sewage disposal. The nature of the evidence presented by the microscopical examination is both direct and indirect. In water supply, direct information is obtained on the number, mass, or bulk of the different genera present and on the known effects of these organisms upon the quality of the water in which they have their habitat. Immediate effects include (1) the production of odors and tastes, and of color and turbidity; (2) the release of oxygen and utilization of carbon dioxide by photosynthetic activities of chlorophyllaceous organisms during hours of daylight; (3) the reverse by their respiration during the night; (4) the possible clogging of conduits and filters; and (5) the production of water blooms. Surveys of the distribution of algae and related organisms are needed if their growth is to be controlled or prevented. These surveys must encompass both their horizontal and vertical distribution in lakes and reservoirs and in tributary waters. Organisms widely associated with odors and tastes in drinking water are shown in Figure 11-5.

In sewage disposal, the microscopical examination provides a measure of the pollutional status of receiving waters and their natural purification. It is of assistance, too, in explaining the mechanism of biological treatment processes.

The discharge into natural bodies of water of sewage and related wastes provides a wide variety of food materials that can be used by water-dwelling organisms, large and small. As a result there is established in the polluted waters a flora and fauna commensurate with and characteristic of the amount and quality of food material as well as the conditions of existence that are created by changes in the physical, chemical, and biological environment resulting from pollution. The ecological systems that are developed can tell the experienced biologist much about the pollutional status of the water. The many types of living things encountered can be broadly classified as *pollutional* and *cleaner-water* organisms. The relative preponderance of the one or the other group will then be a measure of pollution. Organisms that are *tolerant* to both polluted and clean water are of little value as biological indicators of water quality. Some of the

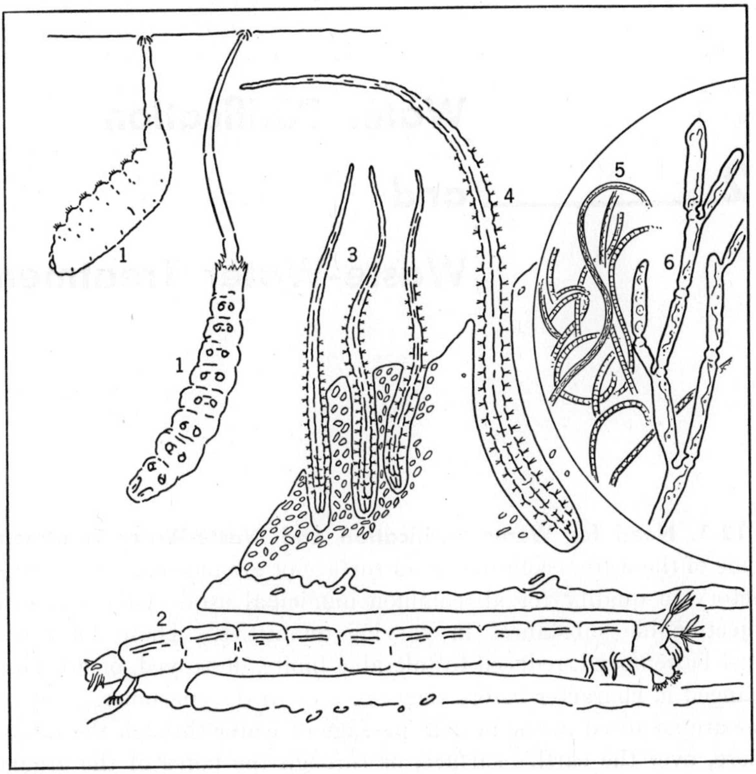

Figure 11-6. "Indicator organisms" of polluted waters. 1. Rat-tail maggot, *Eristalis,* the larva of the drone fly, ×5. 2. Blood worm, *Chironomus,* the larva of the midge fly, ×5. 3. Sludge worm, *Tubifex,* a bristle worm, ×5. 4. Sludge worm, *Limnodrilus,* a bristle worm, ×5. 5. Sewage fungus, *Sphaerotilus,* a higher bacterium, ×500. 6. Sewage fungus, *Leptomitus,* a mold, ×500.

"type organisms of heavy pollution" are shown in Figure 11-6. They include the rat-tail maggot, *Eristalis,* or larva of the drone fly; the blood worm, *Chironomus,* or larva of the midge fly; the sludge worms, *Tubifex* and *Limnodrilus;* and the so-called sewage fungi, *Sphaerotilus* and *Leptomitus. Sphaerotilus* is actually a higher bacterium.

Microscopic organisms are an integral part of the food economy of fish, shellfish, and other aquatic organisms. The microscopic organisms may, however, be a hindrance as well as an aid to the growth of higher aquatic life.

The collection of plankton and other organisms may involve the use of specialized equipment, as may their concentration for the determination of their quantitative presence.

12 Water Purification and Waste-Water Treatment

12-1. Need for Water Purification and Waste-Water Treatment. Some of the waters collected from surface or ground sources are satisfactory in quality for all common municipal uses. Others contain objectionable substances in varying quantities. These substances must be removed, reduced to tolerable limits, destroyed, or otherwise changed in character before they are sent to the consumer. Impurities are acquired in the normal passage of water through the atmosphere, over the earth's surface, or through the pores of the ground. They are associated in their pollutional aspects with man's activities and, in particular, with his own use of water in household and industry and his discharge of spent water into natural water courses. Water can acquire impurities also within the water-supply system. Some of the heavy metals, such as lead, copper, zinc, and iron, are traceable to corrosion of metallic pipes that convey the water to its point of use, and there are opportunities for contamination of the water through cross-connection with impure water supplies and through back-flow in plumbing systems.

The nature of the raw water in its relation to the required standards of water quality determines the method of treatment to be employed. Purification works in a public water-supply system must be selected and designed to deliver water that, if not already so, has been made (1) hygienically safe, (2) esthetically attractive and palatable, and (3) economically satisfactory for the uses to which it is to be put.

The water-carriage system of sewerage provides a simple and economical means for transporting unsightly, putrescible, and dangerous waste matters away from household and industry. However, it concentrates potential nuisances and dangers at the terminus of the collecting system, where the sewage must be discharged either into a natural drainage channel (dilution) or, more seldom, onto land (irrigation). Normally, sewage matters must be unloaded from the transporting water prior to its disposal in order that receiving waters may be protected against damage in one or more of the following forms: (1) contamination of water supplies, bathing places, shellfish layings, and ice supplies; (2) pollution sufficient in concentration to render the receiving waters unsightly or malodorous; (3) destruction of food fish and other valuable aquatic life; and (4) other impairment of the usefulness of natural waters for recreation, commerce, or industry. This unloading operation is assigned to sewage-treatment plants. The required degree of treatment depends (*a*) upon the nature and relative volume of the receiving water and (*b*) upon the purposes the water is to serve in the water economy of the region.

12-2. Unit Operations of Water and Sewage Treatment. Fundamentally, water purification and waste-water treatment do not differ in principle, but only in the degree of pollution of the influent water with which they have to contend and the quality of the effluent that they must turn out. For this reason, they share in most essentials the same unit operations of treatment, operations that are employed for the removal of unwanted or objectionable substances, or for the transformation of these substances into acceptable form. But they do not share them in the same intensity. An outline of the most important unit operations follows.

1. *Gas Exchange.* An operation by which gases are precipitated from water or taken into solution by water through exposure of the water to air or to special atmospheres under normal, increased, or reduced pressures. Examples of gas exchange are: (1) the addition of oxygen to water or waste water by spray or bubble aeration for deferrization and demanganization (water) and for the creation or maintenance of aerobic conditions (waste water); (2) the removal of carbon dioxide, hydrogen sulfide, and volatile, odorous substances from water by spray or bubble aeration for odor and corrosion control; (3) the addition of ozone or chlorine to water or waste water in ozone towers and gas chlorinators respectively for disinfection; and (4) the removal of oxygen from water by evacuation in degasifiers for corrosion control. The release of methane and carbon dioxide from sewage sludge that is undergoing decomposition is, in principle, also a form of gas exchange. On the other hand, the oxygenation of water for deferrization and demanganization is, in principle, also a form of chemical precipitation.

2. *Screening.* An operation whereby floating and suspended matter that is larger in size than the openings of the screening device is strained out and removed for disposal. Shredding devices combined with screens convert coarse matter into fine matter. This is normally returned to the water to be removed by sedimentation. Examples are: (1) the removal from water of leaves, sticks, and other debris by racks and screens, and the straining out of algae by what are called microscreens; and (2) the removal from sewage of coarse suspended and floating matter by racks and of finer suspended matter by screens. The comminution of substances intercepted by screens within the sewage is a special use of screens. Rakings and screenings must be removed from racks and screens for disposal by burial, incineration, or digestion (including composting). Comminution of screenings and their return to the flowing sewage is an indirect method of screenings disposal. They become a part of the sewage sludge (Chapter 17).

3. *Sedimentation.* An operation by which the carrying and scouring powers of flowing water are reduced in magnitude until suspended particles settle out by gravitational pull and are not resuspended by scour. Examples are: (1) the removal of sand and heavy silt from water in settling basins; (2) the collection of heavy mineral solids from waste waters by differential sedimentation and scour (grit chambers); (3) the removal of settleable, suspended sewage solids in settling tanks; and (4) the removal from water and sewage of non-settleable substances that have been rendered settleable by chemical or biological coagulation or precipitation. The settled substances are known as sludge. This must be removed from the sedimentation devices for disposal with or without treatment.

4. *Flotation.* An operation by which (*a*) the transporting power of flowing water is reduced by quiescence or (*b*) the suspending power of water is overcome by quiescence and by the addition of flotation agents. Substances lighter than water rise to the water surface and are skimmed off. Flotation agents include fine air bubbles and chemical compounds that, singly or in combination, are wetting and foaming agents. If these agents are also hydrophobic, their power of flotation is increased. Examples are: (1) the removal of grease and oil from waste waters with or without the benefit of aeration in skimming tanks or tanks that serve the primary purpose of sedimentation; (2) the release of air into waste waters by the diffusion of compressed air or by precipitation of dissolved air through reduction of the pressure of the overlying atmosphere, the fine air bubbles attaching themselves to suspended particles, imparting buoyancy to them, and lifting them to the surface; and (3) the addition to water and waste water of flotation agents that attach themselves to suspended matter or attach suspended matter to bubbles of air and lift the particles to the surface. The skimmings or foam must be removed from the flotation device and disposed of. Examples of flotation agents are the anionic, neutral, or cationic detergents, and also oil, grease, resin, and glue.

5. *Chemical Coagulation.* An operation of chemical treatment in which floc-forming chemicals are added to water and waste water for the purpose of enmeshing, or combining with, settleable, but more particularly with non-settleable, suspended and colloidal matter. Rapidly settling aggregates, or flocs, are created. The added chemicals, called coagulants, are soluble, but

they are precipitated by reacting with substances in or added to the water or waste water. In water purification, the floc that has not been removed by sedimentation (see 3) is generally removed by filtration. The most common coagulants are aluminum and iron salts while the precipitating substances are, usually, naturally present alkalinity or, more rarely, added alkalinity released by substances such as soda ash. Examples are: (1) the addition of aluminum sulfate to water and (2) of ferric chloride to water or waste water.[1] Dosing, mixing, and flocculating (or stirring) devices are needed adjuncts to the required settling basins.

6. *Chemical Precipitation.* An operation whereby dissolved substances are thrown out of solution. The added chemicals are soluble and react with chemicals in the water or waste water to precipitate them. Examples are: (1) flocculation of iron by the addition of lime to iron-containing water or waste water, the reaction being carried to completion by dissolved oxygen, and sedimentation of suspended solids being enhanced by the resulting coagulation; (2) precipitation of iron and manganese from water by aeration, the reaction being one of oxidation by dissolved oxygen; (3) softening of water by the addition of lime (carbonate hardness) and soda ash (noncarbonate hardness); and (4) precipitation of fluorides from water by the addition of tricalcium phosphate, or by their precipitation along with magnesium in connection with water softening. Dosing, mixing, and flocculating devices are needed adjuncts to required settling basins (see 5 and 3).

7. *Ion Exchange.* An operation by which certain ions in water are exchanged for complementary ions that are part of the complex of a solid exchange medium. Examples are: (1) the exchange of calcium and magnesium for sodium by passage of water through a bed of sodium zeolite which is regenerated by brine (base or cation exchange); (2) the exchange of sodium and potassium as well as calcium and magnesium by synthetic organic cation exchangers and absorption of the acids produced on other synthetic organic anion exchangers, the cation exchanger being regenerated with acid, the anion exchanger with sodium carbonate; and (3) the precipitation of iron and manganese on manganese zeolite and the regeneration of the zeolite with potassium permanganate. In a sense the last example is one of surface or contact precipitation rather than ion exchange. The by-products of ion exchange are the spent, regenerating washes.

8. *Physical Adsorption and Contact.* An operation in which adsorptive and other physical interfacial forces combine to remove substances from solution and to concentrate them at the interface, sometimes as precipitates. Examples are: (1) the adsorption on beds of coke, crushed stone, or other granular materials, of iron and manganese that are precipitating from water; and (2) the adsorption of odor- and taste-producing molecules on beds of granular carbon or on powdered activated carbon that is suspended in water and removed by sedimentation or filtration. Biological contact processes are outlined in the next paragraph of this section. Contact beds are regenerated by washing. Spent powdered activated carbon is wasted.

[1] The addition of coagulating chemicals to waste water is erroneously, but generally, referred to as chemical precipitation. The explanation of this usage of the term precipitation is traceable to the fact that flocculation of sewage was first employed with sewages rich in iron wastes to which only lime had to be added to produce settling flocs.

9. *Biological Flocculation and Precipitation.* A contact operation in which the formation of biologically active flocs or slimes of living organisms is promoted under aerobic conditions for the purpose of transferring to the floc or slime interface putrescible, principally finely divided and dissolved, substances. These substances are partially stabilized by biological activity, some of the soluble and stable end products of biological activity being returned to the water. Examples are: (1) the biological treatment of sewage on trickling filters and (2) the aeration of sewage in activated-sludge units. The filtration of water through slow sand filters is, in part, biological contact. The treatment of sewage on intermittent sand filters and the disposal of sewage by irrigation are likewise, in part, biological contact. The biological slimes are unloaded intermittently from trickling filters as settleable solids or trickling-filter humus, and more or less continuously as excess activated sludge from the settling tanks that follow activated sludge units.

10. *Filtration.* An operation in which straining, sedimentation, and interfacial contact combine to transfer suspended matter onto grains of sand, coal, or other granular materials from which it must later be removed. Examples are: (1) the slow filtration of water through beds of sand, the clogged surface layers of which are scraped off successively but relatively infrequently and washed before being returned to the bed; (2) the even slower filtration of sewage through beds of sand (usually natural deposits) that are allowed to rest and reaerate between dosings; and (3) the rapid filtration of water through beds of sand, the accumulated impurities being scoured from the filter medium in place through the action on it, singly or in combination, of water, air, or mechanical rakes. The wash water is a by-product of water filtration.

11. *Disinfection.* An operation by which infectious organisms are killed. Examples are: (1) the chlorination of water and sewage (chemical disinfection) and (2) the boiling of water (heat disinfection). Dosing, mixing, and detention are ancillary operations. Since disinfection is a time-concentration phenomenon, the use of detention tanks as well as dosing devices is important.

12. *Chemical Stabilization.* A variety of operations in which chemicals are added for the purpose of converting objectionable substances into unobjectionable forms without their removal. Examples are: (1) the chlorination of water for the oxidation of hydrogen sulfide into sulfate; (2) the liming of water or passage of water through chips of marble or limestone for the conversion of carbon dioxide into soluble bicarbonate; (3) the recarbonation of water (that has been softened by excess-lime treatment) to convert excess lime into soluble bicarbonate; (4) the superchlorination of water or addition of chlorine dioxide for the oxidation of odor-producing substances; (5) the removal of excess chlorine by reducing agents such as sulfur dioxide; (6) the addition to water of complex phosphates to keep iron in solution; and (7) the addition to water of lime, complex phosphates, or sodium silicate to protect metallic surfaces by forming deposit coatings on them or otherwise reducing the corrosive action of water.

13. *Fluoridation.* An operation whereby the fluoride content of water is raised to a desirable value by the addition of soluble fluorine compounds for the control of dental caries in children.

14. *Odor and Taste Control.* An operation that may include a number of different activities. Examples are: (1) the destruction of algae or prevention of algal growths by the addition of copper sulfate or other copper compounds to water; (2) the use of powdered activated carbon to black out reservoirs, preventing the growth of algae and adsorbing odors and tastes; and (3) the addition to water of oxidants such as chlorine (superchlorination and breakpoint chlorination) or chlorine dioxide for the destruction of odor- and taste-producing substances rather than, or in addition to, disinfection.

This list, although fairly complete, by no means includes all of the unit operations of water purification and waste-water treatment. There are specialized operations in connection with the preparation of boiler feed-water, other industrial process waters, and industrial waste-waters. Some of these are identified in Chapter 20. The unit operations of sludge treatment and methods of sludge disposal are considered in Section 17-2.

The unit operations of water purification and waste-water treatment are applied in treatment works in many different combinations to meet (1), in water-purification works, existing conditions of raw-water quality and requirements of pure-water quality, and (2), in sewage-treatment works, prevailing situations of sewage concentration, composition, and condition and specifications of effluent quality. The selection and elaboration of the unit operations to be employed constitutes the process design of the treatment works.

The design of water-purification and sewage-treatment works is based (1) upon an understanding of the operation of the various treatment processes and devices (process design); (2) upon a knowledge of the factors affecting the flow of the water, waste-water, sludge, and often air through the various structures and conduits employed (hydraulic design); and (3) upon a comprehension of the structural behavior of these works (structural design). Structural design is not considered in this book.

12-3. Municipal Water Purification Plants. In order to direct attention to feasible combinations of water-treatment operations, the attributes of water affected by the more conventional unit operations and processes of treatment are listed in Table 12-1. There, the relative degree of effectiveness of each unit operation or process is indicated by the number of plus signs (+) up to a limit of four; adverse effects are shown by minus signs (−) also to degree; and indirect effects are recorded by parentheses placed around the signs. Limitations and other factors are explained in footnotes.

As shown in Table 12-1, the most common classes of municipal water-purification works and their principal functions are:

TABLE 12-1. Common Attributes of Water Affected by Conventional Unit Operations and Water-Treatment Processes

Attribute (*a*)	Aeration (*b*)	Coagulation and Sedimentation (*c*)	Lime-Soda Softening and Sedimentation (*d*)	Slow Sand Filtration without (*c*) (*e*)	Rapid Sand Filtration Preceded by (*c*) (*f*)	Disinfection (Chlorination) (*g*)
Bacteria	0	++	(+++) (1,2)	++++	++++	++++
Color	0	+++	0	++	++++	0
Turbidity	0	+++	(++) (2)	++++ (3)	++++	0
Odor and taste	++ (4)	(+)	(++) (2)	++	(++)	++++ (5) −− (6)
Hardness	+	(−−) (7)	++++	0	(−−) (7)	0
Corrosiveness	+++ (8) −−− (9)	(−−) (10)	(11)	0	(−−) (10)	0
Iron and manganese	+++	+ (12)	(++)	++++ (12)	++++ (12)	0

(1) When very high *p*H values are produced by excess lime treatment; (2) by inclusion in precipitates; (3) but filters clog too rapidly at high turbidities; (4) not including chlorophenol tastes; (5) when break-point chlorination is employed or superchlorination is followed by dechlorination; (6) when (5) is not employed in the presence of intense odors and tastes; (7) some coagulants convert carbonates into sulfates; (8) by removal of carbon dioxide; (9) by addition of oxygen when it is low; (10) some coagulants release carbon dioxide; (11) variable, some metals are attacked at high *p*H values; (12) after aeration.

1. Filtration plants [2] that remove objectionable color, turbidity, and bacteria as well as other harmful organisms by filtration through sand after necessary preparation of the water by coagulation and sedimentation.

2. Deferrization and demanganization plants [2] that remove excessive amounts of iron and manganese by oxidizing the soluble ferrous and manganous compounds and converting them into insoluble ferric and manganic compounds which are removable by sedimentation and filtration.

3. Softening plants [2] that remove excessive amounts of scale-forming, soap-consuming compounds, chiefly the soluble bicarbonates, chlorides, and sulfates of calcium and magnesium (*a*) by the addition of lime and soda ash which precipitate calcium as a carbonate and magnesium as a hydrate, or (*b*) by passage of the water through cation-exchange media that exchange sodium for calcium and magnesium ions and are themselves regenerated by brine.

[2] In North America, there are many filtration plants, large and small, that incorporate the treatment processes sketched in Figure 12-1*a*. Among them are the filter plants of (1) Buffalo, N. Y., Cleveland, Ohio, Detroit, Mich., and Milwaukee, Wis., on the Great Lakes; (2) Cincinnati, Ohio, Louisville, Ky., Minneapolis and St. Paul, Minn., St. Louis, Mo., and New Orleans, La., in the drainage basin of the Mississippi River; and (3) Cambridge, Mass., Albany, N. Y., and Providence, R. I., which filter impounded upland supplies. Deferrization plants like that outlined in Figure 12-1*b* are numerous in New England, among them those at Lowell and Amesbury, Mass., both of which treat ground waters. Slow sand filters not employed in connection with deferrization and, therefore, without coke prefilters are in operation (1) at Springfield, Mass., and Hartford, Conn., for impounded upland waters, and (2) at Philadelphia and Pittsburgh, Pa., and Washington, D. C., for the waters of large streams. Softening plants (Figure 12-1c) are found at Columbus, Ohio (Scioto River); Springfield, Ill. (impounded supply); Kansas City, Mo. (Missouri River); Los Angeles, Cal. (Colorado River); and numerous smaller places.

Diagrammatic sketches of purification plants of this kind are presented in Figure 12-1. Today, all but unusually well-protected ground-water supplies are chlorinated to assure their disinfection. Many waters are treated with lime or other chemicals to reduce their tendency to corrode iron and other metals with which they come into contact and so to maintain their quality during distribution as well as to insure longer life to the metallic portions of the water works. Waters containing odor- or taste-producing substances are treated with activated carbon that adsorbs most of these undesirable substances, or with taste-destroying doses of chlorine or chlorine dioxide. Numerous other treatment methods have been devised to meet special needs. Allowable pollutional loadings of water-filtration plants are discussed in Section 15-13.

12-4. Purification of Rural Water Supplies. The sources available for rural water supplies are the same as those for municipal water supplies. Hence the quality and need for purification of rural and municipal supplies are also much alike. Because most water-purification operations require skillful management which is rarely obtainable under rural, individualistic practices, it is advisable to seek, wherever possible, waters that do not need to be purified. Many ground waters fall into this category. Roof water and surface water are best passed through sand filters at low rates (Section 15-1). Iron-bearing waters are either aerated or filtered or treated in manganese-cation exchange units (Section 14-5). Soft, corrosive ground waters rich in carbon dioxide are rendered less aggressive by passage through a bed or tank of marble or limestone chips. Waters that must be disinfected are normally chlorinated by dosing devices that proportion the addition of a chlorine solution to the flow of water. Often the householder prefers to boil drinking water in order to insure its bacteriological safety.

12-5. Composition of Municipal Sewage. The wastes discharged from households and related establishments, including hotels, hospitals, restaurants, offices, and commercial buildings, are composited within the sewerage system to produce relatively constant per capita amounts of suspended solids, of organic matter as measured in terms of biochemical oxygen demand, and of other substances that are of special concern in the disposal of sewage. Average values for domestic sewage are presented in Table 12-2. The per capita contribution of BOD, for example, is 54 grams or 0.119 lb. If the nature and capacity of the industries of the community are known, an estimate can be made also of the per capita contribution, or better the popu-

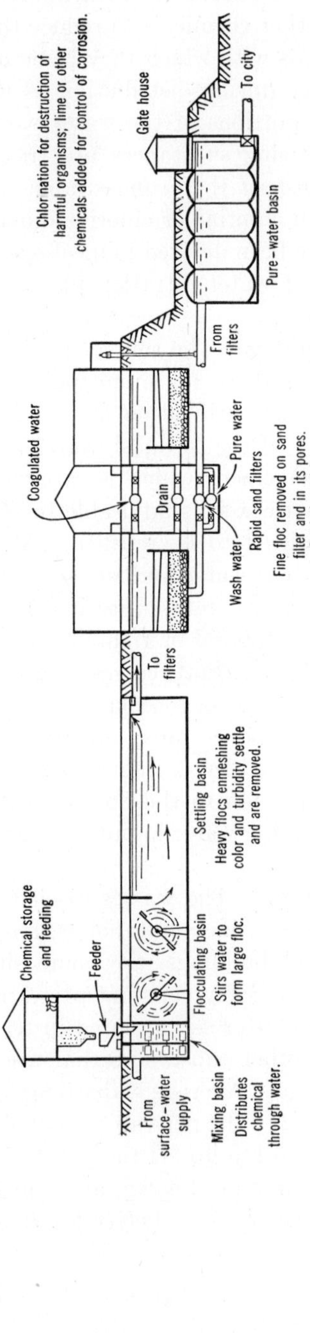

a. Filtration plant including coagulation, settling, filtration, chlorination, corrosion control, and pure-water storage.

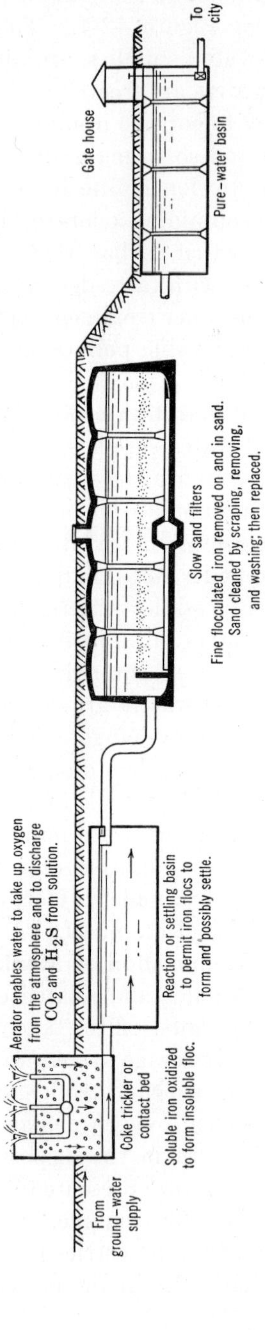

b. Deferrization plant including aeration, contact treatment, filtration, and pure-water storage.

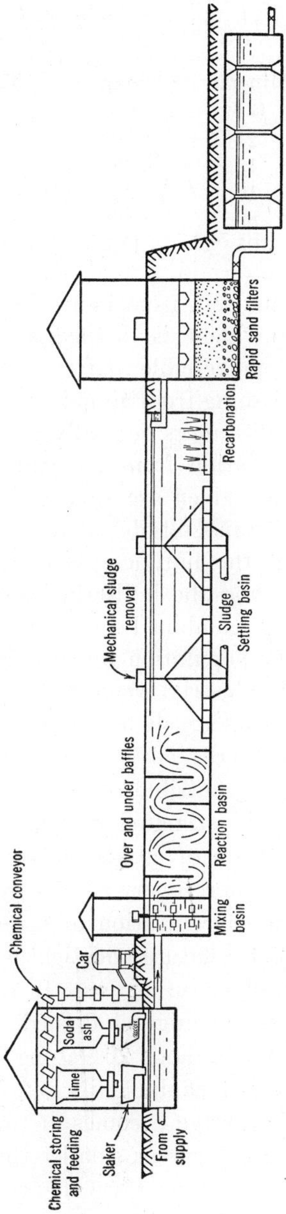

c. Softening plant including addition of softening chemicals, settling, recarbonation, filtration, and pure-water storage.

Figure 12-1. Common types of water-purification plants.

TABLE 12-2. Average Per Capita Solids and BOD in Domestic Sewage

[grams/capita/day (1 gram per capita = 2.2 lb per 1,000 population)]

State of Solids (1)	Mineral (2)	Organic (3)	Total (4)	5-Day, 20 C BOD (5)
1. Suspended	25	65	90	42
a. Settleable	15	39	54	19
b. Non-settleable	10	26	36	23
2. Dissolved	80	80	160	12
3. Total	105	145	250	54

lation equivalent, of waste matters from industrial sources (Section 20-7). The population equivalent is defined as the ratio of the amount of suspended solids, putrescible matter in terms of BOD, or other significant substances issuing from an industry to the per capita amount of these respective substances normally found in domestic or combined sewage. Some variation from the figures in Table 12-2 must be expected. The values given are affected by the wealth and habits of the population. The magnitudes of the dissolved and total solids are functions, too, of the hardness and other mineral substances in the water supply and the infiltering ground water. The BOD population equivalent of combined sewage varies widely. It is about 1.4 times the tributary population for combined systems that include a normal amount of industrial waste water.

Of the organic matter in average domestic sewage about 40% is composed of nitrogenous substances, 50% of carbohydrates, and 10% of fats. The daily per capita contribution of nitrogen (as N) and fats (as ether-soluble matter) is estimated at 10 and 15 grams respectively. These general figures are of interest in connection with the fertilizing value of sewage or the recovery of fats from sewage.

The strength of sewage or concentration of sewage matters in it depends upon water use, general nature and tightness of the system, and the degree of admission of storm waters. In the United States, the volume of domestic sewage averages 100 gpcd. Since 1 gram of waste substance per capita daily equals $264/Q$ mg/l, where Q is the sewage flow in gpcd, 1 gram per capita daily = 2.64 mg/l, and the average strength of domestic sewage becomes of the order shown in Table 12-3. For sewage flows larger or smaller than 100 gpcd, the concentrations of the various substances are changed more or less in inverse proportion, unless the municipal water or infiltering ground water contains unusually large amounts of solid matter.

TABLE 12-3. Average Composition of Domestic Sewage, mg/1

State of Solids (1)	Mineral (2)	Organic (3)	Total (4)	5-Day 20 C BOD (5)
1. Suspended	65	170	235	110
a. Settleable	40	100	140	50
b. Non-settleable	25	70	95	60
2. Dissolved	210	210	420	30
3. Total	275	380	655	140

The condition of sewage at the outfall of the sewerage system, or at the treatment works, is a function of the time of travel in the collecting system and the temperature of the sewage. Long lines, low grades (sluggish flow), and high temperatures decrease the freshness of the sewage. Fresh domestic sewage has little odor; it is gray in color; the sewage solids are only slightly comminuted; and dissolved oxygen is present. As decomposition becomes active, the sewage becomes stale, and it may become septic if the dissolved oxygen is exhausted. Septic sewage has a foul odor (hydrogen sulfide); its color is black; and the floating and suspended solids are disintegrated.

In the course of the day, sewage varies in strength as well as in flow. The interrelationship is idealized in Figure 12-2. The volume of flow generally reaches a maximum about noon, and the strength of the sewage is also greatest at that time. The collection of representative samples is not a simple matter. Daily samples must be composited in proportion to flow if they are to reflect average conditions. Attention must be paid also to the vertical distribution of suspended solids in conduits. They are generally most concentrated near the bottom.

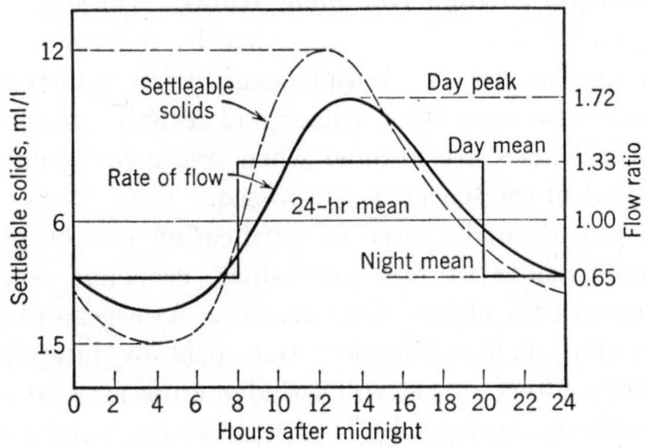

Figure 12-2. Hourly variation in flow and strength of municipal sewage. *After Imhoff.*

The nature and composition of industrial waste waters are discussed in Section 20-7.

12-6. Synthetic Detergents in Sewage. Synthetic detergents are finding their way into sewers in increasing quantities from both household and industry. When the detergents are present in sufficient concentration, some of the properties that make them good cleansing agents will cause them to interfere with the normal operation of certain waste-water treatment processes. For this reason they are of special interest. Even in great dilution, the synthetic detergents lower the surface, or interfacial, tension of water and increase its ability to wet substances with which it comes into contact. They are little affected in their cleansing action by acid or alkali, or by the alkaline earth metals. Other properties are: (1) the emulsifying of grease and oil; (2) the peptizing or deflocculating of colloids; (3) flotation and foaming; and (4) destruction of bacteria and other living organisms. There are three general types of synthetic detergents: anionic (commonly containing as their soluble groups sodium sulfates and sulfonates), cationic (mainly quaternary ammonium compounds), and non-ionic (condensation products of ethylene oxide with phenolic materials or fatty acids). The anionic detergents are in widest general use. Their cost is small, and they are stable in hard waters. The cationic detergents are quite expensive, but they possess the best bactericidal and bacteriostatic properties. Their use is normally confined to the disinfection of eating utensils. The BOD of the synthetic detergents is much smaller than that of soap, but their emulsification of grease and oil may carry a larger than normal BOD load through settling basins onto biological treatment units.

12-7. Municipal Sewage Treatment Works. The degree of waste-water treatment that can be accomplished by individual unit operations and treatment processes may be gaged from Table 12-4.

Discrepancies between these values and recorded results are to be expected. Efficiencies are lowered when treatment plants are overloaded and part of the sewage is by-passed.

Although any desired degree of purification can be obtained by suitable combinations of unit operations, economic considerations ultimately govern the choice of operations. As a general rule, treatment works that include complete treatment by intermittent sand filters, trickling filters, or activated-sludge units may be expected to turn out an effluent having a BOD of 10 to 20 mg/l and a suspended-solids content of less than 30 mg/l. Such effluents ordinarily are

TABLE 12-4. Relative Efficiencies of Sewage-Treatment Operations and Processes

Percentage Removal

Treatment Operation or Process (a)	5-Day, 20 C BOD (b)	Suspended Solids (c)	Bacteria (d)
1. Fine screening	5–10	2–20	10–20
2. Chlorination of raw or settled sewage	15–30	.....	90–95
3. Plain sedimentation	25–40	40–70	25–75
4. Chemical precipitation	50–85	70–90	40–80
5. Trickling filtration preceded and followed by plain sedimentation (high and low rate)	65–95	65–92	80–95
6. Activated-sludge treatment preceded and followed by plain sedimentation (high and low rate)	65–95	65–95	80–98
7. Intermittent sand filtration	90–95	85–95	95–98
8. Chlorination of biologically treated sewage	.....	.....	98–99

stable for 10 days or more. Partial treatment calls for modification of the treatment operations.

Combinations of unit operations often used in sewage-treatment practice are illustrated in Figure 12-3. Numerous other methods or combinations of methods are in use. The plants shown in Figure 12-3 give complete treatment to sewage and sludge.[3] Partial treatment of either or both is often adequate to satisfy local needs. Seasonal operation of plants or parts of plants to secure a higher degree of treatment at critical times of the year is sometimes sufficient, for example during periods of low runoff and high recreational use of the receiving water: bathing, boating, etc.

The works shown can be operated to remove from 80 to 95% or more of the suspended solids, putrescible matter, and bacteria. Chlorination of the effluent can increase the destruction of bacteria

[3] The combination of sedimentation and sludge digestion in a two-storied tank or in separate settling and digestion tanks, followed by biological treatment of the clarified sewage on a trickling filter (examples *a* and *b* in Figure 12-3), has found wide favor in North America, particularly in cities of moderate size: Fitchburg and Worcester, Mass.; Reading, Pa.; Schenectady, N. Y.; Trenton, N. J.; and Atlanta, Ga. Plain sedimentation followed by activated-sludge treatment with or without separate sludge digestion has found widest use in large treatment works (example c in Figure 12-3): the Tallman's Island, Bowery Bay, and Jamaica Bay plants of New York, N. Y.; the North Side and Southwest Side plants of Chicago, Ill.; the Easterly Works of Cleveland, O.; and many smaller places.

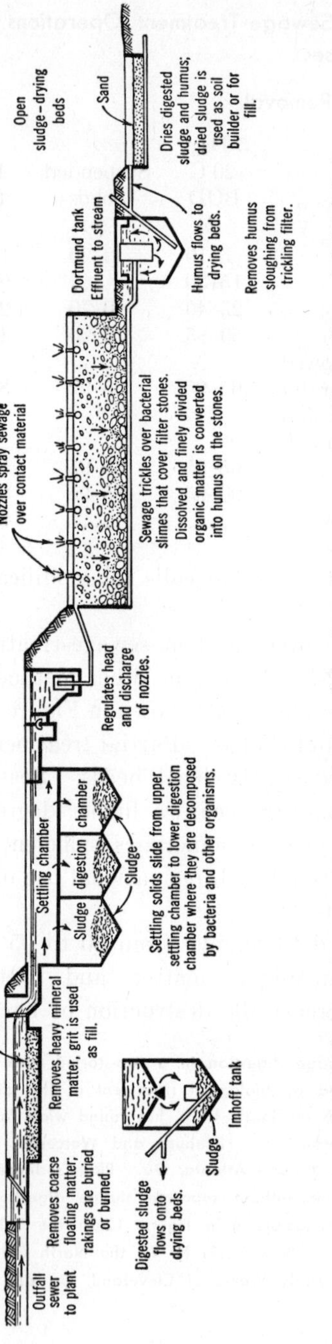

a. Trickling filter including coarse screening, grit removal, plain sedimentation, contact treatment, final settling, and sludge drying.

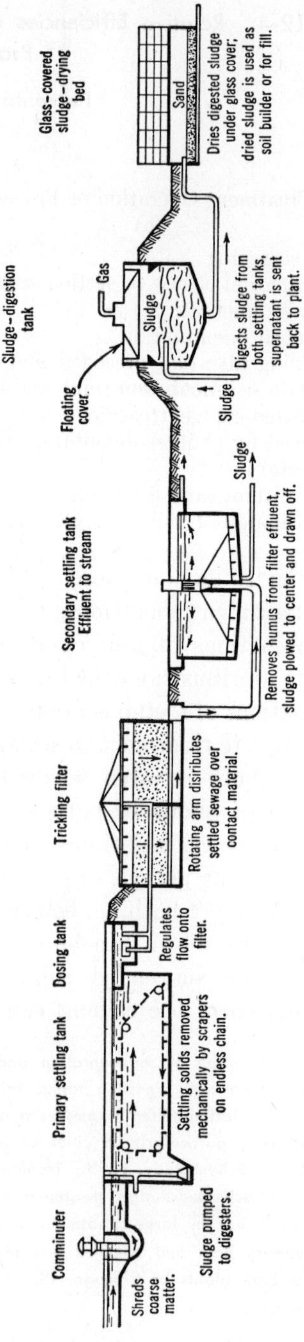

b. Trickling filter including comminution, plain sedimentation, contact treatment, final settling, and digestion and drying of sludge.

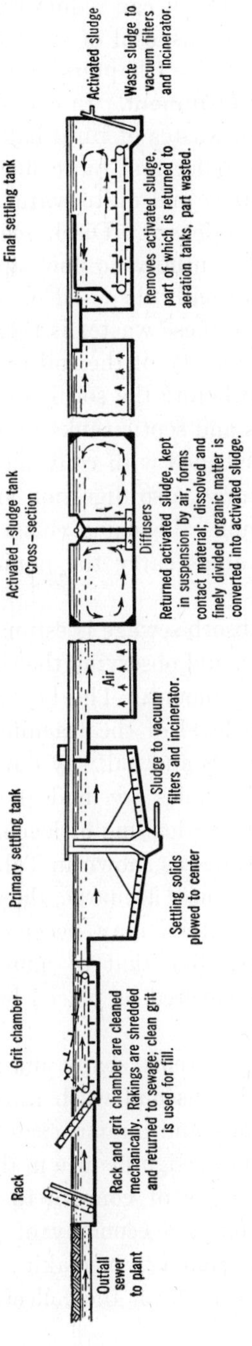
Outfall
sewer
to plant
Rack
Grit chamber
Rack and grit chamber are cleaned mechanically. Rakings are shredded and returned to sewage; clean grit is used for fill.
Primary settling tank
Settling solids plowed to center
Sludge to vacuum filters and incinerator.
Air
Activated-sludge tank
Cross-section
Diffusers
Returned activated sludge, kept in suspension by air, forms contact material; dissolved and finely divided organic matter is converted into activated sludge.
Final settling tank
Removes activated sludge, part of which is returned to aeration tanks, part wasted.
Activated sludge
Waste sludge to vacuum filters and incinerator.

***c.* Activated-sludge plant including coarse screening, grit removal, plain sedimentation, contact treatment, and final settling. Sludge is partly dewatered on vacuum filters and then incinerated.**

Figure 12-3. Common types of sewage-treatment plants.

to 99% or more. Partial treatment can reduce the removal values to between 40 and 70%. For the disposal of sewage onto land (irrigation) or into water (dilution), see Chapters 15 and 19, respectively.

12-8. Rural Waste-Water Treatment. In comparison with municipal sewage, the water-carried wastes of rural habitations and similar buildings are likely to be smaller and more fluctuating in volume; fresher and more concentrated; and quite warm, greasy, and soapy as flushes of wash water are released. Discharge is largely confined to 16 hr of the day, with substantially no flow at night.

Rural waste waters are normally disposed of in the ground. The capacity of the soil to receive these wastes is then of controlling importance. The absorptive capacity of the soil is greatly increased if settleable solids are removed before the soil is called upon to receive the waste waters. Cesspools and septic tanks incorporate sedimentation and, since they can be cleaned with convenience only after long intervals of time (1 to 3 years), also digestion and consolidation of the deposited sludge and scum. Leaching cesspools and subsurface irrigation fields or seepage areas carry the liquid fraction into the soil.

The ability of the soil to absorb sewage is estimated by digging test holes, filling them with water, and observing the time required for the water level to drop a given amount. The bottom of the test hole should be at the percolating level of the leaching device, i.e., 18 to 36 in. deep for irrigation laterals and halfway down the dry masonry for leaching cesspools. If test holes are made 1 ft square and filled with 6 in. of water, the allowable loading of leaching devices may be estimated from the seepage times as shown in Table 12-5.

When the volumes of waste water are large, the use of Imhoff tanks and sand beds, or trickling filters, may become more economical. Their design and operation is like that of municipal installations. However, they are generally covered or placed below the surface of the ground.

In the absence of plumbing systems, soapy and greasy waters from the kitchen and from hand basins and wash tubs are emptied onto the ground or into soakage pits and human excreta are deposited in privies. Apart from their general significance in the protection of the health of rural areas, privies are of concern to sanitary engineers (1) in evaluating the need for and economy of private and public sewerage and sewage disposal and (2) in making privy construction an integral part of the general plan for the collection and disposal of

TABLE 12-5. Required Area of Absorption Trenches

Square feet of trench bottom per bedroom

U. S. Public Health Service, *Studies on Household Sewage Disposal Systems*, Part III, 1954

Time for Water in Test Hole to Fall 1 in., min	No Garbage Grinder or Automatic Washer	With Garbage Grinder	With Automatic Washer	With Garbage Grinder and Automatic Washer
2 or less	50	65	75	85
3	60	75	85	100
4	70	85	95	115
5	75	90	105	125
10	100	120	135	165
15	115	140	160	190
30	150	180	205	250
45	180	215	245	300
60	200	240	275	330
over 60	Unsuitable for shallow absorption systems			

sanitary wastes. In North America, the pit privy is most widely used because of its economy and sanitary safety.

12-9. Treatment Works and Water-Quality Standards. In the evolution of standards of water quality and the creation of works for the attainment of existing standards, engineers have progressed from a prescription of removal efficiencies to one of defined quality. At one time, for example, 99.99% removal of bacteria by water-purification plants was an accepted standard without adequate regard to the bacterial load imposed upon the plants by the raw water that they received (Section 15-13). Such a standard is no longer honored. Instead, progress in water-treatment methods has permitted the establishment of defined standards of drinking-water quality. Although these standards are, in a sense, still standards of expediency (the equivalence of sterile, distilled water not yet being prescribed for drinking water), they are standards which, experience has shown, provide the greatest possible protection to health, enjoyment, and usefulness justifed by the existing economy.

In North America, the step from prescription of removal efficiency to that of defined quality has not yet been taken so fully in the treatment and disposal of sewage and other waste waters. It stands to reason, however, that completion of the step is but a matter of time and that standards for sewage-treatment plant performance will eventually involve standards that define the quality of the effluent to be discharged into a given receiving water rather than the percentage removal of impurities to be obtained in a treatment plant. The advances that have already been made in waste-water treatment methods support this judgment.

The sanitary control of water and waste water, furthermore, is not merely a matter of suitable water purification and waste-water treatment. It enters into every phase of water-works and waste-water works activity.

For water, sanitary control starts with the preparation and supervision of the catchment area or source of supply; it follows the conduits through the purification works into the distribution system; and it terminates only at the fixture or equipment into which water is drawn. Each part of the works presents problems of control that are peculiar to it. For all parts, however, eternal vigilance is the price of safety.

For waste-water, sanitary control starts, where water supply ends, at the fixtures or appurtenances that receive water for discharge into the waste-water system; it follows the collecting system through the treatment works; and it terminates only after the streams or other bodies of receiving water have been returned to the condition of relative purity desired for them.

12-10. Treatment-Plant Design. Ordinarily, water-purification and sewage-treatment works are designed either by consulting engineers or, in large communities, by an engineering staff recruited for this purpose. Sound engineering thinking, unhampered by participation in the profits from construction materials, supervision of labor, and items of equipment, is needed if efficient and economical treatment works are to be built for small as well as large communities.

Proper engineering studies must precede design. Works must be fitted to existing conditions. Climate, degree of water use, nature of industrial operations, location of treatment works, and the economic status and size of the community are important factors. Generally speaking, highly mechanized and especially sensitive operations require a quality of plant supervision that can be provided economically only in large treatment works. Small works may be cheaper and safer to operate if they include only simple structures in which treatment can be accomplished with a minimum of attention.

13 Screening, Sedimentation, and Flotation

13-1. Racks and Screens. Of the coarse substances suspended or floating in water or sewage some are of such size that they can be strained or screened out of the flowing water. Screening devices fall into three general categories: (1) racks or bar screens; (2) perforated plate or fine screens; and (3) comminuters or cutting screens. Comminuters are used only in the treatment or disposal of sewage.

a. Water screens. In water-works practice, racks and screens protect intakes against debris and keep sticks, leaves, and the like out of the water drawn. The clear openings of bar racks are as small as ½ in. Intake screens normally have from 2 to 8 meshes to the inch and are made of corrosion-resistant metal. They are cleaned by water jets or a hose stream after withdrawal by hand or as a series of frames attached to a rotating, endless band. Microstrainers [1] are revolving drums covered with stainless steel wire fabric offering an opening only 35 μ in nominal size to the passage of water. They are cleaned by water sprays. They have been installed ahead of slow sand filters to remove algae and other finely suspended matters and thereby to increase filter runs appreciably (Section 15-12).

b. Waste-water screens. In the treatment of waste water, racks and screens are employed (1) to protect pumps against trash and other clogging matter and (2) to remove coarse, floating solids that are unsightly and that clog valves and nozzles.

[1] Richard Hazen, Application of the microstrainer to water treatment in Great Britain, *J. Am. Water Works Assoc., 45,* 723 (1953).

Coarse racks of steel bars have clear openings of 1 to 2 in. or more. The openings of fine racks may be as small as ⅝ in. Fine screens are expected to collect sewage matters down to $\frac{1}{16}$ in. in size. They may possess openings as small as $\frac{1}{32}$ in. in their smallest, or controlling, dimension, but they may be many inches long. Racks are cleared by hand, long-handled rakes being used for this purpose,

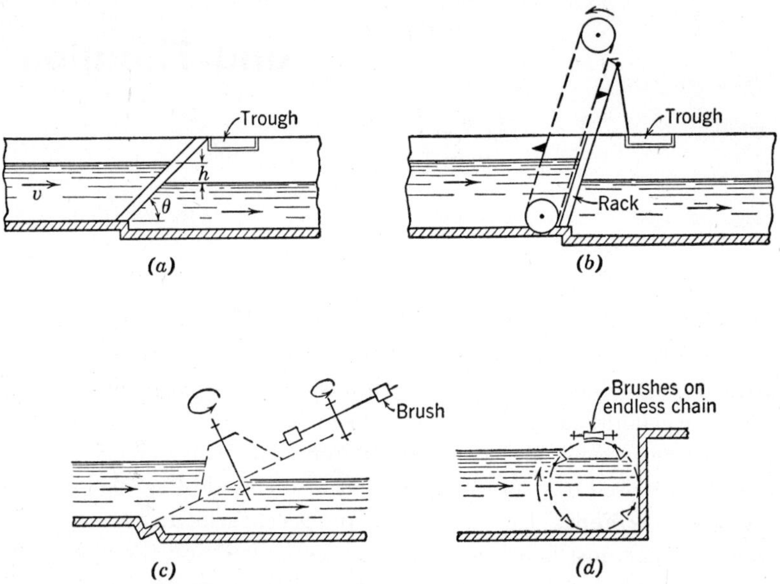

Figure 13-1. Racks and screens: (*a*) hand-cleaned inclined rack; (*b*) mechanically cleaned rack; (*c*) brush-cleaned disk screen (*Riensch-Wurl*); (*d*) brush-cleaned drum screen (*Link-Belt* Co.), sewage leaves through open end of drum.

or they are stripped by mechanical scrapers (*a* and *b* in Figure 13-1). The rack area is increased by placing the bars on a slope. Ratios of 1 vertical to 1, 2, or 3 horizontal are common. Cage racks are arranged in pairs (in series). For clearing, they are lifted from the sewage channel by elevator mechanisms. Screens are always mechanically driven. They rotate through the water as endless bands, disks, or drums and are cleaned by brushes, jets of water, or blasts of air (*c* and *d* in Figure 13-1).

Hydraulic requirements are (1) that the approach velocity of the sewage in the raking or screening channel shall not fall below a self-cleaning value or rise to a magnitude at which the rakings or screenings will be dislodged from the bars or screens; and (2) that the loss of head through the rack or screen shall not back up the flow sufficiently to place the entrant sewer under pressure. The loss of head through racks and screens can be formulated as an orifice loss. As such, it is a function of the velocity head. Kirschmer[2] has developed the following empirical relationship for racks constructed of bars of different shapes:

$$h = \beta(w/b)^{4/3} h_v \sin\theta \qquad \text{13-1}$$

Here h is the loss of head in feet, w is the maximum width of the bars facing the flow, b is the minimum width of the clear openings between pairs of bars, h_v is the velocity head (in feet) of the water as it approaches the rack (face velocity), θ is the angle of the rack with the horizontal, and β is a bar shape factor. Kirschmer's values of β are 2.42 for sharp-edged rectangular bars, 1.83 for rectangular bars with semicircular upstream face, 1.79 for circular bars, 1.67 for rectangular bars with semicircular upstream and downstream faces, and 0.76 for bars with semicircular upstream face and tapering in a symmetrical curve to a small, semicircular, downstream face (tear-drop). The effective velocity is assumed to be the geometric mean of the horizontal, longitudinal, approach velocity v and the component of the velocity at right angles to the rack ($v \sin\theta$), i.e., $v\sqrt{\sin\theta}$.

The maximum head loss through clogged racks and screens is generally held to about 2.5 ft. Racks with clear openings of 0.5, 1, and 2 in. collect respectively about 0.2, 0.1, and 0.02 cu ft of rakings per capita annually. Fine screens remove 0.2 to 1.0 cu ft of screenings or from 2 to 20% of the suspended solids, depending upon the size of the openings. Peak collections of rakings and screenings may be as high as 5 times the average quantity.

Rakings and screenings are unsightly. Their water content is high but can be reduced to about 65% in presses or centrifuges. Disposal may be by digestion with other solids, by burial, or by incineration. Removal of rakings or screenings and their separate disposal are avoided if they are shredded and returned to, or comminuted in, the flowing sewage. To this purpose, cutting devices have been added to the cleaning mechanism of racks and cylindrical, revolving, cutting screens with fine openings (comminuters) have been developed (Figure 13-2).

[2] O. Kirschmer, Untersuchungen über den Gefällsverlust an Rechen, *Trans. Hydraulic Inst.*, Munich, R. Oldenbourg, 21 (1926).

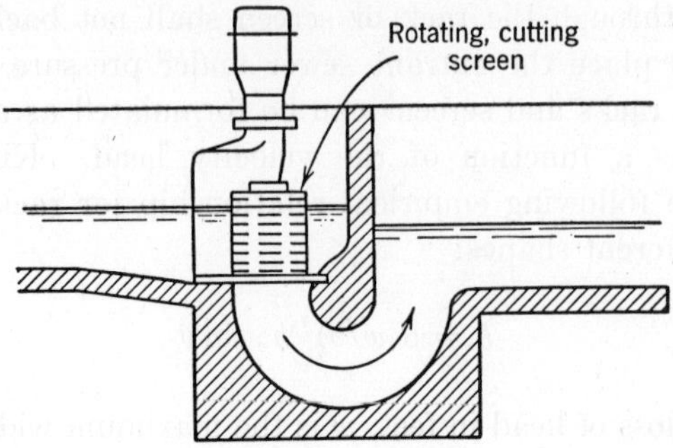

Figure 13-2. Cutting screen or comminuter. *Chicago Pump Co.*

The revolving, slotted drum of comminuters is equipped with cutters that shear the coarse materials collected on the drum against a comb. The solids are chopped down until they can pass through the $\frac{3}{16}$-in. to $\frac{3}{8}$-in. slots of the drum. Materials of this size do not tend to float at the water surface or to clog pumps. Revolving and vibrating screens are employed in the treatment of industrial waste waters (Figure 20-3).

13-2. Sedimentation. Sedimentation or the removal, by gravitational settling, of suspended particles that are heavier than water is an important factor in the natural purification of streams, lakes, and tidal waters. It is also the most widely useful operation in the treatment of water and sewage.

In modern water-purification works, settling tanks are included for the removal of (1) flocculated impurities, such as color and turbidity, and (2) precipitated impurities, such as hardness and iron. River waters that carry a heavy load of silt may be subjected to sedimentation both in advance of flocculation and afterwards.

In the treatment of sewage and industrial wastes, sedimentation is a function of: (1) grit chambers that separate heavy mineral or otherwise inert solids from the flowing liquid by differential sedimentation and scour; (2) primary, or preliminary, settling tanks that collect much of the suspended load of impurities prior to the discharge of the clarified effluent into receiving waters or prior to its further treatment; and (3) secondary, or final, settling tanks that collect those matters which have been converted into settleable solids, or otherwise rendered settleable, by biological or related treatment processes. The addition of flocculating or precipitating agents to sewage or industrial wastes may precede sedimentation and improve its efficiency.

Fill-and-draw operation of settling tanks is confined, nowadays, very largely to the preparation of boiler feed waters and the treatment of industrial wastes that are discharged in batches. Continuous-flow basins are built, almost exclusively, in modern municipal water-purification and sewage-treatment works.

Principles of Sedimentation and Flotation

13-3. Settling and Rising Velocities of Discrete Particles. When a discrete particle is falling or rising through a quiescent fluid, it will accelerate until the frictional resistance, or drag, of the fluid equals the impelling force acting upon the particle. Thereafter the particle will settle or rise at a uniform velocity.

The impelling force equals the effective weight of the particle or its weight in the suspending fluid, i.e.,

$$F_I = (\rho_s - \rho)gV \qquad 13\text{-}2$$

where F_I is the impelling force, g is the gravity constant, V is the volume of the particle, and ρ_s and ρ are respectively the mass density of the particle and of the fluid.

The drag force F_D of the fluid, on the other hand, is a function of the dynamic viscosity μ and mass density ρ of the fluid and of the velocity v_s and a characteristic diameter d of the particle. Dimensionally, therefore,

$$F_D = \phi(v_s, d, \rho, \mu)$$

or, designating dimensional relations by square brackets,

$$[F_D] = [v_s^x d^y \rho^p \mu^q]$$

Introducing the fundamental units of mass m, length l, and time t of the various parameters into this equation,

$$[mlt^{-2}] = [m^{p+q} l^{x+y-3p-q} t^{-x-q}]$$

and solving for x, y, and p in terms of q,

$$F_D = v_s^2 d^2 \rho \phi(v_s d\rho/\mu) = v_s^2 d^2 \rho \phi(\mathbf{R}) \qquad 13\text{-}3$$

where **R** is the Reynolds number.

This dimensionally derived relationship for the frictional drag has been verified experimentally.

If we substitute the cross-sectional, or projected, area A_c at right angles to the direction of settling for d^2, the dynamic pressure $\rho v_s^2/2$ for ρv_s^2, and Newton's *drag coefficient* C_D for $\phi(\mathbf{R})$,

$$F_D = C_D A_c \rho v_s^2/2 \qquad 13\text{-}4$$

The value of C_D is not constant, as Newton [3] assumed, but varies [4] with **R** as shown in Figure 13-3. For spheres, the observational relationships between C_D and **R** shown in this figure are approximated by the following equation (upper limit $\mathbf{R} = 10^4$):

$$C_D = \frac{24}{\mathbf{R}} + \frac{3}{\sqrt{\mathbf{R}}} + 0.34 \qquad 13\text{-}5$$

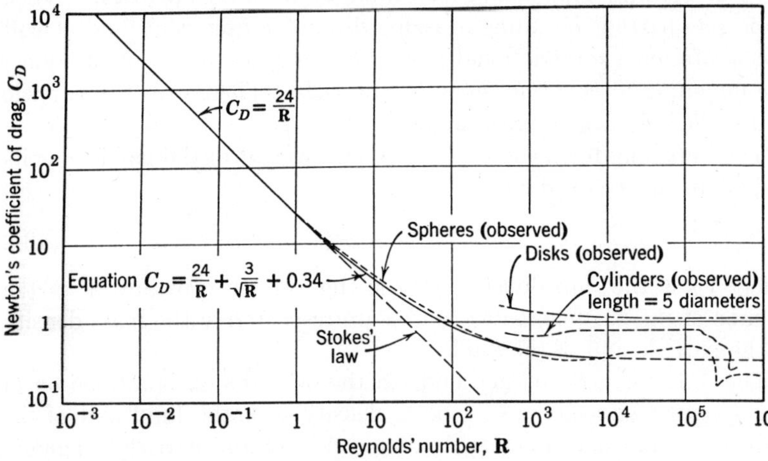

Figure 13-3. Newton's coefficient of drag for varying magnitudes of Reynolds number. "Observed curves after Camp," *Trans. Am. Soc. Civil Engrs.*, *103*, 897 (1946).

We can now equate F_I and F_D (Equations 13-2 and 13-4) and establish a general equation for the settling or rising of free and discrete particles, as follows:

$$v_s = \sqrt{\frac{2g}{C_D}\frac{\rho_s - \rho}{\rho}\frac{V}{A_c}} \qquad 13\text{-}6$$

or, for spherical particles, $V = (\pi/6)d^3$ and $A_c = (\pi/4)d^2$,

$$v_s = \sqrt{\frac{4}{3}\frac{g}{C_D}\frac{\rho_s - \rho}{\rho}d} \quad \text{or closely} \quad \sqrt{\frac{4}{3}\frac{g}{C_D}(s_s - 1)d} \qquad 13\text{-}7$$

Here s_s is the specific gravity of the particle and $d = \frac{3}{2}V/A_c = 6V/A$ where A is the surface area of the particle.

[3] *Mathematical Principles of Natural Philosophy.*

[4] This variation is similar to that for pipes.

For eddying resistance at high Reynolds numbers ($\mathbf{R} = 10^3$ to 10^4), C_D has a value of about 0.4, and

$$v_s = \sqrt{3.3g(s_s - 1)d} \qquad 13\text{-}8$$

For viscous resistance at low Reynolds numbers ($\mathbf{R} < 0.5$), $C_D = 24/\mathbf{R}$, and Equation 13-7 reads as follows:

$$v_s = \frac{g}{18}\frac{\rho_s - \rho}{\mu}d^2 \quad \text{or closely} \quad \frac{g}{18}(s_s - 1)\frac{d^2}{\nu} \qquad 13\text{-}9$$

This is Stokes's law,[5] and ν is the kinematic viscosity. Values of ν are given in Table A-3 in the back of the book.

To cover the range of possible grain sizes, curves such as those shown in Figure 13-4 are useful.

Example 13-1. Find: (*a*) the settling velocity in water at 20 C of spherical particles 5×10^{-3} cm in diameter and specific gravity 2.65; (*b*) the rising velocity of particles of the same diameter but a specific gravity of 0.80; and (*c*) the settling velocity in water at 10 C of spherical particles 10^{-1} cm in diameter and specific gravity 2.65.

a. Settling velocity of particle 5×10^{-3} cm in diameter and specific gravity 2.65.

1. From Table A–3, $\nu = 1.010 \times 10^{-2}$ cm²/sec.
2. From Equation 13-9, $v_s = \dfrac{981}{18}\dfrac{(2.65 - 1.00)}{1.01 \times 10^{-2}}(5 \times 10^{-3})^2 = 0.222$ cm/sec.
3. $\mathbf{R} = (2.22 \times 10^{-1})(5 \times 10^{-3})/(1.01 \times 10^{-2}) = 1.1 \times 10^{-1}$, and Stokes's law applies.

b. Rising velocity of particle 5×10^{-3} cm in diameter and specific gravity of 0.80.

1. From Equation 13-9, $v_s = 0.222(0.80 - 1)/(2.65 - 1) = -2.69 \times 10^{-2}$ cm/sec.
2. $\mathbf{R} = (1.1 \times 10^{-1})(2.69 \times 10^{-2})/(2.22 \times 10^{-1}) = 1.3 \times 10^{-2}$, and Stokes's law applies.

c. Settling velocity of particle 10^{-1} cm in diameter and specific gravity of 2.65.

d. From Figure 13-4, the velocity is 21 cm/sec, and Stokes's law does not apply.

The suspended matter in water and sewage is seldom truly spherical. As shown in Figure 13-3, irregularities in shape exert their greatest influence on drag at high velocities.

[5] Stokes derived his law from theoretical considerations of the motion of a spherical pendulum in a fluid. [*Trans., Cambridge Philosophical Soc., 8,* 287 (1845).]

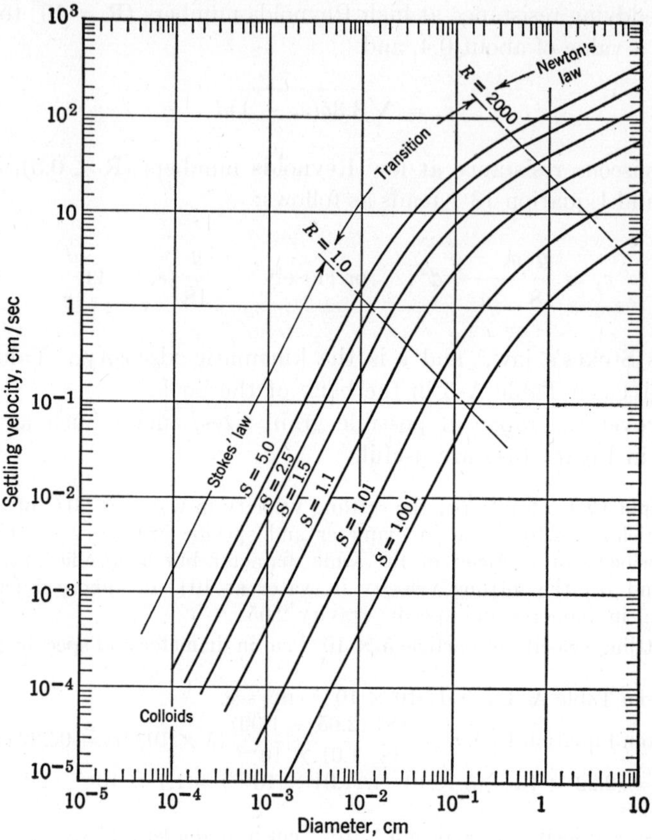

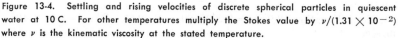

Figure 13-4. Settling and rising velocities of discrete spherical particles in quiescent water at 10 C. For other temperatures multiply the Stokes value by $\nu/(1.31 \times 10^{-2})$ where ν is the kinematic viscosity at the stated temperature.

13-4. Hindered Settling of Discrete Particles. In a suspension of discrete particles, the settling velocity of each particle remains unchanged throughout the settling period except when the particles are so closely spaced in the suspending medium that their velocity fields interfere. Under these conditions, there is an appreciable upward displacement of the fluid, and settling is hindered. Natural and induced aggregation of particles increase the volume concentration of suspended matter, but most suspensions that are subjected to sedimentation in water and sewage treatment, with the exception of activated sludge, may be considered to settle freely. If the solids suspended in water or sewage are well graded, the settling velocities may be such as to crowd the particles together when they catch up with one another as they approach the bottom of the settling tank. Settling may then be hindered locally. Crowding is produced also in vertical-flow tanks in which those particles that possess a settling velocity closely approximating that of the rising fluid accumulate in a blanket or suspended filter layer through which the rising fluid must pass. There is hindered flotation as well as hindered sedimentation.

Hydraulically, the process of hindered settling is analogous to the expansion of filtering materials in backwashing and can be formulated in those terms (Section 15-6).

13-5. Settling of Flocculent Suspensions. Most granular solids settle as discrete particles. Organic matter and the flocs formed by coagulants or zoogleal growths tend to agglomerate when they collide and to form clusters of different size, shape, and weight. The settling velocity of the clusters is ordinarily increased, and they are more readily removed. Particles collide when fast-settling particles overtake slower ones or when turbulence bumps particles together within the liquid. In vertical-flow tanks, rising particles collide with settling particles. It follows that contact, and with it possible aggregation, is greatest for a large concentration of particles of large size, large relative weight, and large size-difference in a liquid of small viscosity (Section 14-4).

Most flocs formed in water and waste water are quite fragile. As they grow in size, the velocity gradient across them increases, and they tend to be broken up. This creates a limiting size. As a rule, flocculent suspensions entering settling tanks in water and waste-water treatment works have not yet reached this limit, and sedimentation is improved materially by further floc growth. Floc formation, depending upon the nature of the settling process, may either be self-induced or promoted by the addition of coagulating substances.

The composition of flocculating suspended solids and the opportunities for contact are so complex that there is no satisfactory method for evaluating the acceleration of settling by the aggregation of flocculent particles.

Flocculated aggregates entrain more or less water and thereby enlarge their over-all size while decreasing their gross density.

The expansion and coalescence of gas bubbles rising through a liquid are somewhat analogous to the settling of flocculating particles.

13-6. Efficiency of an Ideal Settling Basin. For purposes of discussion, we may divide a continuous-flow basin into four zones: (1)

an inlet zone in which influent flow and suspended matter disperse over the cross-section at right angles to flow; (2) a settling zone in which the suspended particles settle within the flowing water; (3) a sludge zone adjacent to the bottom, in which the removed solids accumulate and from which they are withdrawn for disposal; and (4) an outlet zone in which the flow and remaining suspended particles assemble and are carried to the effluent conduit. These zones are shown in Figure 13-5 for a horizontal-flow tank. Similar zones exist in vertical-flow tanks.

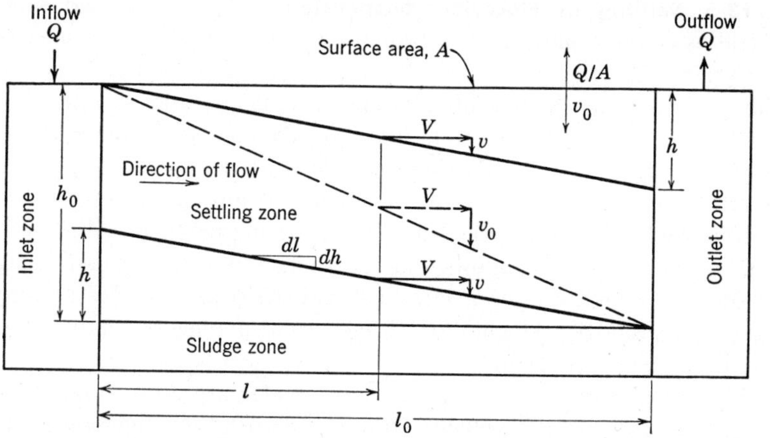

Figure 13-5. Settling paths of discrete particles in a horizontal-flow tank (idealized). The capacity of the settling zone is C, and its surface area is A.

In order to devise a framework for the formulation of sedimentation in continuous-flow basins, certain simplifying assumptions must be introduced. For horizontal-flow tanks, these include the following:

1. Within the settling zone of the tank, sedimentation takes place exactly as in a quiescent container of equal depth.
2. The flow is steady, and, upon entering the settling zone, the concentration of suspended particles of each size is uniform throughout the cross-section at right angles to flow.
3. A particle that enters the sludge zone is and stays removed.

The paths traced by discrete particles that are settling in a rectangular basin are shown in Figure 13-5. They are determined by the vector sums of the settling velocity v_s of the particle and the displacement velocity V of the basin. All particles with a settling velocity $v_s \geqq v_0$ are removed, v_0 being the velocity of that particle that falls through the full depth h_0 of the settling zone in the detention time t_0. Since $v_0 = h_0/t_0$ and $t_0 = C/Q$, where Q is the rate of flow and C is the volumetric capacity of the settling zone, and since $C/h_0 = A$, the surface area of this zone, it is true, furthermore, that $v_0 = Q/A$, the surface loading or overflow velocity of the basin. In vertical-flow basins particles with velocity $v_s < v_0$ are not removed. In horizontal-flow basins such particles can be removed, but only if they are within a vertical striking distance $h = v_s t_0$ from the sludge zone. If y_0 particles possessing a settling velocity $v_s \leqq v_0$ compose each size represented in the suspension, the proportion y/y_0 of particles that are removed in a horizontal-flow tank is

$$\frac{y}{y_0} = \frac{h}{h_0} = \frac{v_s\,t_0}{v_0\,t_0} = \frac{v_s}{v_0} = \frac{v_s}{Q/A} \qquad \text{13-10}$$

This equation can be derived also from the geometric relations shown in Figure 13-5.

For a rectangular basin of width W, $dh/dl = (v_s\,dt)/(V\,dt) =$ constant because both v_s and V are constant. Hence, $h = (v_s/V)l$, and

$$\frac{h}{h_0} = \frac{v_s}{V}\frac{l}{h_0} = \frac{v_s}{V}\frac{lW}{h_0 W} = \frac{v_s}{Q/A}$$

Derived by Hazen[6] in somewhat different fashion, the relationship represented by Equation 13-10 states that, for discrete particles and unhindered settling, the efficiency of a basin is solely a function of the settling velocity of the particles and of the surface area and rate of flow of the basin which, in combination, constitute the surface loading or overflow velocity. The efficiency is independent of the depth of the basin and of the displacement time or detention period. It follows from this equation, furthermore, that all particles with velocity $v_s \geqq v_0$ are removed and that particles with velocity $v_s < v_0$ can be fully captured in horizontal-flow basins if false bottoms or trays are inserted in the tank at intervals $h = v_s t_0$ ideally. The greater the number of these trays, the smaller may be the settling velocity of the particles all of which are to be removed. Water or sewage filters approximate, in a sense, settling basins equipped with a very large number of trays. The number of trays that can actually

[6] Allen Hazen, On sedimentation, *Trans. Am. Soc. Civil Engrs.*, *53*, 63 (1904).

be included in a sedimentation basin is limited, however, by required clearances and needed cleaning facilities.

13-7. Reduction in Basin Efficiency by Currents. The efficiency of settling basins is reduced (1) by eddy currents which are set up by the inertia of the incoming fluid; (2) by wind-induced currents when basins are not covered; (3) by convection currents that are thermal in origin; and (4) by density currents that cause cold or heavy water to underrun a basin and warm or light water to flow across its surface. All of these currents may contribute to short-circuiting of the flow.

In an ideal basin, displacement is steady and uniform, and each unit volume of fluid is detained for a time $t = C/Q$. In actual operation, on the other hand, straying currents cause some of the inflow to reach the outlet in less than the theoretical detention period and some to take much longer. The degree of short-circuiting and extent of retardation can be measured by adding a dye, electrolyte, or other tracer substance to the basin influent and observing the time required for the substance to reach the outlet. After the first measurable amount of tracer substance has arrived, its concentration in the effluent rises, as shown in Figure 13-6, until a maximum is reached. Then the concentration drops off, usually more slowly

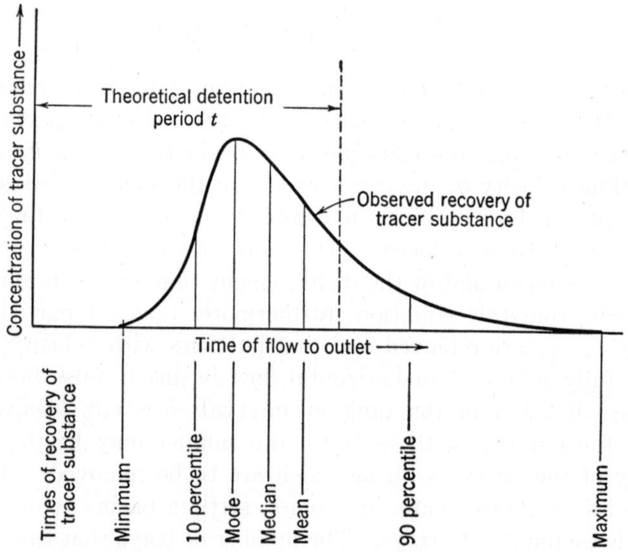

Figure 13-6. Dead spaces and short-circuiting in a settling basin as reflected by the concentration and time of recovery of tracer substances.

than it has risen. In accordance with the principles of Chapter 3, modal, median, and mean flowing-through periods characterize the central tendency of the time-concentration distribution. Relating the observed times to the theoretical detention period t permits making comparisons between different basins. The theoretical period and mean period are closely equal.

If a tank contains spaces in which the flow rotates upon itself, these spaces receive no suspended solids and can do no work. Hence, they reduce the effective capacity of the basin and the flowing-through times relative to the theoretical detention period. In the absence of such currents, the ratio of the mean time to t must equal unity. In the absence of short-circuiting, the mean, median, and mode must coincide. Short-circuiting is characterized, therefore, by the ratio of the mode or median to the mean being less than unity or by the ratio of the difference between the mode and mean, or the median and mean, to the mean being large.

If there is some interchange of flow between the ineffective spaces and the active portions of the tank, the time-concentration curve becomes unduly elongated as small amounts of tracer material are released to the moving water for capture in the effluent. The proportion of tracer substance that arrives at the outlet in a given time is measured by the ratio of the area under the curve up to the given time to the total area or total dose of tracer substance. Percentile ratios, such as the quartile or decentile ratio, then identify the degree of variability of exposure to sedimentation. Morrill[7] has suggested that the ratio of the 10-percentile to the 90-percentile be used as a parameter of the volumetric efficiency of settling tanks.

If the time-concentration curve of a basin cannot be reproduced reasonably well in repeated tests, the flow through the tank is not stable, and the performance of the tank will be erratic. Radial-flow tanks have been shown to be quite unstable.

The surface area of settling tanks must be increased over the theoretical value if the efficiency of removal is to be held constant in spite of turbulence. Ratios that rest upon Hazen's theory of sedimentation[6] are shown in Table 13-1 for different removal efficiencies and basin characteristics. These values are also the ratios of the actual to the theoretical subsidence values of the particles that are removed under different conditions of tank performance.

[7] Arthur B. Morrill, Sedimentation basin research and design, *J. Am. Water Works Assoc.*, *24*, 1442 (1932).

TABLE 13-1. Ratios of Required to Theoretical Surface Areas of Settling Basins and of Actual to Theoretical Settling Velocities, $v_0/(Q/A)$, of Particles at Different Removal Efficiencies

Performance of Basin	Removal Efficiency, %					
	70	75	80	85	90	95
(1)	(2)	(3)	(4)	(5)	(6)	(7)
Very good	1.3	1.5	1.8	2.2	2.7	3.6
Good	1.4	1.7	2.0	2.5	3.2	4.8
Poor	1.7	2.0	2.5	3.2	4.4	6.9
Very poor	2.3	3.0	4.0	5.9	10	19

Example 13.2. Find the settling velocity and size of particles of specific gravity 1.001 of which 80% are expected to be removed in a very good settling basin at an overflow rate of 1,000 gpd/sq ft, if the water temperature is 10 C (50 F).

1. $Q/A = 1{,}000 \times 1.547 \times 10^{-6} \times 30.48 = 4.72 \times 10^{-2}$ cm/sec.
2. From Table 13-1, $v_0/(Q/A) = 1.8$ for a very good basin. Hence $v_0 = 1.8 \times 4.7 \times 10^{-2}$ cm/sec $= 8.5 \times 10^{-2}$ cm/sec.
3. From Figure 13-4, $d = 0.15$ cm.

13-8. Bottom Scour of Deposited Sludge. As shown in Section 9-2, the channel velocity that will initiate the scour of deposited particles is

$$V_0 = \sqrt{(8k/f)g(s_s - 1)d} \qquad \text{9-6}$$

The critical displacement velocity V_0 must, therefore, not be exceeded if deposited solids are not to be lifted into the flowing waters from the sludge zone. Values of k are 0.04 for unigranular sand and 0.06 or more for non-uniform (interlocking) sticky materials. If scouring velocities are to be avoided, the ratio of length to depth of basin, or of surface area A, to cross-sectional area a, must be kept below a value of

$$l_0/h_0 = A/a = (V_0/v_0)(t/t_0) = (t/t_0)\sqrt{(6k/f)C_D} \qquad \text{13-11}$$

where t/t_0 equals unity for an ideal basin.

Example 13-3. Find (*a*) the velocity at which coal dust ($s_s = 1.5$) 10^{-2} cm in diameter can be removed from the wash water of a colliery without danger of resuspension by scour, and (*b*) the limiting length/depth ratio of the basin in which this removal can be effected.

a. Assuming $k = 0.04$ and $f = 0.03$ in Equation 9-6,

$$V_0 = \sqrt{\frac{8 \times 4 \times 10^{-2}}{3 \times 10^{-2}} 981 \times 0.5 \times 10^{-2}} = 7.2 \text{ cm/sec} = 0.24 \text{ fps}$$

b. By Stokes's law, Equation 13-9, $v_0 = 2.1 \times 10^{-1}$ cm/sec for $s_s = 1.5$ and 10 C (50 F). Hence $l_0/h_0 = (7.2/0.21)(t/t_0) = 34.2t/t_0 = 34.2$ for an ideal basin ($t/t_0 = 1$). For a poor basin, l_0/h_0 or A/a must be about twice as great or about 68.

Settling and Skimming Tanks

13-9. Elements of Tank Design. Each of the four functional zones of sedimentation basins or flotation tanks—(1) the inlet zone, (2) the settling or rising zone, (3) the sludge or scum zone, and (4) the outlet zone—presents special problems of hydraulic and process design that depend upon those properties of the suspended matter which govern its behavior, within the tank, during removal, and after deposition as sludge or scum.

The size, density, and flocculating properties of the suspended solids, together with their tendency to entrain water, as we have seen, determine the geometry of the settling or rising zone. Their concentration by volume and length of storage establish the dimensions of the sludge or scum zone. However, the design of both the settling and sludge or scum zone must also take account of the possible putrescence of liquid and sludge. Otherwise, the liquid may become septic during treatment, and gas-lifted sludge may damage the quality of the effluent or form unsightly scum that is removed with difficulty from the tank surface.

Where sludge volumes are large or where putrefaction of sludge in contact with the flowing water is to be avoided, sludge removal must become a more or less continuous operation. On a volume basis, use of mechanical sludge-removal devices is estimated to become economical when the volume of settleable matter (including entrained water) is more than 0.1% of the volume of the flowing liquid.[8] The devices used for this purpose influence tank design as well as operation. Thermal convection currents and wind-induced motion are prevented by housing or covering the tanks. Choice of tank number is governed by desired flexibility of operation and economy of design.

Use of flocculating or flotation agents may add as many as three ancillary functions to settling or flotation: (1) rapid distribution of the agent throughout the water to be treated; (2) provision of reaction time or time for floc growth to take place; and (3) return of floc to the influent for the purpose of promoting flocculation. These func-

[8] J. R. Baylis, Recent developments in water treatment and filtration, *Water Works, 67,* 38 (1928).

tions are best accomplished in separate units designed for each particular purpose (Section 14-4). They are sometimes made part of the joint performance of the settling basin, especially in water-treatment works.

Horizontal-flow tanks and vertical-flow tanks have been constructed in great variety. Thumbnail sketches of representative designs are shown in Figures 13-7 and 13-8. Circular, square, or

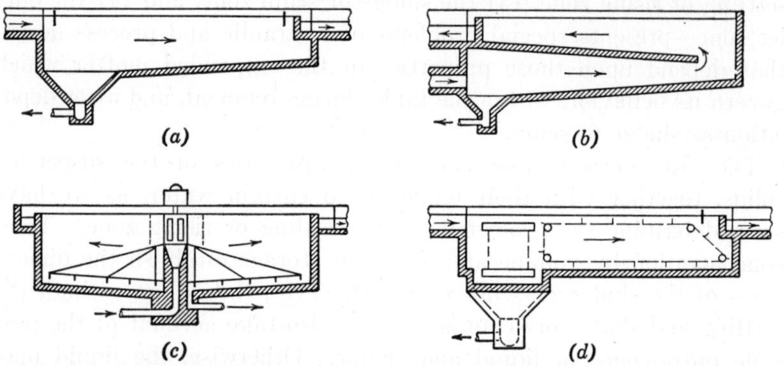

Figure 13-7. Representative designs of horizontal-flow settling tanks. (*a*) Rectangular tank with longitudinal flow. Tank is thrown out of operation for cleaning. Sludge is flushed to sump for removal from the dewatered tank. (*b*) Rectangular tank with longitudinal flow and single tray. (*c*) Circular tank with radial flow. Sludge is scraped to central sump and withdrawn during operation. The rotary mechanism carries plows. (*d*) Rectangular tank with longitudinal flow. Sludge is scraped to influent end and thence to sump to be withdrawn during operation. In some designs the sludge is collected at the effluent end. Tanks *a* and *b* are normally used in water purification, tanks *c* and *d* in sewage treatment.

rectangular in plan, they vary in depth from 7 to 15 ft, 10 ft being an average value. Circular tanks are as large as 200 ft in diameter with a 100-ft maximum commonly preferred. Square tanks are generally smaller, a side length of 70 ft being common. Rectangular tanks have reached lengths of almost 300 ft, but 100 ft is common. The width of mechanically cleaned, rectangular tanks is dictated by the available length of wooden scrapers. This is 16 ft, but scrapers can be arranged in parallel. A width of 30 ft is common. The diameter of circular tanks is governed by the structural requirements of the trusses that carry the scraping mechanisms. Unless it is broken up into steep hoppers, the bottom of most settling tanks slopes gently. The slope is ordinarily about 8% for circular or square tanks and 1% for rectangular tanks. Foothold on a slippery sur-

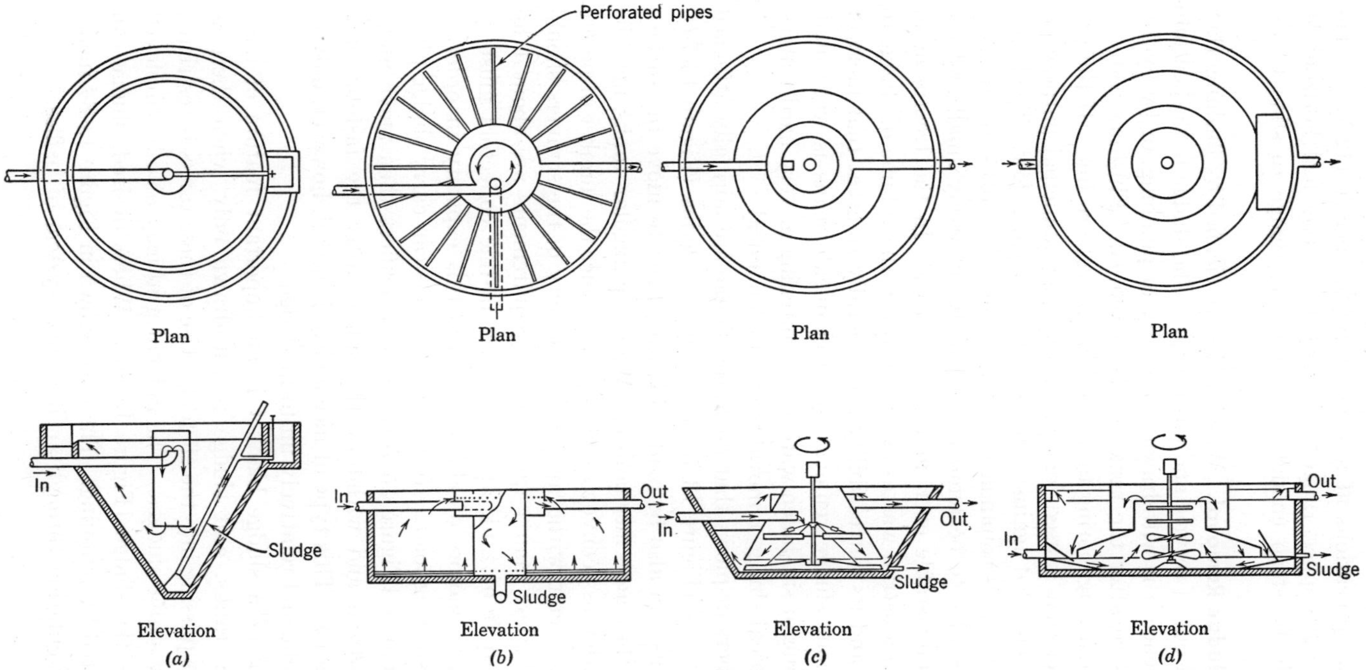

Figure 13-8. Representative designs of vertical-flow settling tanks. (*a*) Flaring circular or square settling tank. Sludge is removed during operation; in this case hydrostatically. (*b*) Circular settling tank with central mixing and flocculating chamber. Pipe grid distributes flow and collects sludge. (c) Circular, flaring, settling tank with central mixing and flocculating chamber. *Spaulding Precipitator*. (*d*) Circular settling tank with central mixing and flocculating chamber, and means for sludge recirculation. *Accelerator*. Tank *a* is normally used in sewage treatment, tanks *b*, *c*, and *d* in water purification.

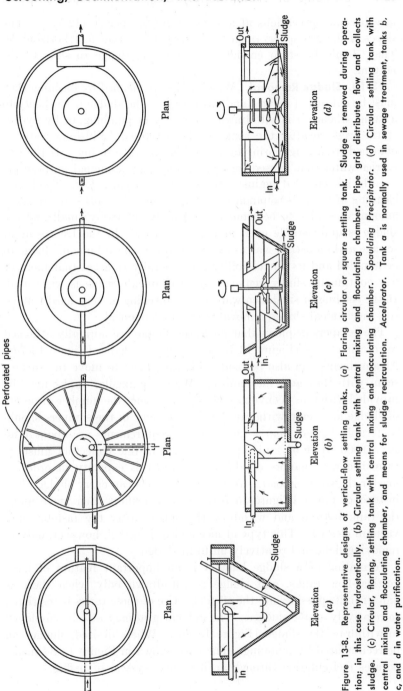

face becomes precarious at a slope of 1½ in. per ft (12.5%). The slopes of sludge hoppers range from 1.2:1 to 2:1 (vertical:horizontal). They should be steep enough to permit the sludge to slide to the bottom.

13-10. Sludge Removal. When tanks are cleaned by flushing, they must be cut out of service and unwatered. The sludge is washed into a sump, whence it is withdrawn by gravity or pumping, or by hydrostatic pressure after the tank has been refilled. Flushing water is obtained from neighboring tanks or from a pressure line. If the line carries water that is used for general plant or municipal purposes, it must be safeguarded against contamination by back-flow. The hand-cleaning of tanks is common in water purification works, because the amount of sludge to be removed is usually relatively small and the sludge is quite stable even in warm weather. In the treatment of sewage and industrial waste-waters, however, the volume of sludge to be handled and its putrescibility are generally so great that more or less continuous sludge removal by mechanical means is warranted. In the settling of silt-laden waters and softening of very hard waters, too, mechanical sludge removal is often economical.

The scrapers or plows that move the sludge are normally attached to rotating arms (Figure 13-7*c*) or to endless chains (Figure 13-7*d*). Arrangements can also be made (Figure 13-7*d*) to move the surface scum with the same mechanism. Wide rectangular tanks may be provided with cross-conveyors in order to reduce the number of points of sludge and scum withdrawal. The velocity of the scrapers should preferably be less than 1 fpm. Power requirements are about 1 hp for 10,000 sq ft of tank area, but straight-line collectors must be furnished with motors of about 10 times this capacity in order to master the starting load. Rotary mechanisms can carry sludge pipes instead of plows (Figure 13-7*c*). Suction orifices then move along the tank bottom and withdraw the sludge after the fashion of a vacuum cleaner. This type of mechanism is useful, however, only in removing light and relatively uniform sludge.

Formation of a sludge blanket is an important feature of most vertical-flow tanks, and sludge is withdrawn only when there is danger of its passing into the effluent. Use of these tanks is restricted to relatively stable sludges. The influent grid may also be employed to withdraw the sludge (Figure 13-8*b*). Where desired, sludge can be recirculated by pumping. The tank shown in Figure 13-8*d* incorporates recirculation through an ingenious system of baffles.

By contrast, full separation of accumulating sludge from flowing sewage is aimed for in two-story tanks (Figure 13-9). The sewage is then kept fresh, and storage space can be provided for the digestion of the accumulating solids. The two chambers are so constructed that rising gas bubbles and sludge particles cannot escape from the sludge hopper into the settling compartment.

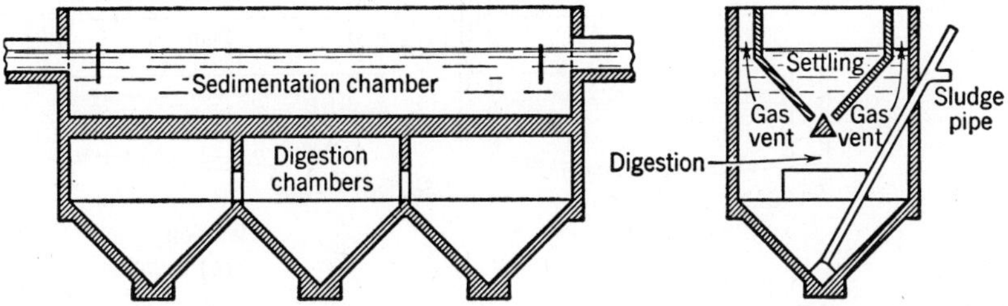

Figure 13-9. Two-storied Imhoff or Emscher tank for sewage treatment.

13-11. Inlets. For high efficiency, inlets must distribute flow and suspended matter as uniformly as possible between tanks and within tanks. Hydraulic balance is obtained either by subjecting the dividing flow to equal frictional resistances or by inserting at each point of discharge a controlling loss of head that is large in comparison with the frictional resistances between inlets. The water levels in the different tanks are held the same by outflow regulation. If suspended matter moves along the bottom of the influent conduit, equality of loading is not necessarily insured by these arrangements, and adjustments must then be made by trial. The principles involved in flow regulation, when referred to Figure 13-10, are as follows:

1. The flow originating at I in a traverses identical paths before its discharge at A, B, C, and D. Hence inflow at these four points must be equal except when the elevation of the water surface in the two tanks is not the same. Equality will then be restricted to pairs of points in each tank.

2. The flow originating at I in b is to be subdivided in such manner that the discharge q_n at any inlet will be held to mq_1, where $m < 1$ and q_1 is the discharge at the first inlet. Considering the inlet an orifice, the discharge head, or head lost, must be

$$h_n = kq_n^2 = k(mq_1)^2 = m^2h_1 \qquad 13\text{-}12$$

or, if h_λ is the lost head between points of discharge (1 and n),

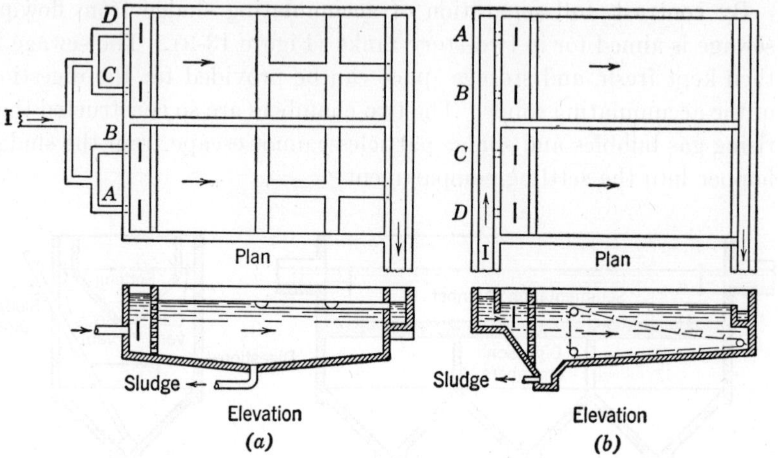

Figure 13-10. Inflow and outflow structures of settling tanks. (a) Uniformity of inflow is secured by equality of resistance. (b) Uniformity of inflow is secured by control of resistance.

$$h_n = h_1 - h_\lambda = m^2 h_1$$

and

$$h_1 = h_\lambda/(1 - m^2) \qquad 13\text{-}13$$

The magnitude of h_λ can be estimated from friction losses and changes in velocity. Distribution of flow by the piping shown in Figure 13-8*b* and in filter underdrains (Section 15-8) can also be secured in this manner.

Example 13-4. In a settling tank, the inlet farthest from the point of supply is to discharge 99% of the flow delivered by the nearest inlet. Find, in terms of the friction head h_λ, the required head loss through the nearest inlet and the associated head loss through the farthest inlet.

1. From Equation 13-13, $h_1 = h_\lambda/[1 - (0.99)^2] = 50.3h_\lambda$.
2. From Equation 13-12, $h_n = (0.99)^2 h_1 = 0.980h_1 = 49.3h_\lambda$.

Baffle boards in front of inlet openings will destroy the kinetic energy of the incoming water and assist in distributing the flow laterally and vertically over the basin.

Training or dispersion walls perforated by holes or slots (Figure 13-10) operate on the principle demonstrated in Equation 13-13 by introducing a controlling head loss. Frictional resistance in advance of the openings is a function of the velocity head of the eddy currents. Baffles of this kind contribute also to stability of flow.

Velocities in inlet conduits and orifices should be high enough to prevent deposition of solids but sufficiently low to keep fragile floc from being broken up. Model analysis of inlet structures is often rewarding.

13-12. Outlets. Control of outflow is generally secured by a weir attached to one or both sides of single or multiple outlet troughs. If the weirs in different tanks are placed at the same elevation and discharge freely, the loading of equal basins will be kept within the limits of inflow variation. If the effluent weir is submerged, the degree of submergence will vary along the trough. Draw-off then becomes unequal and induces short-circuiting, unless a training wall similar to the inlet training wall again introduces a controlling loss of head.

Outlet troughs are lateral spillways. Required dimensions are given by the drawdown curve of the water surface in the trough (Figure 13-11). As shown for wash-water troughs of rapid filters

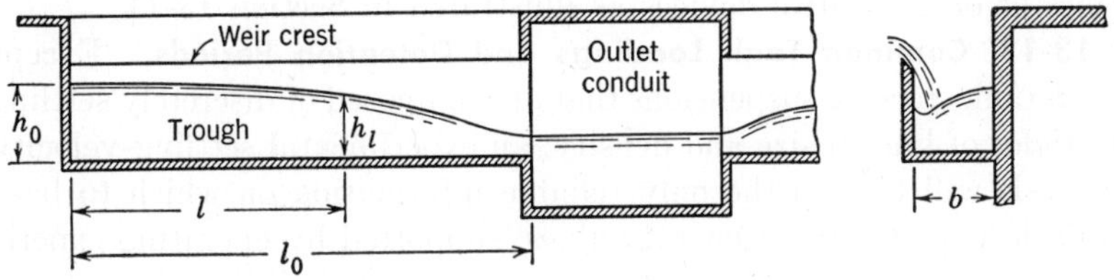

Figure 13-11. Drawdown of water surface in an outlet trough.

(Section 15-9), the depth of water h_0 at the upstream end of a trough with level invert can be estimated from Equation 13-14. If friction is neglected,

$$h_0 = \sqrt{h_l^2 + \frac{2(nql)^2}{gb^2h_l}} \tag{13-14}$$

Here h_l is the depth of water at a distance l from the upstream end, $n = 1$ when one side weir receives the flow and $n = 2$ when there are two weirs, q is the discharge per unit length of weir, g is the gravity constant, and b is the width of the trough. For long troughs an allowance for friction must be made.

Weir length relative to surface area determines the strength of outlet current. A unit length of weir at the end of a rectangular tank serves an area equal to the length of the tank. In a circular tank, the area served by a unit length of peripheral weir equals ¼ the tank diameter.

Multiplying these values by the surface loading of the tank gives the rate of weir discharge. Experience shows that this should be held below 20,000 gpd per ft if surges are to be avoided. When weirs are very long in relation to flow, it may be difficult for discharge to be uniform over their entire length unless a saw-toothed edge breaks up the weir into triangular notches with jets of adequate thickness.

In sewage treatment, a scum board, or shallow baffle plate, placed in front of the outlet weir, will hold back floating solids, grease, and oil.

Variations in flow are ordinarily of little concern in the operation of settling tanks, provided that the maximum design flow is not exceeded. In the design of grit chambers that are to collect only heavy, inert solids, on the other hand, the conditions of sedimentation and scour must be kept unchanged within relatively narrow limits. To assure this, outlet weirs are replaced by proportional-flow weirs or other control devices as illustrated in Section 13-14.

13-13. Common Tank Loadings and Detention Periods. Except when tanks receive suspensions that are composed of discretely settling particles of known size and density, an experimental settling-velocity analysis will furnish the only reliable information on which to base tank design. Certain general values, supported by operating experience, will indicate the order of magnitude of permissible tank loadings.

Sand, silt, and clay have a specific gravity of about 2.65. The grain-size range of particles of this kind ordinarily subjected to plain sedimentation extends upward from 10^{-3} cm and creates settling velocities at 10 C as low as 6.9×10^{-3} cm/sec corresponding to a maximum surface loading [9] as low as $21{,}200 \times 6.9 \times 10^{-3} = 146$ gpd per sq ft of tank surface and a minimum detention period [10] as high as $8.47 \times 10^{-2}/6.9 \times 10^{-3} = 12.3$ hr in a 10-ft basin.

Alum and iron flocs possess specific gravities as low as 1.002 because of adsorbed and entrained water, but they may be as large as 0.1 cm in diameter. Their settling velocities at 10 C are then about 8.3×10^{-2} cm/sec, corresponding to a maximum surface loading of 1,760 gpd per sq ft and a minimum detention period of 1.02 hr in a tank 10 ft deep. Similar values are associated with the precipitation of calcium, the crystals of calcite and adsorbed water being about 10^{-2} cm in diameter and possessing a specific gravity close to 1.2.

[9] 1 cm/sec = 21,200 gpd per sq ft, and surface loading varies directly with velocity.

[10] 1 cm/sec = 8.47×10^{-3} hr of detention per ft of basin depth, and the detention period varies directly with depth and inversely with velocity.

In practice, smaller surface loadings (<900 gpd per sq ft) and longer detention periods (>2 hr) are employed.

Sewage solids, excepting grit, vary in specific gravity from less than 1.0 to about 1.2 on a dry basis. They may be several centimeters in diameter, and their wet specific gravity is about 1.001. If their size is 10^{-1} cm, they will have a settling velocity of about 4.2×10^{-2} cm/sec and will be removed, at 100% efficiency, in a tank loaded to a maximum of 890 gpd per sq ft and affording a minimum detention period of 2.0 hr in a 10-ft tank.

In general, therefore, coagulated and lime-softened water, as well as sewage that is to be subjected to plain sedimentation or coagulation in primary tanks, should be given a detention period of about 2 hr, corresponding in a 10-ft tank to a surface loading of 900 gpd per sq ft. Tank space assigned to the sludge zone is additional.

Activated sludge is so bulky that settling is generally hindered, the free settling velocity of particles 10^{-1} cm in diameter with a specific gravity of 1.005 being reduced from 2×10^{-1} cm/sec to about 10^{-1} cm/sec. Under ideal conditions, the surface loading of secondary settling tanks treating activated sludge may, therefore, be as high as 2,000 gpd per sq ft, and the detention period as low as 8.47×10^{-1} hr or 50 min in a tank 10 ft deep. In practice, a loading value of 1,200 gpd per sq ft makes allowance for poorly settling sludge.

In sewage treatment, smaller capacities than normal are employed when removal of coarse solids alone meets the needs of the situation; e.g., when effluent is discharged into a receiving water of large capacity, or when sewage is settled in advance of chemical precipitation or activated-sludge treatment. Capacities larger than normal are provided when stress is laid on removal of BOD as well as suspended solids (Figure 13-12), when settling tanks serve as buffers against surges of sewage and industrial wastes (especially toxic wastes), and when abnormally large amounts of combined sewage are to receive some treatment in settling units. For different efficiencies of BOD removal, the Upper Mississippi Board of Public Health Engineers and Great Lakes Board of Public Health Engineers have suggested the loading curve shown in Figure 13-13.

13-14. Tank Performance. Most settling basins that are incorporated in water-purification works are preceded by or include coagulation or chemical precipitation processes. Interest then centers on the removal of substances, such as color, turbidity, hardness, and iron.

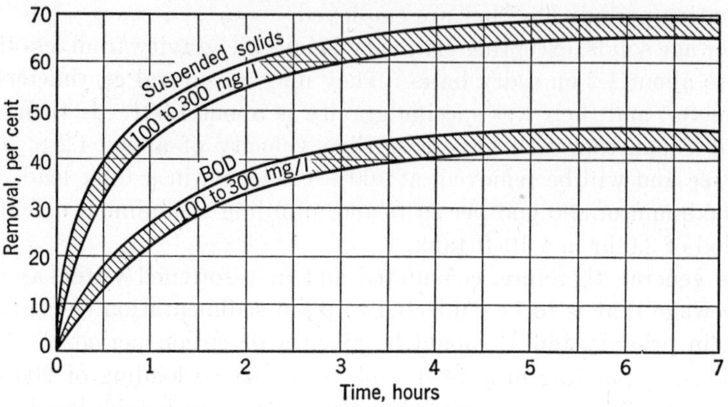

Figure 13-12. Removal of suspended solids and biochemical oxygen demand from sewage by plain sedimentation in primary tanks.

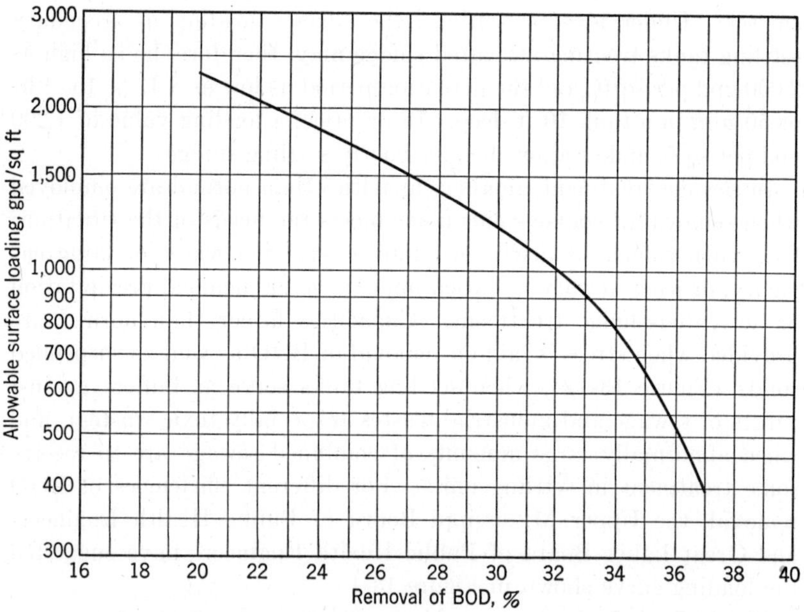

Figure 13-13. Normally allowable loadings of settling tanks for sewage for different BOD removals (*Standards of Sewage Treatment,* Upper Mississippi Board of Public Health Engineers and Great Lakes Board of Public Health Engineers, 1952).

The performance of settling tanks is allied, therefore, to the performance of the preparatory processes. It is not generally a unique measure of settling efficiency. Only when turbid river waters are subjected to plain sedimentation is it common practice to report the percentage removal of the suspended solids. The weight of suspended matter in turbid river waters is often measured in thousands of milligrams per liter. Recorded efficiencies vary widely for different rivers and different stretches of the same river. As little as 30% and as much as 75% of the suspended matter may settle out in 1 hr, and as little as 50% and as much as 90% in 2 hr. That long periods of settling may be required when the silt is fine has already been indicated in Section 13-13.

By contrast, the settling tanks of sewage-treatment works are generally devoted to plain sedimentation by itself. Performance is usually related to the removal of suspended solids and biochemical oxygen demand. Typical settling curves for primary tanks are shown in Figure 13-12.

13-15. Grit Chambers. Grit chambers are included in sewerage systems when combined sewage, industrial wastes, or illicit storm drainage transport significant quantities of sand or other heavy and inert matter in suspension. Removal of these substances in advance of pumps and treatment units prevents wear of machinery and unwanted accumulation of grit in settling tanks. It also facilitates the handling of the sludge produced by the various treatment processes. Grit chambers may be installed, too, in advance of inverted siphons.

Removal of suspended matter in grit chambers is desirably confined to the inert components, because the exclusion of decomposable solids simplifies the problem of grit disposal. Purposeful inclusion of organic matter with the grit converts grit chambers into *detritus tanks*.

Grit chambers are generally constructed as fairly shallow and elongated channels that capture particles of specific gravity 2.65 and 2×10^{-2} cm in diameter. Depth of flow is normally governed by the size of the outfall sewer. Except for the space assigned to grit storage, the invert of the chamber is made continuous with that of the outfall sewer.

The problem of selective deposition of heavy inert particles is complicated by fluctuations in rate of flow, especially those that accompany storm rainfalls. Aside from subdividing the grit chamber into several compartments that can be shunted in and out in succession, a solution is sought by combining (1) opportunity for sedimentation of wanted particles with (2) scour or resuspension of unwanted particles. This implies (1) provision of adequate surface area and (2) maintenance of adequate displacement velocity. Fluctuations in flow require, ideally, that both (1) a constant value of Q/A and (2) a constant displacement velocity V be maintained in the chamber. Ordinarily a compromise solution is offered in order to keep the required structure simple. The cross-section of the chamber at right angles to the direction of flow is made uniform throughout its length, and its shape is so chosen that the displacement velocity is held substantially constant at all depths of flow. To this purpose, a flow control device, such as a proportional-flow weir, a vertical throat, or a standing-wave flume, may be placed at the end of the chamber. The area of the water surface at maximum flow is then made large enough to insure deposition of wanted large and heavy particles, the selective movement and resuspension of smaller and lighter particles, which will settle as flow is reduced, being cared for by the constant scouring action of the flowing water.

Two outlet control devices are shown in Figure 13-14: (1) a proportional-flow weir and (2) an adjustable throat. A standing-wave flume attached to the grit chamber can serve both as a control and measuring device. The discharge Q through devices such as these is a simple function of channel depth or head, $Q = kh^n$, where k and n are constants. To have these control devices produce a constant displacement velocity in the chamber, therefore, the width w of the chamber, as shown in Figure 13-14, must be so chosen that $Q = kh^n = V\int_0^h w\,dh$. As shown by Camp,[11] this condition is satisfied when

$$w = nkh^{n-1}/V \qquad 13\text{-}15$$

If flow is controlled by a proportional-flow weir, for example, $Q = kh$ or $n = 1$. Then $w = k/V =$ constant, and the channel must be rectangular. If flow is controlled by a throat, $Q = kbh^{3/2}$, or $n = 3/2$, and $w = 3/2(kbh^{1/2}/V) = 3/2(Q/hV)$. This is the equation of a parabola, and the channel must be parabolic in cross-section or approach a parabola sufficiently closely.

Example 13-5. Two grit chambers, controlled by outlet throats 3 in. wide, are to remove particles of specific gravity $s_s = 2.65$ and diameter $d = 2 \times 10^{-2}$ cm from combined sewage. The maximum rate of flow Q_{max} is 15 cfs; the minimum rate of flow Q_{min} is 3 cfs. Find the settling velocity v at 10 C, the dis-

[11] T. R. Camp, Grit chamber design, *Sewage Works J.*, *14*, 368 (1942).

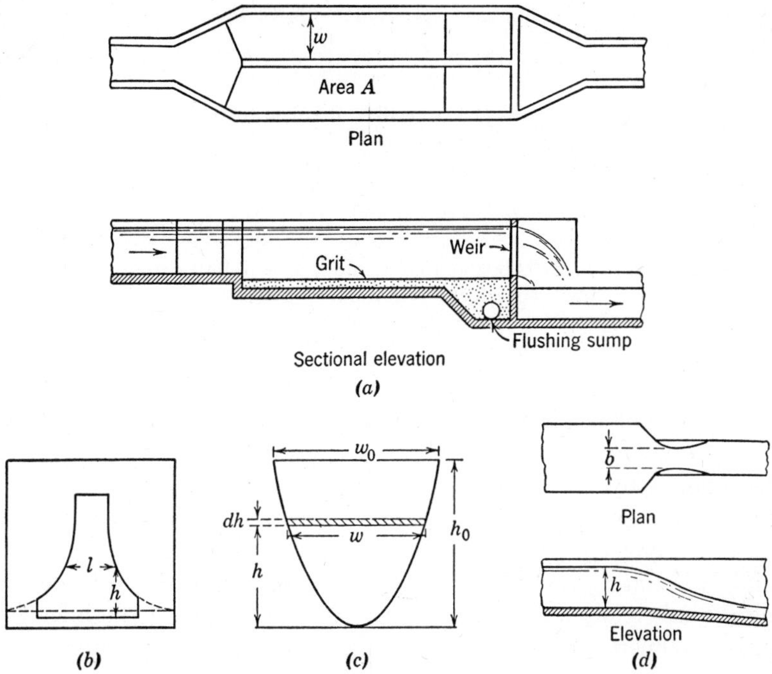

Figure 13-14. Grit chamber and outlet control devices. *(a)* Twin-compartment grit chamber with weir control. *(b)* Proportional-flow weir plate. Narrowing opening at base is replaced by rectangular notch. $Q = kh$ because sides of opening are curved to make $lh^{1/2}$ constant. *(c)* Hypothetical cross-section of channel controlled by throat. Cross-sectional area $a = \int_0^h w\,dh$. *(d)* Outlet throat. $Q = kbh^{3/2}$.

placement velocity V, maximum and minimum depths of flow, $h_{\max}$ and $h_{\min}$ respectively, the maximum and minimum width of channel, $w_{\max}$ and $w_{\min}$ respectively, and the maximum and minimum required length of channel $l_{\max}$ and $l_{\min}$ respectively.

1. From Figure 13-4 for $d = 2 \times 10^{-2}$ cm, $v_s = 2.1$ cm/sec $= 0.0689$ fps.
2. From Equation 9-6, assuming $k = 0.06$ and $f = 0.03$,

$$V = \sqrt{(8 \times 0.06/0.03) \times 32.2 \times 1.65 \times (2 \times 10^{-2}/30.48)} = 0.75 \text{ fps}$$

3. For a discharge of $Q = kbh^{3/2}$, where $b = 0.25$ ft and k approximates 3.5,

$$h = \left(\frac{Q}{3.5 \times 0.25}\right)^{2/3}$$

and

$$h_{\max} = \left(\frac{7.5}{3.5 \times 0.25}\right)^{2/3} = 4.18 \text{ ft} \qquad \text{or} \qquad h_{\min} = \left(\frac{1.5}{3.5 \times 0.25}\right)^{2/3} = 1.43 \text{ ft}$$

4. From Equation 13-15, $w = \frac{3}{2}kbh^{1/2}/V = \frac{3}{2}(Q/hV)$,

$$w_{\text{max}} = (\tfrac{3}{2})\ 7.5/(4.18 \times 0.75) = 3.59 \text{ ft}$$

and

$$w_{\text{min}} = (\tfrac{3}{2})\ 1.5/(1.43 \times 0.75) = 2.10 \text{ ft}$$

5. From Equation 13-10, $y/y_0 = v_s/(Q/A)$, and for 100% removal $Q/A = v_s$, or

$$hwV/(lw) = v_s \qquad \text{and} \qquad l = h(V/v_s)$$

Hence $l_{\text{max}} = 4.18(0.75/0.069) = 45.5$ ft, and $l_{\text{min}} = 1.43(0.75/0.069) = 15.5$ ft. The settling zone must, therefore, be given a length of 45.5 ft. If the chamber has some short-circuiting (poor performance), its over-all length should be made up to twice as much, or 90 ft (Table 13-1), to insure 75% removal of wanted particles.

The amount of grit that is collected in grit chambers varies from 1 to 12 (average 4) cu ft per million gallons treated and depends upon the topography, surface cover, type of roadway and sidewalk, size of intercepter, and intensity of storm rainfall on the area sewered. Daily maxima of 10 to 30 cu ft per mg and as high as 80 cu ft per mg have been reported. Grit storage is generally provided by lowering the invert of the chamber 6 to 18 in. below that of the inlet and outlet channels. In small plants, the accumulated solids are removed from the unwatered channels by hand or by flushing the grit onto a disposal area. In large plants, some type of mechanical grit conveyor is generally employed to remove grit without draining the compartment to be cleaned.

13-16. Detritus Tanks. Short-period sedimentation in a tank that operates at substantially constant level produces a mixture of grit and organic solids, called detritus. The light organic solids can be washed out of the mixture before, during, or after removal from the tank in one of the following ways:

1. Compressed air is blown through the deposited detritus from time to time and resuspends the light solids.
2. The removed detritus is washed in a grit washer, the wash water being returned to the effluent from the detritus tank. A sand washer such as that shown in Figure 15-5 can be used for this purpose.
3. A scraper delivers the detritus to a conveyor that moves the solids through and out of the water in such a way that the organic solids are flushed back into the flowing sewage. The scrapers are like those illustrated in Figure 13-8. Some conveyors are patterned after classifying machinery used in the mining industry for the separation of ores.

13-17. Skimming Tanks. These tanks are commonly designed as long, trough-shaped structures. Surface area, in accordance with the principles of sedimentation and flotation, is a governing factor. Detention periods are short and seldom exceed 3 min. In the tank shown in Figure 13-15, provision is made to blow air into the sewage from diffusers situated in the bottom. This keeps heavy solids from settling and captures light solids in the surface froth. Vertical baffle walls separate the tanks into a central aerated channel and two lateral stilling chambers in which oil and grease gather at the surface. The baffles are slotted near the flowline to provide entrance into the stilling compartments. Settleable matter slides back into the central channel which moves it forward and eventually delivers it to the

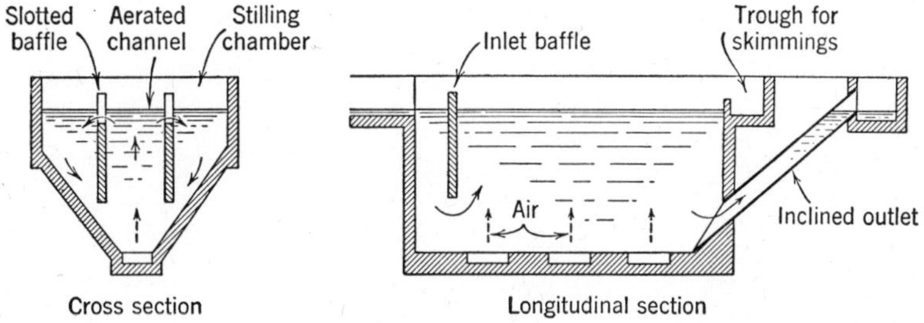

Figure 13-15. Aerated skimming tank. *After Imhoff.*

inclined outlet from the tank. The outlet velocity is sufficient to resuspend the solids. Oil and grease are drawn off from time to time into a channel that leads to a separator. Air requirements are small, about 0.03 cu ft per gallon of sewage. Flotation is hastened and extended to particles that are heavier than water by introducing or otherwise releasing finely divided air or gas bubbles that attach themselves to the particles. These bubbles not only impart buoyancy to the particles but also entangle them in the surface foam that the bubbles create. The addition of wetting and foaming agents in connection with flotation corresponds to the addition of coagulating or precipitating agents in connection with sedimentation. The mechanisms that remove sludge from settling tanks can be arranged to serve also as scum collectors (Figure 13-7*d*). Unless some advantage is to be secured from the aeration of the sewage that takes place in an aerated skimming tank, or unless the unsightliness of the scum is objectionable, separate skimming tanks may be omitted where the settling tanks can be provided with scum-removal mechanisms.

The grease removed from tanks that include domestic or municipal sewage is generally too polluted to be of commercial value. If it includes much mineral oil, it is best buried or burned together with rakings and screenings. If grease predominates, the skimmings can be added to sludge that is to be digested anaerobically to produce gas of high fuel value (Section 17-6). The volume of skimmings from municipal sewage is estimated at 0.1 to 6.0 cu ft per mg, or 0.003 to 0.2 cu ft per capita per year. Some industrial wastes, wool-scouring wastes for example, contain much grease which can be recovered for sale.

14 Chemical Treatment

14-1. Reasons for Chemical Treatment. Some of the unit operations of chemical treatment are aimed at the removal of suspended and colloidal substances; others at the removal of dissolved substances; yet others at the conversion of dissolved substances from an objectionable to an unobjectionable form. Some chemicals, finally, are added for their own sake; fluorides are an example.

Not all the chemical processes that are useful in the treatment of water and waste water will be discussed in this chapter. Some find a better place in other chapters of this book. Chlorination and copper sulfate treatment are examples.

14-2. Chemical Coagulation. The principal function of *chemical coagulation* is the destabilization, aggregation, and binding together of colloids. Chemical coagulation is commonly accomplished by the addition of one of the following floc-forming substances: filter alum, or aluminum sulfate, $Al_2(SO_4)_3 \cdot 14H_2O$; copperas, or ferrous sulfate, $FeSO_4 \cdot 7H_2O$; ferric sulfate, $Fe_2(SO_4)_3$; ferric chloride, $FeCl_3$; and chlorinated copperas, a mixture of ferric sulfate and ferric chloride.

a. Mechanisms of coagulation. The colloids found in natural waters are principally clay particles and tealike organic color; those in waste waters include colloidal proteins and carbohydrates along with numerous other substances. All of them are commonly stabilized by negative charges at their surfaces. Neutralization of the charge, which leads to destabilization and coagulation, is achieved by (1) interaction with ions of opposite charge or (2) mutual coagulation with colloids of opposite charge.

The coagulating power of ions of opposite charge rises rapidly with their valence. This is known as the Schulze-Hardy Rule. The ions, Al^{+++}, for example, are several hundred times as effective as Na^+ ions in bringing about coagulation of negative colloids and $SO_4^=$ ions are much more effective than Cl^- ions in the coagulation of positively charged colloids.

Particle size is a factor in destabilization and coagulation. The presence of colloidal particles smaller than 1 μ is important. If such particles are not present in the water or waste water to be treated, it may be advisable to add them. Fine clay, activated silica, and other so-called coagulant aids serve this purpose. Larger particles also assist coagulation for they provide nuclei on which floc can grow; and they add weight.

b. Properties of common chemical coagulants. The compounds of iron and aluminum that are generally used for removing turbidity, bacteria, color, and other finely divided matter from water and waste water make use of both mechanisms for coagulation. They produce cations of high valence and react with alkalinity to form insoluble hydrous oxide colloids that are positively charged. The cations destabilize the negatively charged colloidal materials in the water. The positively charged hydrous ferric or aluminum oxides flocculate them by processes of mutual coagulation. The reactions are sensitive to the *p*H of the water and to the ion balance. Negatively charged particles, particularly color colloids, coagulate best at low *p*H values, whereas hydrous oxides are generally least soluble and flocculate best at somewhat higher values. Overdosing with electrolytes may interfere with the coagulation of colloids. Sulfates of aluminum and sulfates and chlorides of iron are normally employed because they are the cheapest available chemical coagulants.

Aluminum and iron coagulants react in much the same manner. Stated in the simplest terms, the first reaction is one of solution; the second, one of combination with OH^- ions made available by the alkalinity of the water. The reactions of alum, for example, are: [1]

$$Al_2(SO_4)_3 \cdot 14H_2O \rightarrow 2Al^{+++} + 3SO_4^= + 14H_2O \qquad 14\text{-}1$$

and

$$2Al^{+++} + 6OH^- \leftrightharpoons Al_2O_3 \cdot xH_2O \downarrow \qquad 14\text{-}2$$

[1] Filter alum contains a slight excess of alumina and less water of crystallization. An empirical formulation is $Al_2(SO_4)_{2.87} \cdot 15H_2O$ for the slightly basic commercial product that contains 17% water-soluble Al_2O_3.

In these reactions, the vertical arrow indicates precipitation. If the natural alkalinity of the water is inadequate, it must be brought to needed concentration by the addition of substances such as hydrated (slaked) lime, $Ca(OH)_2$, soda ash, Na_2CO_3, or lye, NaOH. In practice, more than the amount required for reaction is added in order to leave a residual of unreacted alkalinity in the water. Needed amounts are generally less than those that can be calculated stoichiometrically from reactions such as the following:

$$Al_2(SO_4)_3 \cdot xH_2O + 3Ca(HCO_3)_2 \rightarrow 3CaSO_4 + 2Al(OH)_3 \downarrow + 6CO_2 + xH_2O \quad 14\text{-}3$$

Taking the molecular weight of alum as 600 [it is 594.3 for $Al_2(SO_4)_3 \cdot 14H_2O$] and the reacting weight of the natural bicarbonate alkalinity as 3×100 (as $CaCO_3$), the indicated relative amount of reacting alkalinity is 300:600, or 1:2. Similarly, the relative amount of free CO_2 (mol wt 44) released from bicarbonate alkalinity is 264:600, or about 1:2. As a rule, the actual amount of CO_2 liberated is also less than its possible value. Although the reaction presented is an oversimplification of what actually takes place, it does indicate orders of magnitude and the facts that hardness is converted to the non-carbonate form and that CO_2 will be formed in the reaction of both aluminum and iron coagulants, unless lime or lye is added to the water.

The solubility constants K_s(mols/l) of the hydrated oxides of aluminum and iron are given in Table 14-1. Their values are affected by both temperature and dissolved solids.[2] The hydrous oxide of aluminum is an *amphoteric* [3] substance, i.e., it dissolves both in the

TABLE 14-1. Calculated Solubilities of the Hydrous Oxides of Aluminum and Iron in Pure Water at 25 C

Ion Product	K_s	Solubility, mg/l	pH	Decrease in Solubility with pH
$(Al^{+++})(OH^-)^3$	1.9×10^{-33}	51 as Al	4.0	1,000-fold for each unit rise
$(AlO_2^-)(H^+)$	4×10^{-13}	11 as Al	9.0	10-fold for each unit fall
$(Fe^{+++})(OH^-)^3$	4×10^{-38}	2.2 as Fe	3.0	1,000-fold for each unit rise
$(Fe^{++})(OH^-)^2$	1.65×10^{-15}	92 as Fe	8.0	100-fold for each unit rise

[2] A solubility equation, such as $(Al^{+++})(OH^-)^3 = K_s$, defines the condition of saturation. If the ion product $(Al^{+++})(OH^-)^3$ is less than K_s, the solution is unsaturated with respect to that substance and further solution will occur in the presence of additional solid until the solubility equation is satisfied.

[3] From the Greek *amphoteros*, both.

presence of H^+ and OH^- ions. In the presence of caustic alkalinity (in connection with the softening of water by lime, for example) aluminum oxide dissolves as an aluminate, or

$$Al_2O_3 + 2OH^- \rightleftharpoons 2AlO_2^- + H_2O \qquad 14\text{-}4$$

Iron does not behave in this way.

The calculated solubilities of the hydrous oxides of aluminum and iron in pure water are shown in Table 14-1. The amount of dissolved aluminum (mol wt of Al = 27.0) at pH 4, for example, is $1.9 \times 10^{-33} \times 27 \times 10^3/10^{-3(14-4)} = 51$ mg/l.

The amounts of coagulant ordinarily used vary upward from 0.3 grain per gal for relatively clear waters to 10 or 20 times this dosage for highly turbid waters and waste waters. Since 1 grain per gal is equivalent to 17.1 mg/l, the mg/l of Al or Fe released by the common coagulants for each grain per gal of coagulant are: 1.54 mg/l Al for filter alum (mol wt 600); 2.38 mg/l Fe for ferric sulfate [$Fe_2(SO_4)_3$]; 5.89 mg/l Fe for ferric chloride ($FeCl_3$); and 3.43 mg/l Fe for copperas ($FeSO_4 \cdot 7H_2O$).

Ordinarily, the best precipitates are obtained at points of low solubility. The time required for floc to form is likewise least at points of low solubility. The rate of floc formation and the effect of various ions on the time of floc formation may be gaged from fundamental studies such as those of Bartow [4] and his associates. Figure 14-1 presents but a partial series of results of this kind.

The following statements summarize the practical aspects of the indicated properties of colloids and the indicated dosage and behavior of common coagulants:

1. The pH range of relative insolubility is 5 to 7 for aluminum, above 4 for ferric iron, and above 9.5 for ferrous iron.

2. Because of the high solubility of $Fe(OH)_2$ below pH 9.5, ferrous sulfate is a useful coagulant only in highly alkaline waters. Otherwise lime must be added to raise the pH. The combined use of copperas and lime is known as the *iron and lime* process. The hydrous ferrous oxide is oxidized to the ferric state in the presence of dissolved oxygen $4Fe(OH)_2 + O_2 \rightarrow 2(Fe_2O_3 \cdot H_2O) + 2H_2O$. This causes precipitate to form at lower pH values and extends the range of usefulness of ferrous sulfate down to a pH value of about 8.5. Aeration of the water prior to liming will make oxygen available and blow out lime-consuming CO_2 (Section 14-3). The use of large amounts of lime may render the process uneconomical, unless treatment in-

[4] Edward Bartow, A. P. Black, and W. E. Sansbury, Formation of floc by ferric coagulants, *Trans. Am. Soc. Civil Engrs.*, *100*, 263 (1935).

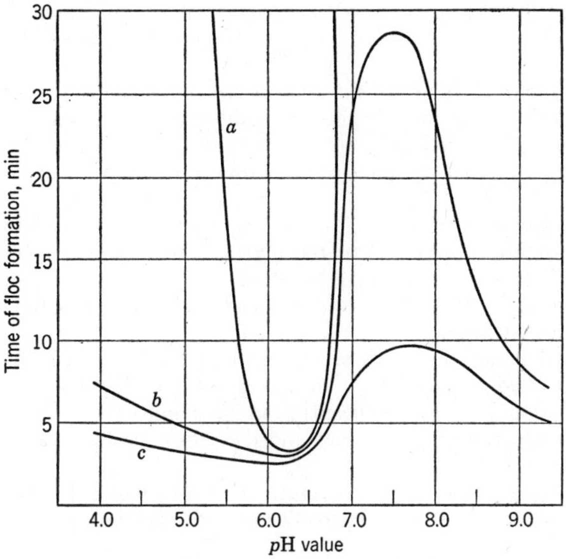

Figure 14-1. Zone and time of floc formation by ferric sulfate at various *p*H values and effect of added sodium sulfate. (*a*) Ferric sulfate only; 1.6 grains per gal of $Fe_2(SO_4)_3 \cdot 9H_2O$. (*b*) Ferric sulfate and 50 ppm of $Na_2SO_4 \cdot 10H_2O$. (*c*) Ferric sulfate and 250 ppm of $Na_2SO_4 \cdot 10H_2O$. *After Bartow, Black, and Sansbury.*

cludes lime softening. At high *p*H values, natural color colloids are stabilized, and calcium carbonate may be precipitated on sand and other surfaces with which the water comes in contact during purification and distribution. This is a nuisance.

3. If ferrous sulfate is to be used as a source of coagulant at low *p*H values, the ferrous iron may first be oxidized at the plant to the ferric state by adding a solution of chlorine to dissolved ferrous sulfate. The oxidation reaction is

$$6(FeSO_4 \cdot 7H_2O) + 3Cl_2 \rightarrow 6Fe^{+++} + 6SO_4^{=} + 6Cl^- + 42H_2O \qquad 14\text{-}5$$

About $(3 \times 71):(6 \times 278)$, or 1 lb of Cl_2 to 8 lb of ferrous sulfate is required. Chlorine is generally added in excess because of some consumption in side reactions.

4. The presence or addition of negative ions extends the useful range of *p*H in the acid region. In accordance with the Schulze-Hardy rule, bivalent $SO_4^=$ ions are more effective than monovalent Cl^- ions. Conversely, the presence or addition of positive ions extends the useful *p*H zone in the basic region, bivalent Ca^{++} ions being more effective than monovalent Na^+ ions.

5. In soft waters, negatively charged color colloids are coagulated most effectively at *p*H values of 4 or less. The trivalent ions of aluminum and iron are then the precipitating agents. Excess amounts of Al^{+++} and

Fe^{+++} may have to be removed as hydrous oxides by subsequent addition of alkaline substances. In practice, a *p*H value as low as 4 is seldom attained.

6. Color removal is sometimes improved by prechlorination of alum-treated waters. This may be due to oxidation of ferrous iron. Iron in organic combination in highly colored waters has also been effectively oxidized and precipitated by potassium permanganate at a *p*H of 8.8 to 9.8 (Section 14-3).

7. The coagulation of very clear waters may be improved by the addition of finely divided clay (15 to 100 mg/l), activated silica (colloidal silica prepared from sodium silicate), or other coagulant aids. These provide nuclei about which the precipitate can collect. They also weight the floc and hasten its settling.

8. Iron and manganese naturally present in water can be called into use as coagulants and to speed their own removal (Section 14-3).

9. Coagulation is a time-concentration phenomenon. Concentration increases the opportunity for contact and decreases the time required for floc formation.

10. Stirring increases the opportunity for contact and decreases the time for floc formation. It also promotes floc growth (Section 14-4).

c. Determination of coagulant dose. Because waters and waste waters vary and change in quality, and because coagulation is so complex a reaction, the optimum dosage of coagulants must be determined in practice by trial. Ordinarily, a single chemical coagulant is applied, its dosage being regulated to the minimum amount necessary for rapid and adequate coagulation. Only if such treatment is uneconomical or gives poor results, are alkalinity or colloidal particles added or chemicals used to regulate the *p*H.

Trial determinations of coagulant dosage, commonly called *jar tests,* are made in a laboratory stirring device of the type shown in Figure 14-2. The amount of coagulant is increased stepwise, and all jars are mixed simultaneously for 10 to 30 min. The jar in which floc first makes its appearance is generally assumed to have received the most economical dose. However, the size of floc and its settling characteristics and filterability must also be taken into consideration

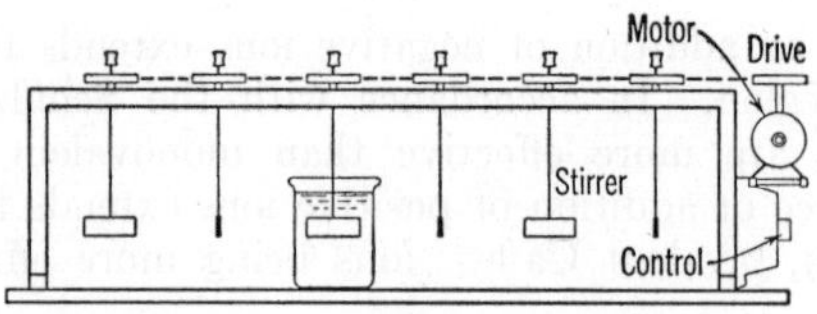

Figure 14-2. Laboratory apparatus for determination of the optimum dosage of coagulating chemicals and needed stirring. A variable-speed motor is provided. Tyndall beams directed through the beakers are of assistance.

in relation to available flocculation chambers, settling basins, and filter capacities. The usefulness of alkalies, *p*H regulation, and the introduction of coagulant aids such as clay, activated silica, or synthetic organic materials may have to be investigated. Jar tests also provide essential data for controlling the dosage of sewage sludge with chemicals in order to speed and improve its filtration or drying. This is called sludge conditioning (Section 17-15).

14-3. Chemical Precipitation. The two most important classes of dissolved substances in water and waste water that are amenable to precipitation by added chemicals are: (1) hardness and (2) iron and manganese. In water purification, removal of hardness is called water softening, removal of iron and manganese respectively deferrization and demanganization.

Natural waters, more particularly well waters, may contain hundreds and even thousands of milligrams per liter of hardness as $CaCO_3$. The iron content of natural waters rarely exceeds 10 mg/l, but it may go above 50 mg/l. The manganese content is generally lower. It rarely exceeds 3 mg/l. Ground water is the most common offender.

a. Precipitation of hardness. The relationship of the hardness-forming constituents, principally the ions of calcium and magnesium, to other mineral ions in water is shown schematically in Figure 14-3. Chemical precipitation of hardness is generally accomplished by lime or by lime and soda ash, the *lime-soda* process of water softening developed by Clark in 1841. In the removal of Ca^{++}, lime converts CO_2 and bicarbonate ion to normal carbonate ion. Relatively insoluble precipitates of calcium carbonate ($K_s = 4.82 \times 10^{-9}$) are formed and removed by settling. For the precipitation of Mg^{++}, hydroxyl ion must be provided in order to form an insoluble precipitate of magnesium hydroxide ($K_s = 5.5 \times 10^{-12}$). The solu-

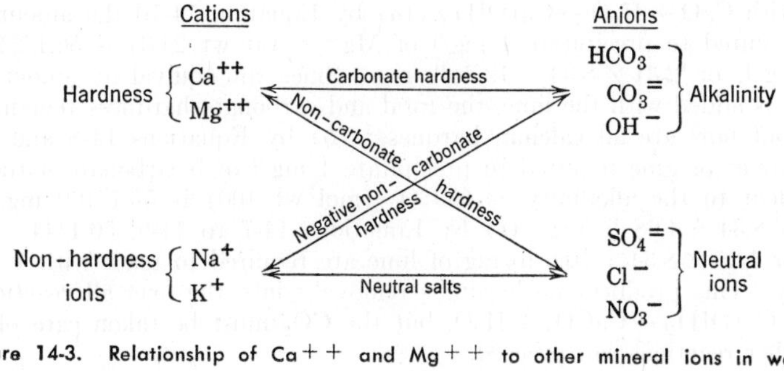

Figure 14-3. Relationship of Ca + + and Mg + + to other mineral ions in water.

bility of magnesium carbonate $MgCO_3 \cdot 3H_2O$ is relatively high ($K_s = 1 \times 10^{-5}$). An excess of 2 or 3 grains per gal of hydrated lime is needed to promote the formation of $Mg(OH)_2$.

If the amount of $SO_4^=$, Cl^-, and NO_3^- exceeds the amount of Na^+ and K^+ naturally present in the water, i.e., if the water contains non-carbonate hardness, there is insufficient carbonate ion to remove the Ca^{++}. Soda ash is then added to provide carbonate ion for this Ca^{++} and for the Ca^{++} associated with the excess lime used for Mg^{++} removal. Cold-process softening falls short of Ca^{++} and Mg^{++} removals that are theoretically possible. Final precipitations are slow and could be completed only in outsized reaction and settling tanks. In order to prevent cementing of filters and incrustation of pipes by $CaCo_3$ and to rid the water of unwanted causticity, excess-lime treatment must be followed by carbonation with CO_2 gas. This stops the precipitation of Ca^{++} and Mg^{++} and stabilizes the water (see Section 14-6). The softening and recarbonation reactions are:

$$Ca(OH)_2 \leftrightarrows Ca^{++} + 2OH^- \qquad 14\text{-}6$$

$$CO_2 + OH^- \leftrightarrows HCO_3^- \qquad 14\text{-}7$$

$$HCO_3^- + OH^- \leftrightarrows CO_3^= + H_2O \qquad 14\text{-}8$$

$$Ca^{++} + CO_3^= \leftrightarrows CaCO_3 \downarrow \qquad 14\text{-}9$$

$$Mg^{++} + 2OH^- \leftrightarrows Mg(OH)_2 \downarrow \qquad 14\text{-}10$$

In the presence of Mg^{++}, the amount of lime must be sufficient not only to convert all the CO_2 and HCO_3^- to $CO_3^=$ but also to produce $Mg(OH)_2$ with the required excess of OH^-.

The quantities of lime and soda ash required for softening can be calculated by means of these equations as follows:

1. Lime, CaO (mol wt 56.1) needed for precipitation of carbonate hardness, with $CaO + H_2O \rightarrow Ca(OH)_2$: (*a*) by Equation 14-10 the amount of lime required to precipitate 1 mg/l of Mg^{++} (at wt 24.3) is 56.1/24.3 = 2.31 mg/l, or $2.31 \times 8.34 = 19.3$ lb/mg. Since an equivalent amount of Ca^{++} is added with the lime, the total and carbonate hardness remain the same but now are all calcium hardness; (*b*) by Equations 14-8 and 14-9 the amount of lime required to precipitate 1 mg/l of bicarbonate hardness, equivalent to the alkalinity as $CaCO_3$ (mol wt 100) is 56.1/100 mg/l or $0.561 \times 8.34 = 4.68$ lb/mg; (*c*) by Equations 14-7 to 14-9, 56.1/44 = 1.28 mg/l or $1.28 \times 8.34 = 10.6$ lb/mg of lime are required to react with 1 mg/l of CO_2. This produces no hardness removal, since the over-all reaction is $CO_2 + Ca(OH)_2 \rightarrow CaCO_3 + H_2O$, but the CO_2 must be taken care of before other reactions can proceed.

2. Soda ash, Na_2CO_3 (mol wt 106.0) needed for precipitation of non-carbonate hardness: for 1 mg/l of non-carbonate hardness 106/100 = 1.06 mg/l or $1.06 \times 8.34 = 8.84$ lb/mg are required.

The calculated amounts of lime and soda ash must be adjusted for purity and an allowance must be made for the excess lime used to hasten and complete precipitation. Normally this amounts to 25 to 50 mg/l of caustic alkalinity.

Example 14-1. Calculate the necessary amounts of lime to soften a raw water of the following composition: total hardness as $CaCO_3$ 215 mg/l; alkalinity as $CaCO_3$ 185 mg/l; magnesium as Mg 15.8 mg/l; non-carbonate hardness as $CaCO_3$ 29.5 mg/l; and carbon dioxide as CO_2 25.8 mg/l.

The required amount of pure lime is $10.6 \times 25.8 = 274$ lb/mg for the carbon dioxide plus $4.68 \times 185 = 866$ lb/mg for the bicarbonate hardness plus $19.3 \times 15.8 = 305$ lb/mg for the magnesium, a total of 1445 lb/mg. The excess lime is additional.

For the non-carbonate hardness, the required amount of pure soda ash is $8.84 \times 29.5 = 260$ lb/mg.

The required degree of softening is effected in one of the following ways:

1. Part of the water is subjected to excess-lime or lime-soda treatment and the settled effluent is mixed with unsoftened water. This *split treatment* generally makes carbonation unnecessary.

2. Lime softening is combined with ion-exchange softening (Section 14-5). The lime throws down most of the carbonate hardness, while the ion exchanger eliminates the remaining amount as well as the non-carbonate hardness.

3. Coagulants are added to increase removals of precipitates or to shorten the requisite time of settling. Filter alum, sodium aluminate, and activated silica have been found useful either singly or in combination.

4. A portion of the settled sludge or slurry is recirculated. This accelerates precipitation and may reduce the consumption of chemicals.

5. Free CO_2 is reduced by aeration prior to softening. Then the lime ordinarily wasted in converting CO_2 to $CaCO_3$ is no longer required.

6. Recarbonation after excess-lime treatment is made to serve more than the single purpose of removing causticity. If the amount of CO_2 added is such that caustic alkalinity is converted to carbonate alkalinity (Equations 14-7 and 14-8), a fine precipitate of $CaCO_3$ is formed and further softening results. The precipitate may be removed by filtration or by coagulation and secondary settling. A pH in the vicinity of 9.5 will effect these changes.

7. The water is subjected to secondary carbonation just before it is applied to filters. This reduces precipitation of $CaCO_3$ on sand grains and supporting gravel.

8. Incrustation of sand is prevented by the addition of small amounts of polyphosphate.

9. The advantages of softening by recarbonation are balanced against those of producing a stable water (see Section 14-5). It may be better to

add sufficient CO_2 to reach the equilibrium point between carbonate and calcium ions and to forego some reduction in hardness.

10. Efficiencies of removal of Ca^{++} and Mg^{++} are increased by raising the water temperature. This decreases solubilities and increases rates of precipitation. Hot-process softening is common in boiler-water treatment (Section 20-5).

In practice, the softening of water by chemical precipitation generally aims at the following targets: (1) reduction of calcium alkalinity by lime softening to values of 75 to 100 mg/l in the absence of significant amounts of Mg^{++}; (2) reduction of calcium and magnesium alkalinities by excess-lime treatment to values of 30 to 50 mg/l in the absence of significant amounts of non-carbonate hardness; (3) reduction of calcium and magnesium hardness by the lime-soda process to 30 to 40 mg/l; and (4) reduction of calcium and magnesium hardness by the hot, lime-soda process to less than 10 mg/l.

An important side reaction in the excess-lime treatment of high-magnesium waters is a reduction in fluorides when they are present. Removal appears to be due to adsorption of F^- on the $Mg(OH)_2$ floc. Scott[5] and his associates have suggested the following empirical relationship:

$$P = 7\sqrt{\mathrm{Mg}} \qquad 14\text{-}11$$

Here P is the percentage removal of fluoride as F, and Mg is the mg/l of magnesium precipitated. Reduction of 3.3 mg/l of F^- to 1.0 mg/l, for example, requires the precipitation of 100 mg/l of Mg^{++}. In the absence of adequate amounts of magnesium, a magnesium salt can be added to bring about the desired fluoride removal.

b. Precipitation of iron and manganese. Since the solubilities of inorganic ferrous (Fe^{++}) and manganous (Mn^{++}) carbonates and hydroxides are high compared to hydrous ferric (Fe^{+++}) and manganic oxides, inorganic iron and manganese normally occur in solution in highest concentration when water is devoid of dissolved oxygen. However, very acid wastes, such as those draining from mines, may hold large amounts of iron in solution even in the presence of oxygen. The anions present in iron- and manganese-bearing waters are much the same as those found in hard waters (Figure 14-3). In combination with organic matter, iron and manganese are extremely difficult to precipitate.

[5] R. D. Scott, A. E. Kimberley, H. L. van Horn, L. F. Ey, and F. H. Waring, Jr., Fluoride in Ohio water supplies, *J. Am. Water Works Assoc.*, 29, 9 (1937).

Iron and manganese are precipitated from water either by aeration and contact treatment (filtration) or by liming and filtration.

Aeration of water low in dissolved oxygen and high in CO_2 will add oxidizing oxygen and raise the *p*H value by flushing out CO_2. Both effects aid in oxidizing the iron and manganese to insoluble ferric and manganic hydroxides. However, the amounts present are relatively so small and the amounts that may be left in solution are relatively so minute (Fe and Mn together <0.3 mg/l), that self-precipitation is protracted. Rates of flocculation are, therefore, accelerated in practice by contact and by catalysis. For these purposes, the water is generally caused to trickle over coke, or crushed stone, or to flow upward through the contact material. Deposits of hydrated oxides of iron and manganese accumulate on the contact surfaces and catalyze further oxidation to ferric and manganic oxides. Limestone is an effective contact medium because of its basic reaction. Pyrolusite (MnO_2 ore) possesses high catalytic power. Iron and manganese bacteria may grow luxuriantly on the contact media. Filters are generally made part of the treatment works because they, too, provide contact and because they remove finely divided precipitates.

But 0.14 mg/l O_2 is needed to convert 1 mg/l Fe^{++} to ferric hydroxide. Therefore little aeration is required for the purpose. Vigorous aeration may remove more than the excess CO_2 (Section 14-6) and shift the calcium carbonate equilibrium of hard water to precipitate finely divided $CaCO_3$ that retains ferric ions in colloidal suspension. Waters high in organic matter, too, may have to be aerated sparingly, because overaeration may produce relatively stable colloids. Oxidation of the organic matter by potassium permanganate or chlorine may be more helpful. The oxidants destroy the complex compounds of iron and manganese and oxidize the iron and manganese released. Oxide precipitates are formed. The settling of precipitates can be hastened by coagulation. Alum, but preferably iron, coagulants will, indeed, remove small amounts of iron and manganese from some waters without preparatory treatment. Chlorination may then be of assistance.

The contact beds of deferrization and demanganization plants are normally 6 to 10 ft deep with surface loadings of 40 to 80 mgad. They are operated either as down-flow tricklers or as up-flow submerged beds. Submerged flow makes for a longer period of contact. The contact medium is ordinarily 1½ to 2 in. in size, but coarse and fine gravels have also been employed successfully. The aerators of trickling contact beds are ordinarily proportioned to the size of the beds above which they operate. Heads on aerators are commonly kept to a few feet. Accumulations of iron and manganese are flushed out of coarse beds by rapid drainage, if necessary after filling the beds to near overflow level. Gravel beds are washed in much the same way as rapid sand filters. A flocculating and settling basin is generally interposed between the contact unit and slow or rapid filters where these are used. An hour or two of detention is normally provided. The rates of filtration are in the vicinity of 10 mgad for slow filters and 125 mgad for rapid filters. Precipitation of manganese is normally much slower than that of iron. Most of the manganese load may, therefore, fall on the filters.

Precipitation of iron and manganese from hard waters by lime is quite similar to, and fully as effective as, the precipitation of calcium and magnesium. If oxygen is kept out of the system, iron precipitates as ferrous hydroxide, $Fe(OH)_2$, or ferrous carbonate, $FeCO_3$; manganese as manganous hydroxide, $Mn(OH)_2$. The solubility of $Mn(OH)_2$ calculated from its solubility product $(Mn^{++})(OH^-)^2$ of 7.1×10^{-15} is 3.90 mg/l as Mn at a *p*H of 9.0. It decreases 100-fold for each unit rise in *p*H. The solubility of $Fe(OH)_2$ is somewhat smaller (Table 14-1). Precipitation of Fe^{++} and Mn^{++} as hydroxides can, therefore, proceed only above *p*H values of about 9.5 and 10 respectively. Because of the cost, the use of lime for deferrization and demanganization is commonly restricted to hard waters that are to be softened at the same time or to waters that need to be stabilized (Section 14-6).

The hydrous oxides of iron and manganese precipitated from water by lime in the absence of oxygen are removed effectively by filtration. Enclosed (pressure) units are used for this purpose (Section 15-1).

14-4. Flocculation. In their initial phases, coagulation and precipitation produce finely divided, or colloidal, suspensions. These suspensions are converted into settleable solids by agglomeration. In a quiescent fluid, colloids collide because of their Brownian movement, and finely divided solids come into contact with one another when more rapidly settling solids overtake more slowly settling ones (Section 13-5). As a result, flocs of ever-increasing size are formed. Floc growth is exceedingly slow unless it is hastened by stirring the water. This increases the number of collisions or contacts. The increased opportunity for contact is called *flocculation.* It may be provided by hydraulic or mechanical means, including the injection of air.

a. Theoretical considerations. The stirring of water or waste water imparts velocity gradients that are the controlling factor in flocculation. It stands to reason that the number of contacts between particles in a unit of time varies directly with the velocity gradient and, in addition, with the number and size of particles. In a given suspension, the number of flocculating particles decreases rapidly as their size increases. The total available binding energy also declines with neutralization of charge and increase in size of particle, until the floc attains a size at which the shearing action of the fluid overbalances any further tendency for aggregation. Under favorable conditions, the flocs may attain a size about equal to the dimensions of snowflakes.

The temporal mean velocity gradient in a shearing fluid, designated by the letter G, is the difference in velocity dv in a given distance dy at right angles to the direction of flow,[6] is a function of the power input P, the volume of the vessel V, and the viscosity of the fluid μ. Dimensionally, therefore,

$$G = \phi(P, V, \mu)$$

Hence, as in Section 13-3, $[G] = [P^x, V^y, \mu^z]$ and $[lt^{-1}l^{-1}] = [t^{-1}] = [m^{x+z}l^{2x+3y-z}t^{-3x-z}]$, whence

$$G = \sqrt{P/(V\mu)} \qquad 14\text{-}12$$

Experience has shown that the value of G should be greater than 10 fps per ft in order to promote flocculation but less than 75 fps per ft if disintegration of the floc by shear is to be avoided. Optimum values appear to lie between 30 and 60 fps per ft. The detention period should be at least 10 min. Longer times (30 min or more) are indicated for low values of G, and there is reason to believe that for satisfactory performance the dimensionless product Gt may range within the limits of 10^4 and 10^5. If the value of G is adjusted to floc size and growth requirements by being given a high initial value and being decreased progressively, the initial values of G may be made as high as 100 fps per ft. The final values may then be dropped to as low as 10 fps per ft in order to preserve floc structure.

For baffled channels of length l and cross-sectional area a in which a loss of head h is incurred by a flow Q,

[6] T. R. Camp and P. C. Stein, Velocity gradients and internal work in fluid motion, *J. Boston Soc. Civil Engrs.*, *30*, 219 (1943). Also, T. R. Camp, Flocculation and flocculation basins, *Trans. Am. Soc. Civil Engrs.*, *120*, 1 (1955).

$$P/V = Qwh/(al) = vwh/l = v\rho gs = wh/t = \rho gh/t \qquad 14\text{-}13$$

or

$$G = \sqrt{v\rho gs/\mu} = \sqrt{vgs/\nu} = \sqrt{gh/\nu t} \qquad 14\text{-}14$$

Here ρ is the mass density of the fluid, g is the gravity constant, ν is the kinematic viscosity of the fluid, s is the slope of the water surface and t is the period of detention. In practice, velocities vary between 0.3 and 3 fps, detention times between 10 and 90 min, and head losses between 1 and 3 ft.

For mechanical mixers, operated by paddles, the useful power input is a function of the drag of the paddles. If F_D is the drag in lb, C_D is the coefficient of drag for plates moved face-on to the fluid, A is the area of the paddles in sq ft, v is the velocity of the paddles relative to that of the liquid in fps, and V is the volume of the flocculator in cu ft, the drag (Equation 13-4) is

$$F_D = C_D A w v^2/2g = C_D A \rho v^2/2 \qquad 14\text{-}15$$

and the power input, which equals force times velocity, becomes

$$P = F_D v = C_D A \rho v^3/2 \qquad 14\text{-}16$$

or

$$G = \sqrt{C_D A v^3/(2\nu V)} \qquad 14\text{-}17$$

In practice peripheral speeds of paddles range from 3 fps to 0.3 fps.

For diffused-air aeration, the work done is $\int p\,dv$, where p is the pressure and v the volume of the air. For isothermal expansion of the air pv = constant and $\int p\,dv$ = constant $\int dv/v$ = constant $\times \log_e v$ between the limiting volumes of compressed air and free air (air at atmospheric pressure). Hence the work done is $pv_{\text{free}} \log_e (p_{\text{compressed}}/p_{\text{free}})$. For Q_a cfm of free air and p in feet of water H, the work done is $(14.7 \times 144 \times 2.303/60)Q_a \log [(H + 34)/34]$, and

$$P = 81.5 Q_a \log [(H + 34)/34] \qquad 14\text{-}18$$

or

$$G = 9.0\sqrt{Q_a \log [(H + 34)/34]/\mu V)} \qquad 14\text{-}19$$

Example 14-2. A flocculator designed to treat 20 mgd is 100 ft long by 40 ft wide by 15 ft deep. It is equipped with 12-in. paddles supported parallel to and moved by four horizontal shafts which rotate at a speed of 2.5 rpm. The center line of the paddles is 6.0 ft from the shaft which is at middepth of the tank. Two paddles are mounted on each shaft, one opposite the other. If the mean velocity of the water is approximately ¼ the velocity of the paddles (as is generally true in this type of stirring device), find: (*a*) the velocity differential between the paddles and the water, (*b*) the hydraulic power and energy consumption if the velocity differential between the water and the paddle is 75% of the linear velocity of the paddle blades and the coefficient of drag for flat plates is 1.8, (*c*) the time of flocculation, and (*d*) the value of G.

a. Speed of rotation. If n is the number of revolutions per minute and r is the distance of the center of the paddle blade from the center of the shaft, $2\pi rn = 60\,v_p$, or $v_p = 2\pi \times 6 \times 2.5/60 = 1.57$ fps, where v_p is the linear velocity of the paddle blades. Therefore, the velocity differential between the paddles and the water is $0.75 \times 1.57 = 1.18$ fps.

b. Power consumption. Since the area of the paddles is $A = 40 \times 2 \times 4 \times 1 = 320$ sq ft, and the coefficient of drag $C_D = 1.8$, the total power input, P_t, by Equation 14-16 is: $P_t = 1.8 \times 320 \times 62.4 \times (0.75 \times 1.57)^3/(2 \times 32.2) = 918$ ft-lb per sec, and $918/550 = 1.67$ hp, or 1.24 kw.

The energy consumption per mg, therefore, is $1.67 \times 24/20 = 2.0$ hp-hr per mg, or 1.5 kwh per mg treated. For electrical drive, there must be added the energy required to overcome mechanical friction and to provide for electrical losses in the lines and motor. (In practice, flocculators consume 2 to 6 kwh per mg treated.)

c. Time of flocculation. Since the volume of the tank is $4 \times 100 \times 15 = 6 \times 10^4$ cu ft, the detention period $t = 6 \times 10^4 \times 7.48 \times 24 \times 60/(20 \times 10^6) = 32.5$ min.

d. Value of G. By Equation 14-17:

$$G = \sqrt{1.8 \times 320 \times (1.18)^3/(2 \times 1.41 \times 10^{-5} \times 6 \times 10^4)} = 24 \text{ fps per ft}$$

and

$$Gt = 24 \times 32.5 \times 60 = 4.7 \times 10^4$$

b. Mixing and flocculating devices. The suspended or dissolved chemicals added to water or waste water must be dispersed uniformly through the water or waste water treated. The more rapidly this can be done, the less time is wasted in setting the chemicals to work. To this purpose, the chemicals may be introduced (1) in advance of hydraulic structures in which the water is agitated violently but which have some other function to perform as well or (2) into special mixing units. Examples of the first are turbines, pumps, and spray or injection aerators; examples of the second are heavily baffled basins, or tanks equipped with mechanical stirrers or air diffusers. Exposures of 30 to 60 sec are commonly enough.

By contrast, floc growth is encouraged by gentle stirring. This, too, may be accomplished by hydraulic means such as baffling, by mechanical means such as revolving paddles, or by air diffusion. Detention periods must be adjusted to chemical dosage. They may be as low as

10 min, but are more commonly 30 to 60 min. The velocity in conduits connecting flocculation chambers with settling tanks should lie between 0.5 fps and 1.0 fps. These values are large enough to prevent deposition of floc but small enough to prevent its disintegration. A combined mixing and flocculation basin is illustrated in Figure 14-4 and a number of units incorporating mixing, flocculation, and settling are shown in Figure 13-9. Slurry or sludge may be returned in order to promote floc formation and growth. Activated-sludge units are biologically activated flocculating units.

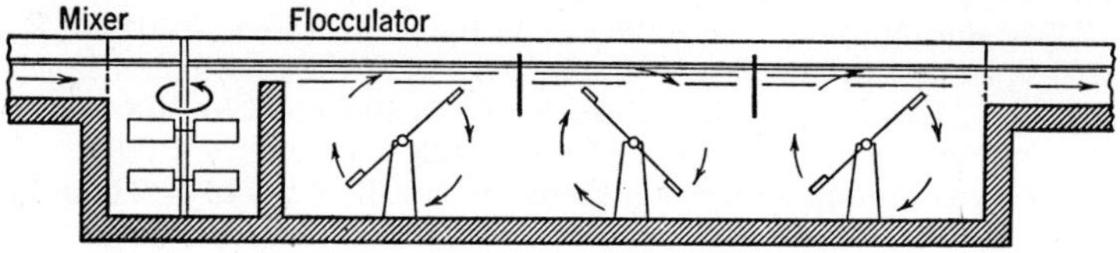

Figure 14-4. Mixing and flocculation basin.

14-5. Ion Exchange and Demineralization. Ion exchange is the displacement of one ion by another. Deionization, demineralization, or de-ashing embraces the removal of substantially all ionizable materials that will leave a residue on evaporation.

Both cations and anions may be exchanged between a liquid and a solid exchange medium. Cation or base exchange is employed to soften water and to remove iron and manganese. It has been used experimentally to remove and recover ammonia as NH_4^+ from sewage, and it may be employed in the laboratory to prepare ammonia-free water. In industry, both cation and anion exchangers find use in the preparation of boiler feed-water and in numerous industrial processes. The exchange media are packed in beds not unlike pressure, rapid sand filters (Section 15-1).

For the treatment of water, ion-exchange media must possess the following properties: (1) they must be of large surface, since rate of ion exchange is dependent on diffusion, but their resistance to flow must be compatible with hydraulic requirements; (2) they must possess a high exchange capacity and be readily cleaned by back-washing and regenerated by suitable chemicals; (3) they must be physically durable (not subject to attrition) and resistant to chemical attack (chemically stable); (4) they must be relatively inexpensive and capable of being regenerated by relatively inexpensive chemicals; and (5) they must be non-toxic and must not discolor the water (free from color throw). Effective sizes of 0.25 to 0.6 mm and uniformity coefficients of 1.7 to 2 are common and in line with sand-filter practice (Section 15-3). The porosity of exchange beds, too, accords with that of sand filters. The grains of exchange media are, themselves, quite porous.

The exchange capacity of a bed is commonly expressed in terms of the number of kilograins (1 lb = 7 kilograins) of substance removed from the liquid by passage through 1 cu ft of exchange medium. Because ion exchangers were first used for the softening of water, comparisons of exchange capacity are generally made by expressing the substance removed in terms of hardness as $CaCO_3$. When a bed is no longer capable of useful ion exchange, it is said to be exhausted and in need of regeneration.

The water that is to be treated in ion exchangers must be relatively free from suspended matter, oil, H_2S, and iron. Otherwise, the active surfaces become coated and lose their exchange capacity, and the beds clog and must be washed too frequently. The applied water must also be free from chemicals that will attack the exchange medium. The regenerating wash must likewise be free from interfering substances.

The regenerating requirements of a bed are expressed in pounds of chemical per cubic foot of exchanger or per kilograin of substance removed from the liquid. The minimum depth of bed is generally 24 in., the loading 2 gpm per cu ft, and the rate of flow of the regenerant 1 gpm per cu ft. Rinse-water requirements after regeneration vary from 30 to 100 gal per cu ft. Wash-water needs and rates depend respectively upon the quality of the water treated and the degree of bed expansion to be employed (Section 15-6). When dry resins are immersed in water, they swell; when they are converted from the Na^+ or H^+ to the Ca^{++} or Mg^{++} form, they shrink. This may lead to channeling and thus to inefficient operation. The swelling of most organic exchangers is less than 5%, but it is as high as 55% for some of them.

a. Zeolite exchangers.[7] Zeolites are insoluble sodium aluminosilicates that are capable of exchanging monovalent sodium ions (1) for multivalent ions of the alkaline earth group, (2) for ammonia, and (3) for the divalent ions of some of the metals in water. They are employed in particular for the removal of Ca^{++} and Mg^{++} in water softening, and for the removal of relatively small amounts of

[7] Zeolites (from the Greek words *zein* to boil and *lithos* stone) are a family of hydrous silicates originally occurring as secondary minerals in the cavities of lavas. The term *zeolite* has been applied loosely to all cation exchangers. This should not be done.

Fe^{++} in deferrization. The chemical structure of the sodium zeolites is portrayed by the formula $Na_2O \cdot Al_2O_3 \cdot xSiO_2 \cdot yH_2O$. For convenience, this formula may be written Na_2Z, the letter Z symbolizing that part of the zeolite which is not exchanged. The common exchange reactions may be written as follows:

$$Na_2Z + \begin{Bmatrix} Ca^{++} \\ Mg^{++} \\ Fe^{++} \end{Bmatrix} \rightleftharpoons \begin{Bmatrix} Ca \\ Mg \\ Fe \end{Bmatrix} Z + 2Na^+ \qquad 14\text{-}20$$

When natural, fresh waters are passed through a column of sodium zeolite, these reactions are driven to the right. The reactions are reversed, and the zeolite is regenerated by a solution of common salt, or brine, of high Na^+ concentration. The reciprocal exchange of Na^+ creates the sodium cycle.

Two types of zeolites are in common use: (*a*) natural, greensand (glauconite [8]) zeolites and (*b*) synthetic, porous, gel zeolites. The synthetic zeolites are prepared from solutions of Na_2SiO_3 and alum or sodium aluminate ($NaAlO_2$). The specific gravity of all zeolites, when dry, is 2.1 to 2.4, i.e., not much smaller than that of quartz sand (2.65). Natural zeolites, however, retain about 10% water, synthetic zeolites as much as 50%. This reduces their apparent specific gravity, and their weights become 100 lb per cu ft (natural) and 55 to 70 lb per cu ft (synthetic). The exchange capacity of the zeolites and their regeneration requirements are summarized in Table 14-2.

Natural zeolites are durable and chemically stable. Their use is preferred for water relatively low in hardness (never $>$ 850 to 1,000 mg/l as $CaCO_3$), relatively high in Fe^{++} (but $<$ 1.5 to 2 mg/l), relatively low in silica (which is picked up from the zeolite), and either high or low in *p*H value. Synthetic zeolites are less durable and less stable chemically. They disintegrate in the presence of 15 mg/l or more of CO_2. Their use is preferred for waters relatively low in Fe^{++} and possessing normal *p*H values. If the formation of surface coatings of iron is to be prevented, dissolved oxygen must be kept out of the water; otherwise Fe^{++} will precipitate as Fe^{+++}.

Example 14-3. Find (*a*) the length of time during which a bed of natural zeolite 42 in. deep and operated at a rate of 6 gpm per sq ft will continue to remove 100.5 mg/l of Ca^{++}, 47.5 mg/l of Mg^{++}, and 2.0 mg/l of Fe^{++} all as $CaCO_3$, and (*b*) the amount of salt required for regeneration of the bed at

[8] From the Greek word *glaucos*, blue-green.

TABLE 14-2. Approximate Exchange Capacities and Regeneration Requirements of Ion Exchangers

Exchanger and Cycle (1)	Exchange Capacity: Observed Kilograins per cu ft as $CaCO_3$ (2)	Regenerator (3)	Regeneration Requirements: Observed Pounds per Kilograin Exchanged (4)	Regeneration Requirements: Theoretical Pounds per Kilograin Exchanged (5)
Cation Exchangers:				
Natural zeolite, Na	3–6	NaCl	0.5–1	0.167
Synthetic zeolite, Na	6–16	NaCl	0.4–0.5	0.167
Carbonaceous and resin, Na	5–40	NaCl	0.3–0.6	0.167
Carbonaceous and resin, H	5–40	H_2SO_4	0.3–0.6	0.137
Anion Exchangers:				
Resin	12–25	NaOH	0.6–1.0	0.120
Tricalcium phosphate	0.4–0.9	NaOH	1.4–3.3	0.300
	as F	HCl	0.7–1.7	0.275

Columns 2 and 4: Reported values. (1 lb = 7,000 grains = 454 grams.)

Column 4: To obtain lb per cu ft multiply Column 4 by Column 2. The efficiency of regeneration is 100 × Column 5/Column 4.

Column 5 (Equivalent wt of regenerator)/(7 × 10^3 × equivalent wt of substance removed/10^3), e.g., 58.5/(7 × 50) = 0.167 for NaCl and $CaCO_3$.

the end of this period. Use the average values given in Columns 2 and 4 of Table 14-2 for the necessary computations.

a. The volume of the bed is 42/12 = 3.5 cu ft per sq ft. Assuming that the bed will remove 4.5 kilograins/cu ft as $CaCO_3$, the exchange capacity of the bed is 4.5 × 3.5 = 15.8 kilograins per sq ft. Since the sum of the substances to be removed is 150 mg/l, or 150/17.1 = 8.77 grains/gal, 15.8 kilograins are removed from $15.8 \times 10^3/8.77$ = 1,800 gal per sq ft. Therefore, the length of the softening cycle is 1,800/6.0 = 300 min or 5 hr.

b. Assuming a salt requirement of 0.75 lb per kilograin exchanged, the amount of regenerating salt is 0.75 × 15.8 = 11.9 lb per sq ft of bed. The salt requirement per million gallons of water treated then becomes $11.9 \times 10^6/(1.8 \times 10^3) = 6.6 \times 10^3$ lb or 3.3 tons.

If the desired Ca^{++}, Mg^{++}, and Fe^{++} content of the treated water is to be 25 mg/l, (150 − 25)/150 = 5/6 of the water should be passed through the exchanger and 1/6 by-passed to be mixed with the softened water.

For the removal of iron and manganese by contact oxidation, zeolites may be treated with manganous sulfate and potassium permanganate. Higher oxides of manganese are deposited on the zeolite granules by this treatment, and both iron and manganese in water are oxidized by the manganese oxides to insoluble hydrous oxides. They are washed from the bed when the head loss becomes excessive. Potassium permanganate serves as the regenerant.

b. Carbonaceous and resinous exchangers. Carbonaceous cation exchangers are prepared from substances containing humates (coal), lignins (wood), or tannins (tan bark). Resinous cation exchangers are composed of substances such as sulfonated phenol-formaldehyde resins, and polymethyl acrylic acid.

These cation exchangers may be operated either on the sodium or the hydrogen cycle. For the removal of hardness from water, the sodium cycle is common. Regeneration is by salt. The hydrogen cycle is employed when sodium and potassium as well as hardness must be removed. Regeneration is then by an acid such as sulfuric acid. Letting the letter *R* stand for that part of the exchanger which is not exchanged, the reactions for operation on the sodium and hydrogen cycles, respectively, are:

$$Na_2R + \left\{\begin{matrix} Ca^{++} \\ Mg^{++} \end{matrix}\right. \rightleftharpoons \left.\begin{matrix} Ca \\ Mg \end{matrix}\right\} R + 2Na^+ \qquad 14\text{-}21$$

$$H_2R + \left\{\begin{matrix} Ca^{++} \\ Mg^{++} \\ 2Na^+ \\ 2K^+ \end{matrix}\right. \rightleftharpoons \left.\begin{matrix} Ca \\ Mg \\ Na_2 \\ K_2 \end{matrix}\right\} R + 2H^+ \qquad 14\text{-}22$$

The ions removed by hydrogen cation exchanges are replaced by hydrogen ions, and the *p*H of the water is lowered. The carbonate equilibrium is displaced, and CO_2 is freed. Its removal by aeration or by degasification, through heat and vacuum, will reduce the solids concentration of waters to the extent that carbonate ion was present. The other acids formed, HCl and H_2SO_4, can be neutralized economically by split treatment. They can also be removed in an anion exchanger, sometimes called an acid absorber. This will further deionize the water. In the presence of much Na^+ and $SO_4^=$ or Cl^-, hydrogen cation exchangers may permit the passage, *elution*, or *slippage* of Na^+. This can be reduced by recirculating water treated in an anion exchanger to the influent to the cation exchanger (Figure 14-5).

Two classes of anion resin exchangers exist: (1) weak base types in which the active centers in the resin matrix are R_3NH^+ groups, and (2) strong base types in which the active centers are quaternary ammonium groups, R_4N^+.

The weak base resins when regenerated with soda ash function as acid absorbers rather than as true exchangers. For these, equations may be written as follows:

$$(R_3NH)_2\begin{cases}Cl_2\\SO_4\end{cases} + Na_2CO_3 \rightarrow 2R_3N + Na_2\begin{cases}Cl_2\\SO_4\end{cases} + H_2O + CO_2 \quad 14\text{-}23$$

$$2R_3N + \begin{cases}2HCl\\H_2SO_4\end{cases} \rightarrow (R_3NH)_2\begin{cases}Cl_2\\SO_4\end{cases} \quad 14\text{-}24$$

These resins are ineffective absorbers of weak acids like carbonic acid or silicic acid and so may be used economically ahead of aerators or degasifiers in the treatment system.

The strong base resins are regenerated with NaOH rather than soda ash and function as true exchangers. The reactions may be written

$$2R_4NOH + \begin{cases}2Cl^-\\SO_4^=\end{cases} \leftrightarrows (R_4N)_2\begin{cases}Cl_2\\SO_4\end{cases} + 2OH^- \quad 14\text{-}25$$

$$(R_4N)_2\begin{cases}Cl_2\\SO_4\end{cases} + 2NaOH \leftrightarrows 2R_4NOH + Na_2\begin{cases}Cl_2\\SO_4\end{cases} \quad 14\text{-}26$$

Since these resins will also exchange anions of weak acids like carbonic and silicic acids, they are often used in boiler-water treatment. Silica and the silicates of calcium and magnesium form hard scales in boilers. Sodium chloride and carbonate may cause foaming and priming, and the decomposition of sodium bicarbonate promotes corrosion (by CO_2) and caustic embrittlement (by NaOH) (Section 20-1).

The approximate exchange capacities and regeneration requirements of carbonaceous and resinous ion exchangers are included in Table 14-2. These exchangers are resistant to attack by chemicals. They do not pick up silicon and are relatively light, weighing but 30 to 50 lb per cu ft when dry. The operation of cation and anion exchangers is outlined in Figure 14-5. Columns of mixed cation and anion exchangers give efficient removal of all ionizable impurities from waters in a single-step operation (mixed-bed deionization).

c. Fluoride exchangers. A processed tricalcium phosphate composed of granules of $Ca_3P_2O_8 \cdot H_2O$ and $3Ca_3P_2O_8 \cdot Ca(OH)_2$ has been found to remove fluoride by ion exchange. Degreased, protein-free bone functions in much the same way. Removals attained and regeneration requirements are included in Table 14-2.

d. Desalting processes other than ion exchange. These are two in number: (1) electrochemical desalting and (2) distillation. *Electrochemical desalting* is accomplished by membranes that are se-

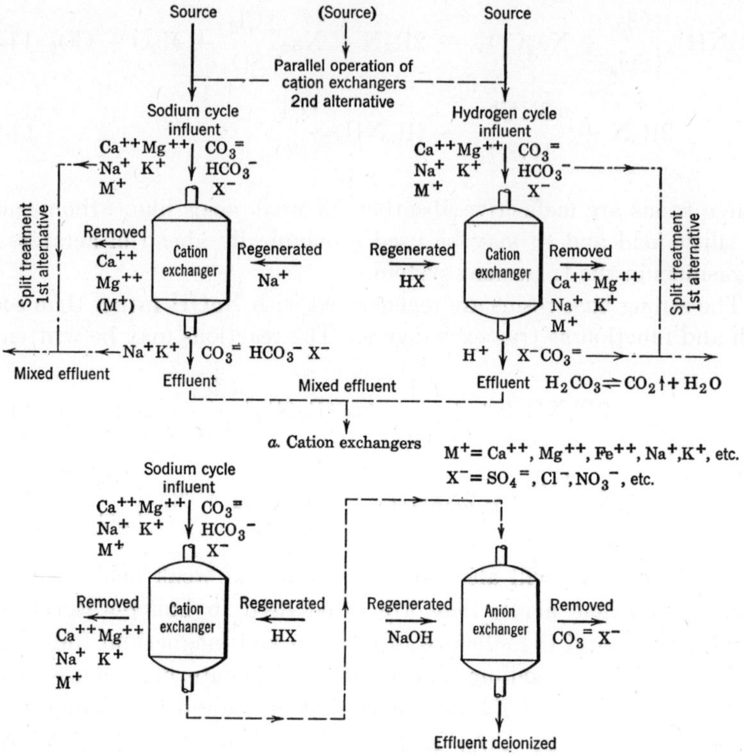

b. Cation and anion exchangers

Figure 14-5. Operation of cation and anion exchangers.

lectively permeable to cations or anions. The membranes are, in a sense, ion exchangers, but the driving force is electrochemical. *Distillation* is the oldest method of demineralization. It is currently also the only method by which water containing more than 5,000 mg/l of dissolved solids can be demineralized economically and effectively. Single-effect, multiple-effect, and vapor compression stills are employed.

14-6. Chemical Stabilization. Stabilization is the adjustment of the *p*H and alkalinity of a water to its calcium carbonate saturation-equilibrium value. At this point the water will neither dissolve nor deposit calcium carbonate, and protective coatings of this substance on the interior walls of pipes are thereby stabilized. The fundamental relationship involved is expressed by the reversible reaction

$$CaCO_3 + H^+ \rightleftharpoons Ca^{++} + HCO_3^- \qquad 14\text{-}27$$

If the pH lies below the equilibrium values, no protective coatings of $CaCO_3$ are formed, and the water has free access to the metal. Natural waters of low alkalinity and hardness, or of high CO_2 content, and coagulated, ion-exchange-softened, or demineralized waters fall into this category. If the pH lies above the equilibrium value, deposits of calcium carbonate accumulate in distribution mains, meters, hot-water heaters, and other equipment. This reduces their carrying capacity, or it causes poor heat transfer or the overheating of metals in boilers. Other problems, such as the incrustation of sand or gravel in filters, are also created. Since the equilibrium point shifts with temperature, it is not possible to attain a perfect balance for both cold-water and hot-water systems at the same time.

The pH associated with calcium carbonate equilibrium is designated pH_s and can be calculated or determined by test. The equations developed by Langelier [9] form the basis for the necessary calculations. In laboratory tests, the equilibrium point is assumed to have been reached after water has stood overnight in contact with pure, washed calcium carbonate powder. The equilibrium equation is constructed from Equation 11-4 and the equation

$$[Ca^{++}][CO_3^{=}] = K_s \qquad 14\text{-}28$$

where K_s is the solubility constant of calcium carbonate in mol/l. Equating the two expressions for $[CO_3^{=}]$ and neglecting the molar concentrations of H^+ and OH^- when they are sufficiently small (unless the saturation pH value is greater than about 10.3), the following logarithmic approximation of the equilibrium equation is obtained:

$$pH_s = (pK_2 - pK_s) + pCa + pA \qquad 14\text{-}29$$

where pK_2 is the negative logarithm of the second dissociation constant of carbonic acid, pK_s is the negative logarithm of the solubility constant of calcium carbonate, pCa is the negative logarithm of the molal concentration of calcium, and pA is the negative logarithm of the equivalent concentration of alkalinity or titratable base. The values of the constants vary with the temperature and salinity of the water and suitable corrections must be made for them.[10]

[9] W. F. Langelier, The analytical control of anticorrosion water treatment, *J. Am. Water Works Assoc.*, *28*, 1500 (1936).

[10] T. E. Larson and A. M. Buswell, Calcium carbonate saturation index and alkalinity interpretations, *J. Am. Water Works Assoc.*, *34*, 1667 (1942).

In order to provide a measure of the stability of a given water, Langelier has proposed naming the difference between the measured pH of the water and its calculated or observed $p\text{H}_s$ the saturation index I. A value of $I = p\text{H} - p\text{H}_s = 0$ indicates that the water is in equilibrium; a positive value that the water is oversaturated with $CaCO_3$ (or lacking in excess CO_2) and will tend to deposit $CaCO_3$; a negative value, conversely, that the water is undersaturated (or possessed of excess CO_2) and will tend to dissolve existing deposits of $CaCO_3$.

Example 14-4. A sample of water has a pH of 7.0 at 25 C and contains 7.5 mg/l of Ca^{++}, and 15 mg/l of alkalinity as $CaCO_3$. Find the saturation index at 25 C, the ionization and solubility constants being $K_2 = 4.69 \times 10^{-11}$, and $K_s = 4.82 \times 10^{-9}$.

Since $4.69 \times 10^{-11} = 10^{-10.33}$ and $4.82 \times 10^{-9} = 10^{-8.32}$, $pK_2 = 10.33$ and $pK_s = 8.32$. Furthermore, 7.5 mg/l of Ca^{++} equals $7.5/(40.1 \times 10^3) = 1.87 \times 10^{-4}$ mol/l, and 15 mg/l of alkalinity equals $15/(50 \times 10^3) = 3 \times 10^{-4}$ mol/l, whence $p\text{Ca} = 3.73$ and $p\text{A} = 3.52$. By Equation 14-29, therefore, $p\text{H}_s = (10.33 - 8.32) + 3.73 + 3.52 = 9.26$ and $I = 7.0 - 9.3 = -2.3$ (uncorrected for salinity).

14-7. Corrosion Control. The corrosion of metals is a complex and, as yet, poorly understood electrochemical process by which metals deteriorate and are eventually destroyed.

a. Processes of corrosion. The processes involved in corrosion are best exemplified by the corrosion of a metal such as iron in contact with water. Three principal steps may be distinguished: (1) an anodic reaction by which the metal goes into solution and electrons are freed to flow through the metal to a cathode, (2) a cathodic reaction that makes use of the liberated electrons, and (3) a series of reactions of the metal ions with the water and substances dissolved

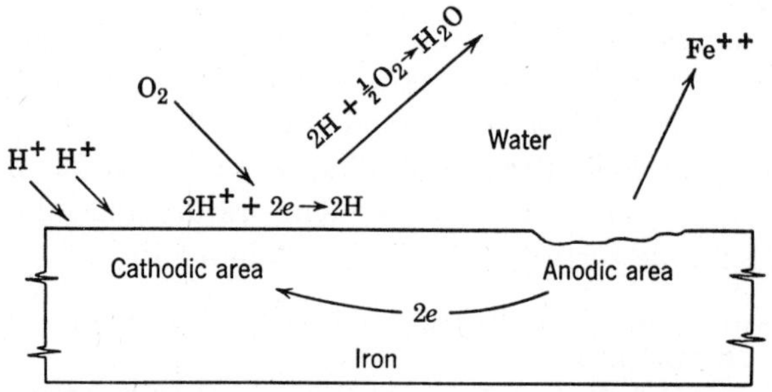

Figure 14-6. Corrosion cell on surface of iron in water. *After Eliassen and Lamb.*

in it (Figure 14-6). The last step, ordinarily, results in the formation of insoluble products of corrosion which are precipitated from the water. This completes the cycle of corrosion and clears the way for renewed solution of the metal. Interruption of, or interference in, any one of these steps will alter the course or the rate of corrosion. The chemistry of corrosion may be summarized as follows:

1. The anodic reaction is a function of the oxidation potential of the metal, or that of its alloy or oxide, whichever happens to be present at the metal-water interface.[11] The anodic reaction (or first step) of pure iron, for example, is: $Fe = Fe^{++} + 2e$ with a standard half-cell potential of +0.409 volts.

2. The cathodic reaction is more complex and less well understood. At *p*H values below 4.5, gaseous hydrogen is evolved according to the reaction:

$$2H^+ + 2e = H_2 \qquad 14\text{-}30$$

In these circumstances *p*H is an important factor in determining the rate of corrosion. At higher *p*H values (5 to 11) and in the presence of oxygen, the over-all cathodic reaction is best represented by the equation:

$$2H_2O + O_2 + 4e = 4OH^- \qquad 14\text{-}31$$

In this range, the rate of corrosion is not appreciably dependent on *p*H but, rather, on the oxygen supply. In the absence of oxygen, the cathode becomes polarized, and the rate of corrosion is inappreciable.

3. The metal ions produced at the anode react with hydroxide or carbonate ions from the cathode and, in the case of iron, with additional oxygen to produce insoluble hydroxides or carbonates. For iron this reaction may be written

$$4Fe^{++} + 8OH^- + O_2 \rightarrow 2Fe_2O_3 \cdot H_2O + 2H_2O \qquad 14\text{-}32$$

The end result is the deposition of an insoluble hydrous oxide of iron, or *rust.*

The composition of natural waters is so varied that present knowledge of what takes place in the three steps that have been outlined does not, as yet, offer a satisfactory explanation, and especially not a quantitative evaluation, of corrosion effects. However, the following qualitative observations are of interest:

[11] A chemical substance is *oxidized* when it loses electrons to a second substance that is *reduced* as it acquires the transferred electrons. Although oxidation and reduction always occur together, the processes may be written separately as half-reaction equations. A potential difference between a metal and a solution, called an electrode potential, is created as part of the establishment of an equilibrium. The magnitude of the potential is measured by connecting two electrodes and their solutions to make a complete circuit or electrochemical cell. If one electrode is chosen as standard (such as the hydrogen electrode) and assigned an arbitrary potential, the potential of the other electrode can be expressed with respect to the standard.

1. Oxygen and water are essential to corrosion. In the absence of either one, there is essentially no corrosion.

2. Contact between dissimilar metals or the existence of areas of dissimilar oxidation potentials in the same metal promotes corrosion. A galvanic cell is formed, and the rate of corrosion is stepped up.

3. The anodic metal or area, which possesses the highest oxidation potential, corrodes; the cathodic metal or area does not. The relative behavior of different metals may be gaged from the electromotive force series, or better from a galvanic series which applies to the particular environmental conditions encountered in water. An applicable galvanic series of metal and alloys suggested by Eliassen and Lamb [12] is listed in Table 14-3.

TABLE 14-3. Galvanic Series of Metals and Alloys

Corroded end (anodic or least noble)	Magnesium
	Zinc
	Aluminum (commercially pure)
	Steel or iron
	Cast iron
	Lead
	Tin
	Brasses
	Copper
	Bronzes
	Chromium-iron (passive)
	Silver
	Graphite
Protected end (cathodic or most noble)	Gold
	Platinum

Zinc, for example, is anodic to copper or iron. This accounts for the dezincification of yellow brass and for the reduced corrosion of iron in galvanized-iron pipes until the zinc coating has been destroyed. Iron, in turn, is anodic to copper. Red or rusty water may therefore issue from a bronze faucet attached to an iron pipe.

4. Since the rate of reduction of oxygen at the cathodic area, which depends upon the rate at which oxygen has access to the area, governs the transfer of electrons from the metal to the solution, the area to which oxygen has easiest access tends to become the cathodic area and the area to which oxygen has access with difficulty tends to become the anodic area. The resulting corrosion cell is called a differential-aeration cell. In water supply and waste-water disposal, such cells are observed in many forms. Examples of anodic areas, or areas sheltered against oxygen, are (*a*) pits or depressions in the metal, (*b*) areas underlying mill scale or products of corrosion, and (*c*) areas underlying biological growths. In water pipes, the rate of cor-

[12] Rolf Eliassen and J. C. Lamb III, Mechanism of internal corrosion of water pipe, *J. Am. Water Works Assoc., 45,* 1281 (1953).

rosion is decreased with time owing to the accumulation of rust or similar oxidation products, and it is increased by high velocities of flow owing to the more rapid removal of corrosion-retarding substances and the replenishment of corrosion-promoting substances.

5. The presence of electrolytes promotes corrosion by facilitating the flow of electricity.

6. Corrosion is more rapid in acid than in alkaline solutions. In the range of *p*H values encountered in water treatment, this factor relates more closely to the stability of protective films on the metal than to the actual rate of corrosion.

7. Direct-current electricity corrodes the metal of the pole that serves as the anode. Underground pipes are corroded by stray electrical currents at points where positive electricity leaves the pipe.

b. Control of corrosion. The selection of materials and of methods of corrosion control are directed toward interrupting or controlling one or more of the three steps in the cycle of corrosion. The materials and methods commonly employed include the following:

1. Corrosion-resistant metals or alloys. They are materials that either possess low solution potentials or that lay down protective coatings of dense oxides when they are corroded. Stainless steel, Monel metal, tin, and copper are examples.

2. Non-metallic materials. Poor conductors of electricity and non-electrolytes resist attack by most waters. Such materials include reinforced-concrete, asbestos-cement, fiber, and plastic pipes.

3. Coatings. Coatings interrupt both anodic and cathodic reactions by preventing escape of cations and denying access of water and oxygen. Either metallic (for example, zinc, tin, and chromium) or non-metallic coatings (for example, paints, cement, bituminous materials, and plastics) are suitable.

4. Deactivation. Deactivation is the removal of oxygen. It may be accomplished by heating and degasification, by the direct application of a vacuum, or by passage of water over iron filings or turnings.

5. Cathodic protection. Cathodic protection is provided (*a*) by using direct-current electricity to feed electrons into a metal and render it cathodic or (*b*) by attaching a metal of higher oxidation potential which, being anodic, will corrode and be sacrificed to provide the desired protection. Electrical bleeding of distribution mains and other underground utilities and cathodic protection of steel water-storage tanks are examples of the first method. Attaching plates of zinc to the hulls or other underwater metal parts of ships and the insertion of magnesium plugs in hot-water heater tanks are examples of the second.

6. Insulation. Insulation is the creation of resistance to the flow of electrical currents. Examples are (*a*) the insertion of insulating couplings or connectors between dissimilar metals to prevent the production of galvanic currents and (*b*) the use of insulating joints in water mains to oppose the flow of stray electrical currents.

7. Deposition of protective coatings. The deposition of coatings of calcium carbonate on pipes has been discussed in Section 14-6. Silicate films have also been employed. Small amounts of sodium silicate ($Na_2O \cdot 3.25SiO_2$ or $Na_2O \cdot 2SiO_2$) will deposit dense, adherent but slightly permeable films. An initial dosage of 12 to 16 mg/l as SiO_2 is introduced into the water for about a month. After that, dosage is reduced to the amount necessary to maintain a residual of 1 mg/l in remote parts of the distribution system.

8. Inhibitors. Inhibitors are substances that are believed to form adsorbed films on the metals they are to protect. Polyphosphates are reported to reduce corrosion by forming protective films on cathodic areas so as to interrupt the cathodic reaction. Sodium hexametaphosphate and sodium heptaphosphate are common names under which polyphosphates are sold. Initial dosages of 6 to 12 mg/l are later reduced to 2 to 6 mg/l to maintain a minimum residual of about 0.5 mg/l. The polyphosphates also function as inhibitors for the precipitation of calcium, magnesium, and iron.

14-8. Handling, Storing, and Feeding Chemicals. The properties of chemicals that are commonly used in the treatment of water and waste water are listed in the Appendix. This information permits a determination of the handling facilities, storage requirements, and feeding arrangements that must be provided for the safe, economical, and satisfactory operation of a given treatment works. Size and location of plant as well as available sources of supply and shipping facilities for chemicals are also important elements in the engineering design. In small plants, chemicals may be handled satisfactorily by simple hoisting equipment and two-wheeled trucks (1) to be stored on open floors in their shipping containers and (2) to be moved to the feeding devices. Receiving and feeding weights may be determined by simple beam scales with platforms placed at floor level for convenience. Large plants generally require the installation of mechanical or pneumatic material-handling equipment to unload dry bulk chemicals from freight cars or automotive trucks and to transport them to storage bins, similar to grain storage bins, whence they can flow by gravity to weighing and feeding machines. In such plants, liquids are pumped to storage and to feeding devices. Liquefied gases such as chlorine and ammonia will generally flow under their container pressure.

With rare exceptions, the chemicals are dissolved or suspended in water before they are introduced into feed lines. Feeding devices regulate the amounts of chemicals to be added to the water or wastewater. Dry-feed machines control the dosage by the rate of volumetric or gravimetric displacement of dry chemicals. Volumetric machines generally plow, push, or shake the chemical off a receiving table onto which the chemical drops from a hopper-shaped supply bin, as in a "chicken-feed" device. Solution feed depends upon the regulated displacement of liquid chemicals or of dry chemicals that have been dissolved or suspended in water to produce solutions of known strength or suspension of known concentration. Measurement is by constant-head orifices or by pumps. Pumped flow may be proportioned automatically to the rate of flow of the water or waste water to be treated.

The dissolved or suspended chemical is conveyed to the point of application through pressure or gravity pipelines. These pipelines must be resistant to attack by the chemical transported. Suitable materials are indicated in the list mentioned above. To avoid clogging and permit cleaning, lines are liberally dimensioned and laid out in straight runs. Clean-outs are provided.

For the carbonation of water, CO_2 is commonly generated at the plant in a coke, oil, or gas burner. The gas may be cooled, scrubbed, and dried by passage through limestone chips and steel turnings before it is compressed and delivered to diffusers or bubblers in the carbonation chamber. A gas-flow meter measures the amount added. For the feeding of gaseous chemicals other than CO_2, see Section 18-11. Carbon dioxide, ozone, chlorine dioxide, and chlorinated copperas are the only chemicals that must be produced at the site or that can ordinarily be produced there more economically than in commercial chemical plants.

Flow sheets for chemicals can be elaborated in wide variety depending upon the treatment processes involved. The points of application should be kept as flexible as possible. Treatment methods and with them the points best suited to the introduction of chemicals are subject to change with the development of new chemicals and treatment processes, with varying quality of the water or waste water, with seasonal requirements, and with demands for higher standards of performance.

14-9. Disposal of Waste Products of Chemical Treatment. The waste products of chemical coagulation, precipitation, and ion exchange include both sludges and liquids. Liquids are normally discharged into waste-water systems or directly into receiving waters. The treatment and disposal of sludges are considered in Chapter 17. The possible recovery of the chemicals from sludges and liquids continues to be a challenge. Recovery of the large amounts of calcium needed for the softening of hard waters and of the calcium thrown down in the process is particularly attractive. To be used again, the dewatered, dried, and calcined sludge must not contain much magnesium. Calcining is the heating of the dried solids to drive off carbon dioxide. Both CaO and MgO are produced. Incidentally, carbon dioxide may be provided in this way for needed carbonation of the softened water.

15 Filtration

15-1. Types of Filters. Discussion of filters and the processes of filtration is confined in this chapter to the passage of water through fine-grained materials, the voids of which are filled with the flowing water. Sewage treatment on trickling filters is considered in Chapter 16, and the dewatering of sludge on vacuum filters in Chapter 17.

Filtration is an important process in the natural purification of ground water. Observation of the relative freedom of such waters from objectionable impurities may indeed explain the first large-scale use, in 1829, of beds of sand by James Simpson for the clarification of river water pumped from the Thames by the Chelsea (London) Water Company.

a. Granular water filters. There are two common types of granular water filters. These differ hydraulically and structurally (1) because the filter beds are intended to be operated either at relatively low rates (1 to 10 mgad) or at relatively high rates (100 to 200 mgad), and (2) because penetration of suspended matter and its subsequent removal during cleaning operations are purposely confined to the surface layer of "slow" filters, whereas substantially the full depth of "rapid" filters is intended to contribute to purification and hence also to require cleaning. Natural silica sand is the common filtering medium, but there are other fine-grained filtering materials, such as crushed anthracite.

Figure 15-1 shows typical sections and plans of a slow sand filter and a rapid sand filter, and a rough comparison of the general features of the two filters is presented in Table 15-1. It is seen that

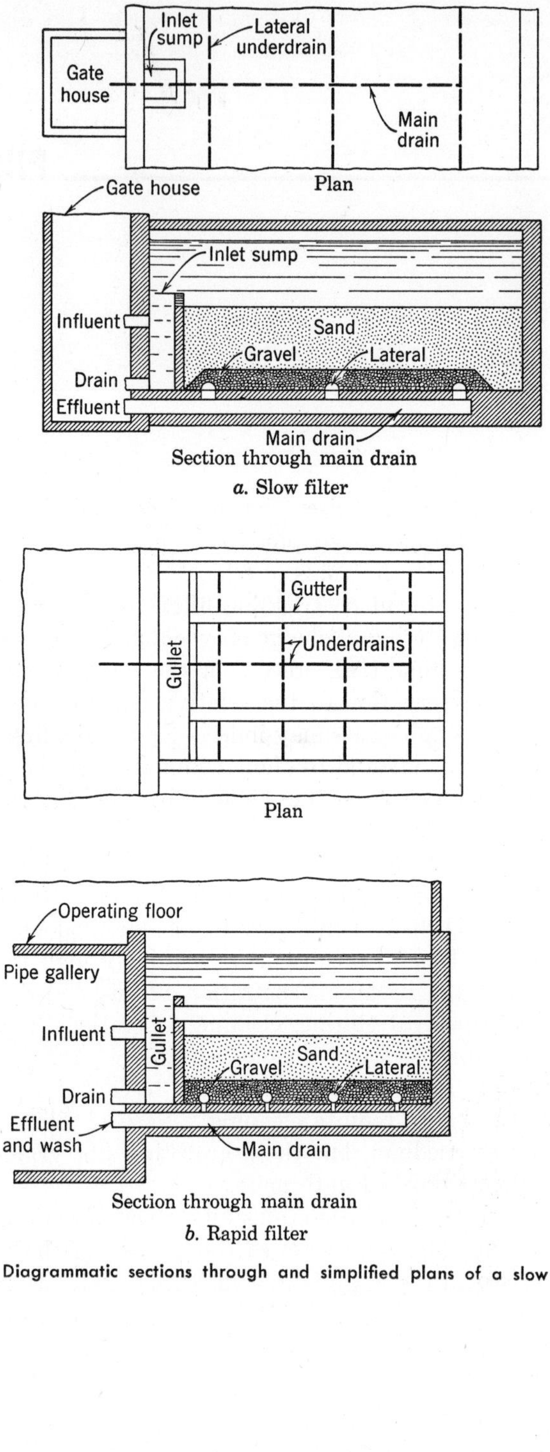

Figure 15-1. Diagrammatic sections through and simplified plans of a slow and a rapid sand filter.

TABLE 15-1. General Features of Construction and Operation of Slow and Rapid Sand Filters *

	Slow Sand Filters	Rapid Sand Filters
Rate of filtration	1 to **4** to 10 mgad	100 to **125** † to 200 mgad
Size of bed	Large, ½ acre	Small, 1/100 to 1/10 acre
Depth of bed	12 in. of gravel; 42 in. of sand, usually reduced to 24 in. by scraping	18 in. of gravel; 30 in. of sand, or less
Size of sand ‡	Effective size 0.25 to **0.3** to 0.35 mm; uniformity coefficient 2 to **2.5** to 3	0.45 mm and higher; uniformity coefficient 1.5 and lower
Grain size distribution of sand in filter	Unstratified	Stratified with smallest grains at top and coarsest at bottom
Underdrainage system	Split tile laterals laid in coarse stone and discharging into a tile or concrete main drain	(1) Perforated pipe laterals discharging into main pipe, or (2) diffuser-plate bottom
Loss of head	0.2 ft initial to 4 ft final	1 ft initial to 9 ft final
Length of run between cleanings	20 to **30** to 60 days	12 to **24** to 40 hr
Penetration of suspended matter	Superficial	Deep
Method of cleaning	(1) Scraping off surface layer of sand and washing removed sand, (2) washing surface sand in place by traveling washer	Scour by mechanical rakes, air, or water; and removal of dislodged suspended matter by upward flow or backwashing which stratifies the bed
Amount of wash water used in cleaning sand	0.2 to 0.6% of water filtered	1 to **4** to 6% of water filtered
Preparatory treatment of water	Generally confined to aeration, but could also include flocculation and sedimentation	Flocculation and sedimentation are common
Supplementary treatment of water	In absence of flocculation, confined to chlorination	Chlorination and other supplementary treatment are common
Cost of construction	Higher	Lower
Cost of operation	Lower	Higher
Depreciation of plant	Lower	Higher

* The most common values are shown in boldface type.
† 125 mgad = 2 gpm per sq ft.
‡ For a definition of sand-size terms, see Section 15-3.

rapid filters operate at approximately thirty times the rate of slow sand filters, and it is understandable that they should need to be cleaned about thirty times as often. Back-washing the filter, with or without the assistance of added mechanical scour (1) by stirring the suspended sand with rakes,[1] (2) by blowing air into the bed before or during back-washing (generally the former), or (3) by directing jets of water into the expanded sand, is a distinguishing feature of the rapid sand filter. The rapid filter has essentially dis-

[1] Use of rotating rakes led to the name "mechanical filter."

placed the slow sand filter in North American practice where it has proved itself to be a flexible, adaptable, and economical water-purification device. A very high degree of purification can be reached by placing slow filters in series with rapid filters. However, this arrangement is generally confined to plants in which the performance or capacity of existing slow filters has had to be supplemented.

When rapid filters must be placed under pressure, they are housed in a pressure-resisting shell and called pressure filters. Their use is normally confined to industrial and swimming-pool installations. In case of trouble, many of their parts are not as accessible, and their space requirements are not as favorable as those of gravity filters.

b. Granular waste-water filters. Where natural sand deposits are available, they have been successfully converted into sand filters that treat sewage and industrial waste-waters intermittently at rates varying from between 20,000 and 80,000 gpd per acre to between 400,000 and 800,000 gpd per acre, depending upon the degree of pretreatment to which the sewage has been subjected. The lower range of values is a minimum for raw sewage, the higher one a maximum for biologically treated sewage. An intermediate range of 40,000 to 120,000 gpd per acre holds for settled sewage. At these rates, intermittent sand filters produce an excellent effluent.

Construction of an intermittent sand filter is illustrated in Figure 15-2. Drainage pipes, laid with open joints, are ordinarily placed at depths of 3 to 4 ft and surrounded with graded layers of gravel and coarse stone that keep the sand out of the drains. In deep sand deposits, the effluent may seep into the ground-water stream, and drains may not be needed. Waste water is piped to the beds and discharged onto a protective stone or concrete apron or into a con-

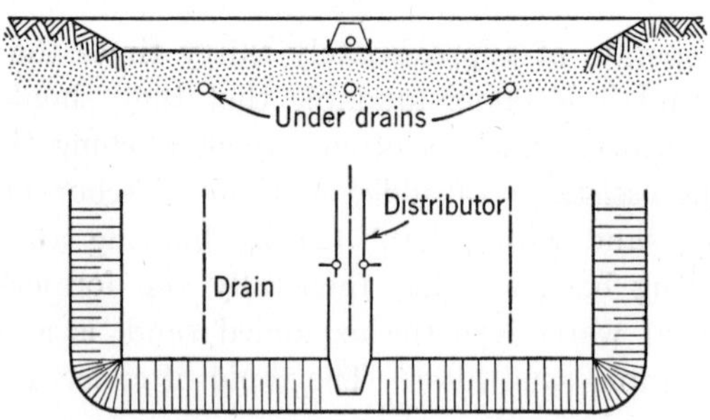

Figure 15-2. Intermittent sand filter with central distribution. *After Imhoff and Fair.*

crete flume or carrier which distributes the waste water over the bed. The depth of flooding is 1 to 4 in. in 7 to 20 min. Each dose carries from 25,000 to 100,000 gal onto an acre of bed. One or more doses are applied each day. Surface accumulations of solids and, where necessary, surface sand are scraped off from time to time. They are ordinarily disposed of by burying or filling. Beds are re-sanded when they become too shallow. In cold climates, the beds are furrowed and then dosed deeply on a cold night to create a surface sheet of ice that will span the furrows and keep the bed itself from freezing and cracking.

Rapid filters using a thin layer (about 3 in.) of granular magnetite ore as the filtering medium have in some instances been attached to the effluent weirs of settling tanks or built as separate structures. The magnetite is relatively coarse (6×10^{-2} to 1.5×10^{-1} cm) and weighs about twice as much as sand. It is lifted by a traveling solenoid and washed by influent sewage that is pumped through the expanded magnetite.

c. *Diatomaceous-earth filters.* In this water filter, a layer of diatomaceous earth is built up on a supporting medium or septum that simultaneously acts as the drainage device. Water is then filtered through this layer (precoat). If the water is very turbid, additional diatomaceous earth (body feed) must be carried onto the precoat. Diatomaceous earth consists of the skeletons of diatoms 0.5 to 12 μ in size. Precoating requires the addition to recirculating water of 0.1 to 0.5 lb of earth per sq ft of septum. If the water to be filtered contains inorganic silts or organic slimes, body feed must be added. Total requirements lie between 800 and 1,000 lb of filter aid per million gallons of water treated. Filtration is at a rate of 1.0 to 15 gpm/sq ft with 2 to 3 gpm/sq ft common. Back-washing at rates of 7 to 10 gpm/sq ft removes the filter cake. Figure 15-3 shows a diagram of the operation of a diatomaceous-earth filter. Filters such as this can be made portable for emergency use.

15-2. Theory of Filtration. A number of different operations combine to produce the over-all removal of impurities by filtration. The most important of these operations are straining, sedimentation, flocculation, and, for heavily polluted waters and sewage, biological activity.

a. Straining. Straining takes place, almost entirely, at the surface of the filter where the water enters the pores of the filter bed. Initially, straining removes only those substances that are larger than the pore openings. As filtration is continued, the substances strained out accumulate on the surface

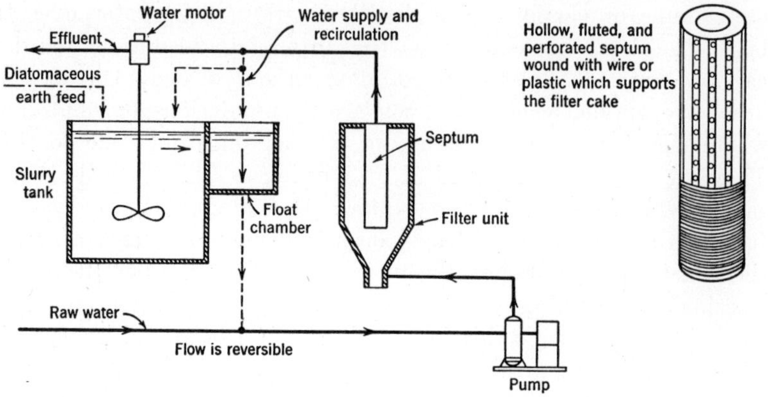

Figure 15-3. Operation of a small diatomaceous earth filter.

of the filter in a mat [2] through which the water must pass before it can reach the filter medium itself. Removal of impurities is thereby further restricted to the surface of the filter.

Where the water to be filtered contains much organic matter, adventitious organisms, principally saprophytic bacteria, utilize these substances for energy and growth within the surface mat, provided that the mat is left in place for days rather than hours (slow and intermittent sand filters). Multiplication of zoogleal organisms then renders the mat sticky or slimy, and the effectiveness of the straining process is further enhanced. The resulting progressive increase in efficiency is referred to as the ripening or breaking-in of the filter. The time consumed in ripening the filter varies principally with the concentration and availability of the impurities as food for microorganisms and with the temperature of the water. Removal of the mat and of the supporting surface layer of the filter medium becomes necessary when the resistance to filtration has mounted to excessive values or when the surface mat is in danger of being ruptured.

Water that has been coagulated or from which iron has been precipitated generally contains enough residual floc to build up a mat of the floc upon the filter surface. Addition of filter aids, such as diatomaceous earth, creates a cake upon the supporting medium. Such mats also act as straining media.

b. Sedimentation. Hazen [3] has proposed that the removal by filters of particles that are smaller than the pore space is analogous to sedimentation in a basin filled with a very large number of trays. In this connection it is well to realize that a cubic meter of spherical sand grains 5×10^{-2} cm in diameter, for example, contains, together with 40% void space, $0.6 \times 10^6/[(\pi/6) \times 125 \times 10^{-6}] = 9.15 \times 10^9$ particles with a gross surface area of $9.15 \times 10^9 \times \pi \times 25 \times 10^{-4} \times 10^{-2} = 7.2 \times 10^3$ sq m. If we assume with

[2] This mat was called a *Schmutzdecke* or cover of filth by early German investigators. The German expression, perhaps because it was less objectionable in its connotation than its literal meaning, has been adopted into the English language as a technical term.

[3] Allen Hazen, On sedimentation, *Trans. Am. Soc. Civil Engrs., 53,* 63 (1904).

Hazen that but $\frac{1}{6}$ of the area is horizontal and facing upwards, $\frac{1}{2}$ being in contact with other sand grains, and $\frac{1}{3}$ of the remainder being exposed to scour, the effective surface area of an equivalent settling basin would be $(\frac{1}{6} \times \frac{1}{2} \times \frac{2}{3} = \frac{1}{18}) \times 7.2 \times 10^3 = 400$ sq m, or 400 trays, per meter of depth. In accordance with Equations 13-9 and 13-10, the settling velocity of removable particles is thereby $\frac{1}{400}$ and their diameter $\frac{1}{20}$ that of a particle that can be deposited in a settling basin of equal loading. Since slow sand filters are made about 1 m deep and ordinarily receive but $\frac{1}{10}$ the amount of water per unit surface that settling basins do, it follows that a slow sand filter, in comparison with settling basins, can be expected to remove particles with $\frac{1}{4{,}000}$ the settling velocity and of less than $\frac{1}{60}$ the diameter.

The efficiency of filtration, like that of sedimentation, is observed to decrease with temperature, although the resistance to filtration increases.

c. Flocculation. Floc formation in a filter is explained by the principles laid down in Section 14-4. In addition, a filter offers opportunity for contact between the impurities contained in water and waste water and the large surface of the grains composing the filter. As the floc builds up in size, it becomes large enough to be retained in the constrictions between the individual pores in spite of increasing pore velocities. Encroachment of the waterway, however, carries non-flocculated solids deeper and deeper into the filter. At low temperatures, the viscosity of water is high and flocculation is decreased. Also the shearing force of the water is increased. When this force exceeds the shearing strength of the floc, the floc particles are torn apart. Again they penetrate farther into the bed. For these reasons, too, the efficiency of filtration decreases with temperature.

d. Biological Activity. How microorganisms may take part in the straining process has already been described. They may also contribute to sedimentation and flocculation by forming sticky, gelatinous coatings on the surface of the filter grains. To these coatings finely divided solids adhere, while colloidal and even dissolved solids are utilized for energy and growth. The mechanism of biological activity is that described in connection with biological flocculation and precipitation (Chapter 16). It produces chemical as well as physical changes in water quality. These can be of considerable magnitude in highly polluted waters and waste waters. In such waters the oxygen requirements of the saprophytes are relatively so great that filter beds treating them would quickly become septic if the beds were not operated intermittently and in such manner as to permit the drawing of fresh air into the filter for the maintenance of aerobic conditions. In the treatment of relatively clean waters, on the other hand, or waters that have been suitably prepared by coagulation and sedimentation, biological activity is unimportant.

Granular Filtering Materials

15-3. Grain Size and Shape. Granular filtering materials differ in size and size distribution, in shape and shape variation, and in density and chemical composition. Size is three-dimensional and generally implies volume. Shape is, in particular, a matter of surface area in relation to volume. Only in the ideal case of regular solids can a single measurement identify both the volme and surface area of a solid. The so-called diameter of irregular particles, whatever its means of determination, can but approximate volume and surface area. Unfortunately there is, as yet, no satisfactory method of measuring the shape of irregular particles, and the assumption has to be made that the particles behave like spheres with the measured diameter.

For a sample of sand or other granular material, size and size distribution are commonly determined by means of a series of calibrated sieves. The American (U. S.) standard sieve series is based on a sieve opening of 1 mm (produced by approximately 18 meshes to the inch). Sieves in the "fine series" stand successively in the ratio of $\sqrt[4]{2}$ to one another, the largest opening in this series being 5.66 mm (produced by approximately 3½ meshes to the inch), and the smallest 0.037 mm (produced by approximately 400 meshes to the inch). The sieves are generally calibrated directly by measurement of a representative number of screen openings in a given sieve, if necessary with the aid of a microscope. This method is known as the manufacturer's rating.

The size distribution or variation of a sample of granular material is determined by sieving the sample through a series of standard sieves. Starting with the weighing of the portion of the sample caught on the pan, successive portions of the sample held between adjacent sieves are added, and the cumulative weights are recorded. Converted into percentages by weight equal to or less than the size of separation of the overlying sieve, the cumulative frequency distribution can then be plotted for purposes of generalization. For many natural granular materials this curve approaches geometric normality. Logarithmic-probability paper (Section 3-8), therefore, assures an almost straight-line plot in which interpolation is facilitated (Figure 15-4). The geometric mean M_g and geometric standard deviation σ_g are then useful parameters of central tendency and variation. The parameters most commonly used, however, are the effective size E, or 10-percentile P_{10}, and the uniformity coefficient U, or ratio of the 60-percentile to the 10-percentile P_{60}/P_{10}. The 10-percentile was suggested by Allen Hazen[4] because he had observed that the resistance to the passage of water offered by a bed of sand within which the grains are distributed homogeneously remains

[4] Allen Hazen, *Annual Report of the Massachusetts State Board of Health*, 1892.

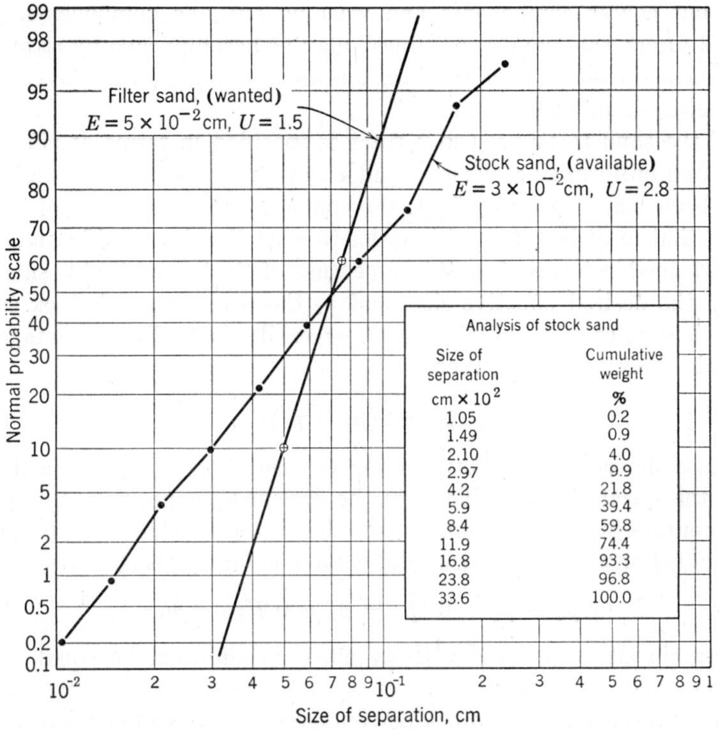

Size of separation cm × 10^2	Cumulative weight %
1.05	0.2
1.49	0.9
2.10	4.0
2.97	9.9
4.2	21.8
5.9	39.4
8.4	59.8
11.9	74.4
16.8	93.3
23.8	96.8
33.6	100.0

Figure 15-4. Grain size distribution of a stock sand and required sizing of a filter sand.

almost the same, irrespective of size variation (up to a uniformity coefficient of about 5.0), provided that the 10-percentile remains unchanged. Hydraulic effectiveness is, therefore, implied. It is of interest, in this connection, that a size frequency distribution of the *number of particles* rather than their *weight* will show that the 10-percentile by weight corresponds in size closely to the median by count. This is to be expected since it is the number of particles rather than their weight that determines the frictional surface of the filter. Use of the ratio of the 60-percentile to the 10-percentile as a measure of uniformity [5] was suggested by Hazen because this ratio covered the range in size of half the sand.

15-4. Preparation of Filter Sand. Run-of-bank sand may be too coarse, too fine, or too non-uniform for use in filters. Within economical limits, proper sizing and uniformity are obtained by screen-

[5] It would be more logical to speak of this ratio as a coefficient of non-uniformity because the coefficient increases in magnitude as the non-uniformity increases.

ing out coarse components and washing out fine components. In rapid filters, the removal of "fines" may be accomplished by stratifying the bed through back-washing and then scraping off the layer that includes the unwanted sand.

If the sand to be used in a filter is specified in terms of effective size and uniformity coefficient, and a sieve analysis of the stock sand has been made (Figure 15-4), the coarse and fine portions of stock sand that must be removed in order to meet the size specification are ascertained in terms of p_1, the percentage of stock sand that is smaller than the desired effective size, and p_2 the percentage of stock sand that is smaller than the desired 60-percentile size. The percentage of usable stock sand p_3 is then

$$p_3 = 2(p_2 - p_1) \qquad 15\text{-}1$$

because the sand lying between the P_{60} and P_{10} sizes will constitute half the specified sand. To meet the specified composition, this sand can contain but $0.1p_3$ of sand below the P_{10} size. Hence the percentage p_4 below which the stock sand is too fine for use, becomes

$$p_4 = p_1 - 0.1p_3 = p_1 - 0.2(p_2 - p_1) \qquad 15\text{-}2$$

The grain size associated with p_4 must, in addition, be equal to or greater than the smallest size of sand to be included in the filter. We have now accounted for a percentage of stock sand equal to $p_3 + p_4$ of which p_3 is usable and p_4 too fine. Therefore, the percentage p_5 above which the stock sand is too coarse is

$$p_5 = p_3 + p_4 = p_1 + 1.8(p_2 - p_1) \qquad 15\text{-}3$$

A sand or grit washer can be used to separate fines from stock sand before it is placed in a filter. The same device can be employed also to wash sand removed from a filter—a slow sand filter, for example—and to wash grit that contains too much organic matter. As shown in Figure 15-5, such a washer is essentially an upward-flow, settling tank. Ideally, therefore, the rate of overflow of the washer must not exceed the settling velocity of the smallest particle to be retained while at least equaling, insofar as the first restriction permits, the settling velocity of the largest particle to be removed. Turbulence (Section 13-7) and sand concentration (Sections 13-4 and 15-7) reduce the needed rate of overflow appreciably. The sand or grit that settles to the bottom is ejected hydraulically, or it is withdrawn by gravity through a shear gate. About 1 cu yd of sand per hour can be washed per sq ft of washer surface.

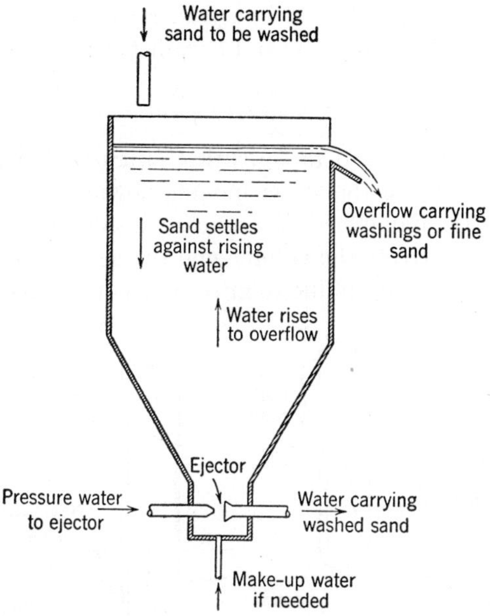

Figure 15-5. Sand washer.

Example 15-1. What must be done to the stock sand of Figure 15-4 to convert it into a filter sand of effective size 5×10^{-2} cm and uniformity coefficient 1.5?

a. From Figure 15-4, the proportion of sand p_1 less than the desired effective size of 5×10^{-2} cm is 30.0%, and the proportion of sand p_2 less than the desired sixty percentile of $5 \times 10^{-2} \times 1.5 = 7.5 \times 10^{-2}$ cm is 53.5%. Hence by Equation 15-1, the proportion p_3 of usable sand is $p_3 = 2(53.5 - 30.0) = 47.0\%$.

b. The percentage p_4 below which the stock sand is too fine is given by Equation 15-2 as $p_4 = 30.0 - 4.7 = 25.3\%$, and the diameter of this sand from Figure 15-4 is 4.4×10^{-2} cm. The settling velocity of this sand, and hence the overflow rate of an ideal washer, from Figure 13-4, is 7 cm/sec or 100 gpm per sq ft at 10 C (50 F).

c. The percentage p_5 above which the stock sand is too coarse is given by Equation 15-3 as $p_5 = 47.0 + 25.3 = 72.3\%$, and the diameter of this sand from Figure 15-4 is 1.10×10^{-1} cm.

d. It follows that all stock sand finer than 4.4×10^{-2} cm and all stock sand coarser than 1.10×10^{-1} cm must be wasted in order to create the desired filter sand.

15-5. Hydraulics of Filtration. The resistance offered by granular materials to the passage of fluids is analogous both to the resistance offered by small pipes to fluids carried by them and to the resistance offered by a fluid to the settling of particles.

For purposes of dimensional analysis, Rose[6] has set up equations that include the following essential parameters:

$$(h/l) = \phi\{(vd/\nu)(v^2/gd)(f)\} \qquad 15\text{-}4$$

Here h is the loss of head in a depth l (Figure 15-6), v is the face velocity, or velocity of the water moving down upon the sand bed, d is a characteristic diameter of the sand grains defined as $6V/A$, where V and A are respectively the volume and surface area of the sand particles, g is the acceleration due to gravity, ν is the kinematic viscosity

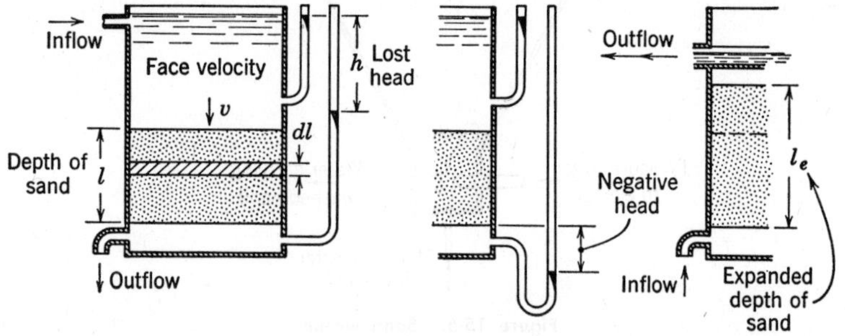

Figure 15-6. Head loss in filtration, and expansion in back-washing.

of the water, and f is the porosity ratio of the filter bed. It can be deduced from experimental investigations of beds composed of closely graded, smooth, spherical particles that $(h/l) \propto (v^2/gd)$; that $(h/l) \propto (1/f)^4$; and that the equation can be balanced by a resistance coefficient which is a function of the Reynolds number and equal to $1.067C_D$, where C_D is the coefficient of drag as recorded in Equation 13-4.

a. General equation. Substitution of these relationships in Equation 15-4 establishes the following general equation for the resistance to flow offered by beds of granular material:

[6] H. E. Rose, On the resistance coefficient-Reynolds number relationship for fluid flow through a bed of granular material, *Proc. Inst. Mech. Engrs.*, *153*, 154 (1945); also Further researches in fluid flow through beds of granular material, *160*, 493 (1949).

Equation 13-3 states that the drag force exerted on a particle settling in a fluid is $v_s^2 d^2 \rho\phi(v_s d/\nu)$. Translated to the conditions of flow in filtration, the drag force also equals the difference in pressure (loss of head) between two horizontal planes through a sand bed 1 grain diameter apart and 1 grain diameter square in area. Hence $h\rho g d^2 \times d/l$ varies as $v_s^2 d^2 \rho\phi(v_s d/\nu)$. If a function of the porosity f is included to allow for the packing of sand grains in filters, the relationship shown in Equation 15-4 is obtained.

$$\frac{h}{l} = 1.067 \frac{C_D}{g} \frac{1}{f^4} \frac{v^2}{d} = 0.178 \frac{C_D}{g} \frac{v^2}{f^4} \frac{A}{V} \qquad 15\text{-}5$$

where

$$C_D = 24/\mathrm{R} + 3/\sqrt{\mathrm{R}} + 0.34 \qquad 13\text{-}5$$

and by definition,

$$A/V = 6/d \qquad 15\text{-}6$$

When the flow is laminar, C_D approaches a value of 24/R and Equation 15-5 becomes[7]

$$\frac{h}{l} = 25.6 \frac{\nu}{g} \frac{1}{f^4} \frac{v}{d^2} = 0.711 \frac{\nu}{g} \frac{v}{f^4} \left(\frac{A}{V}\right)^2 \qquad 15\text{-}7$$

whence, for v in m/day, d in mm, and $f = 0.4$,

$$v = 850 d^2 \frac{h}{l} \frac{\nu_{10}}{\nu_t} = c d^2 \frac{h}{l} \frac{T + 10}{60} \qquad 15\text{-}8$$

This is Hazen's[4] classical formula for the flow of water through homogeneously packed sand, d being the effective size of the sand, and T the temperature of the water in degrees F. The value of the coefficient of compactness c was reported by Hazen to vary from 600 to 1,200. Hazen's equation was derived empirically for sharp sands with a uniformity coefficient of less than 5 and offers the basis for his suggesting the effective size as a measure of hydraulic central tendency. The earliest formulation of laminar flow through granular materials is that of Darcy (Equation 5-2).

b. Area-volume ratio. Except for the diameter term $d = 6V/A$, evaluation of the various factors that enter into Equation 15-5 is straightforward. If all the grains in a filter are uniform in size and shape, the value of A/V for a single grain is the same as that for the bed as a whole. If the grains vary in size, they may either be packed homogeneously within the bed, or they may be arranged, or stratified, in order of magnitude from the coarsest to the finest. Homogeneous packing obtains in slow sand filters that are cleaned by scraping off the surface layer; stratification is induced by the back-washing of rapid filters.

[7] This equation yields substantially the same values as the Kozeny equation in which the term $(1 - f)^2/f^3$ replaces the term $1/f^4$ and the numerical constants are about 7 times as great. *Wasserkraft und Wasserwirtschaft,* 22, 67 (1927).

For *homogeneous packing* of equally shaped particles, the area-volume relationship for any portion of the bed or for the bed as a whole is

$$A/V = 6\int_{P=0}^{P=1} dP/d \qquad 15\text{-}9$$

where dP is the proportion of particles of size d. Assuming that the particles lying between adjacent sieves are substantially uniform in size, the area-volume relationship in terms of the component sieve separations p becomes

$$A/V = 6\Sigma(p/d) \qquad 15\text{-}10$$

Stratification separates the grains into individual filtering layers that are piled up one upon another like the sieve separations in a grain size analysis but in inverse order. If the porosity is uniform, the thickness of each layer $dl = l\,dP$, and the loss of head through it is

$$\frac{dh}{dl} = 0.178\,\frac{C_D}{g}\,\frac{v^2}{f^4}\,\frac{A}{V} = \text{constant } C_D\,\frac{1}{d} \qquad 15\text{-}11$$

It follows that the total loss of head

$$h = \int_0^h dh = \text{constant} \int_0^l C_D\,dl/d = \text{constant } l\int_{P=0}^{P=1} C_D\,dP/d \qquad 15\text{-}12$$

because $dl = l\,dP$. Again assuming that the particles between adjacent sieves are substantially uniform in size,

$$h/l = \text{constant } \Sigma C_D p/d \qquad 15\text{-}13$$

It follows that the product of the area-volume relationship and the coefficient of resistance, $C_D'A'/V'$, for an equivalent bed of uniform particles is

$$C_D'A'/V' = 6\Sigma C_D p/d \qquad 15\text{-}14$$

The area-volume ratio of gravel is small and makes for a low loss of head. During filtration, the lines of flow curve towards the underdrains, but flow is viscous over most of the path. Rates of wash may be sufficiently high, however, to create transitional flow and a significant loss of head. Approximate values for h/l are 0.001, 0.025, and 0.075 for gravel 1 in., ½ in., and ¼ in. in size when the rate of wash-water rise is 24 in. per min. For other rates, h/l varies about as the 3/2 power of the velocity.

Example 15-2. Find the loss of head for the sharp filter sand shown in the first three columns of the accompanying schedule of computations (Table 15-2). This sand is being used (*a*) in a slow filter 30 in. in depth and operated at a rate of 10 mgad (1.08×10^{-2} cm/sec) and (*b*) in a rapid filter 30 in. in depth and operated at a rate of 125 mgad (1.35×10^{-1} cm/sec). The sand has a specific gravity of 2.65, an effective size of 2.55×10^{-2} cm, and a uniformity coefficient of 1.63. Its surface area-volume ratio equals $6.0/d$. The porosity ratio of the unstratified sand bed is 0.394, that of the stratified sand bed 0.414. The lowest temperature of the water to be filtered is 4 C (39.2 F) and the kinematic viscosity, accordingly, 1.568×10^{-2} stoke. Necessary calculations are included in Table 15-2.

TABLE 15-2. Calculation of Loss of Head in Sand Filters (Example 15-2)

Sieve Number (1)	Geometric Mean Size $100d$, cm (2)	Percentage of Sand $100p$ (3)	$\frac{p}{d}$ (4)	C_D (5)	$C_D \frac{p}{d}$ (6)
14–20	10.0	0.92	0.09	31.3	3
20–28	7.0	4.71	0.67	43.8	30
28–32	5.4	14.67	2.72	56.3	153
32–35	4.6	17.9	3.89	65.5	255
35–42	3.8	17.5	4.61	78.8	363
42–48	3.2	19.8	6.19	94.0	582
48–60	2.7	15.4	5.71	109.5	626
60–65	2.3	7.1	3.09	128.2	396
65–100	1.8	2.0	1.11	162.7	181
Sums		100.0	28.08		2,589

Columns 1 to 3 record the results of the sieve analysis of the sand. Column 4 = Column 3 ÷ Column 2, the sum being 28.08. Column 5 gives the value of C_D for the rapid filter in accordance with Equation 13-5. Column 6 = Column 5 × Column 4, the sum being 2,589.

a. Loss of head in slow filter. By Equation 15-10: $A/V = 6.0 \times 28.1 = 169$. Since $\mathbf{R} = \frac{1.08 \times 10^{-2}}{1.568 \times 10^{-2}} \frac{6}{169} = 2.45 \times 10^{-2}$, the value of the coefficient of drag becomes, by Equation 13-5, $C_D = 1{,}000$. Making the necessary substitutions in Equation 15-5, therefore:

$$\frac{h}{l} = 0.178 \frac{1{,}000}{981} \times \frac{(1.08)^2 \times 10^{-4}}{(0.394)^4} \times 169 = 0.15$$

and $h = 0.15 \times 2.5 = 0.38$ ft.

By Equation 15-8, assuming that $c = 1{,}200$ for clean, compacted sand:

$$h/l = 10 \times 0.935 \times 60/[1{,}200 \times (2.55)^2 \times 10^{-4} \times 49.2] = 0.15$$

and $h = 0.15 \times 2.5 = 0.38$ ft.

b. Loss of head in rapid filter. By Equation 15-14: $C_D'A'/V' = 6.0 \times 2{,}589 = 15{,}534$. Making the necessary substitutions in Equation 15-5, therefore:

$$\frac{h}{l} = \frac{0.178}{981} \frac{(1.35)^2 \times 10^{-2}}{(0.414)^4} \times 15{,}534 = 1.76$$

and $h = 1.76 \times 2.5 = 4.4$ ft.

It is obvious that use of so fine a sand results in excessive head loss in a rapid filter. Removal of the five smallest sieve separations of sand (61.8%) will leave 38.2% of the sand and reduce $\Sigma C_D p/d$ to $\frac{441}{0.382} = 1{,}155$ and h/l to $1.76 \times 1{,}155/2{,}589 = 0.786$. If the depth is held at 30 in., $h = 0.786 \times 2.5 = 1.96$ ft.

15-6. Hydraulics of Filter Washing. The burden of suspended matter collected in filters and on their grains is removed and the bed restored to capacity either by washing the filter material in place or by removing the clogged portions of the bed. The scouring of granular materials in place is accomplished by water that rises through the bed and lifts the filter grains into suspension. This is called *sand expansion* (Figure 15-6). Substances that have been transferred into the bed during filtration are then flushed upward through the suspended or expanded bed and wasted with the wash water. At the same time, the substances adhering to the filter grains are dislodged either by the shearing action of the rising water or by the rubbing together of the suspended grains. Scour is important and can be promoted by stirring the expanded filter mechanically with rakes, pneumatically with air (either during or, more commonly, before expansion), or hydraulically with jets of water that are directed into the suspended sand.

As against this, the washing of granular materials after removal from the filter—or for that matter before placement as a means of cleaning or sizing—is also in the nature of differential sedimentation. The relatively coarse and heavy filter grains are allowed to settle against rising water which carries away the dislodged fine and light suspended matter. The washing of detritus for the removal of putrescible organic matter also follows this pattern.

Traveling washers that move over the surface of drained slow sand filters jet water into the sand and pump the rising water out of the filter.

a. General equations. The maximum frictional resistance that individual filter grains or collections of grains that are free to move can offer to a fluid is their weight in water. The cleansing action of water upon filter grains is not increased, therefore, by rates of wash that are higher than necessary to suspend the active portion of a filter. Increased flow merely separates the grains more widely. But this may be necessary in order to permit the enmeshed suspended matter to escape from the pores. If we call l_e the depth of bed that is expanded and f_e its porosity ratio, the mass density of the grains and fluid being ρ_s and ρ respectively, and the specific gravity of the grains being s_s,

$$h\rho g = l_e(\rho_s - \rho)g(1 - f_e)$$

and

$$h/l_e = [(\rho_s - \rho)/\rho](1 - f_e) = (s_s - 1)(1 - f_e) \quad \text{closely} \qquad 15\text{-}15$$

This is the loss of head h incurred in expanding the filter.

The grains are kept from settling, because the drag exerted on them by the rising water equals the settling force. The settling force is given by Equation 13-2 as $(\rho_s - \rho)gV$, the drag force by a modification of Equation 13-4 as $C_D A_c \rho (v^2/2)\phi(f_e)$. The function of f_e is introduced because v is the face, or approach, velocity of the wash water, whereas the drag is due to the settling velocity, v_s of the particles. To bring the settling force into equilibrium with the drag force, therefore,

$$\phi(f_e) = (v_s/v)^2 \qquad 15\text{-}16$$

By experiment, $(v_s/v)^2 = (1/f_e)^9$, whence

$$v_s = v/f_e^{4.5}; \quad v = v_s f_e^{4.5}; \quad f_e = (v/v_s)^{0.22}; \quad \text{and} \quad f_e^{4.5} = v/v_s \qquad 15\text{-}17$$

Since the volume of sand per unit area of bed is constant and equal to $(1 - f)l$ or $(1 - f_e)l_e$, where l is the unexpanded depth of the bed and l_e is the expanded depth, the relative expansion of a layer of thickness dl is

$$dl_e/dl = (1 - f)/(1 - f_e) \qquad 15\text{-}18$$

For a bed of uniform sand grains, therefore,

$$l_e/l = (1 - f)/(1 - f_e) = (1 - f)/[1 - (v/v_s)^{0.22}] \qquad 15\text{-}19$$

and the rate of rise of wash water required to maintain the same degree of expansion at different water temperatures varies directly as the settling velocity of the grains at these temperatures.

b. Expansion of non-uniform beds. Each grain size in a stratified bed is carried into suspension in succession as the drag of wash water equals the weight of the particles. Only those sizes are lifted, therefore, for which $v > f^{4.5}v_s$.

If dP is the proportion of sand of a given size, the ratio of the fully expanded depth L_e to the unexpanded depth of sand L becomes

$$L_e/L = (1 - f) \int_{P=0}^{P=1} dP/(1 - f_e) \qquad \text{15-20}$$

Assuming that the particles lying between adjacent sieves are substantially uniform in size,

$$L_e/L = (1 - f)\Sigma p/(1 - f_e) \qquad \text{15-21}$$

Here f_e must be calculated by means of Equation 15-17.

Example 15-3. A sand with the grain size distribution shown in Table 15-3 is placed in a bed 30 in. deep which is washed at a rate of 24 in. per min (1.016 cm per second) when the water temperature is 10 C (50 F), or $\nu = 1.31 \times 10^{-2}$ stoke. The porosity ratio of the stratified bed is 0.414 and the area-volume ratio is $6/d$. Find (a) the degree of expansion of the bed, and (b) the loss of head through the expanded portion. Fundamental calculations are included in Table 15-3.

TABLE 15-3. Calculation of Sand Expansion (Example 15-3)

Sieve No. (1)	100d cm (2)	100p (3)	v_s cm/sec (4)	$100\frac{v}{v_s}$ (5)	f_e (6)	$\frac{100p}{1-f_e}$ (7)
8–10	21.8	0.5	30.7	3.31	0.473	0.9
10–14	15.4	2.3	23.7	4.29	0.500	4.6
14–20	10.0	9.3	15.9	6.39	0.543	20.3
20–28	7.0	24.8	11.1	9.15	0.591	60.2
28–32	5.4	20.6	8.36	12.2	0.630	55.3
32–35	4.6	16.4	6.69	15.2	0.661	47.9
35–42	3.8	12.1	5.58	18.2	0.687	38.4
42–48	3.2	14.0	4.18	24.3	0.733	53.2
Sum						280.8

Columns 1 to 3 record the results of the sieve analysis of the sand. Column 4 is read from a plotting such as that in Figure 13-4. Column 5 is 100 × 1.016 ÷ Column 4. Column 6 is $(v/v_s)^{0.222}$. Column 7 is Column 3 ÷ (1 − Column 6).

a. Since f for the unexpanded bed is 0.414, all the sand is expanded. By Equation 15-21, therefore, $L_e/L = (1 - 0.414) \times 2.81 = 1.65$, i.e., the bed is expanded 65%, and

$$L_e = 30 \times 1.65 = 49.5 \text{ in.}$$

b. Since all the sand is expanded, the loss of head through the lifted sand is $^{30}\!/_{12} \times 1.65 \times (1 - 0.414) = 2.42$ ft, in accordance with Equation 15-15.

c. Back-wash scour. The scouring action associated with the washing of filters may be calculated in accordance with the principles laid down in Section 14-4. The power input equals the drag force times the settling velocity. Hence

$$F_D v_s = C_D A_c \rho v_s^3/2 \qquad 15\text{-}22$$

and the power input P per unit volume of expanded sand $V/(1 - f_e)$ is

$$\frac{P}{V}(1 - f_e) = \frac{C_D A_c \rho v_s^3 (1 - f_e)}{2V} = \frac{3}{4} C_D \rho \frac{v_s^3}{d}(1 - f_e) = \mu G^2 \qquad 15\text{-}23$$

It follows that G, the velocity gradient, must be

$$G = \sqrt{\frac{3}{4}\frac{C_D}{\nu}\frac{v_s^3}{d}(1 - f_e)} = \sqrt{\frac{g}{\nu}(s_s - 1)(1 - f_e)v_s} \qquad 15\text{-}24$$

and that the number of contacts between soiled particles is greatest when that portion of the bed which has been penetrated by floc or other impurities is only just fully lifted. Expansion greater than this makes for fewer contacts. However, the bed must be opened up enough to permit included floc to escape.

d. Auxiliary scour. Means for stirring the sand in order to improve scour are illustrated in Figure 15-7. Only surface wash is currently included in new designs in North America.

The rakes used for mechanical agitation of the sand should penetrate the active or expanded sand. They generally reach within 2 or

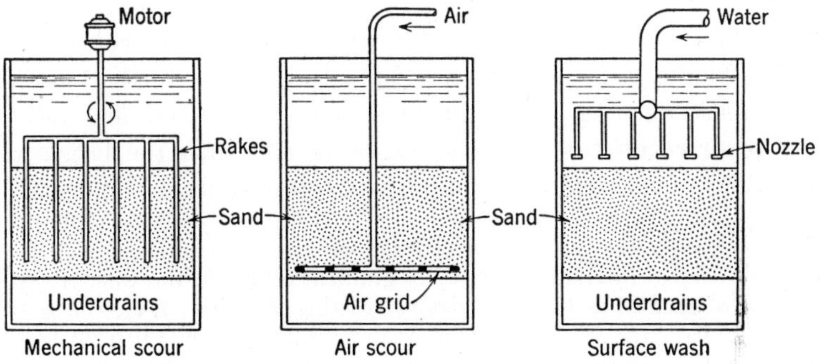

Figure 15-7. Auxiliary scour of rapid filters.

3 in. of the gravel. The raking arms revolve at a rate of 8 to 9 rpm. The teeth are often wedge shaped and are spaced 6 in. on centers. Upward flow is held to between 12 and 18 in. per min.

Air scour generally proceeds at a rate of 3 to 5 cfm per sq ft of filter for several minutes before back-washing the filter at a rate of 12 to 18 in. per min. The air is normally introduced above the gravel line from a pipe grid similar in its principles of design to the perforated pipe systems that underdrain the filters.

Surface wash by jets of water adds from 3 to 11 in. per min of water to the back-wash (about 16 in.). A basic expansion of about 10% is induced before the jets are directed into the sand. The jets issue under a pressure of 10 psig or more. They may be supplied from a stationary grid or a rotating arm.

e. Hindered settling and time of settling of expanded beds. As suggested in Section 13-4, expansion and hindered settling are complementary phenomena. Hence the velocity of fall in hindered settling is identified by Equation 15-17 rather than Equations 13-6 or 13-7, and the time t_s required for the smallest and hence most highly expanded grain size in an expanded bed to settle back into place becomes

$$t_s = (L_e - L)/(v_s f_e^{4.5}) \qquad \text{15-25}$$

where v_s is the settling velocity of the smallest sand grains. The finest grains obviously take the longest time and fix the length of time required for the sand bed to consolidate after washing is discontinued. Since $v_s f_e^{4.5} = v$, the rate of rise of the wash water that suspended the bed, $t_s = (L_e - L)/v$ also.

f. Hindered rising and time of rising of expanding beds. Whereas an expanded bed settles back into place at a uniform rate, its rate of rise is non-uniform because the porosity increases in the course of expansion from a value of f to one of f_e. In practice, furthermore, the rate of back-washing is increased gradually to its maximum value in order to drive off first the *schmutzdecke* and then the larger concentrations of floc and other impurities from the upper layers of the expanding bed.

Example 15-4. Find: (a) the velocity gradient G and (b) the time of settling t_s of a bed of sand 30 in. (76.2 cm) deep consisting of grains ($A/V = 6/d$) 4.6×10^{-2} cm in diameter when the rate of washing is 24 in./min (1.016 cm/sec) and the water temperature is 10 C (50 F), or $\nu = 1.31 \times 10^{-2}$ stoke. In accordance with Example 15-3, the settling velocity of the grains is $v_s = 6.69$ m/sec, and the bed is expanded from a porosity ratio $f = 0.414$ to one of $f_e = 0.661$. The specific gravity of the grains is 2.65.

a. By Equation 15-24:

$$G = \sqrt{\frac{981(2.65 - 1)(1 - 0.661)6.69}{1.31 \times 10^{-2}}} = 530 \text{ cm/(sec)(cm) or } 530 \text{ ft/(sec)(ft)}$$

b. By Equation 15-19: $L_e = 76.2(1 - 0.414)/(1 - 0.661) = 131.7$ cm, and the rise of the bed is $(131.7 - 76.2) = 55.5$ cm. By Equation 15-25: $t_s = \dfrac{55.5}{6.69(0.661)^{4.5}} = 54$ sec, or $t_s = 55.5/1.016 = 55$ sec.

Design of Filters

15-7. Required Depth of Filters. The existing body of knowledge on the behavior of filters under load is inadequate. As a result, the depths of different types of filters have been kept substantially constant since their first use, and rates of filtration have been allowed to vary only within a narrow range. In the hydraulically most heavily loaded filter (the rapid sand filter), the one significant change in the course of a half century has been a shift towards the use of coarser sand or crushed anthracite. New, too, is the construction of beds with a layer of coarse crushed anthracite overlying finer but heavier sand. By this means, the applied load of impurities is distributed more uniformly through the depth of the bed than in a filter that is graded, as is normally the case, from fine sand at the top to coarse sand at the bottom.

The depth to which impurities will penetrate in a filter is a function of many factors. They fall into two broad categories: (1) the composition, concentration, and condition of the substances to be removed from the applied water and (2) the reaction of these substances to removal by filtration. Their reaction is a function of readily measurable factors such as (1) the rate of filtration; (2) the size of the filter grains and their variation with depth; (3) the packing of the sand grains or the porosity of the bed; (4) the temperature of the water; and (5) the terminal loss of head or the increase in loss of head beyond that of the clean bed.

When water is coagulated and settled prior to filtration, the load imposed on the filter consists largely of a carry-over of coagulant flocs. At a given time and place, the flocs are relatively uniform in nature and amount. In these circumstances, the load can be expressed, with fair satisfaction, in terms of the amount of aluminum or iron contained in the flocculated water. In the absence of preparatory treatment, on the other hand, the applied load may vary widely and defy significant numerical identification. Depth of penetration of impurities into a uniform bed of sand would be reflected by a logarithmic law, were it not for the fact that some impurities are intercepted by the accumulating surface film while other impurities are carried deeper and deeper into the bed as pore space is reduced by the accumulating solids and velocities of flow are raised sufficiently to prevent further deposition or to induce scour of accumulating substances. In the absence of a more significant parameter, therefore, the applied load is normally related to the surface area of the bed and not to its volume.

a. Uniform sand. A formulation by Hudson [8] identifies some of the factors that affect the requisite depth of rapid sand filters. Addition of a viscosity coefficient establishes the relationship

$$l = k'Qhd^3[60/(T + 10)] = kQhd^3 \qquad 15\text{-}26$$

where l is the requisite depth of uniform sand, Q is the rate of filtration in gpm/sq ft, h is the terminal loss of head in ft, d is the sand-grain size in cm, T is the water temperature in degrees Fahrenheit, and k' is a measure of the stress under which the filter is placed by the applied water. Values of $k = k'[60/(T + 10)]$ for filtered water free of flocculated turbidity, based on a filterability index suggested by Hudson, are shown in Table 15-4.

TABLE 15-4. Values of k for Various Waters and Conditions of Pretreatment

(After Hudson)

Type of raw water	Conditions of pretreatment	Value of k
Difficult to coagulate	Average	2,500
Average	Average	1,000
Average	High-grade	500
Average	Highest grade	167

b. Non-uniform sand, unstratified. On a weight basis, non-uniformity of the sand in an unstratified bed makes (1) for a small surface area per unit volume by the inclusion of large particles and (2) for small void space by fine particles filling the voids between large particles. On the assumption that these two factors offset each

[8] H. E. Hudson, Factors affecting filtration rates, *J. Am. Water Works Assoc.*, *48*, 1151 (1956).

other to a considerable extent, the required depth of an unstratified bed of non-uniform sand is, therefore, a function of the effective size of the sand.

c. Non-uniform sand, stratified. The requisite depth of a stratified bed of non-uniform sand can be based on a relationship, such as that suggested in Equation 15-26, by making the following assumptions:

1. The depth of a layer of sand composed of a given sieve separation is assumed to bear the same relation to the total depth that the sieve separation does to the total amount of active sand. This presupposes that the porosity of the bed is constant throughout its depth. By the term "active sand" is meant that fraction of the sand which is held responsible for the removal of impurities. Neither the supporting layer of coarse sand nor the surface layer of fine sand that is scraped off before the bed is first put into normal use can be considered to be active.
2. The effectiveness of each constituent layer of sand is assumed to equal the ratio of the actual depth of the layer to the depth that would be required if the filter had to be built up in its entirety of sand of a size equal to that composing the layer.

If we let l_0 equal the total active depth, l the requisite depth of a given constituent layer of substantially uniform sand, and dP the proportion of this sand in an elemental layer of active sand, 100% efficiency is implied when

$$\int_{P=0}^{P=1} \frac{l_0\,dP}{l} = 1 \qquad \text{or} \qquad \int_{P=0}^{P=1} \frac{dP}{l} = \frac{1}{l_0} \tag{15-27}$$

Substituting the value of l from Equation 15-26,

$$\frac{1}{l_0} = \frac{1}{kQh} \int_{P=0}^{P=1} \frac{dP}{d^3} \tag{15-28}$$

In terms of a sieve analysis, therefore,

$$\frac{1}{l_0} = \frac{1}{kQh} \Sigma \frac{p}{d^3} \tag{15-29}$$

d. Gravel. It is the function of gravel to support the overlying sand and to conduct the filtered water to the underdrains of slow and rapid filters, while acting as a dispersing medium for the wash water of rapid filters. To these ends, the gravel must be carefully graded from coarse to fine vertically. The over-all depth of gravel is usually 12 in. in slow filters and 18 in. in rapid filters. If the particles are sized by screening, the depth l in inches of a layer of size d in inches, where $d > 3/64$ in., may be estimated from the following observational equation:[9]

$$l = k(\log d + 1.40) \qquad 15\text{-}30$$

Here k varies in magnitude from 10 to 14 and averages 12. Stones as large as 3 in. may be placed near the filter underdrains, but a maximum size of 1 to 2 in. is more common. To preserve its stability under back-washing, the screened gravel should be carefully packed, the larger sizes being placed by hand.

Example 15-5. A rapid sand filter is to purify a relatively clear lake water that becomes as cold as 40 F in winter.

a. How deep must the bed be made (assuming that Equation 15-26 applies), if the sand to be used is constituted as shown in the first three columns of Table 15-5 and, for purposes of illustration, no sand equal to or larger than

TABLE 15-5. Calculation of Filter Depth (Example 15-5)

Sieve No. (1)	Size of Separation, cm × 10^2 (2)	Proportionate Weight of Sand on Sieve, $p \times 10^2$, % (3)	Geometric Mean Size of Sand Held between Sieves, d, cm × 10^2 (4)	Corrected Proportionate Weight: $p \times 10^2$ (5)	Corrected Proportionate Weight: $\frac{p}{d^3}$ (6)
35	5.0	6.20	5.4	7.03	446
30	5.9	47.0	6.5	53.3	1940
25	7.1	20.2	7.7	22.9	502
20	8.4	6.83	10.0	7.75	78
16	11.9	7.92	14.1	8.98	32
12	16.8	6.26	20.0	......	....
8	23.8	5.59	28.3	......	....
6	33.6	......	....	......	....
Sums	....	100.0	....	100.0	2998

Columns 1 to 3 record the results of the sieve analysis of the stock sand. It is seen that (5.59 + 6.26) = 11.85% of the sand is greater than number 12 sieve.

Column 4 gives the geometric mean size of sand held between adjacent sieves; for example, $\sqrt{5.0 \times 5.9} = 5.4$.

Column 5 gives the corrected proportionate weight of the sand smaller than number 12 sieve; for example, $(6.20 \times 100)/(100 - 11.85) = 7.03$.

Column 6 = Column 5 ÷ (Column 4)^3.

number 12 sieve is to be considered active in purification? Needed calculations are included in Table 15-5 for $Q = 2$ gpm/sq ft and $h = 8$ ft.

[9] J. R. Baylis, Filter-bed troubles and their elimination, *J. New Eng. Water Works Assoc.*, *51*, 17 (1937).

For $k = 2{,}500$, $\frac{1}{l_0} = \frac{2{,}998}{2{,}500 \times 2 \times 8} = 0.075$ by Equation 15-29, and $l_0 =$ 13.2 in. To include the coarse sand, the depth must be $\frac{13.2 \times 100}{100 - 11.85} = 15.1$ in. Adding 100% for safety, the depth becomes 30 in.

b. The sand is to be supported on gravel $\frac{3}{32}$ to $1\frac{1}{2}$ in. in size. What are the requisite depths?

Based upon Equation 15-30 and a value of $k = 12$, the calculations are as follows for sieve ratios of 2:1:

Size, in.	$\frac{3}{32}$	$\frac{3}{16}$	$\frac{3}{8}$	$\frac{3}{4}$	$1\frac{1}{2}$
Depth, in.	4.4	8.2	11.8	15.3	19.0
Increment, in.	4.4	3.8	3.6	3.5	3.7

The total required depth of gravel is 19 in. composed of five layers that are about 4 in. in thickness.

15-8. Filter Underdrains. The underdrainage system of a filter is intended to collect the filtered water and, where necessary, to distribute the wash water in such fashion that all portions of the bed perform nearly the same amount of work and, if washed, receive nearly the same amount of cleansing. Since the rate of wash is many times the rate of filtration, the former is the governing factor in the hydraulic design of filters that are cleaned by back-washing.

Equality of filtration and washing is created most conveniently by introducing a controlling loss of head at the contact between the filtering medium and the underdrainage system. The magnitude of this loss can be fixed in accordance with Equation 13-13.

a. Perforated pipes. The underdrainage system of rapid filters commonly consists of a main, or manifold, and perforated pipe laterals. The velocity of the jets issuing from the perforations or orifices is destroyed by directing the openings downward against the filter bottom and into the coarse gravel surrounding the pipes. The lost head, therefore, equals the driving head. In practice, this controlling head loss is set between 3 ft and 15 ft. At a wash-water rate of 36 in. a minute, this corresponds to a ratio of orifice area to bed area of $(\frac{3}{60})/(0.75\sqrt{2gh}) = 0.5\%$ to 0.2%, on the assumption that the coefficient of discharge of the orifices is 0.75. If the orifice farthest away from the first orifice in the lateral adjacent to the manifold or main is to be held to a value mq_1 and $m = 0.9$, for example, the permissible friction loss in the lateral, according to Equation 13-13, becomes $h_f = (1 - m^2)h_1 = 0.19h_1 = 0.57$ to 2.85 ft.

As shown in Figure 15-8, flow through perforated laterals decreases substantially uniformly, but actually stepwise at each orifice. If the

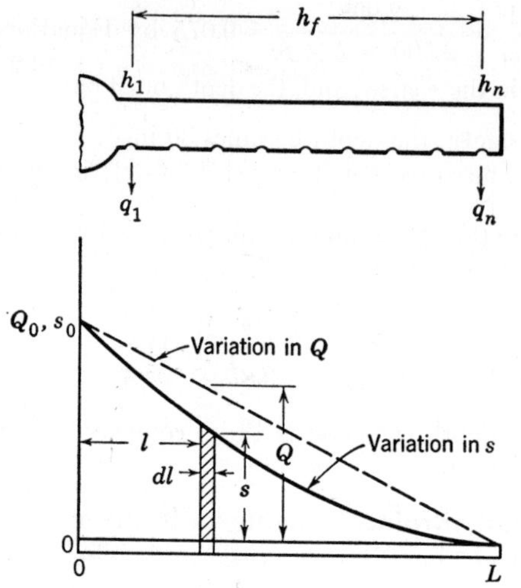

Figure 15-8. Frictional resistance to uniformly decreasing flow (idealized).

diameter is kept constant, the friction loss from the entrance of the lateral to the farthest opening is approximately equal to the loss of head due to the entrant flow passing through ⅓ the length of lateral. In terms of the Chezy formula, for example, $s = v^2/c^2r = Q^2/c^2a^2r = kQ^2$, the value of c^2a^2r being almost constant. The loss of head h_f in a length l then becomes

$$h_f = \int_0^l s\,dl = k\int_0 Q^2\,dl = \frac{kQ_0^2}{L^2}\int_0^l (L - l)^2\,dl \qquad 15\text{-}31$$

because in a portion l of a total length L, flow decreases from the entrant flow Q_0 to a flow $Q = Q_0(L - l)/L$. Integration of Equation 15-31 gives

$$h_f = \frac{kQ_0^2}{L^2}\left(L^2l - Ll^2 + \frac{1}{3}l^3\right) = s_0\left(l - \frac{l^2}{L} + \frac{1}{3}\frac{l^3}{L^2}\right) \qquad 15\text{-}32$$

and for $l = L$, $h = \frac{1}{3}s_0L$ as stated at the outset. Collection of water during filtration, like distribution of water during washing, induces losses that can be formulated in exactly the same way. The flow pattern is simply reversed.

Additional losses include entrance losses, losses in fittings, and losses at each orifice corresponding to sudden enlargement of section but produced by the withdrawal of water and consequent slowing up of velocity. These losses are offset in part, and are sometimes even exceeded, by recovery of velocity head at each point of withdrawal. Losses through manifolds and main drains are analogous to losses through laterals and can be formulated in the same manner.

Certain rules of thumb, based upon calculation and experimentation, are used to strike a first trial balance of the underdrainage system. These rules apply to filters that are washed at rates of 6 to 36 in. per min and may be summarized as follows:

1. Ratio of area of orifice to area of bed served: $1.5 \times 10^{-3}:1$ to $5 \times 10^{-3}:1$.
2. Ratio of area of lateral to area of orifices served: 2:1 to 4:1.
3. Ratio of area of main to area of laterals served: 1.5:1 to 3:1.
4. Diameter of orifices: ¼ in. to ¾ in.
5. Spacing of orifices: 3 in. to 12 in. on centers.
6. Spacing of laterals: closely approximating spacing of orifices.

Once installed, underdrains are relatively inaccessible. Therefore, they should be corrosion resistant or protected against corrosion.

b. Other systems of underdrainage. There are a number of other arrangements of underdrains that are similar to perforated pipe systems and that employ a layer of gravel to support the sand, disperse the wash water, and conduct the filtrate to the collecting system. Notably different from them is the porous-plate bottom. Here the sand rests directly on a diaphragm, septum, or false bottom of porous plates like the diffuser plates of the activated-sludge process (Section 16-11). A sufficient waterway must be provided between the bottom and the plates to reduce head differentials to workable magnitudes. Whereas gravel-bottomed filters require the use of sand that grades into the supporting gravel (if the sand is not to slip through the gravel into the underdrains), sand of any wanted uniformity can be placed on porous-plate septums. Clogged plates are cleaned from time to time with acid or alkali.

Vitrified-tile pipe laid with open joints (about ⅜ in. apart) generally furnishes the underdrainage of filters that are not backwashed. The laterals of slow sand filters, for example, are usually constructed of split-tile (half-round) pipe, whereas agricultural-tile pipe or sewer pipe makes up the laterals of intermittent sand filters and of sludge-drying beds (Section 18-18). The pipe is surrounded by layers of graded gravel that gradually taper off in size to that of the filter layer of sand.

15-9. Wash-Water Gutters. If the static head on the underdrainage system is to be nearly equal over all parts of a filter bed, the wash water must be carried away without being forced to travel far over the surface. A system of weirs and troughs is ordinarily used for this purpose. Corresponding in their action to the effluent weirs and troughs of settling tanks (Section 13-12), these collecting devices are called wash-water troughs.

If certain simplifying assumptions are made, the momentum theorem can be employed to develop a general relationship for the water-surface curve of wash-water troughs and related hydraulic structures.[10] The simplifying assumptions are (1) the kinetic energy of the water falling into the trough does not contribute to longitudinal velocity; (2) friction can be neglected; (3) flow is substantially horizontal in direction; and (4) the water-surface curve is approximated by a parabola. The forces acting to change the momentum are then solely the unbalanced static pressure forces P_1, P_2, and P_3 shown in Figure 15-9. They have the following magnitudes: $P_1 = \frac{1}{2}wbh_0^2$; $P_2 = -\frac{1}{2}wbh_l^2$; and[11] $P_3 = wbli(\frac{2}{3}h_0 + \frac{1}{6}il + \frac{1}{3}h_l)$. Here w is the unit weight of water; b, l, and i are respectively the width, length, and slope of the trough; and h_0 and h_l are respectively the initial and terminal depths of the collected

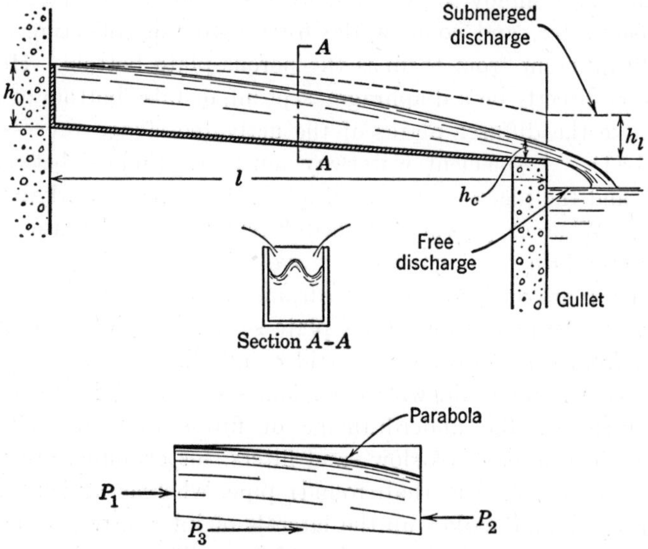

Figure 15-9. Water-surface curves in a wash-water gutter.

[10] For a general discussion of this problem, see T. R. Camp, *Trans. Am. Soc. Civil Engrs.*, *105*, 606 (1940).

[11] Because the volume of water in the trough is

$$bl[h_0 + il - \tfrac{1}{2}il - \tfrac{1}{3}(h_0 + il - h_l)].$$

water. The change in momentum, Qv_lw/g, equals wbh_c^3/h_l, because $Q = bh_cv_c$; $v_l = h_cv_c/h_l$; and $v_c = \sqrt{gh_c}$. Here Q is the rate of discharge, and v_l and v_c are the velocities of flow at the submerged depth h_l and at the critical depth h_c respectively. Equating the sum of the forces to the change in momentum and solving for h_0:

$$h_0 = \sqrt{(2h_c^3/h_l) + (h_l - \tfrac{1}{3}il)^2} - \tfrac{2}{3}il \qquad 15\text{-}33$$

For level inverts ($i = 0$) and for the critical depth $h_c^3 = Q^2/gb^2$, where Q is the total rate of discharge, and b is the width of a rectangular trough,

$$h_0 = \sqrt{h_l^2 + \frac{2Q^2}{gb^2h_l}} = \sqrt{h_l^2 + 2\frac{h_c^3}{h_l}} \qquad 15\text{-}34$$

When discharge is free, h_l closely equals h_c, and

$$h_0 = h_c\sqrt{3} = 1.73h_c \qquad 15\text{-}35$$

or

$$Q = 2.49bh_0^{3/2} \qquad 15\text{-}36$$

Equations 15-35 and 15-36 hold also for troughs of other than rectangular cross-section. Additional drawdown of the water surface by friction can be estimated on the basis of turbulence increasing the roughness factor up to about twofold.

Lateral travel of the water overflowing into the gutters is commonly limited to between 2.5 and 3.5 ft, i.e., the clear distance between gutters is held to between 5 and 7 ft in order to keep the head of water on the underdrains, and with it the rate of wash, as uniform as possible. The vertical distance of troughs above the sand bed is determined by the degree of sand expansion. The bottom of the trough must be kept above the surface of the expanded sand if reduction in the waterway by the troughs and consequent increase in upward velocity between them is not to result in loss of sand.

Troughs are arranged to run the length or the width of the filter. They discharge into a gullet, the hydraulics of which are like that of the tributary gutters except that flow increases stepwise instead of uniformly. Choice of trough cross-section depends somewhat on the material of construction. Rectangular, semicircular, semihexagonal, and semioctagonal shapes are common. Of them, the semicircle interferes least with the upward streaming of wash water and possesses the best hydraulic properties as well.

Example 15-6. Troughs 24 ft long, 18 in. wide, and 7 ft on centers are to serve a filter that is washed at a rate of 30 in. per min.

a. How deep must the troughs be made if their invert is to be kept level and they are to discharge freely into the gullet?

b. How high must the top of the trough be placed above the sand if a 30-in. bed is to be expanded 50%?

Since $Q = 24 \times 7 \times 30/(12 \times 60) = 7$ cfs, find the following:

a. By Equation 15-36: $h_0 = \left(\frac{7}{2.49 \times 1.5}\right)^{2/3} = 1.52$ ft, or, say, 18½ in.

b. The troughs should be placed $(0.5 \times 2.5 + 1.52) = 2.77$ ft, or, say, 2 ft 9½ in. above the sand surface plus the depth of freeboard in, and thickness of, the trough.

15-10. Sizing of Filters and Conduits. The size and number of filter beds to be included in a plant become a matter of economics, once provision has been made for a sufficient number of units to permit routine cleaning or washing of beds and occasional repairs. Essential factors are the cost of the filter area, the walls, and the appurtenances. A rough estimate of the number of rapid sand units N is given by Morrill and Wallace[12] as $N = 2.7\sqrt{Q}$ where Q is the plant capacity in mgd ($Q \gtreqless 100$). As stated before, double filter units are resorted to when it is necessary to keep the size of the wash-water system within reasonable working limits.

Allowance must be made in the sizing of filters for their time out of service. The time required to clean slow filters may be as much as three days in every thirty-day period. Rapid filters are normally expected to be thrown out of operation for about 10 min during each cycle, normally a day. For these filters, the time out of service is composed of the following: (1) the time necessary to draw down the water to trough level or lower, either by filtration under a falling head, or by direct wasting of the water above the level of the wash-water troughs; (2) the time required to expand the sand, which is purposely extended in order to permit surface deposits and the suspended matter in the top layers of sand to escape before the whole bed is suspended; (3) the time of wash, which by experience is about 2 min per ft of sand; (4) the time required for the smaller sand grains to settle back into place after the wash water has been shut off (Equation 15-25); and (5) the time required to refill the filter box to the flowline. Allowance must be made, furthermore, for the amount of filtered water consumed in washing the beds. Including

[12] A. B. Morrill and W. M. Wallace, The design and care of rapid sand filters, *J. Am. Water Works Assoc.*, *26*, 446 (1934).

a freeboard of 1 ft, the depth of both slow and rapid filter tanks is commonly 10 ft.

Pipes and other conduits, including valves and gates, are ordinarily designed to carry water at the following velocities approximately:

	fps
Influent conduits carrying raw water	3–6
Influent conduits carrying flocculated water	1–2
Effluent conduits carrying filtered water	3–6
Drainage conduits carrying used wash water	4–8
Wash-water conduits carrying clean wash water	8–12
Filter-to-waste connections	12–15

Wash-water tanks must refill between washes and must hold for safety about 1.5 times the amount of water needed for a single bed. In large plants, wash-water is often pumped directly to the filters up to maximum rate.

15-11. Filter Appurtenances. Filter appurtenances include manually, hydraulically, or electrically operated gates on the influent, effluent, drain, and wash-water lines; measuring devices such as Venturi meters; rate controllers activated by the measuring device; loss-of-head and rate-of-flow gages; sand-expansion indicators; wash-water controllers and indicators; operating tables and water-sampling devices; sand ejectors and sand washers; and wash-water pumps and tanks. The larger the plant and the higher the rate of filtration, the greater is the justification for the inclusion of mechanical and automatic aids to operation.

Much of the equipment and piping of modern rapid sand filters is shown in Figure 15-10. Attention is called to the "filter-to-waste" connection which serves the purpose of wasting the water held in the filter after washing. This connection, also called the "rewash connection," was in regular use when filters were washed with raw water. This is no longer done in modern plants, and the filter-to-waste connection is needed only when beds must, upon occasion, be cleaned with deterging chemicals such as sodium hydroxide. The chemical is then drawn into the bed from the surface and, after a sufficient contact time, washed from the bed by opening the filter-to-waste connection. This connection should lead from the filter effluent in advance of the rate controller. It consists generally of a valved stub of pipe, proportioned to discharge at about the maximum rate of filtration when the bed is clean. The waste connection should not endanger the normal filtrate by providing an opportunity for backflow of polluted water.

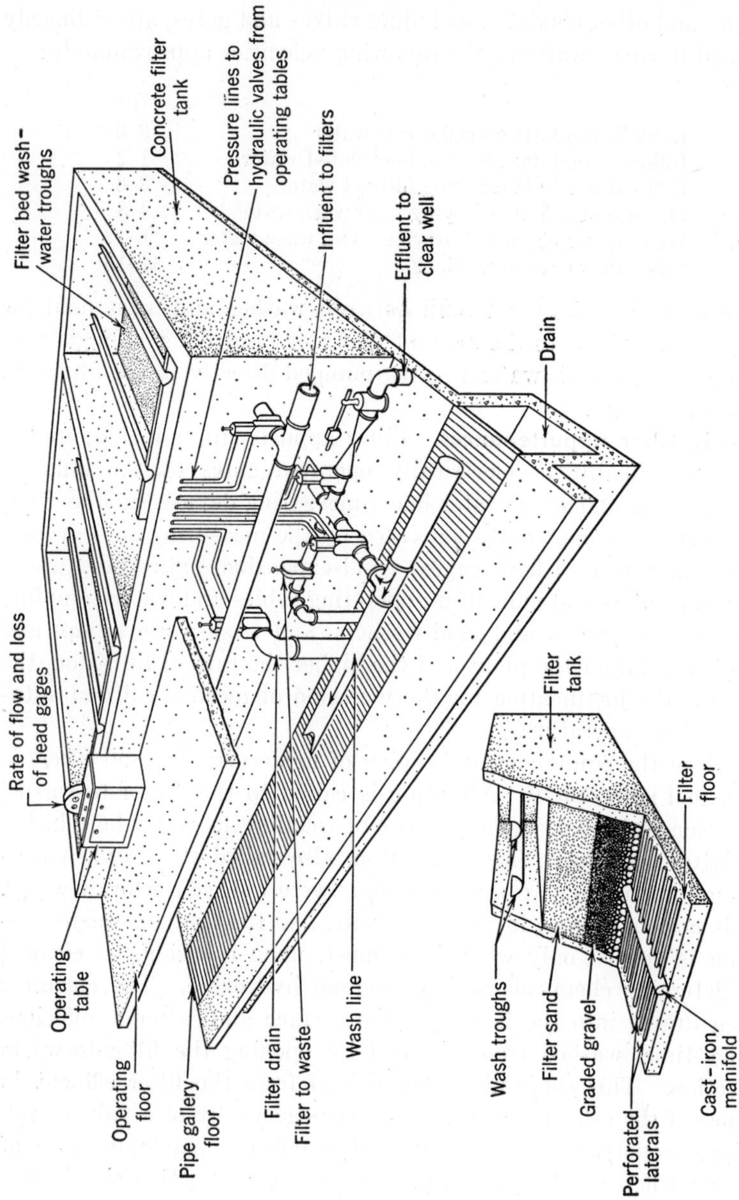

Figure 15-10. Rapid filters and accessory equipment. *After C. P. Hoover, Water Supply and Treatment, National Lime Association.*

Special appurtenances of slow sand filters are sand ejectors, sand washers (Figure 15-5), and sand-storage bins. These appurtenances are useful also in the general handling, washing, transportation, and placement of sand and other granular materials, such as grit.

Operation of Filters

15-12. Length of Filter Runs. The impurities that are transferred from the water to the filter, together with their coagulating or precipitating agents, clog the pores of the filter and increase the loss of head through it. The time rate at which head loss is increased, dh/dt, determines the "length of run" or "period of service" of the filter. Because clogging of the pores progresses downward during operation, dh/dt increases slightly with time. The magnitude of dh/dt is directly proportional to the amount of suspended matter carried onto the filter when the factors included in Equation 15-5 are held constant. For a given water, the length of run is expected to vary directly as the square of the grain size and the fourth power of the porosity, and inversely as the $\frac{3}{2}$ power of the rate of filtration.[13] When flow is substantially laminar (Equation 15-7), the head loss varies approximately as the first power of the rate of filtration, the reciprocal of the square of the sand size, and the reciprocal of the fourth power of the porosity. It follows that the length of filter run may be expected to vary approximately inversely as the product of the initial loss of head of the clean sand bed and the square root of the rate of filtration.

Filters are normally cleaned when a loss of head has been established at which the bed and its underdrainage system are under partial vacuum or negative head (Figure 15-6). The head at a given elevation in a filter becomes negative when the loss of head through the overlying portion exceeds the static head at the point. Most filters operate under a partial vacuum at their lower levels towards the end of their run. Dissolved gases begin to be released when this happens. At atmospheric pressure and normal water temperatures, water can hold about 3% of air (i.e., oxygen and nitrogen) by volume in solution. Since the amount of air precipitated from solution is about $100/34 = 3\%$ per foot of negative head, it does not take long to fill much of the pore space or underdrainage system. The filter then becomes "air bound" and loses capacity.

[13] H. E. Hudson, Filter materials, filter runs, and water quality, *J. Am. Water Works Assoc.*, *30*, 1993 (1938).

Resistance to flow being least along the walls of a filter, the head loss adjacent to the walls is less, and the pressure at any depth is greater, than in the body of the filter. This pressure differential produces inward as well as downward flow within the filter and causes the filter grains to pull away from the walls. Water short-circuits through the resulting shrinkage cracks and fills them with caking suspended matter. Pressure differentials associated with inequalities of flow may open shrinkage cracks also in the body of the bed. Shrinkage is least for coarse sand that is well compacted and kept clean. Such sand will consolidate by less than 1% as the loss of head rises to its maximum value.

Poor distribution of wash water and inadequate scour and cleaning of the sand grains permit the accumulation of suspended matter on the grains and in the voids of the bed. Depending upon the nature of the suspended matter removed, the dirtiness of the sand can be measured in terms of the concentration of alumina, iron, color, or turbidity that is freed from a known weight or volume of sand by shaking it vigorously with a known volume of water to which a detergent or dissolving agent has been added. When the washing of a filter is inadequate, turbidity and floc, together with some sand, are cemented together to form "mud balls." The intensity of mud-ball formation can be determined by washing a known volume of sand through a 10-mesh sieve and measuring the volume of the retained mud balls by displacement in a graduated cylinder of water.[9] In a filter that is well designed and well operated, mud balls should not occupy more than about 0.1% of the volume of the top 6 in. of sand. Badly clogged filters can be improved by ejecting the sand and cleaning it in a sand washer, by agitating the expanded bed by hand with long-tined rakes, by directing hose streams into the expanded bed, or by the addition of a detergent such as a 2 to 5% solution of caustic soda (¼ to 2 lb per sq ft of filter covered with 2 to 3 in. of water).

15-13. Performance and Permissible Loading of Filters. Some of the matters relating to filter performance have been discussed in Sections 1 and 2 of this chapter. It is the purpose of this section to carry this discussion further and to report, in particular, on the allowable coliform loading of rapid filtration plants. This is important not only in water purification but also in stream sanitation.

a. Bacterial efficiency. Studies by engineers of the U. S. Public Health Service[14] have established the following empirical relationship

[14] *U. S. Public Health Service Bull.* 172 (1927) and 193 (1929); also *U. S. Public Health Repts., 48,* 396 (1933).

between the effluent concentration E and the influent, or raw-water, concentration, R of coliform organisms in water that has been subjected to certain water-purification processes:

$$E = cR^n \qquad \text{or} \qquad \log E = \log c + n \log R \qquad 15\text{-}37$$

Here c and n are coefficients that reflect respectively the magnitude of the effluent count for a given raw-water count and the relative shift in effluent count with changing raw-water count. A low value for c represents high fundamental efficiency, and a low value for n great constancy of performance with varying raw-water quality. Observed values of c and n and of the probable number of coliform organisms per 100 ml in the raw water (R_0) that can be reduced, by different treatment processes, to the current Public Health Service standard for drinking water of about 1 per 100 ml in the effluent are shown in Table 15-6. Since filter performance alone does not govern the

TABLE 15-6. Permissible Coliform Loading of Rapid Sand Water Filters Including Related Treatment Processes

$E = cR^n$; $R = R_0$ when $E = 1$ per 100 ml.

	Turbid River Water *			Clear Lake Water †		
Treatment Process	$c \times 10^3$	n	R_0	$c \times 10^3$	n	R_0
1. Chlorination	15	0.96	80	50	0.76	50
2. Flocculation, settling, and rapid sand filtration	70	0.60	80	87	0.60	60
3. (2) and prechlorination	..	....	3,500	..	....	.....
4. (2) and postchlorination	11	0.52	6,000	40	0.38	4,500
5. (2) and double chlorination	..	....	20,000	..	....	.....
6. (4) and double settling	64	0.25	60,000	..	....	.....

* Ohio River plants.
† Great Lakes plants.

quality of the effluent, the efficiency of related treatment processes is included in this table.

A comparable value of R_0 for slow sand filters treating relatively clean waters that are not pretreated by flocculation or chlorination is 50 or about the same as for chlorination alone and is not far below the value of R_0 for rapid sand filtration preceded by flocculation and sedimentation. It should be noted that the values of c and n for a combination of treatment processes cannot be synthesized from the values of these coefficients for the component processes, because each component changes the quality of the water to be treated. It should be noted, too, that relatively clear lake waters are paradoxically not as amenable to treatment as is turbid river water. The "reaction to filtration" of clear waters is, therefore, generally poorer than that of turbid waters. Mechanical flocculation and other improvements in the preparation of water for filtration, better control of filtration, and more efficient chlorination have raised the safe loading limits of rapid filtration over those shown in Table 15-6 and may be expected to continue to do so.

b. Removal of color, turbidity, and iron. On an average, but 30% of the natural color in water is removed by slow sand filters without the aid of coagulants. By suitable flocculation and settling prior to filtration, however, a colorless water can be produced by both slow and rapid filters. Turbidity responds well to slow sand filtration without the aid of coagulation; but it clogs these filters so quickly that raw water containing turbidities in excess of about 40 units should not be applied to slow filters, unless it has previously been subjected to coagulation and sedimentation. Rapid filtration, as has been stated before, generally presupposes that the applied water has been suitably flocculated and settled. Diatomaceous-earth filters also perform most satisfactorily when the applied water has been flocculated and settled.

Both slow and rapid sand filters will remove oxidized iron and manganese. However, oxidized manganese precipitates so slowly that it responds better to slow filtration than to rapid filtration, unless it has been flocculated (Section 14-3). The presence on the sand of a coating of manganese hastens precipitation of this substance by catalysis.

c. Removal of larger organisms. The larger microorganisms, including the algae and diatoms, are readily removed by filtration; but the odors and tastes associated with the algae and diatoms may remain unchanged in intensity unless treatment processes especially adapted to the removal of odor- and taste-producing substances are included in the treatment works. The cells of diatoms are bad clogging agents because they interlock to form a tenacious mat.

The eggs and adults of the common, intestinal, parasitic worms, as well as the cysts of the pathogenic amoebae, are relatively so large that they cannot normally pass through a bed of sand. However, the cercariae of the blood flukes, although larger than amoebic cysts, are reported to be sufficiently motile to wriggle through beds of sand of normal depth. These worms, as well as amoebic cysts, are held back by diatomaceous-earth filters.

d. Oxidation of organic matter. As shown in Table 12-4, the efficiency of intermittent sand filters for the removal of bacteria and for the removal or oxidation of organic matter from sewage is very good. It is accomplished, however, only by reducing the rates of filtration to relatively small figures. Except in extraordinary circumstances, the biological oxidizing power of filters is not utilized in the purification of municipal water supplies. Apart from their improving the hygienic and esthetic qualities of water, therefore, rapid and slow filters leave the remaining, largely chemical, qualities of the applied water substantially unaltered.

16 Biological Treatment

16-1. Biological Treatment Units. Historically, the development of aerobic biological treatment of sewage and other waste waters proceeds from sewage farms or irrigation areas through intermittent sand filters to contact beds and thence to trickling filters and activated-sludge units. With certain modifications, all these methods are still in use for the treatment of sewage and related waste waters. On rare occasion, the intermittent sand filter has been employed also in the treatment of a municipal water supply that was exceptionally rich in organic matter. All the methods so far developed are based, at least in part, upon the capacity of adventitious microorganisms (1) to abstract needed food substances from suitable waste waters and (2) to elaborate gelatinous films that, together with the organisms themselves, constitute the essential elements of the most advanced aerobic, biological treatment systems. Because of their high microbial population and their viscous, jellylike nature, these films are called *zoogleal*[1] films. These biological creations possess the signal ability (1) to transfer to themselves, among other things, energy-yielding substances that were dissolved or suspended in the carrying water and (2) to release to the water some of the end products of their metabolism including water, carbon dioxide, nitrate, and sulfate. The mechanisms involved in the exchange of substances from and to the carrying water are complex and variable. For want of a better definition, they are classed as "surface," "contact," or "interfacial forces"

[1] From *zoo* and the Greek word *gloios*, a glutinous substance.

and as "biological oxidation." Since, in the most advanced methods, the important contribution is the conversion of finely divided suspended and colloidal matter and, more important still, dissolved matter into film substance, the over-all accomplishment may be thought of as biological flocculation and precipitation, as contrasted to chemical flocculation and precipitation.

a. Irrigation areas. The disposal of sewage on agricultural areas has two objectives: (1) the raising of crops and (2) the treatment of the applied sewage. The agricultural utilization of sewage is concerned both with its water value and its content of fertilizing elements. The degree of treatment received by the sewage is not necessarily proportionate to its agricultural utilization. Conflicts in the sanitary and agricultural management of irrigation areas are the result.

Irrigation methods are rationally made to conform to local needs. They vary with the characteristics of the soil, the magnitude and distribution of rainfall, the other climatic conditions that influence the raising of crops, the height of the ground-water table, the topography of the land, and the nature of the crops raised. In most areas of the world, the annual water requirements of irrigable lands are in the vicinity of 10 in., or from ½ to ⅓ of the annual precipitation in well-watered regions. This is equivalent to about 750 gpd per acre. Therefore, very large areas of land are needed if agricultural needs are to govern the disposal of the sewage. If they are made subservient to it, the water load can be increased, under the best conditions, to about 3,000 gpd per acre for cultivated, agricultural lands and up to 25,000 gpd per acre for grasslands. Sanitary needs are met by suitable pretreatment of the sewage.

Sewage is carried to the irrigation areas in open channels or in closed pipes. It is applied to the land (1) by large revolving spray nozzles attached to movable pipelines (spray irrigation); (2) by surface flowage from ridge distributors in the form of ditches or pipes with side outlets (surface, ridge, or bed irrigation; also land filtration). Surface and flood irrigation are illustrated in Figure 16-1. For the disposal of sewage from isolated dwellings or small numbers of people, subsurface irrigation is often employed (Section 12-8). Purposeful agricultural utilization of the sewage is then dispensed with.

In *surface irrigation*, the sewage flows over the cropped land. Some of it seeps into the soil, some of it is evaporated, much of it is collected after but moderate contact with soil and crops. This form of irriga-

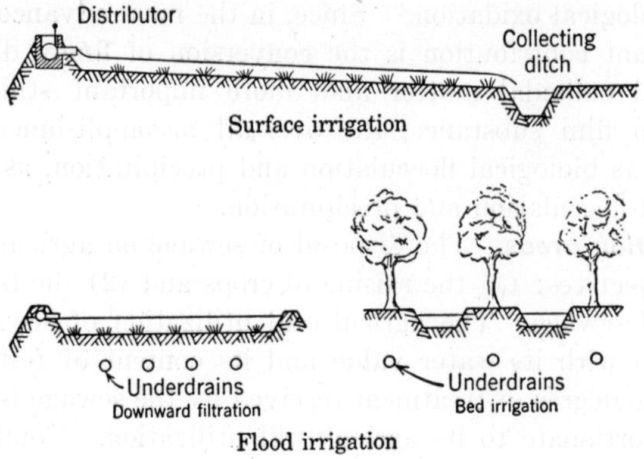

Figure 16-1. Surface and flood irrigation. *After Imhoff and Fair.*

tion is, at best, a process of partial biological treatment. Purification ceases in cold weather. In *flood irrigation,* the sewage percolates through the soil and is collected, if necessary, in underdrains. The mechanical and biological purifying powers of the soil are utilized, and treatment becomes more complete. For sanitary reasons, the sewage can be kept from contact with crops by being confined to furrows between cropped beds. Spray irrigation is a form of surface irrigation (Section 20-12*d*).

The sanitary management of sewage farms is beset by a number of difficulties. Unless the sewage is fully treated before use for irrigation, odors cannot be avoided. Unless it is applied to crops not intended for human consumption, sanitary hazards are introduced. Spray irrigation is a particularly bad offender. At times of heavy rainfall, the crops do not need watering, whereas sewage volumes are often swollen by storm-runoff or ground-water infiltration. The simplest solution for some of these difficulties is the holding in reserve of about 25% of the area or, better, the shunting in of treatment devices that are routinely used for pretreatment or that stand by for times when the irrigation area is overwatered or must be laid dry in the interest of agriculture. Harvesting periods as well as rainy periods must be considered in this connection.

Operation of irrigation areas must be intermittent. Otherwise the land will not remain sweet. Overloaded areas and soils that cannot absorb large quantities of water, or that are easily clogged by suspended matter or growths, become "sewage sick." The biological films that are established on the soil grains are eventually converted to humus and may contribute to the fertility of the soil.

b. Intermittent sand filters. These relatively fine, granular sewage filters are described in Section 15-1 and illustrated in Figure 15-2. They are logical developments from sewage farming in regions where sandy soils prevail and direct agricultural utilization of sewage can be dispensed with in favor of intensive sewage treatment. Rates of application of sewage are thereby raised to as much as 80,000 gpd per acre without pretreatment and to as much as 800,000 gpd per acre with biological pretreatment. Heavy surface accumulations of suspended matter must be removed from time to time, but the biological films that form on the sand grains within the filter undergo continuous stabilization. Anaerobic conditions are avoided by intermittent dosing and resting of the sand beds.

c. Coarse-grained beds and related structures. Whereas biological flocculation and precipitation are more or less incidental to irrigation and intermittent sand filtration, the purposeful building up of biological slimes has become the governing principle in the management of coarse-grained beds for sewage treatment. The need for maintaining aerobic conditions has led to the evolution of two treatment devices from the prototype contact, or bacteria, bed. The design and operating features of the different devices are illustrated in Figure 16-2.

1. The fill-and-draw bed—*contact* or *bacteria bed* (Figure 16-2*a*)—consists of a tank of moderate depth filled with coarse granular ballast or other materials of large surface area. The tank is filled with sewage, allowed to stand full, and drained. It is then allowed to rest. Air is drawn into the tank or bed while it is being filled or emptied and circulates through it to some extent while it stands idle. Beds are operated as single units or in series as double or triple units. They are generally preceded by settling tanks and must be followed by such tanks, if they unload their accumulated slimes from time to time and if these partly stabilized slimes are to be kept out of the plant effluent. The loading of contact beds is 100,000 to 300,000 gpd per acre-ft. Contact beds are now largely obsolete.

2. The percolated bed—*trickling* or *sprinkling filter* (Figure 16-2*b* and *c*)—is a logical development of the fill-and-draw bed.[2] The bed is similar to the contact bed in its basic design but differs in method of dosage and film contact. Sewage is distributed over the bed from fixed or movable nozzles, or sprays, to trickle downward over the contact surfaces, while currents of air, induced chiefly by differences in the specific weights of the atmosphere inside and outside of the bed, sweep through the interstices to carry needed

[2] It should be remarked parenthetically that fill-and-draw or intermittent operation has generally preceded continuous operation in the development of most sewage-treatment processes. The history of past experience is, more often than not, a useful signpost for possible future progress; but past experience must not be allowed to create prejudice that will shackle the mind and hand of the investigator, designer, or operator.

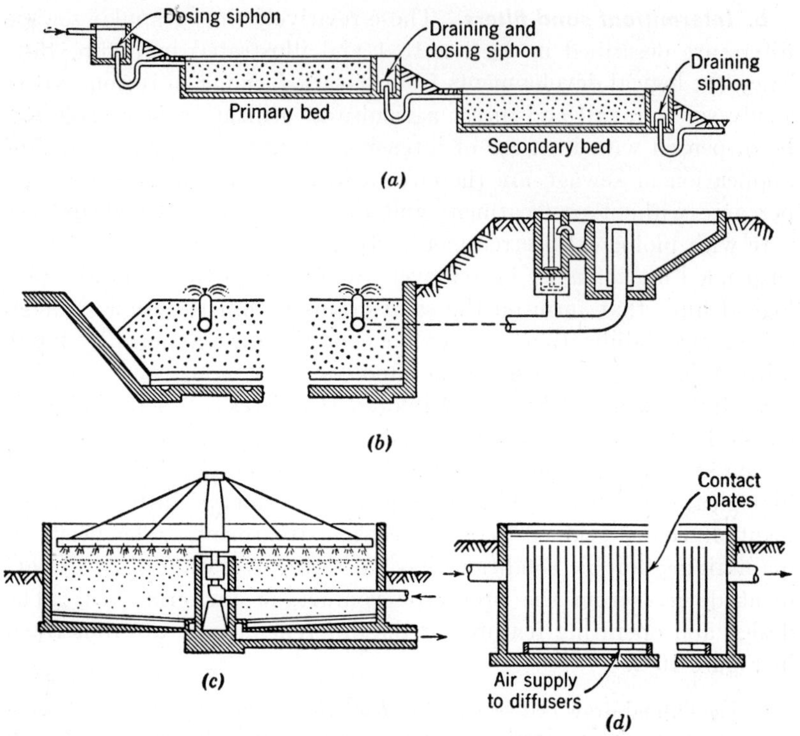

Figure 16-2. Sewage treatment in coarse-grained beds and related structures. (*a*) Double-contact beds with dosing and draining siphons. (*b*) Trickling filter with fixed nozzles and automatic dosing tank. (*c*) Trickling filter with rotary distributor. (*d*) Contact aerator. ***In part after Imhoff and Fair.***

oxygen to the film. Distribution of sewage, originally intermittent by projection of the experience with sand filters and contact beds, has, to good purpose, become substantially continuous.

Removal of settleable solids from the influent sewage and removal of sloughed film from the effluent are essential adjuncts to trickling-filter operation. The design and operation of these filters are elaborated later in this chapter. For purposes of comparison, it may be stated that the loading of trickling filters is 300,000 to 600,000 gpd per acre-ft in low-rate operation and above 2 mgd per acre-ft in high-rate operation, yet efficiencies greater than those of contact beds are attained.

3. The aerated filled bed—*contact aerator, aerated contact bed,* or *Emscher filter* (Figure 16-2*d*)—is again similar in basic design to the contact bed but differs from it in method of air supply and introduction of sewage. The bed operates as a submerged unit. The sewage is displaced through the unit continuously and in a generally horizontal direction, while compressed air is

blown through the bed to maintain circulation of the sewage and supply the oxygen requirements of the film. Removal of influent settleable solids and of sloughed film are necessary. For equal loading on an acre-ft basis, contact aerators are less efficient than trickling filters. Their further installation is not expected.

d. Activated-sludge units. In the activated-sludge process, the biological slimes are produced within the sewage itself while it is gently stirred and kept aerobic as it flows through the treatment tanks. Zoogleal masses are either generated about suspended particles, or they are constructed of colonial growths of bacteria and other living organisms. Needed food materials are precipitated from solution in addition to the colloidal as well as finely divided, suspended solids that are included in the aggregates. The flocs team with living organisms (Figure 16-4) that, by voracious feeding, cleanse or restore the active contact surfaces; hence they are called *activated* sludge flocs. The oxygen requirements of the flocs are high and cannot be satisfied by the dissolved oxygen normally available in the sewage entering the treatment tanks. Needed dissolved oxygen is supplied by forced absorption either from the atmosphere above the flowing sewage or from air blown into it. The amount of floc that can be generated in a given volume of sewage in a given time is small and would not provide sufficient contact area to effect wanted purification in economically justifiable times of exposure. For this reason, a large concentration of floc is caused to accumulate in the treatment unit. In the normal activated-sludge process, this is done by separating formed floc from the effluent sewage by sedimentation and returning it to the influent sewage (*returned sludge*) until the desired concentration of floc is attained. After the breaking-in period, more than the required amount of floc is captured from the effluent, and some floc must be wasted (*excess or waste sludge*). Since the settled floc includes much water, the process involves a proportionate degree of recirculation of effluent. Common arrangements of activated-sludge units are shown in Figure 16-3. The loading of such units is 1 to 2 mgd per acre-ft. This is about the same as for trickling filters that are operated at high rates, but the efficiency of treatment is substantially greater. The activated-sludge process, although delicate, is highly flexible. Modifications in operation, including degree of pretreatment, have been introduced to meet local needs, and the economy of the method is bound to be further improved by an imaginative approach to the design and operation of treatment units.

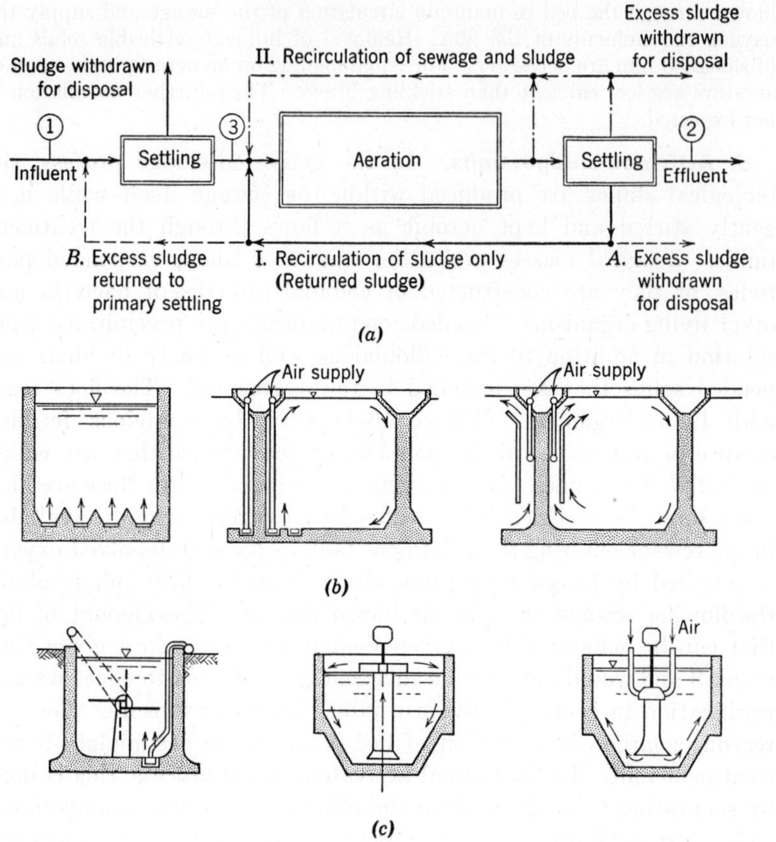

Figure 16-3. Sewage treatment in activated-sludge units. (*a*) Flow diagram. Excess sludge is either withdrawn directly for disposal or returned to primary settling. Recirculation of sewage as well as sludge is possible. (*b*) Diffused-air units: longitudinal furrows; spiral flow with bottom diffusers; and spiral flow with baffle and low-depth tubular diffusers. (*c*) Mechanical aeration units: submerged paddles with diffused air spray mechanism, and aspirator mechanism. *In part after Imhoff and Fair.*

Operation of Biological Flocculation and Precipitation Units

16-2. Mechanism of Treatment. An analysis of biological treatment devices will show that they offer the following opportunities in common, although in different degree: (1) direct biological destruction or stabilization of putrescible matter within the sewage undergoing treatment and (2) transfer of putrescible matter onto zoogleal film surfaces followed by (*a*) its biological destruction or stabilization in the film and the return of certain end products of microbial metabolism to the sewage that washes the film and (*b*) the periodic or continuous unloading of film substance and its removal from the washing sewage, normally by sedimentation, a large part of the film substance being returned to the treatment unit in the activated-sludge process. The energy-yielding substances contained in the applied sewage are the primary substrate for the living organisms that seed themselves upon the surfaces and create the active film. The film itself forms a secondary substrate upon which the organisms feed. This they can do continuously. They need no rest. However, if the film interface becomes overloaded with food and other substances abstracted from the sewage, or if its dissolved-oxygen content approaches exhaustion (because it can be replenished only intermittently or is supplied in insufficient quantity), a so-called resting period may be required. During this period, needed oxygen is absorbed and film activity is restored.

The direct biological modification of putrescible matter within the flowing sewage in treatment units is relatively small because the mechanism of biological decomposition is extremely complex and quite time-consuming, whereas the length of time that the applied sewage remains within the unit is never long. Contact periods are a matter of less than an hour in high-rate trickling filters, somewhat longer in low-rate trickling filters and in downward percolation through soil and sand, and but a few hours in activated-sludge units. The reaction velocities that would be required to effect a reasonable degree of purification by direct attack of the sewage during its stay in the treatment unit would, therefore, have to be of extraordinary magnitude. For comparison, it takes more than 3 days to satisfy 75% of the BOD of samples of sewage that are stored at 20 C in glass test bottles.

The most important element of biological flocculation and precipitation would appear to be the transfer of the pollutional load to the film. There it undergoes decomposition commensurate with the duration of its storage and releases its end products to the atmosphere or to the sewage that washes it.

In bed irrigation (or land filtration), subsurface irrigation, and intermittent sand filtration, stabilization of transferred substances must be carried to completion. This cannot be done without a resting period. Otherwise the pores would clog. Resting periods are required also to permit the absorption of oxygen (reaeration). Otherwise the treatment unit would become septic. Interception of substantial amounts of matter at the surface of the soil or sand reduces the subsurface load.

In trickling filters and activated-sludge units, films or flocs are removed, respectively, as trickling-filter humus and waste (or excess) activated floc. They are referred to collectively as biological or secondary sludges. Depending upon the length of their retention, temperature, and other factors (such as film thickness), these biological sludges are of lower energy value than the substances from which they were formed. They contain more or less nitrogen and other fertilizing ingredients, as well as residual energy values that keep them putrescible. The residual energy values of secondary sludges can be made to supplement those of primary sludges in terms of fuel value or of combustible, digester gas.

The amount of film substance that can be retained in trickling filters, and with it the length of time during which the transferred substances can undergo decomposition, is a function of (1) temperature and through it of BOD, or rate of activity, (2) areal dimensions of the supporting surfaces and their exposure to void space and moving liquid films or masses, and (3) the scour engendered by the moving fluids. The amounts are also a function of the rate of diffusion of oxygen to the inner laminae of the accumulating film or growths. Anaerobic decomposition proceeds at a slower rate than aerobic decomposition and may be accompanied by the release of gases and the production of foul-smelling intermediate substances. Anaerobic decomposition also destroys the gelatinous nature of the inner laminae and this, together with gas formation, causes the film or growths to slough. Since transfer of pollutional substances occurs only at the interface and since film substance and growths that are not actively engaged in this work can readily be captured as settleable secondary sludge, a certain degree of film sloughing is, ordinarily, an essential feature of trickling filters. Film sloughing, furthermore, reduces the opportunity for the development of filter flies (Section 16-3).

In the activated-sludge process, the amount of biologically active growth can be varied at will over a wide range of values by regulating the rate of sludge waste and return. If large flocs are allowed to build up, they, like thick films and thick growths, will become anaerobic. They also become heavier as organic matter is mineralized and it becomes more difficult to keep the sludge in suspension. At the same time, the sludge becomes less active. In the interest of effective treatment, these conditions must be avoided.

16-3. Biological Associations. The biological associations that are responsible for the purification of sewage by flocculation and precipitation include many classes of organisms. Some of the type species are shown in Figure 16-4. The principal and most numerous biological workmen are the zoogleal bacteria. The gelatinous masses that are built by them often assume branching shapes and are then known as *Zooglea ramigera.* Closely associated with the lower bacteria are the filamentous higher bacteria and the protozoa. Among the latter, the ciliates abound. The stalked, colonial ciliates find adequate anchorage both in suspended flocs and on attached films. The free-swimming ciliates and flagellates dart in and out among the organic debris, bacterial filaments, and mold hyphae. Viewed under the microscope, the floc shows a lively and busy microbial community. The primary role of the ciliates, if we may judge from observations of their impact upon bacteria in nutrient solutions, is to keep the bacterial population from reaching a stalemate. Destruction of bacteria is then responsible for a constant renewal of bacterial growth and, with it, for a high consumption of energy-containing food materials. The prevalence of ciliates, therefore, is a valuable index of film or floc healthiness. Pathogenic bacteria are ingested along with the common saprophytic forms. This contributes to effluent safety.

In addition to the principal flora and fauna, worms and insect larvae find nutriment in the floc and film. Rotifers and crustaceans scavenge for food. Fungi utilize simple chemical substances, and surface growths of algae join them in this activity where film is exposed to sunlight.

Trickling filters harbor large numbers of aquatic earthworms, bristle worms, and blood worms (see also Figure 11-6). In the spring of the year when large masses of film are sloughed off with the beginning of warm weather and stepped-up decay of accumulated film, masses of worms are often disgorged. During the summer, small mothlike flies of the genus *Psychoda* may infest trickling filters and create a serious nuisance. Conditions favorable to their growth are (1) free entrance into the bed and (2) film thicknesses that will support their larvae which burrow in the film.

The so-called filter fly passes through ordinary window screens. It does not bite but gets into the eyes, ears, nostrils, and mouth of plant attendants and is extremely troublesome. Its radius of flight is short (a few hundred feet), but it may be carried quite far by the wind. The life cycle of the fly varies from 3 weeks at 60 F to a week at 85 F. The adult fly is readily destroyed by DDT residuals on walls and

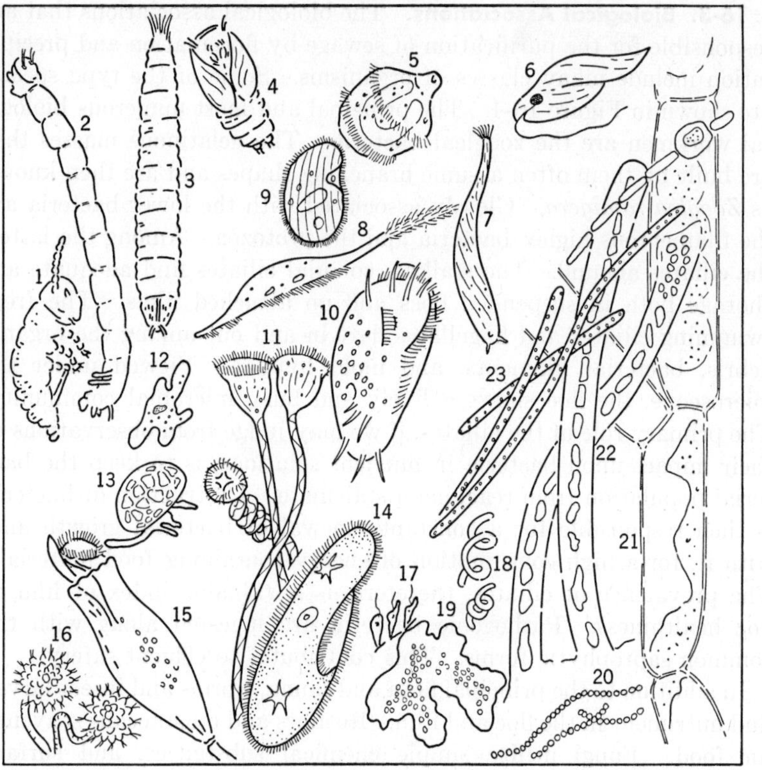

Figure 16-4. Organisms associated with the biological treatment of sewage. *After Imhoff and Fair.*

Numbers 1 to 4, Insects × 5

1. Water springtail, *Podura;* the genus found on trickling filters is *Achorutes.*
2. Larva of blood worm, *Chironomus.*
3. Larva of filter fly, *Psychoda.*
4. Pupa of filter fly, *Psychoda.*

Numbers 5 to 17, Protozoa × 150 *

5. *Didinium*
6. *Euglena*
7. *Choenia*
8. *Lionotus*
9. *Colpidium*
10. *Stylonichia*
11. *Vorticella*
12. *Ameba*
13. *Arcella*
14. *Paramecium*
15. *Opercularia*
16. *Anthophysa*
17. *Oikomonas* × 1,500

Numbers 18 to 23, Bacteria and fungi × 1,500

18. *Thiospirillum*
19. *Zooglea ramigera*
20. *Streptococcus*
21. *Leptomitus*
22. *Sphaerotilus*
23. *Beggiatoa*

* Excepting No. 17, *Oikomonas.*

other surfaces on which it rests. The eggs and larvae are washed out of the filter when the film sloughs. Sloughing may be induced for this purpose (by chlorination of the applied sewage, for example), or film thickness may be held down by operating the filters at high rates of flow.

The appearance of large numbers of filaments of the so-called sewage fungus *Sphaerotilus* is often associated with a phenomenon called the "bulking" of activated sludge (Section 16-10). High carbohydrates appear to promote the growth of this organism. Toxic wastes weaken biological activity. When they are discharged into sewage in high concentration, they may destroy it. Copper and arsenic have been responsible for the breakdown of biological processes (Section 11-12).

16-4. Equalization of Loading. Most water- and sewage-treatment processes operate inherently on a basis of diminishing returns; the amount of work that can be done decreases in proportion to the reduction in the concentration of removable substances. Furthermore, the rate of activity of most biological treatment units (measured by the removal of BOD, suspended solids, or bacteria, for example) may reasonably be expected to be greatest at the beginning, because the substances that best lend themselves to removal are removed first. In order to maintain treatment at a high level of efficiency, therefore, the load impressed upon progressive portions of treatment units should remain relatively constant. This can be attained in some measure by the following means: (1) serial subdivision of the treatment structure into two or more component units, or stages, and alternation of the lead unit; (2) subdivision of the applied sewage into two or more component portions and their progressive introduction along the treatment path; (3) recirculation of the effluent to the influent and subjection of the resultant mixture to treatment; and (4) combinations of recirculation of effluent (*a*) with serial subdivision of the treatment units (alternation of component divisions being optional) and (*b*) with progressive dosing of the treatment unit. The return of sludge in activated-sludge units (about 20% by volume) is a modest form of recirculation. A number of schemes for recirculation and stage treatment are presented in Figures 16-3 and 16-5. They all aim at a more equable distribution of load within units that are substantially constant in their purification capacity along the path of the applied sewage. Adjustment of purification capacity to variation in load within the treatment unit offers a different approach to the problem of decreasing loads. Adjustment of

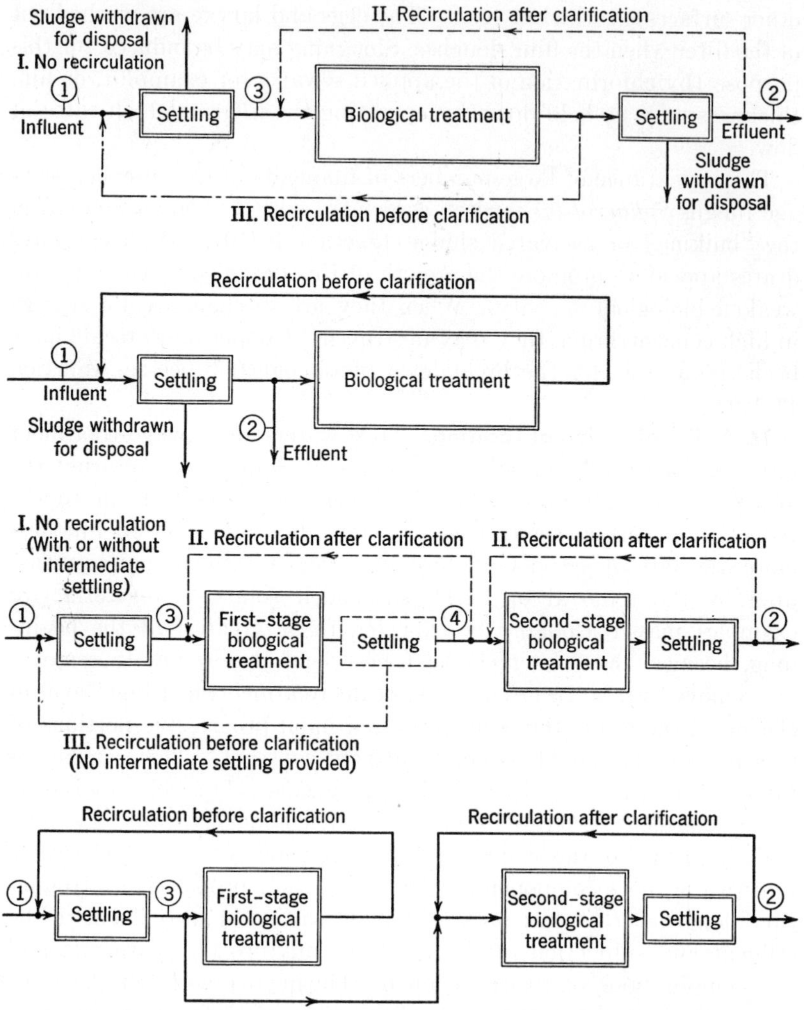

Figure 16-5. Flow diagrams for recirculation and stage treatment of sewage.

air supply to oxygen requirements in contact-aeration and activated-sludge units (tapered aeration) and use of coarse stone in the bottom of trickling filters are examples.

16-5. Recirculation. Recirculation adds much to uniformity and flexibility of plant operation. Besides distributing the load more effectively, an opportunity is afforded for smoothing out the rate of flow of applied sewage. In the best circumstances, the rate of flow of applied sewage can be held substantially constant. The quality of the effluent, on the other hand, is altered appreciably by recirculation. How this comes about is exemplified by contrasting the operation of a trickling filter that treats a unit quantity of sewage on a once-through basis with one that treats the same quantity of sewage on a recirculation basis when a unit quantity of effluent is added to the incoming sewage. In the first instance, the effluent has been produced by exposure of all of the influent sewage to the full treatment time. In the second instance, the effluent is a composite of ½ the influent sewage that has been exposed for ½ the treatment time, ¼ the influent sewage that has been exposed for the full treatment time, ⅛ the influent sewage that has been exposed for 3/2 the treatment time, 1/16 the influent sewage that has been exposed for twice the treatment time, etc. It is seen that the two effluents are by no means identical, although the average exposure of the sewage to treatment is the same with and without recirculation of effluent.

If we call I the rate of incoming sewage and R the rate of recirculation, the recirculation ratio is R/I, and the average number of passages of the incoming sewage through the treatment unit is

$$F' = (I + R)/I = 1 + R/I \qquad 16\text{-}1$$

where F' is called "the recirculation factor." This factor can be represented, in accordance with the reasoning pursued in the preceding paragraph, also by the following series:

$$F' = \frac{I}{I+R} \times 1 + \frac{I}{I+R} \times \frac{R}{I+R} \times 2 + \frac{I}{I+R} \times \left(\frac{R}{I+R}\right)^2 \times 3 \cdots \qquad 16\text{-}2$$

If we assume that the removability of putrescible matter decreases as the number of passages is multiplied, a weighting factor f, where $f < 1$, must be introduced into Equation 16-2 to obtain a satisfactory expression for the average number of "effective" passes F of the putrescible matter through the treatment unit. Equation 16-2 then becomes

$$F = \frac{I}{R+I} \times 1f^0 + \frac{I}{R+I} \times \frac{R}{R+I} \times 2f^1 + \frac{I}{R+I}\left(\frac{R}{R+I}\right)^2 \times 3f^2 \cdots \qquad 16\text{-}3$$

or

$$F = (1 + R/I)/[1 + (1 - f)R/I]^2 \qquad 16\text{-}4$$

If F and R/I are the dependent variables, f being constant, F reaches a maximum value at

$$R/I = (2f - 1)/(1 - f) \qquad 16\text{-}5$$

The magnitude of f appears to be close to 0.9 for trickling filters,[3] but see Section 16-8.

Example 16-1. For a recirculation ratio of unity and a weighting factor of 90%, find (*a*) the average number of passes and (*b*) the average number of effective passes of the sewage through the treatment unit. Find also (*c*) the recirculation ratio needed to produce a maximal value of effective passes and (*d*) the resulting ratio of the magnitude of this value to that of the average number of passes.

a. By Equation 16-1, $F' = 1 + 1 = 2$, or, by Equation 16-2, $F' = \frac{1}{2} + \frac{1}{4} \times 2 + \frac{1}{8} \times 3 \cdots = 2$.

b. By Equation 16-4, $F = \dfrac{1 + 1}{(1 + 0.1)^2} = 1.65$.

c. By Equation 16-5, $R/I = \dfrac{2 \times 0.9 - 1}{0.1} = 8$.

d. By Equation 16-4, $F_{max} = \dfrac{1 + 8}{(1 + 0.8)^2} = 2.78$, and, by Equation 16-1, $F' = 1 + 8 = 9$. Hence $F_{max}/F' = 2.78/9 = 0.31$.

In practice, recirculation has established itself in particular in the operation of trickling filters at high rates of dosage, but it should always be remembered that recirculation is built into the activated-sludge process. Very high rates of recirculation become uneconomical.

16-6. Expression of Loading Intensity. Two kinds of loads are impressed on biological treatment units: (1) water loads which govern the hydraulic design of the treatment unit (hydraulic loads) and (2) loads of removable substance which govern the process design of the treatment unit (process loads). In order to be related to performance, these loads must be expressed as load intensities.

Hydraulic loads are expressed as rates of flow, generally *mgd*. Intensities of hydraulic loads are generally measured in terms of the velocity of the sewage through the treatment unit or the time (direct or inverse) that the sewage remains within the unit. Thus, the intensity of the hydraulic load on irrigation areas, intermittent sand filters, and trickling filters is normally stated in terms of the velocity factor, *mgad*; the loading intensity of trickling filters also in terms of an inverse time factor, *mgd per acre-ft* (sometimes *gpd per cu yd*); the loading intensity of activated-sludge units and contact aerators generally in terms of a time factor, *hours of aeration*.

[3] *Sewage Works J.*, *18*, 791 (1946).

Process loads are rationally expressed in terms of the impurities that are to be removed. Since the BOD is the best over-all determinant of the putrescibility of sewage and related waste waters, the process load of biological treatment units is generally expressed in terms of the weight of BOD applied, normally lb of 5-day, 20 C BOD per day. In special circumstances and for special purposes, other determinants are added or substituted, among them: turbidity, suspended solids, organic nitrogen, ammonia nitrogen, oxygen consumed, and bacteria. The population load can also be usefully employed with due allowance for population equivalents of storm water and industrial wastes in the influent and, where efficiency of treatment is to be established, also for the population equivalent of the effluent.

In order to be expressed as intensities, process loadings must be related to treatment opportunity. Since treatment opportunity involves a complex of design and operating factors, many different parameters of process-loading intensity have been devised.

If we recognize (*a*) area of contact surface or film and (*b*) opportunity for contact as the controlling factors in biological sewage treatment, we arrive at the following complex for a general parameter of loading intensity: (1) weight of removable substance applied in a unit of time to (2) a unit of contact surface for (3) a unit of contact time. The first factor in this complex is readily determined by analytical procedures and measurements of sewage flow. The second factor can be evaluated only indirectly for activated-sludge units and for so-called filtration processes. The third factor is easily ascertained as a statistical average for activated-sludge units but is normally unknown for other treatment devices. Suggested parameters of process-loading intensity i are:

1. *For activated-sludge units:* lb of 5-day, 20 C BOD per day (y_0) per 1,000 lb of suspended solids (W) per hour of aeration (t), or $i = y_0/(Wt)$. Here the weight of suspended solids is an indirect and incomplete measure of the surface area of the sludge floc. It is calculated from the volume of the aeration unit and the concentration of the solids suspended in the mixed liquor. The contact time is given by the quotient of the volume of the aeration unit and the rate of flow of the *incoming* sewage. The rate of flow of the incoming sewage is employed rather than the rate of flow of the mixed liquor because it represents the theoretical average time that a constituent portion of the sewage—which may also find its way from time to time into the sludge liquor—remains in the aeration unit.

2. *For trickling filters:* lb of 5-day, 20 C BOD per day (y_0) per acre-ft, cu yd, or 1,000 cu ft (V), or $i = y_0/V$. Surface of contact, as previously stated, is included only indirectly. Time of contact is also included indirectly, since it is a function of the hydraulic load per acre-ft which is reflected by

the process load. For recirculation, the volume of filter must be multiplied by the recirculation factor F to obtain the equivalent volume FV.

3. *For irrigation areas and intermittent sand filters:* lb of 5-day, 20 C BOD per day (y_0) per acre (A), or $i = y_0/A$. This parameter recognizes that the purifying activity of these treatment units is concentrated at the surface.

That the loading intensities suggested for trickling-filtration and activated-sludge units reflect the performance of these units with a fair degree of reliability is shown in Figures 16-6 and 16-7. The parameters selected imply that it is possible to attain a wanted degree of purification by proper proportioning of the following design and operation elements to the load: (1) in trickling filters—the volume of the bed, the recirculation ratio, or both; and (2) in activated-sludge units—the weight of suspended solids in the aeration unit (per cent of returned sludge), the time of aeration, or both. Recirculation may be presumed to be effective in activated-sludge treatment as well as in trickling filtration. Flexibility is lent to the activated-sludge process by the ability to return more or less sludge to the treatment unit.

16-7. Treatment Efficiency. The most advanced biological treatment systems, as has been indicated, are normally preceded by primary settling tanks. The biological, or secondary, system is composed of the biological unit and its settling tank. However, in some recirculating systems, as shown in Figure 16-5, the primary settling tank is required to settle the secondary solids as well as the primary ones. An analysis of the performance of numerous sewage-treatment works by the Committee on Sanitary Engineering of the National Research Council [3] has led to the following general observational relationship between biological plant performance (expressed as percentage efficiency p_2) and plant loading (expressed in terms of the loading intensity i, discussed in Section 16-6):

$$p_2 = 100/(1 + mi^n) \qquad 16\text{-}6$$

Here m and n are coefficients of performance. Together, they determine the magnitude of the loading intensity that can be impressed on a given process to attain a desired efficiency, the coefficient n being a measure of the variability of efficiency with load intensity. The numerical value of the coefficient m depends upon the units of measurement employed. The parameters of loading intensity i and the magnitudes of m and n that enter into the observational relationships proposed by the National Research Council were derived from the

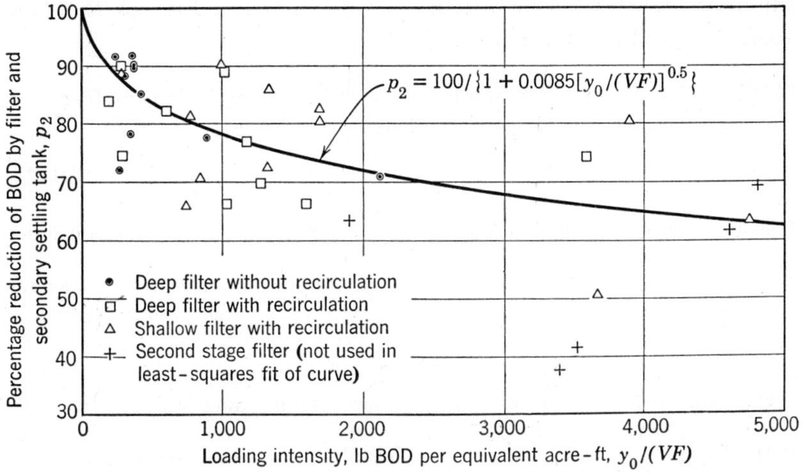

Figure 16-6. Performance-loading relationships for trickling filters. Plotted points represent the results obtained at U. S. military posts.

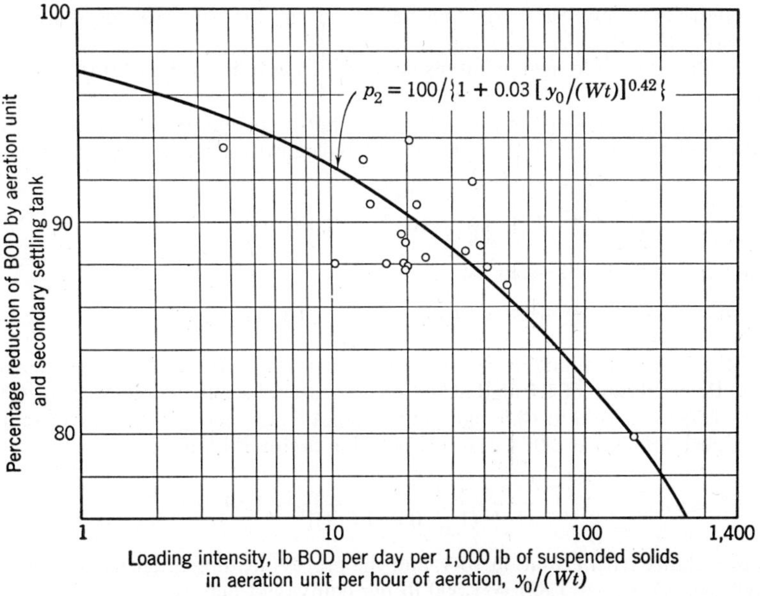

Figure 16-7. Performance-loading relationships for activated-sludge units. Plotted points represent the results obtained at diffused-air plants in North America. Logarithmic scale of abscissa makes plotting more convenient. *After Fair and Thomas.*

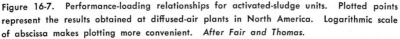

summary plotting of operational results shown in Figures 16-6 and 16-7. They are listed in Table 16-1.

TABLE 16-1. Values of Performance Coefficients for Biological Treatment Units

	n	m	i	Units of i for BOD * Removal
Trickling filters	0.50	8.5×10^{-3}	$y_0/(VF)$	lb/acre-ft × recirculation factor
Activated-sludge units	0.42	3.0×10^{-2}	$y_0/(Wt)$	lb/1,000 lb suspended solids × hr of aeration

* 5-day, 20 C BOD.

Example 16-2. A flow of 1 mgd of sewage containing 307 mg/l of BOD is passed through a primary settling tank, which removes 35% of the BOD, before being applied to a trickling filter and secondary settling tank. The BOD load applied to the filter from the primary tank, therefore, is $307 \times (1 - 0.35) \times 1 \times 8.34 = 1{,}665$ lb per day. If the filter has a surface area of 0.185 acre and its depth is 3.0 ft, estimate the over-all percentage reduction in BOD and the BOD remaining in the plant effluent (*a*) for once-through operation of the trickling filter, and (*b*) for recirculation of 1.5 mgd of plant effluent to the trickling filter.

a. The rate of dosage, or intensity of the hydraulic load, is $1.0/0.185 = 5.4$ mgd per acre, or $5.4/3 = 1.8$ mgd per acre-ft. The process-loading intensity is $y_0/(VF) = 1{,}665/(0.185 \times 3 \times 1) = 3{,}000$ lb per acre-ft. In accordance with Equation 16-6, the efficiency of the biological section of the plant is

$$p_2 = \frac{100}{1 + 8.5 \times 10^{-3} \times (3{,}000)^{0.5}} = 68.2\%$$

The over-all plant efficiency is

$$P = 35 + (100 - 35)68.2/100 = 79.5\%$$

and the BOD remaining in the plant effluent is $(100 - 79.5)307/100 = 63$ mg/l.

b. Recirculation of 1.5 mgd of sewage increases the rate of dosage of the filter $(1 + 1.5) = 2.5$ fold to 13.5 mgd per acre, or 4.5 mgd per acre-ft. If we assume a weighting factor of 90%, the recirculation factor F becomes

$$\frac{1 + 1.5/1}{[1 + (1 - 0.9)(1.5/1)]^2} = 1.89$$

in accordance with Equation 16-4, and the process-loading intensity $y_0/(VF) = 1{,}665/(0.185 \times 3 \times 1.89) = 1{,}590$ lb per equivalent acre-ft.

In accordance with Equation 16-6, therefore, the efficiency of the secondary section of the plant is $p_2 = \dfrac{100}{1 + 8.5 \times 10^{-3} \times (1{,}590)^{0.5}} = 74.6\%$. The resulting over-all plant efficiency is $P = 35 + (100 - 35)74.6/100 = 83.5\%$, and the BOD remaining in the plant effluent is $(100 - 83.5)307/100 = 51$ mg/l.

16-8. Nitrification. Before the introduction of the concept of BOD, great stress was placed, in the biological treatment of sewage, upon the nitrogen load and (1) the conversion of organic nitrogen to ammonia and, more particularly, (2) the subsequent conversion of ammonia to nitrite and nitrate, called nitrification. The quality of the plant effluent was then generally judged by its nitrate content. A nitrate nitrogen concentration of 10 to 15 mg/l was considered desirable. Today we know (1) that the attainment of low BOD values is more desirable in the sanitary management of receiving waters than high nitrification; (2) that the attainment of low BOD values does not necessarily require high nitrification of effluents; and (3) that, although both nitrite and nitrate nitrogen constitute an oxygen reserve that will supplement the DO content of the receiving water, they may, on occasion, stimulate the growth of aquatic plants, large and small, in objectionable quantities. In extreme cases, streams have been known to become choked by growths of rooted or attached plants, while sluggish water-reaches have become covered with masses of floating organisms. Death and decay of these growths has subsequently imposed new, sometimes sudden and heavy, burdens on the oxygen economy of receiving waters. It follows that nitrification should be encouraged only (1) when highly nitrified films or flocs are wanted for the conversion of the sloughed film or waste floc into a remunerative fertilizer or (2) when the sanitary condition of the receiving water is, in fact, benefited by the discharge of a highly nitrified effluent.

Design and Operation of Biological Treatment Units

16-9. Trickling Filters. Aside from structural matters, the problems confronting the designer of a trickling filter are essentially two in number: (*a*) the determination of the required area and depth of the filter and of the amount of effluent to be recirculated (the process design) and (*b*) the determination of the size of the influent conduits, dosing devices, distribution system, and effluent-collecting system and of the size of effluent-recirculating conduits and pumps, if any (the hydraulic design).

a. Process design. The principles underlying the process design of trickling filters have been discussed in preceding sections of this chapter. The fundamental relationships are expressed by the equation noted on Figure 16-6. This equation can be stated in the following form for the purpose of finding the required equivalent acre-foot-age VF of a filter that is to receive a given daily load y_0 and effect a particular degree of purification p_2 which removes a load y.

$$VF = \frac{y_0}{13{,}800}\left(\frac{p_2}{100 - p_2}\right)^2 = \frac{y_0}{13{,}800}\left(\frac{y}{y_0 - y}\right)^2 \qquad 16\text{-}7$$

When effluent is recirculated to the filter, the value of the recirculation factor F is given by Equation 16-4.

A wide range of depths and loadings is employed in practice. For single-stage operation, depths are commonly held between 6 and 10 ft, while hydraulic loads lie between 2 and 6 mgad in low-rate operation and between 15 and 30 mgad in high-rate operation. For multistage operation (generally 2-stage without alternation of the lead filter), filter depths are generally cut in half. For single-stage operation without recirculation, the Upper Mississippi Board of Public Health Engineers and Great Lakes Board of Public Health Engineers have suggested the loading curves shown in Figure 16-8. The effects of high-rate operation and recirculation on performance efficiency are reflected by Equation 16-7.

Example 16-3. Find (*a*) the acre-ft of filter required to effect 85% removal of BOD from 10 mgd of sewage containing 160 mg/l of BOD when it is applied to a trickling filter, (*b*) the BOD loading of the filter per acre-ft and (*c*) the BOD loading and hydraulic loading if the filter is made 6 ft deep. Assume that the sewage is not to be recirculated, i.e., $F = 1$.

a. By Equation 16-7, $V = \dfrac{10 \times 160 \times 8.34}{13{,}800}\left(\dfrac{85}{15}\right)^2 = 31$ acre-ft; also from Figure 16-8, the allowable loading is 10 lb of 5-day BOD daily per 1,000 cu ft, or $V = \dfrac{10 \times 160 \times 8.34}{10 \times 43.6} = 31$ acre-ft.

b. $y_0/V = 10 \times 160 \times 8.34/31 = 440$ lb per acre-ft.

c. $440 \times 6 = 2{,}600$ lb per acre, $31/6 = 5.2$ acres, and $10/5.2 = 1.9$ mgad.

The contact material of trickling filters must be weather resistant, strong enough to support its own weight, and not subject to decay. Crushed stone (trap rock, granite, and limestone) is commonly used, but hard coal, coke, cinders, slag, wood, and ceramic materials have been employed on occasion. The sodium sulfate soundness test [4] has been devised to simulate the effect of alternate freezing and thawing on the disintegration of mineral contact materials. The destructive force of repeated crystal formation within the pores of the rock forms the basis of the test.

[4] Am. Soc. Civil Engrs., *Manuals of Engineering Practice, 13* (1937).

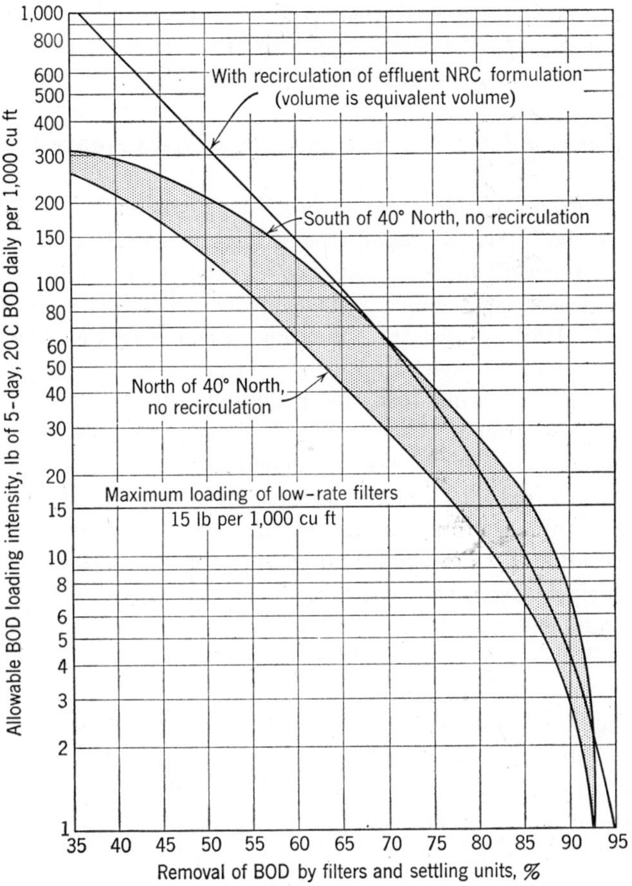

Figure 16-8. **Allowable loading intensities of trickling filters and settling tanks for given BOD reductions (*Standards for Sewage Works,* Upper Mississippi Board of Public Health Engineers and Great Lakes Board of Public Health Engineers, 1952).**

The contact material must be small in order to support a large surface of active film but not so small that its pores are filled by the growths or clogged by accumulating suspended matter or sloughing film. Crushed stone 1½ to 3 in. in size and placed in layers of uniform size with the smallest stone at the top of the bed meets these requirements satisfactorily.

b. Hydraulic design. Sewage is generally applied to the surface of the filter in a fine spray. Uniformity of distribution and opportunity for the absorption of oxygen from the atmosphere are thereby provided. The sprays are either fixed or movable. *Fixed sprays* are formed by nozzles fed from a system of stationary pipes (Figure 16-2*b*). *Movable sprays* are generally produced by rotating distributors (Figure 16-2*c*).[5] Movable sprays have displaced fixed sprays almost fully, but a large acreage of fixed sprays remains in operation.

In a *fixed-spray nozzle,* the sewage issues vertically from a circular orifice and impinges against a deflector mounted on a central spindle to form an umbrellalike spray. Depending upon the shape of the deflector, a circular, square, or hexagonal area of the bed is wetted. Half-sprays are sometimes placed at the edge of the bed. Since wind action modifies the spray pattern, there is little advantage in departing from the simplicity of nozzle construction afforded in the circular spray. The individual nozzles are fed by a system of pipes. The nozzles are generally placed on the apices of equilateral triangles by being staggered in position on adjacent supply pipes. In order to make full use of the bed, the maximum spray limits are allowed to overlap, and the head on the nozzles is allowed to fall during discharge. A dosing device—generally a tank or pair of tanks and automatic flow controls—is normally employed for this purpose. The static head on the nozzles is generally 6 to 10 ft. The pipe grid of trickling filters performs substantially the same distribution function as the pipe grid of rapid sand filters (Section 15-8).

In the *movable spray nozzle,* the sewage issues horizontally from a circular orifice, in the side of a traveling pipe. A spreader plate below the orifice will fan out the sewage onto the bed. Revolving distributors commonly consist of two or more horizontal pipes or arms attached to a central supply shaft. The center line of the pipes lies 10 to 12 in. above the surface of the bed. The arms are driven either by the reaction to the spray or by an electric motor. Self-propelled distributors require a hydrostatic head of 18 to 30 in. Unless the sewage flow is unusually even, a dosing tank must be interpolated between the primary settling tanks and the filters in self-propelled systems. When the rate of inflow to the tank is lower than that required to turn the distributor, the feed to the distributor is cut off until the tank has filled and can supply the required rate of flow. Dosing tanks add from 1 to 5 ft to the head requirements.

[5] Traveling distributors that move up and down the length of a bed are no longer in favor because a relatively long time intervenes between successive passages of the distributor over a given portion of the bed. Dosage is concentrated (therefore at a high local rate) and widely intermittent. Neither of these features is desirable.

The underdrainage system of trickling filters consists of a series of laterals that carry the purified sewage and sloughed film in open-channel flow to main drains that lead to the secondary settling tanks. Suitable arrangements of laterals are illustrated in Figure 16-9. The underdrains must be self-cleansing or accessible for cleaning. Invert gradients of about 1% are common. The laterals may pierce the walls of the filter to assist in the ventilation of the filter and to permit flushing of the underdrainage system. The main drains may be elaborated into inspection and access galleries. Hydraulically, the underdrainage system of trickling filters functions in much the same

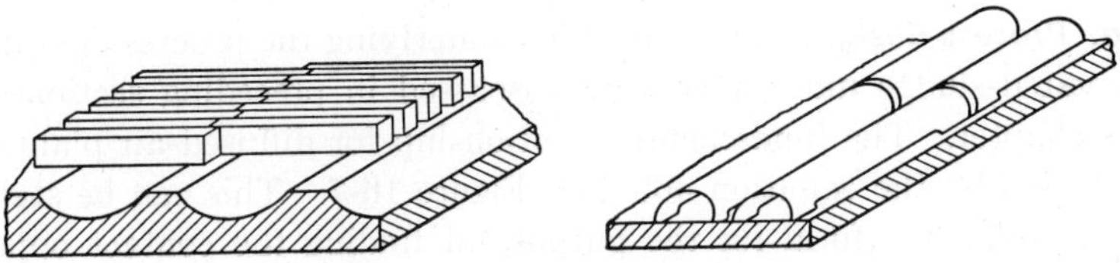

Figure 16-9. Underdrains for trickling filters.

capacity as the wash-water collection system of rapid sand filters (Section 15-9) and is designed accordingly.

Differences in the specific weight of the air within and the atmosphere without the filter are primarily responsible for the vertical displacement of air through the filter.

During warm weather, flow of air through the filter should be encouraged because the oxygen requirements of the treatment process are high. During cold weather, ventilation should be small to avoid unnecessary cooling of the sewage and the active film. Halvorson[6] has suggested an air flow of 1 fpm for high-rate, single-stage, trickling filters. Since the maximum dosage of these filters is about 30 mgad, this corresponds to an air supply of 2.1 cu ft per gal of sewage, compared with an air requirement of diffused-air, activated-sludge units of 1 cu ft per gal. However, allowance must be made for poorer absorption of oxygen by the stationary films of trickling filters. The cross-sectional area of each lateral and of the main drain must be sufficiently large above the sewage flow to permit the ventilating air to travel at reasonable velocities (about 200 fpm) to and from all parts of the bed. Transportation of downward-moving air is aided by the flow of the sewage.

For protection against extreme cold, or avoidance of odor and

[6] H. O. Halvorson, *Sewage Works J.*, 8, 891 (1936).

filter-fly nuisances, trickling filters may be completely enclosed. Forced ventilation is then in order.

16-10. Activated-Sludge Units. The problems that arise in the design of activated-sludge units, aside from structural matters, are also essentially two in number: (*a*) the determination of the required exposure of the sewage to aeration and contact with returned activated sludge (the process design) and (*b*) the determination of the size of the influent conduit, the returned-sludge conduit and pumps, the dimensions of the aeration units, and the air-distribution system and compressors or mechanical agitators (the hydraulic and pneumatic or mechanical design).

a. Process design. The principles underlying the process design of activated-sludge units have been discussed in preceding sections of this chapter. The fundamental relationship for diffused-air plants is expressed by the equation noted on Figure 16-7. This can be stated in the following form for the purpose of finding the contact opportunity as the product of (1) the detention period t that must be provided in the aeration unit and (2) the weight of sludge W that must be returned to it, if a particular degree of purification p_2 is to be obtained and a daily load y is to be removed from an applied daily load y_0.

$$Wt = \frac{y_0}{4{,}200}\left(\frac{p_2}{100 - p_2}\right)^{2.38} = \frac{y_0}{4{,}200}\left(\frac{y}{y_0 - y}\right)^{2.38} \qquad 16\text{-}8$$

The detention period t establishes the volume V of the aeration unit as $V = Qt$, where Q is the rate of flow of the incoming sewage.

Detention periods are commonly 4 to 8 hr for settled sewage of average strength, but they may be as low as 1 to 2 hr for rapid or partial treatment of average sewage and as high as 16 hr for strong industrial wastes. Short periods of aeration may be insufficient to create or maintain an active sludge. The returned sludge may then have to be aerated by itself. This is called "sludge reaeration." Since the concentration of living organisms in the sludge is high, its air requirements are great. If they are not met, the sludge will quickly become septic. It is for this reason, too, that activated sludge which has settled in secondary sedimentation tanks should be withdrawn as rapidly as possible. Detention periods should be short.

In practice, the relative amount of returned sludge is identified in three ways for design and operating purposes: (1) as the volume of activated sludge returned to the influent, expressed as a percentage of the volume of the influent sewage; (2) as the relative volume of suspended matter settling from a known volume of mixed liquor; and (3) as the relative weight of solids settling from a known volume of mixed liquor.

1. The percentage volume of activated sludge P_r returned to the influent varies in practice from 10% to 30% with an average of 20%. This measure is used to determine the capacities of pumps and conduits that transport the returned sludge. It is not a reliable measure of the amount of contact material in the aeration units, because the concentration of active solids in the returned sludge (and with it their relative surface area) varies widely in different plants and periodically in the same plant. A dry-solids concentration in the sludge of 0.2% by weight is undesirably low, one of 2% desirably high.

2. The percentage volume of suspended matter P_v in the mixed liquor of the aeration unit varies normally between 10% and 25%. This ratio is generally obtained by measuring the volume of sludge settling from 1 l of mixed liquor in 30 min. The determination is not analytically exact, because the settling and compacting properties of the suspended matter vary over a wide range. But the test is easily performed and useful in the control of the process. The volume of settleable matter is inherently of the same order of magnitude as the per cent of returned sludge, because the influent sewage adds but a small amount of settleable matter (<0.05% when the sewage is settled before aeration).

3. The dry-weight concentration of suspended solids in the mixed liquor can be determined with high analytical precision. In practice, the percentage concentration of suspended solids by weight P_w varies between 0.06 and 0.4% (600 to 4,000 mg/l) and averages 0.25%. The determination is used in the performance relationship discussed in this chapter, although it is only an indirect measure of the area of contact surface provided. However, no better means is currently available, unless it is the volatile portion of the suspended solids.

The ratio of the second to the third measure is called the *sludge-volume index* I_v. Therefore, $I_v = P_v/P_w$. Specifically, I_v is the volume in ml occupied by 1 gram of sludge, dry weight, after 30 min of settling. Calculations are normally based on the ratio in the mixed liquor of the ml of settling sludge × 1,000 to the mg/l of suspended solids. The sludge-volume index of active sludge varies between 50 and 100. A "bulked" sludge possesses an index of 200 or more. Determination of the sludge-volume index is useful in the management of the treatment process. For example, the amount of return sludge necessary to maintain a desired per cent solids P_w in the mixed liquor may be expressed in terms of the recirculation ratio R/I, and the sludge volume index, as: $100R/I = 100/[100/(P_w I_v) - 1]$. It is assumed here that the solids concentration in the sludge pumped from the secondary settlers is the same as that attained in the sludge volume index test. Since the settling conditions are different, departures from this relationship may be significant. If P_w is to be 0.25% and I_v is 80 ml/gram, the percentage return sludge should be: 100/[100/(0.25 × 80) − 1] = 25%. If I_v rises to 200, the return must be increased to 100/[100/(0.25 × 200) − 1] = 100% or be made equal to the sewage flow. At the same time, operations would be hampered by the poor settling and compacting properties of the bulked sludge. For returned sludge of known percentage solids content P_s or water content $(100 - P_s)$ the following approximate relationship obtains:

$$P_w = P_s \frac{100R/I}{100 + 100R/I} = P_s(R/I)/F' \qquad \text{16-9}$$

where F' is the recirculation factor.

Since $W = 8.34VP_w/(10^2 \times 10^3) = 8.34 \times 10^{-5}VP_w$, where W is measured in thousands of pounds and V is the tank volume in gallons, and since $t = 24V/I$, where t is the detention time in hours and I is the inflow in gallons per day,

$$V = 22.4\sqrt{I(Wt)/P_w} \qquad \text{16-10}$$

and

$$t = 538\sqrt{(Wt)/(IP_w)} \qquad \text{16-11}$$

Example 16-4. Find (*a*) the allowable loading intensity of a diffused-air activated-sludge plant that is to effect 80% removal of BOD from 10 mgd of sewage containing 160 mg/l of applied BOD; (*b*) the necessary time of aeration if the solids concentration is to be maintained at 0.25% in the aeration units; (*c*) the necessary solids concentration if the detention period available in the tanks is 6 hr; (*d*) the approximate percentages of sludge to be returned to the influent under (*b*) and (*c*), if the sludge-volume index is 80; and (*e*) the required approximate solids content of the returned, activated sludge under (*b*) and (*c*).

Since the applied load is 160 × 10 × 8.34 = 13,300 lb, Equation 16-8 states:

a.

$$Wt = \frac{13{,}300}{4{,}200}\left(\frac{80}{20}\right)^{2.38} = 86{,}300 \text{ lb-hr}$$

b. If the suspended-solids concentration in the aeration units is 0.25%, the detention time t is given by Equation 16-11 as $t = 538\sqrt{86.3/(10^7 \times 0.25)} =$ 3.16 hr.

c. If the time of aeration is 6 hr, Equation 16-11 states $P_w = (538)^2 \times 86.3/[10^7 \times (6)^2] = 0.0694\%$.

d. For $I_v = 80$, the percentage of returned sludge would have to be about as follows:

For $P_w = 0.25\%$, $100R/I = 100/[100/(0.25 \times 80) - 1] = 25\%$.
For $P_w = 0.0694\%$, $100R/I = 100/[100/(0.0694 \times 80) - 1] = 5.9\%$.
e. In accordance with Equation 16-9, the approximate solids content of the returned sludge would be:
For $P_w = 0.25\%$ and $100R/I = 25\%$, $P_s = 0.25 \times (100 + 25)/25 = 1.25\%$.
For $P_w = 0.0694\%$ and $100R/I = 5.9\%$, $P_s = 0.0694 \times (100 + 5.9)/5.9 = 1.25\%$.

The age of returned sludge, which has some effect on its purifying efficiency, is calculated by Gould [7] as the ratio of the weight of suspended solids in the aeration tank to the daily weight of solids in the influent. However, if according to Möhle,[8] a pound of BOD in the applied sewage produces a pound of floc (dry weight), the BOD concentration of the influent sewage is a more rational measure than the suspended solids. Nevertheless, the resulting numerical ages are nearly equal. Where the concentration of solids is the same in the returned and wasted activated sludges, sludge age is approximated by the ratio of the volume of returned sludge in circulation to the volume of excess sludge wasted daily.

The process design of activated-sludge plants includes a determination of the oxygen requirements of the process. In diffused-air plants, needed oxygen is obtained from the air diffused into the sewage (bubble aeration) and from the atmosphere in contact with the sewage surface (surface aeration). In mechanical aeration plants, it comes solely from the atmosphere. Oxygen intake is aided in these plants (1) through the formation of droplets by rotating brushlike or turbinelike devices that dip into the sewage or pull sewage upward through draft tubes and shower droplets over the sewage surface (droplet aeration) or (2) through the formation of bubbles of air by rotating turbinelike devices that pull air and sewage downward through draft tubes (Figure 16-3). The transfer of oxygen to droplets of sewage is more rapid than the transfer of oxygen to sewage from bubbles of air, because the interfacial film is about ⅓ as thick. However, the attainable time of exposure of droplets is ordinarily quite short.

The oxygen-transfer efficiency of bubble aeration is normally only 5 to 15%. Since a liter of free air contains about 273 mg of oxygen, from 14 to 41 mg of oxygen are absorbed from each liter of air during aeration.

The rate of oxygen demand of mixed liquor and the basic rate of

[7] Richard Gould, *Sewage Works J.*, 20, 782 (1948).
[8] H. Möhle, *Gas und Wasserfach*, 96, 239 (1955).

returned sludge are idealized in Figure 16-10. A maximum demand of 50 to 80 mg/l per hr per 1,000 mg/l of volatile suspended solids (or 40 to 64 mg/l per hr per 1,000 mg/l of total suspended solids) is exerted near the beginning of the process and approaches the average base rate of the returned sludge of about 20 mg/l per hr per 1,000 mg/l of volatile suspended solids (or about 16 mg/l per hr per 1,000 mg/l of total suspended solids) in the course of 4 to 6 hr. Aeration of activated sludge by itself reduces its initial base rate of 25 to 35

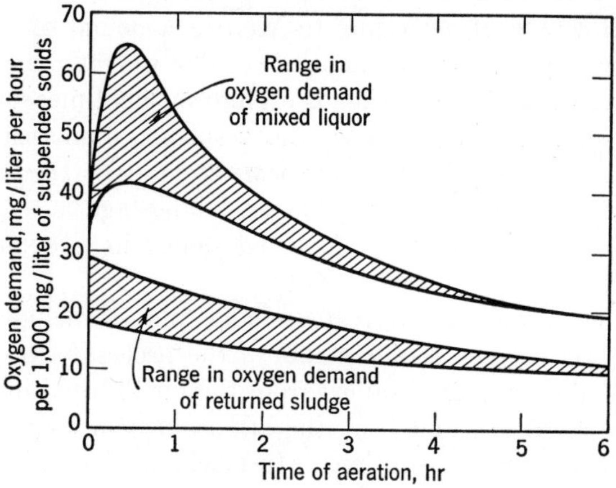

Figure 16-10. Oxygen demands in the activated-sludge process. Idealized.

mg/l per hr per 1,000 mg/l of volatile suspended solids (or 20 to 28 mg/l per hr per 1,000 mg/l of total suspended solids) by about 25 to 50% during 4 to 6 hr. Therefore, a liter of mixed liquor containing 0.25% (2,500 mg/l) of suspended solids must be provided, during 5 hr of aeration (about 6 hr of detention), with $5 \times 2.5\{16 + \frac{1}{3}[(40 - 16) \text{ to } (64 - 16)]\}/[273 \times (0.05 \text{ to } 0.15)] = 7.3 \text{ to } 29.3$ l of air.[9] If it is assumed that half this amount, or 3.7 to 14.7 l, is derived from the atmosphere by surface aeration, the air requirements of diffused-air units may be estimated at 0.5 to 2.0 cu ft per gal of sewage. Actual values range from 0.5 to 1.5 cu ft per gal of sewage of average strength to much higher values for strong industrial wastes. An observational figure, too, is 1,000 cu ft of air per pound of influent BOD. High air supply and long aeration periods are generally required for strong sewage. They produce a highly nitrified effluent. Low air supply and short periods are adequate for weak sewage and

[9] The parabolic nature of the curve introduces the factor ⅓ in the numerator.

unnitrified effluents containing the minimum amount of dissolved oxygen that must ordinarily be maintained in aeration units (about 1 mg/l). Since the oxygen requirements of the process decrease progressively in time (Figure 16-10), air supply is ordinarily proportioned to these requirements when the full amounts of sewage and sludge are brought together at the influent to the aeration units. This proportioning is called tapered aeration. It is accomplished by providing a larger number of diffusers per unit area of tank or diffusers of greater permeability (see (*b*) in this section).

Generally included in the stated air requirements of diffused-air plants is the air supplied to returned-sludge channels for the purpose of (1) keeping the sludge in suspension at velocities of less than 2 fps or (2) keeping the returned sludge in good condition.[10] The air introduced into influent channels to the aeration unit in which the returned sludge is mixed with the incoming sewage is also included in the over-all figure. However, when returned sludge is reaerated for a long period of time to condition it for use, separate account is normally taken of its air requirements.

New approaches to the process design of activated-sludge plants are presented in the following methods:

1. *Step aeration or step loading.* Sewage is added to returned sludge at two or more points along the aeration channel.
2. *Two-stage treatment.* The sewage flows through a pair of aeration and sedimentation units in series. Sludge is either returned and wasted within each stage, or excess sludge from one stage is recycled to the other from which it is wasted together with the sludge of that stage. In this way the purifying potential of the sludge is exploited before the sludge is wasted. Recycling first-stage, excess sludge to the second stage and wasting it from that stage is called activated aeration.[11]
3. *High-rate treatment.* This makes for a partial or intermediate degree of treatment. Short period aeration is combined either with thin mixed liquor (650 mg/l) or with very thick mixed liquor. Use of little returned sludge is called modified aeration.[11]

The prolonged aeration of returned sludge in the influent reaches of aeration channels followed by short-period aeration (15–20 min) of the mixed liquor is reported to have solved operating difficulties in overloaded plants.[12] This is a modified form of reaeration.

[10] The Kutter coefficient of roughness for aerated channels is close to 0.3, because the passageway is reduced by the air.

[11] A. H. Chasick, Activated aeration at the Wards Island sewage treatment plant, *Sewage and Ind. Wastes, 26,* 1059 (1954).

[12] A. H. Ullrich and M. W. Smith, Operation experiences with activated sludge-Biasorption at Austin, Tex., *Sewage and Ind. Wastes, 29,* 400 (1957).

b. Hydraulic and pneumatic, or mechanical, design. Both diffused air and mechanical stirring perform two functions: (1) they supply needed oxygen, and (2) they keep the active sludge in suspension and thereby supply wanted contact between sewage and sludge. Effective velocities of at least 0.5 fps must be maintained if sludge flocs are not to settle out and become septic. Hydraulic circulation, therefore, is an important element in tank design. Circulation is commonly promoted by adding to the relatively slow, longitudinal displacement velocity of the unit (1.5 to 8 fpm) a relatively rapid upward vertical velocity that creates a complementary downward velocity, as well as transverse links. A circulating velocity well above 0.5 fps is induced. If the stirring unit (air or mechanical) is placed on one side of a long tank, the linking flows are across the tank, and the combined motions produce spiral circulation. Spiral flow is well maintained if the channel width to be spanned is not more than three times its depth. Common proportions are more nearly 1.5 (width) to 1.0 (depth).

Gyratory flow is promoted by placing deflectors at the surface of the channel and fillets at the bottom to approximate a circular cross-section in square channels and an elliptical cross-section in rectangular channels. In some designs (Figure 16-3*b*), in which the air is supplied from tubular diffusers that are submerged only a few feet, an air lift is induced by placing longitudinal baffles close to the diffusers. The length of channels is seldom less than 100 ft or more than 400 ft. Depths are generally held at 10 to 15 ft for structural economy. Expansion and coalescence of air bubbles are also factors in circumscribing the depth of diffused-air units.

Since the physical detention period t' equals t/F where t is the average time of treatment used in Equation 16-8 and $F = 1 + R/I$ is the recirculation factor, the hydraulic load Q on aeration units bears the following relations (1) to the width b (ft), depth d (ft), and length l (ft), of aeration channels, (2) to the physical detention period t' (hr), and (3) to the recirculation factor F of the sludge: $Q = 1 \times 7.5 \times 24/(Ft') = 180/Ft'$ gpd per cu ft, or $180bd/(Ft')$ gpd per ft length, or $7.84d/(Ft')$ mgd per acre. The length of channel, conversely, is $l = 5{,}560Ft'/(bd)$ ft per mgd. Good cross-sectional distribution of flow is obtained when channels are made at least five times as long as they are wide. Transverse baffles are sometimes inserted at intervals of about 50 ft in order to reduce longitudinal mixing or short circuiting.

16-11. Air Supply for Diffused-Air Units. The air supply constitutes a unique design feature of diffused-air plants. It includes the following components: (1) diffusers, which inject fine bubbles of air into the sewage, (2) air piping, which carries the air from the compressors to the diffusers, (3) measuring devices, which record the amount of air used, (4) air compressors, which place the air under the required pressure, and (5) air filters, which clean the air drawn into the compressors in order to protect them against abrading substances and to prevent the clogging of diffusers from the air side.

Economic design of the air-distribution system commonly entails an over-all distribution loss of about 25% of the sewage depth. Therefore, the required air pressure is 1.25 × (10 to 15) ft or 5.4 to 8.1 psig. The resistance of the different portions of the system can be gaged from the following average component values:

1. Air filters, ⅛ to ⅜ in. of water for viscous filters and ½ in. for cloth filters.
2. Air meters, 1 to 2 in. of water, or 18 to 24% of the differential head.
3. Piping, $1.0v^2/2g$ ft head of air for 40 diameters of pipe[13] with $0.5v^2/2g$ ft head of air for elbows and $1.5v^2/2g$ ft head of air for globe valves, pipe velocities commonly being held between 2,000 and 3,000 fpm.
4. Diffusers, 2 to 15 in. of water.
5. Sewage, 10 to 15 ft of water.

a. Air diffusers. Commonly, air diffusers are flat plates or circular tubes of porous ceramic materials, but other forms and materials are also available. Plate diffusers are normally 12 in. square and 1 in. thick, tubular diffusers 24 in. long and 1¾ or 3 in. in internal diameter with a wall thickness ⅜ or ⅝ in., respectively. The air release of circular tubes is less uniform than that of plates, because the air bubbles issuing from the bottom half of the tube tend to coalesce as they sweep around the walls of the diffuser. By convention, the *permeability* of diffusers is expressed in terms of the face velocity (fpm) of air at 70 F and 10 to 25% relative humidity that will flow through the pores of the diffuser with a loss of head of 2 in. of water, when the diffuser is tested dry in a room kept at 70 F and a relative humidity of 30 to 50%. Permeabilities of 30 to 60 fpm are commonly specified. A square foot of submerged diffuser will then deliver 1.5 to 3 cfm of air with a pressure loss of 2 to 5 in. of water when the diffuser is new. Losses rise as diffusers become clogged in service. The diffusers are generally cleaned when the loss has increased twofold.

[13] See Equation 6-1, $fl/d = 40f = 1.0$, or $f = 0.025$.

Diffusers clog on the air side when the air carries foreign matter originating in the atmosphere or in the air piping. They are clogged on the sewage side by sewage solids and growths of microorganisms. Clogging on the air side is kept to a minimum by cleaning the air before compression (which also prevents wear on the compressors) and by constructing the air-distribution system of non-corrosive materials or of materials that are protected against erosion. Clogging on the sewage side is reduced, if air pressures are maintained, without interruption, above the hydrostatic head of the sewage. The nature of the clogging substances determines the method of cleaning.

b. Air piping. A satisfactory relation for the resistance of air piping can be based on the Darcy-Weisbach equation for the flow of incompressible fluids in pipes:

$$h_f = f \frac{l}{d} \frac{v^2}{2g} \tag{6-1}$$

Conversion of Equation 6-1 to a useful equation for the flow of air as a compressible fluid in pipes is had by making the following substitutions:

1. $\Delta p = h_f \gamma / 144$, where Δp is the pressure difference in psi and γ is the weight density of the air, the value of γ being 0.076 lb per cu ft at atmospheric pressure (p_0 = 14.7 psia) and a temperature T_0 of 60 F (519.6 F absolute) and varying directly with the absolute pressure p and inversely with the absolute temperature T or $\gamma = 0.076(p/p_0)(T_0/T) = 2.71p/T$.

2. Since the weight of air transported is constant but varies in volume with its density, the rate of flow of the air in the pipe is $0.076Q/(2.71p/T) = 0.0282(T/p)Q$, where Q is the rate of flow of free air in cubic feet per minute. Furthermore, $Q = v \times 60 \times \pi D^2/(4 \times 144)$, where D is the diameter of the pipe in inches; and $T = 519.6(p/14.7)^{0.283}$ for adiabatic compression of the air.[14]

The resulting equation is

$$\Delta p = \frac{f}{38{,}000} \frac{lTQ^2}{pD^5} \tag{16-12}$$

The value of f varies for new piping from 2.5×10^{-2} for 3-in. pipe to 1.6×10^{-2} for 18-in. pipe and for old piping from 4.9×10^{-2} for 3-in. pipe to 2.8×10^{-2} for 18-in. pipe.

In accordance with observations by Fritsche,

$$f = 0.048D^{0.027}/Q^{0.148} \tag{16-13}$$

for pipes less than 10 in. in diameter.

[14] The associated pressure (p)-volume (v) relationship being $pv = RT$, where R is the gas constant and pv^n = constant, the exponent $n = 1.40$ being the ratio of the specific heats of the air at constant pressure and constant volume.

Example 16-5. Find the pressure drop in 500 ft of 6-in. pipe transporting 500 cfm of free air under a gage pressure of 7 psig:

1. The absolute pressure of the air, $p = 7 + 14.7 = 21.7$ psia.
2. The absolute temperature of the air $T = 520(21.7/14.7)^{0.283} = 581$ F.
3. By Equation 16-13, $f = 0.048 \times 6^{0.027}/(500)^{0.148} = 0.020$.
4. By Equation 16-12, therefore,

$$\Delta p = \frac{0.020}{38{,}000} \frac{500 \times 581 \times (500)^2}{21.7 \times 6^5} = 0.23 \text{ psi}$$

The length of pipe that will produce the same loss of head as elbows and tees is approximated by the observational relationship:

$$l = 7.6D/(1 + 3.6/D) \qquad 16\text{-}14$$

Similarly for globe valves:

$$l = 11.4D/(1 + 3.6/D) \qquad 16\text{-}15$$

c. *Air compression.* The work done by air compressors in compressing a unit volume of free air from atmospheric pressure to a pressure p and volume v, consists of (1) the work of compression, $\int p\,dv$, plus (2) the work of expulsion pv minus (3) the work done on the piston by the incoming air p_0v_0. In isothermal compression $pv =$ constant; in adiabatic compression $pv^n = pv^{1.40} =$ constant. Most air compressors employed in sewage works operate adiabatically. The work of compression can therefore be formulated as

$$\int p\,dv = \int_{v_0}^{v} \text{constant} \times v^{-n}\,dv = -\text{ Constant } (v_0^{1-n} - v^{1-n})/(1-n)$$

$$= (pv - p_0v_0)/(n-1)$$

because the constant equals both pv^n and $p_0v_0^n$. It follows that the work done by the compressor is $[(pv - p_0v_0)/(n-1)] + pv - p_0v_0$. Expressing v in terms of v_0 and substituting Q cfm of free air for v_0, the theoretical horsepower requirements P of the compressor are:

$$P = \frac{144}{33{,}000}\left(\frac{n}{n-1}\right) p_0Q\left[\left(\frac{p}{p_0}\right)^{(n-1)/n} - 1\right] \qquad 16\text{-}16$$

or,

$$P = 0.227Q[(p/14.7)^{0.283} - 1] \qquad 16\text{-}17$$

for an atmospheric pressure of 14.7 psia and for $n = 1.40$. Compressor efficiencies being in the vicinity of 80%, the power requirements of a compressor that is to handle 10^6 cu ft of free air per day (694 cfm) against a pressure of 7 psig are $P = 18.4$ hp theoretical and 23 hp actual. The corresponding energy requirements are 24 times as great, or 440 hp-hr theoretical and 550 hp-hr actual, or 330 kw-hr theoretical and 410 kw-hr actual. The energy requirements of mechanical stirring devices are of the same order of magnitude for identical rates of sewage flow.

Rotary and centrifugal blowers are commonly employed to deliver air at the required pressures.

d. Air filters.[15] Two types of air filters are in general use: (1) viscous filters consisting of a mat of non-corrosive metal, glass wool, or hair covered with oil and (2) cloth filters. The viscous filters come in unit frames (20 in. square and about 4½ in. thick) and are suspended in large rectangular frames. With face velocities as high as 300 fpm, their pressure loss, as previously stated, is only ⅛ to ⅜ in. of water. Metallic filters are cleaned by immersing them in a cleansing bath. They are then recoated with oil. Glass-wool and hair filters are discarded when they become clogged. Cloth filters are given face velocities of about 200 fpm and are cleansed by backflows of air or by vacuum-cleaning devices. Their pressure loss is about ½ in. of water. The probable dust loading of filters is from 1 to 3 mg per 100 cu ft of air when the air intake is so placed as to avoid dusty areas such as driveways.

[15] See *Handbook of Air Cleaning*, U. S. Atomic Energy Commission, Government Printing Office, Washington, D. C., 1952.

17 Sludge Treatment and Disposal

17-1. Origin and Constitution of Sludge. The settleable solids that are naturally present in water and waste water, or that are derived from non-settleable matter by chemical coagulation and precipitation and by biological flocculation and precipitation, are removed from settling tanks as *sludge* (Section 13-10). When coagulating and precipitating chemicals are added, their precipitates become part of the sludge (Section 14-9). When sludges contain large quantities of precipitating chemicals they may be referred to as *slurries* (Section 14-9). The wash water from filters also contains sludge-forming substances. In sewage treatment, heavy, largely mineral, settleable solids are classed as *grit* or *detritus* (Sections 13-15 and 13-16). Skimmings introduced into sludge lines (Section 13-17) and screenings comminuted within the suspending sewage or returned to it after removal and disintegration (Section 13-1) are mixed with the sludge.

Sludges are further identified in terms of the treatment processes in which they originate. Examples are the coagulation-basin, water-softening, and iron sludges of water-purification plants, and the plain-sedimentation, chemical precipitation, and activated sludges of sewage-treatment plants. Sloughed trickling-filter slimes are called *trickling-filter humus.*

On reaching the bottom of settling tanks, most sludges form loose structures of particulate matter with included water. The pore space of these structures is large and their water content relatively great. The resulting volume of sludge is many times that of its constituent solids. The great volumes of sludge that must be disposed of are a serious economic problem, especially in sewage treatment. The presence of substantial amounts of organic matter that can serve as food for saprophytic bacteria and other scavenging organisms renders some sludges, including all but exceptional sewage sludges, putrescible. Exceptional sewage sludges are those derived from waste waters containing toxic substances such as copper.

Since bacteria and other organisms are concentrated in sludge and some of them are pathogenic, the hygienic significance of sludge is often as great as its esthetic and economic significance. In the treatment of municipal sewage, thousands of gallons of putrescible and potentially dangerous sludge are removed from each million gallons of sewage treated. For this reason, the present chapter is concerned with sewage sludge more specifically than with water-treatment sludges. However, many of the matters considered apply to both types of sludges, although in different degree. The disposal of water-treatment sludges has been discussed briefly also in Section 14-9.

Many sludges contain substances of economic value. The solids in wastes from the food and beverage industry, for example, may serve as animal foods after the sludge has been adequately dewatered. Other industrial waste waters, too, contain recoverable values including grease, fiber, and chemicals (Chapter 20). Sewage sludge contains constituents that will fertilize the land. Its dry solids are of high calorific power, and wet sewage sludges will yield useful amounts of combustible gas (principally methane) when they are submitted to anaerobic digestion.

17-2. Unit Operations of Sludge Treatment. The primary purposes of sludge treatment are (1) reduction of the volume of sludge to be disposed of and (2) control or destruction of its putrescibility. The unit operations employed for this purpose are listed in the following schedule.

1. *Thickening.* An operation in which sludge is stirred for prolonged periods for the purpose of forming larger, more rapidly settling aggregates of sludge flocs with smaller water content. An example is the thickening of activated sludge to increase its solids concentration to as much as 4% in 8 to 12 hr of stirring, chlorine being added, if necessary, to impede decomposition.

2. *Chemical conditioning.* An operation of chemical treatment, analogous to the chemical coagulation of water and sewage, which improves the dewatering characteristics of sludge. An example is the addition of ferric chloride to sewage sludge that is to be dewatered on vacuum filters.

3. *Elutriation.* A washing operation whereby substances that interfere physically or economically with chemical conditioning and filtration are washed out of sludge. An example is the reduction in required chemical coagulation of digested sewage sludge in advance of filtration.

4. *Biological flotation.* A thickening operation whereby sludge solids are lifted by gases of decomposition. An example is the flotation of primary sludge in 5 days at 35 C and the withdrawal of the subnatant.

5. *Vacuum filtration.* An operation in which moisture is withdrawn from a layer of sludge by suction, the sludge to be dewatered being supported on a porous medium, usually cloth on screening. An example is the dewatering of chemically conditioned activated sludge on a continuous, rotary vacuum filter. A sludge paste or cake is produced.

6. *Air drying.* An operation whereby sludge run onto beds of sand or other granular materials loses moisture by evaporation to the air and by drainage to the drying bed. An example is the air-drying of well-digested sewage sludge on sand beds, a spadable, friable sludge cake being produced.

7. *Heat drying.* An operation of sludge heating or moisture evaporation by which the sludge is reduced to substantial dryness. An example is the drying of vacuum-filtered activated sewage sludge in a continuous flash-drier. If sludge is to be marketed, its moisture content must generally be reduced to less than 10%.

8. *Digestion.* An operation of anaerobic decomposition of putrescible matter accompanied by gasification, liquefaction, stabilization, destruction of colloidal structure, and consolidation or release of moisture. The gases produced generally include, besides carbon dioxide, combustible methane and, more rarely, hydrogen. Examples are (1) the digestion of settled solids in septic tanks (single- or double-storied) and (2) the digestion in heated, separate tanks of sewage solids removed from primary or secondary settling tanks, or both, the gases of decomposition being employed for tank heating and other plant purposes.

9. *Incineration.* An operation by which heat-dried sludge is ignited and burnt, alone or with added fuel, for the purpose of heat-drying the partly dewatered sludge of which it was itself a part. Examples are (1) the incineration of heat-dried sludge for the purpose of supplying heat to a continuous flash-drier and (2) the burning of heat-dried sludge on the lower hearths of a multiple-hearth furnace on the upper hearths of which the sludge to be incinerated is being dried. The end product of incineration is ash.

There are other unit operations of sludge treatment. Among them are (1) conditioning by heating, freezing, or chemical flotation and (2) concentration or dewatering by centrifuging and pressing. They are not described here because they are either inadequately developed or unsatisfactory or uneconomical in performance. Some of them have the further drawback of being discontinuous. None of them is, or has been, widely used.

Common combinations of unit operations are (1) air-drying of digested, plain-sedimentation sewage sludge; (2) heat-drying of thickened, chemically conditioned, vacuum-filtered activated sludge; (3) incineration of digested, elutriated, chemically conditioned, and vacuum-filtered mixtures of trickling-filter humus and plain-sedimentation sewage sludge.

Characteristics and Behavior of Sludge

17-3. Examination of Sludge. *Standard Methods for the Examination of Water and Sewage* [1] includes the schedule of procedures for the examination of sludge and mud samples that is given below. Tests that pertain to the examination of activated sludge only are printed in italics. Unless stated otherwise, they have been discussed in Section 16-10.

Physical and Chemical Examination.

Temperature, color, odor, and physical appearance—all but the temperature test are described in general terms as best suits the individual case.

Specific gravity—by comparative weights of sludge or mud (if necessary diluted with water) in relation to water.

Suspended solids of sludges and aeration-tank liquor—by suction filtration through filter paper supported on a perforated aluminum dish in a Büchner funnel.

Settleability of activated sludge—by recording the volume occupied by the sludge at various time intervals and finding the rate of settling from a volume-time plot. This test is not included in Section 16-10 in this form.

Sludge-volume index (SVI) and sludge-density index (SDI).

Reaction: acidity, alkalinity (phenolphthalein and methyl orange), and *p*H value.

Moisture and solids (total and volatile)—by evaporation and ignition.

Nitrogen—total, ammonia, and organic.

Grease in liquid sludge—by extraction of acidified samples with ether.

Volatile acids in liquid sludge—by steam distillation.

Biological Examination. Bacteriological examination is not specified. Ordinarily, it is conducted by methods used in the examination of water. Results may be expressed in the same terms or based on the weight of the liquid sludge.

Microscopic examination—quantitative estimate of the number, bulk, or weight of organisms or other material retained (1) on a 30-mesh sieve (590 μ openings) and (2) on a 100-mesh sieve (149 μ openings) after passing a 30-mesh sieve.

The significance of most of the standard tests should be clear from what has been said about the examination of water and sewage

[1] American Public Health Association, 10th Ed., New York, 1955.

(Chapter 11). However, there are certain properties of sludge that are deserving of special consideration. These are discussed in succeeding sections of this chapter.

17-4. Moisture-Weight-Volume Relationships. If a sludge contains a weight W_s of dry solids and a weight W of water, the percentage moisture content of the sludge is $p = 100W/(W + W_s)$ and the solids concentration $(100 - p) = 100W_s/(W + W_s)$.

The specific gravity of the dry sludge (or of the sludge solids on a dry basis) is a function of the specific gravities of its component parts. If the two fractions of the solids (volatile and fixed), which are determined by evaporation of the sludge moisture and ignition of the residue, possess specific gravities of s_v and s_f respectively, the specific gravity s_s of the solids as a whole can be calculated from a knowledge of the percentage volatile matter p_v in the sludge. Writing

$$100/s_s = (p_v/s_v) + (100 - p_v)/s_f$$

it follows that

$$s_s = 100s_f s_v/[100s_v + p_v(s_f - s_v)] \qquad 17\text{-}1$$

The specific gravity of the volatile solids is normally close to 1.0 and that of the fixed solids about 2.5, or

$$s_s = 250/(100 + 1.5p_v) \qquad 17\text{-}2$$

The specific gravity of the wet sludge s is the quotient of the sums of the weights of the water and dry sludge and their respective volumes, or

$$s = \frac{p + (100 - p)}{p/s_w + (100 - p)/s_s} = \frac{100s_s s_w}{ps_s + (100 - p)s_w} \qquad 17\text{-}3$$

In terms of Equation 17-2,

$$s = 25{,}000/[250p + (100 - p)(100 + 1.5p_v)] \qquad 17\text{-}4$$

The volume V of the wet sludge equals the sum of the volumes of the water and the solids contained in the wet sludge, or

$$V = \frac{W_s}{s_s w} + \frac{W}{s_w w} = \frac{W_s}{s_s w} + \frac{pW_s}{(100 - p)s_w w} = \frac{100W_s s_w + p(s_s - s_w)}{w(100 - p)s_s s_w} \qquad 17\text{-}5$$

Here w is the unit weight of water. It follows that reduction of the volume of a given sludge by removing water from it, the attributes of the original sludge being given the subscript zero, leaves the volume of the partially dewatered sludge as

$$V = V_0 \frac{[100s_w + p(s_s - s_w)](100 - p_0)}{[100s_w + p_0(s_s - s_w)](100 - p)} \tag{17-6}$$

provided that the voids between the solids remain filled with water.

When s_s is close to s_w in magnitude, as is generally true,

$$V = V_0(100 - p_0)/(100 - p) \tag{17-7}$$

The loss of water from sludge, therefore, changes its volume approximately in the ratio of its solids concentration. Because of this, the solids concentration is, generally speaking, a more useful parameter than the sludge moisture. A reduction in the water content of a given sludge from 95 to 90% or increase in its solids concentration from 5 to 10%, for example, more or less halves its volume. As sludge loses water, it often acquires the plastic properties of a paste. Loss of water to the point where the voids of the sludge are no longer filled with water produces a sludge cake which is generally forkable. Except for some consolidation, the volume of sludge cake remains substantially constant at $V = W_s/[(1 - f)s_s w]$ where f is the porosity ratio (often 40 to 50%).

Example 17-1. A primary sewage sludge, produced by plain sedimentation of domestic sewage, has a moisture content of 95%, 72.2% of the dry solids being volatile matter. Find (*a*) the specific gravity of the dry solids, on the assumption that the specific gravity of the volatile solids is 1.00 and that of the fixed solids 2.50; (*b*) the specific gravity of the wet sludge, on the assumption that the specific gravity of the included water is 1.00; and (*c*) the relative decrease in volume associated with a reduction of the moisture of the wet sludge to 85%.

a. By Equation 17-1 or 17-2: $s_s = 250/(100 + 1.5 \times 72.2) = 1.20$

b. By Equation 17-3: $s = 120/(95 \times 1.2 + 5) = 1.008$

c. By Equation 17-6: $\dfrac{V}{V_0} = \dfrac{(100 + 85 \times 0.20)5}{(100 + 95 \times 0.20)15} = 0.328$

or by Equation 17-7: $V/V_0 = \frac{5}{15} = 0.333$.

17-5. Release of Moisture. The drainability of sludge, or the relative rate at which and extent to which sludge will give up its moisture (and the influence of conditioning agents upon drainability), can be determined in the laboratory by employing an apparatus such as that shown in Figure 17-1. A known weight of sludge is placed on filter paper in a Büchner funnel, or in an aluminum dish supported on a rubber ring in the Büchner funnel, and the volume of filtrate col-

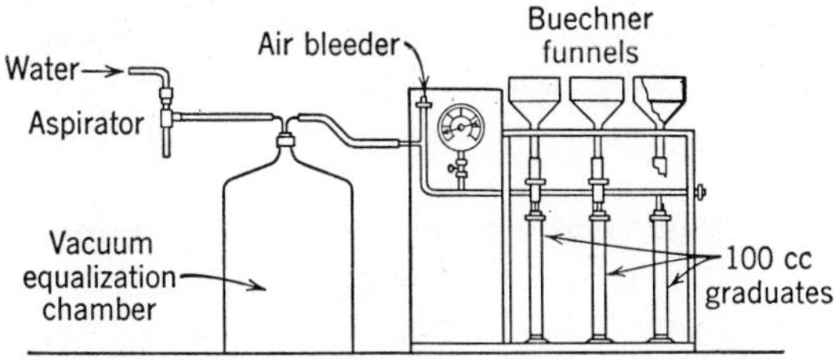

Figure 17-1. Apparatus for determining the release of moisture by sludge.

lected in different time intervals with or without suction is noted.[2] The moisture content of the sludge at the different time intervals is then calculated from a knowledge of the original moisture content of the sludge. If, for example, 50 ml of filtrate are collected in 10 min from 100 grams of activated sludge that contains 98% water, the moisture content of the sludge has been reduced to $(98 - 50)/(100 - 50) = 96\%$ in 10 min. A plot of observed values such as that shown in Figure 17-2 will identify the probable influence of sludge conditioning agents. Laboratory-scale equipment takes the form of miniature vacuum filters and sand beds.

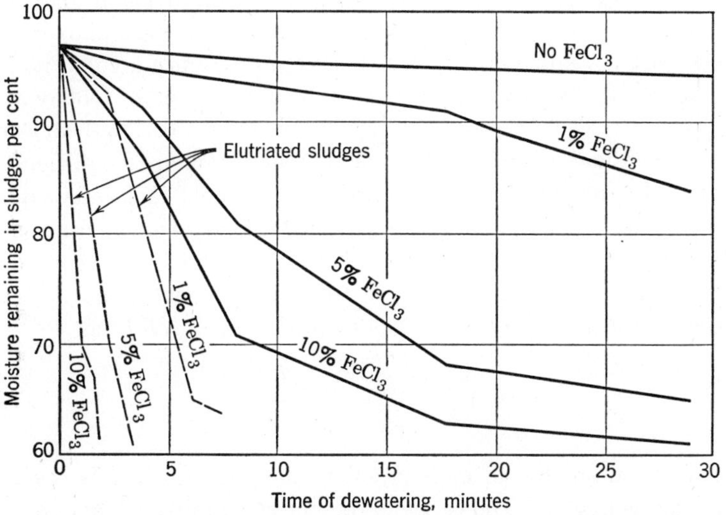

Figure 17-2. Rates of release of moisture by digested, plain-sedimentation sewage sludge.

[2] The Büchner funnel can be replaced by a metal nozzle to the mouth of which filter cloth or screening is clamped. The nozzle is placed under a vacuum and inserted in the sludge to be tested.

The thickening of sludge by stirring can be investigated in a laboratory stirring apparatus (Figure 14-2). The effects of conditioning agents on thickening and flotation can also be studied by these means.

17-6. Digestibility. The rate of digestion of a given sludge can be determined in the laboratory on a batch basis in an apparatus such as that shown in Figure 17-3. Constant temperature is conveniently maintained by placing the sludge bottle in a temperature-controlled water bath. The amount of gas produced in given time intervals and its composition serve as the measures of digestibility. In continuous-digestion (steady-state) experiments, fresh sludge must be added in daily increments to the sludge bottle. The amounts added, after the normal digestion period has been reached, must maintain a steady rate of production of gas of even composition. The gases released by digesting sewage sludges contain about 72% methane, the remainder being substantially all carbon dioxide. The gas is normally saturated with water vapor. Under standard conditions (0 C or 32 F, 1 atm or 29.9 in. mercury, and dryness), gas occupies a volume of 359 cu ft per lb mol. Hence a cubic foot of methane (CH_4) weighs 16/359 = 0.0446 lb and a cubic foot of carbon dioxide (CO_2) 44/359 = 0.1225 lb. The net (or low-heat) fuel value of methane is 963 Btu per cu ft under standard conditions as against 1,080 Btu per cu ft of natural gas. The net fuel value equals the heat liberated in combustion minus the heat of condensation of water (Section 17-14). Reduction of the volume of gas recorded at a given temperature and pressure to standard conditions is made in accordance with the perfect gas equation $pV = NRT$, as

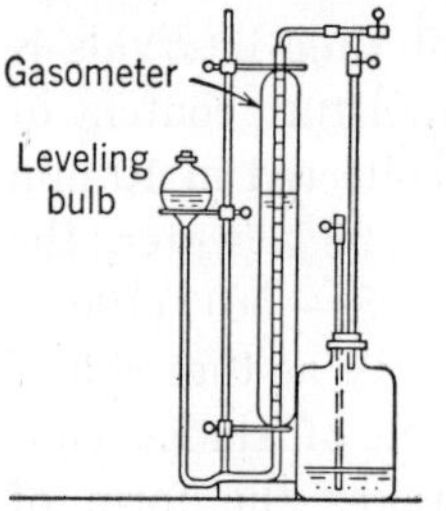

Figure 17-3. Apparatus for determining the digestibility of sludge.

$$V_0 = V \frac{p - p_w}{p_0} \frac{T_0}{T} \tag{17-8}$$

Here N is the number of mols of gas in the volume V; R is the universal gas constant (8.36×10^7 dyne-cm per gram-mol and deg C absolute, or 1,546 lb-ft per lb-mol and deg F absolute); T is the absolute temperature (273.1 + deg C, or 459.7 + deg F); p is the absolute pressure; p_w is the vapor pressure of water; and the subscript zero denotes standard conditions. The vapor pressure of water is subtracted from the observed pressure on the assumption that the gas is saturated with moisture. For p in inches of mercury and T in degrees Fahrenheit,

$$V_0 = 16.4V \frac{p - p_w}{459.7 + T} \qquad 17\text{-}9$$

Example 17-2. A sewage sludge produced by primary (plain) sedimentation of domestic sewage contains 72.2% volatile matter on a dry basis and 95% water. During experimental digestion at 30 C (86 F) of 384 grams of fresh wet sludge, the gas yield is 783 ml per gram of volatile solids, 72% by volume being methane. The wet digested sludge, exclusive of the seeding material, weighs 93 grams and contains 87% water, the volatile matter in the sludge being 38.2% on a dry basis. Find (*a*) the volume in cubic feet and weight in pounds of gas per pound of volatile matter destroyed; (*b*) the net fuel value of the gas in British thermal units per cubic foot and per pound of volatile matter destroyed; (*c*) the volume in cubic feet of gas per cubic foot of wet sludge daily and per capita daily on the assumption that 37.8 cu ft of wet sludge per 1,000 persons are added daily to the digestion unit, and that the daily charge of the digestion unit is proportional to the batch charge of the experimental unit; and (*d*) the relative volume of gas measured at a temperature of 68 F and a barometric pressure of 29.6 in.

a. The weights of volatile matter in the fresh and digested sludges are respectively: $384[(100 - 95)/100](72.2/100) = 13.9$ grams and $93[(100 - 87)/100](38.2/100) = 4.6$ grams. Hence the weight of volatile matter destroyed is $(13.9 - 4.6) = 9.3$ grams and the volume of gas per gram of volatile matter destroyed becomes $783 \times 13.9/9.3 = 1{,}170$ ml. Since 1 cu ft = 28.3 l and 1 lb = 454 grams, the volume of gas is $1.17 \times 454/28.3 = 18.8$ cu ft per pound of volatile matter destroyed. The weight of this gas is $(0.0446 \times 0.72 + 0.1225 \times 0.28)18.8 = 1.25$ lb per pound of volatile matter destroyed. A value of 1.25 lb of gas per pound of volatile matter destroyed is well established for the digestion of plain-sedimentation sewage solids.

b. The net fuel value of the gas is $963 \times 0.72 = 690$ Btu per cu ft, or $18.8 \times 690 = 13{,}000$ Btu per pound of volatile matter destroyed.

c. The gas yield of 783 ml per gram of volatile solids equals $783 \times 0.05 \times 0.722 = 28.3$ ml per gram of wet sludge. In accordance with Example 17-1, the specific gravity of the fresh wet sludge is 1.008. Therefore the gas yield is $28.3 \times 1.008 = 28.5$ ml per ml or cu ft per cu ft, and the daily per capita production of gas is $28.5 \times 37.8/1{,}000 = 1.08$ cu ft. A value of about 1 cu ft of gas per capita daily is a useful background figure for the gas yield of digesting, plain-sedimentation solids.

d. By Equation 17-8 or 17-9: $V/V_0 = (459.7 + 68.0)/[16.4(29.6 - 0.7)] = 1.11$. The vapor pressure of water at 68 F being 0.7 in. of mercury (Table A-4), i.e., 1.11 cu ft of gas will be recorded for each cubic foot of gas under standard conditions.

17-7. Fuel Value. The fuel value of sludge solids is determined in a bomb calorimeter. Since the volatile-solids content of sludge is a measure of its ignitable constituents, estimates of the fuel value may be based on a statistical correlation between pairs of observed fuel values and volatile-solids values of different sludges. For sewage sludges, the correlation may be generalized in the form

$$Q = a\left(\frac{100p_v}{100 - p_c} - b\right)\left(\frac{100 - p_c}{100}\right) \tag{17-10}$$

where Q is the fuel value in British thermal units per pound of dry solids; p_v is the proportion of volatile matter in per cent; p_c is the proportion of chemical, precipitating or conditioning, agent present in per cent; and a and b are coefficients for different classes of sludge. Characteristic magnitudes of these coefficients are: $a = 131$ and $b = 10$ for plain-sedimentation sewage sludge (fresh and digested); and $a = 107$ and $b = 5$ for activated-sludge (fresh).

A comparison of observed or calculated fuel values of sludges can be had with those of the common fuels shown in Table 17-1.

TABLE 17-1. Fuel Values of Common Fuels

Fuel	Btu per lb	lb per gal
Low-grade coal	10,000	...
High-grade coal	14,000	...
Crude petroleum	19,000	7.6
Gasoline	20,000	6.1

Example 17-3. A chemically precipitated sewage sludge contains 68.0% volatile matter on a dry basis and the precipitated chemical is 8.3% of the sludge weight. Estimate: (*a*) the fuel value of the sludge and (*b*) the percentage recovery of fuel value in sludge gas by digestion of these solids, assuming that 67% of the volatile matter is destroyed by digestion and that 72% of the gas by volume is methane, the remainder being carbon dioxide.

a. By Equation 17-10, using the values of a and b for plain-sedimentation sewage sludge,

$$Q = 131\left(\frac{100 \times 68}{100 - 8.3} - 10\right)\left(\frac{100 - 8.3}{100}\right) = 7{,}700 \text{ Btu per lb}$$

b. Since the weight of volatile matter destroyed is $0.67 \times 0.68 = 0.46$ lb per pound of dry sludge and the gas production is 1.25 lb per pound of volatile matter destroyed (Section 17-6), the weight of gas produced is $0.46 \times 1.25 = 0.57$ lb per pound of dry sludge. The volume of methane, therefore, is $(0.72 \times 0.57)/(0.72 \times 0.0446 + 0.28 \times 0.1225) = 6.2$ cu ft per pound of dry sludge, and its fuel value $963 \times 6.2 = 5{,}900$ Btu. This is $100 \times 5{,}900/7{,}700 = 77\%$ of the fuel value of the dry solids.

17-8. Fertilizer Value. A large number of chemical elements are essential to the growth of the higher green plants. The most important ones are:

1. Carbon, oxygen, and hydrogen. They are secured freely from air and water.
2. Nitrogen, phosphorus, potassium, calcium, magnesium, sulfur, and iron. They are obtained in substantial quantities from the soil.
3. Boron, manganese, zinc, copper, and others. They are secured in minute quantities (trace-quantities) from the soil.

In addition, there are elements that, though not beneficial to plants, are valuable components of the food of man and animals: iodine, fluorine, chlorine, and sodium. The value of vitamins and hormones is not fully clarified as yet.

Sludges produced by waste waters contain many of these elements. In competition with commercial fertilizers, they are rated principally on their content of three fertilizing ingredients: nitrogen (N), phosphorus as phosphoric acid (P_2O_5), and potassium as potash (K_2O); but more particularly on the first two. Many sludges are also of value as soil builders or soil conditioners; i.e., as humus.

The concentration of chemical fertilizer-ingredients is expressed as a percentage of the dry weight of the sludge. The nitrogen content of sludges produced by the treatment of domestic sewage varies in fresh sludges from 0.8 to 5% for plain-sedimentation solids (and proportionately less in sludges including chemical precipitating agents) to 3 to 10% for activated sludges. Trickling-filter humus contains 1.5 to 5% nitrogen, decreasing with the length of storage of the sludge in the filter. Digestion reduces the nitrogen content of sludge by 40 to 50%. The phosphoric acid content of most sewage sludges is small (1 to 3%), and that of potash even smaller (0.1 to 0.3%). For purposes of comparison, animal manures contain 1 to 4% of nitrogen and about the same percentage of phosphoric acid and potash. Animal tankage, blood, and fish scraps include 5 to 13% nitrogen and 0.5 to 14% phosphoric acid. Cottonseed meal and castor pomace are about as rich in nitrogen and phosphoric acid as animal tankage, blood, and fish scraps. In addition they contain 1 to 2% potash.

Nitrogen and humus content are ordinarily the determining factors in the utilization of sewage sludges. These sludges are applied directly, or they are used as a fertilizer base (other needed elements being added) or as commercial fertilizer fillers. Not all the nitrogen present in sewage sludges is in forms that are directly available to plants. Because of this, determinations normally include those for nitrate, ammonia, and organic nitrogen. Nitrate is directly available, ammonia after conversion in the soil to nitrate, and organic nitrogen after breakdown and oxidation in the soil (Section 11-7). The true usefulness of fertilizers in meeting the needs of different crops can be fully determined only by field tests. The presence of grease in sludge is not agriculturally desirable.

The utilization of sewage sludges is circumscribed by the hygienic hazards involved. Pathogenic bacteria, viruses, protozoa (cysts), and worms (eggs) can survive sewage treatment and be included in the sludge. There, they will persist for long times and cannot be fully destroyed by digestion or air-drying. Although the numbers of surviving organisms decrease appreciably in the normal course of events, only heat-dried sludge can be considered fully safe.

17-9. Flow Characteristics. Sewage sludges are but pseudohomogeneous materials. The greater the divergence in characteristics of the included solids (for example, fresh plain-sedimentation solids compared with digested solids or activated sludge or any of these solids compared with alum or iron flocs), the greater is their lack of homogeneity. The presence of solids imposes a self-cleaning requirement on the velocity of flow. The solids are of such a nature that plastic or pseudoplastic rather than viscous conditions of flow obtain so long as a significant amount of solid matter is present in the liquid. The hydraulics of sludge flow are complicated by the fact that most sludges are *thixotropic,* i.e., their plastic properties are changed by stirring and turbulence. There may also be a release of gases or air during flow. The friction losses engendered are controlled by the temperature of the sludge, its solids content, and the nature of the solid matter. As might be expected, friction increases with solids content and decreases with temperature. In general, laminar or transitional flow persists up to much higher velocities than for water. For thick sewage sludges, this type of flow has been observed to obtain up to 1.5 to 4.5 fps in pipes 5 to 12 in. in diameter. At turbulent velocities, all sludges behave more like water.

When the flow is turbulent, the loss of head of fairly homogeneous sludges (digested sludges and activated sludge) is increased by not more than 1% for each per cent of solids in the sludge. Fresh, plain-sedimentation sludge is transported at losses that are 1.5 to 4 times those of water. For the transportation of sand and gritty materials, see Section 9-2. When the velocities of flow are too small, the heavier and larger solids may settle out and form obstructions to flow. This reduces the cross-sectional area of the conduit and increases the velocity until there is scour of the deposited material. Under extreme conditions, however, complete stoppage of pipes may be experienced. Rates of sludge withdrawal from tanks must not be made so large that water will break through. Pipe sizes must be selected accordingly.

Sludge pumps, like sewage pumps, must contend with solids of all kinds. For small rates of discharge, plunger and diaphragm pumps and compressed-air ejectors are employed. For higher rates of flow, centrifugal pumps (generally more than 4 in. in size) provide sufficient clearance to prevent clogging. The use of air lifts is normally confined to activated sewage sludge. Then depth of submergence is generally held to twice the head.

17-10. Quantities of Sludge. The nature and characteristics of the solids fractions in domestic sewage may be summarized briefly as follows:

1. *Plain sedimentation* (primary treatment). The fresh sludge is composed of substantially 100% of the settleable solids in the raw sewage. Digestion destroys about 67% of the volatile matter in the sludge, about 25% becoming fixed solids.

2. *Chemical coagulation* (primary treatment). The fresh sludge generally includes the precipitated chemicals and from 70 to 90% of the solids suspended in the raw sewage depending upon the quantity and effectiveness of chemical dosage. Ferric chloride of molecular weight 162.2, for example, is precipitated as ferric hydrate of molecular weight 106.9. Hence each mg/l $FeCl_3$ produces 0.66 mg/l $Fe(OH)_3$. Digestion of the resulting sludge produces changes in composition that are substantially like those for primary sludge.

3. *Trickling filtration* (secondary treatment). Fresh trickling-filter humus is composed of originally non-settleable fractions of solids in the applied sewage that have been rendered settleable by biological flocculation and precipitation and that have been modified subsequently by decomposition during storage in the filter. Fixed-solid residues of decomposing suspended and dissolved volatile matter are largely washed out into the effluent. The proportion of destruction and loss varies with the length of storage. Limits of 30% for low-rate operation and 10% for high-rate operation may be assumed. There results a recovery in the secondary sedimentation units of humus quantities equivalent to 50 to 60% of the non-settleable suspended solids applied to low-rate filters, the range for high-rate filters being 80 to 90%. The humus is generally mixed with primary sludge for digestion, the proportionate changes in composition of the mixture being much the same as for primary solids.

4. *Activation* (secondary treatment). The controlling fraction of sewage solids in fresh, excess activated sludge is substantially the same as that in trickling filters. The subsequent destruction of transferred materials during formation and recirculation of the activated flocs is much like that observed in high-rate trickling filters. A value of 5 to 10% may be assigned to it, depending upon the proportion of sludge return. This proportion governs the length of time that the activated sludge remains in circulation. The

recovery of excess sludge in secondary settling units may be estimated at 80 to 90% of the applied non-settleable suspended solids. The excess sludge is generally allowed to settle with the primary sludge, or the excess sludge is mixed with the primary sludge for treatment and disposal. Digestion brings about much the same proportionate changes in sludge composition as for primary solids.

Calculation of actual quantities of sludge rests fundamentally on the base values for the composition of domestic sewage given in Table 12-2 and the efficiencies of removal indicated in Table 12-4. Corresponding information must be obtained for other waste waters. The commonly observed solids content of domestic sewage sludges is shown in Table 17-2.

TABLE 17-2. Proportion of Solids in Domestic Sewage Sludges

Treatment Process	Condition of Sludge	% Solids
1. Plain sedimentation	*a.* Fresh—depending upon method of sludge removal	2.5–5
	b. Digested—wet	10–15
2. Chemical precipitation	*a.* Fresh—increasing in moisture with amount of chemical used	2–5
	b. Digested—wet	10
3. Trickling filtration	*a.* Fresh humus alone—depending upon length of storage in filter	5–10
	b. Fresh humus mixed with 1*a*	3–6
	c. Digested 3*b*—wet	10
4. Activation	*a.* Fresh *—depending on method of sludge withdrawal	0.5–2
	b. Digested *—alone	2–3
	c. Fresh—settled with 1*a*	4–5
	d. Digested—with 1*a*	6–8

* If primary sedimentation is curtailed, suitable adjustments must be made.

Example 17-4. Estimate for an activated-sludge plant treating domestic sewage and including primary and secondary sedimentation: (*a*) the weight of dry sludge solids in lb per 1,000 persons per day and lb per mg of sewage; (*b*) the volume of wet sludge in cu ft per 1,000 persons per day and gal per mg of sewage. Find in each case the separate and combined amounts of fresh sludge and the amounts of digested sludge if the primary sludge is digested alone and in combination with the secondary sludge. Assume a sewage flow of 100 gpcd and specific gravities of 2.5 for fixed solids and 1.0 for volatile solids.

1. Primary sludge—fresh. From Table 12-2, the daily per capita production of fresh sludge is 54 grams, 39 grams (or 72.2%) being volatile and 15 grams (or

27.8%) fixed. Since 1 lb = 454 grams, the weight of dry solids is: $54 \times 10^3/454 = 119$ lb per 1,000 persons daily, or $119 \times 10^6/(100 \times 10^3) = 1{,}190$ lb per mg. By Equation 17-2, the specific gravity of the dry solids is: $s_s = 250/(100 + 1.5 \times 72.2) = 1.20$. Assuming 5% solids in the wet sludge (Table 17-2), Equation 17-3 gives the specific gravity of the wet sludge as: $s = 120/(95 \times 1.20 + 5) = 1.008$. The volume of the wet sludge is, therefore: $119 \times 10^2/(5.0 \times 62.4 \times 1.008) = 37.8$ cu ft per 1,000 persons daily, or $37.8 \times 10^6 \times 7.48/(100 \times 10^3) = 2{,}830$ gal per mg.

2. Excess activated sludge—fresh. From Table 12-2, the daily per capita production of non-settleable suspended solids is 36 grams, 26 grams being volatile and 10 grams fixed. Assuming that 7.5% of the weight of volatile solids is destroyed during activation and that 87.5% of the remaining weight of solids is captured in the excess sludge, the pertinent figures are: $0.875 \times 0.925 \times 26 = 21$ grams of volatile solids (70%), $0.875 \times 10 = 9$ grams (30%) of fixed solids, and $(21 + 9) = 30$ grams of total solids. Converting as in (1) the dry solids are: 66 lb per 1,000 persons daily, or 660 lb per mg.

Calculating the specific gravity of the solids, as in (1): the specific gravity of the dry solids is found to be $s_s = 1.219$. Assuming 1.5% solids in the wet sludge (Table 17-2), the specific gravity of the wet sludge then becomes $s = 1.002$ and the volume of the wet sludge, again as in (1), 70.4 cu ft per 1,000 persons daily, or 5,270 gal per mg.

3. Combined primary and excess activated sludge—fresh. By addition, the dry solids (grams per capita daily) are: $(54 + 30) = 84$ grams total, $(39 + 21) = 60$ grams (71.4%) volatile, and $(15 + 9) = 24$ grams (28.6%) fixed; and correspondingly $(119 + 66) = 185$ lb per 1,000 persons daily, or $(1{,}190 + 660) = 1{,}850$ lb per mg.

The specific gravity of the dry solids is: $s_s = 1.206$ and, assuming 4.5% solids in wet sludge (Table 17-2), that of the wet sludge is: $s = 1.007$. The resulting volume of wet sludge then becomes 65.4 cu ft per 1,000 persons daily, or 4,900 gal per mg.

4. Primary sludge—digested. Assuming that 67% of the volatile matter is destroyed, 25% being converted into fixed solids, the pertinent figures are: $(1 - 0.67)39 = 13$ grams of volatile solids (37%), $[15 + 0.25(39 - 13)] = 22$ grams of fixed solids (63%), and $(13 + 22) = 35$ grams of total solids, or 77 lb per 1,000 persons daily and 770 lb per mg.

The specific gravity of the dry solids is now: $s_s = 1.607$ and, assuming 13% solids in the wet sludge (Table 17-2), the specific gravity of the wet sludge is: $s = 1.052$. The resulting volume of wet sludge is then: 9.0 cu ft per 1,000 persons daily, or 670 gal per mg.

5. Combined primary and excess activated sludge—digested. Assuming that 67% of the volatile matter is destroyed, 25% being converted into fixed solids, the pertinent figures are: $(1 - 0.67)60 = 20$ grams of volatile solids (37.0%), $[24 + 0.25(60 - 20)] = 34$ grams of fixed solids (63.0%), and $(20 + 34) = 54$ grams of total solids, or 119 lb per 1,000 persons daily, and 1,190 lb per mg.

The specific gravity of the dry solids is now: $s_s = 1.607$ and, assuming 7.0% solids in the wet sludge (Table 17-2), the specific gravity of the wet sludge is: $s = 1.027$. The resulting volume of wet sludge is then: 26.5 cu ft per 1,000 persons daily, or 1,980 gal per mg.

17-11. Sludge-Digestion Units. The anaerobic decomposition, or digestion, of putrescible solids is either made a concurrent function of the settling tank or of a separate unit to which the settled solids are transferred for digestion. Septic tanks perform the first function, separate sludge digestion units, called sludge digesters, the second.

a. Septic tanks. In their simplest form, septic tanks are single-storied, settling basins in which the sludge is held sufficiently long to undergo partial and possibly complete digestion. Single-storied septic tanks possess a number of faults both as sedimentation and as digestion units. Septic action cannot be confined to the sludge proper, and the overlying water is deprived of its freshness. Gas-lifted solids rise into the flowing water. If they reach the tank surface, they may accumulate as unsightly scum in which digestion is retarded. Otherwise they may escape into the effluent. For these reasons, the use of single-storied septic tanks is almost exclusively confined to small, generally residential, installations, where their bad features are counterbalanced by their simplicity (Section 12-8).

b. Two-storied septic tanks. The idea of separating the decomposing sludge from the flowing sewage in a two-storied structure was conceived by Travis and brought to perfection by Imhoff. In the Imhoff, or Emscher,[3] tank, the settling solids slide down the incline of a trough-shaped false bottom of the settling compartment and through slots at the apex of the trough into the underlying digestion compartment (Figure 13-9). The slope of the false bottom is made as steep as possible ($\gtreqless$1.2 vertical:1 horizontal) in order to keep it clean. The slots overlap (about 10 in.), or are otherwise trapped, to keep gases or solids that rise within the digestion compartment out of the settling compartment. However, a small interchange of liquid does occur.

In order to distribute the sludge load as uniformly as possible within the sludge compartment of long tanks, arrangements are generally made to reverse the direction of flow from time to time. Companion flow of sewage through the sludge compartment is reduced by throwing walls across the digestion compartment. For structural economy and ease of sludge withdrawal, the sludge compartments are given hopper bottoms (slope = 1 vertical to 1, or 2, horizontal). They may be dimensioned for temporary storage of the settling solids or for complete digestion of the solids before their removal. The compartments may indeed be made sufficiently large

[3] Named after the Emscher District in which the Travis tank was modified.

to store sludge for protracted periods of time during which digested sludge cannot be air-dried or otherwise disposed of.

Other forms of two-storied tanks that include the essential features of Imhoff tanks have been elaborated.

The digested sludge can be withdrawn through pipes 8 in. or more in diameter reaching into the center of the sludge-compartment hoppers and discharging 4 to 5 ft below the water level of the tank. Sludge gases are allowed to escape to the atmosphere through vents at least 18 in. wide (for access) and of an area equal to about 20% of the total superficial area of the tank; or the gases are captured in gas collectors. The accumulation of scum and foam makes it necessary to provide a freeboard of at least 18 in. in open vents. Two-storied septic tanks cannot compete economically with heated digesters in large installations. In small plants, the ease of operation of two-storied units may justify their use.

c. Sludge digesters. In the order of their development, there are three kinds of sludge digesters: (1) conventional or low-rate digesters, (2) two-stage digesters, and (3) high-rate or continuous digesters. Structurally, they are much the same. They include the tank proper and, in general, the tank roof or cover, a gas-collecting system, a tank-heating system, and sometimes a system of sludge stirring and scum breaking. They differ in method of operation and performance. In low-rate and second-stage digesters, there is an upward stratification of the tank contents into sludge, sludge liquor, and scum. In high-rate and first-stage digesters, gas ebullition permits of no zonal differentiation. In low-rate and two-stage digesters, batches of fresh sludge are introduced and batches of digested sludge and sludge liquor are removed at one or more times during the day. In high-rate digesters, sludge inflow and outflow are more or less continuous. There is no sludge liquor.

Two-stage operation divides the operating space between two tanks. The first stage holds sludge during its period of greatest activity. The sludge mass seethes and boils. Old and new sludge are mixed thoroughly. There is no stratification.

High-rate digestion requires that the sludge be thick enough at normal tank depths to evolve enough gas to keep the sludge in circulation and thoroughly mixed. Ordinarily, this requires that thickened sludge be added to the tank. Concentration of thin sludges to 2 or 3 times their normal solids content is needed. Other methods of inducing sludge circulation are (1) the recycling of sludge from bottom to top, and (2) the blowing of compressed gas into the bottom of the tank. Inclusion of some undigested sludge in the sludge withdrawn is an undesirable feature of high-rate operation. Reduced tank volume, due in part to the admission of thickened sludge, in part to a higher rate of digestion, is the advantage offered by high-rate operation.

Digesters are usually circular in plan with vertical walls and a conical or flat bottom (Figure 17-4). Reinforced concrete tanks have been built up to 100 ft in diameter. The side-water depth is com-

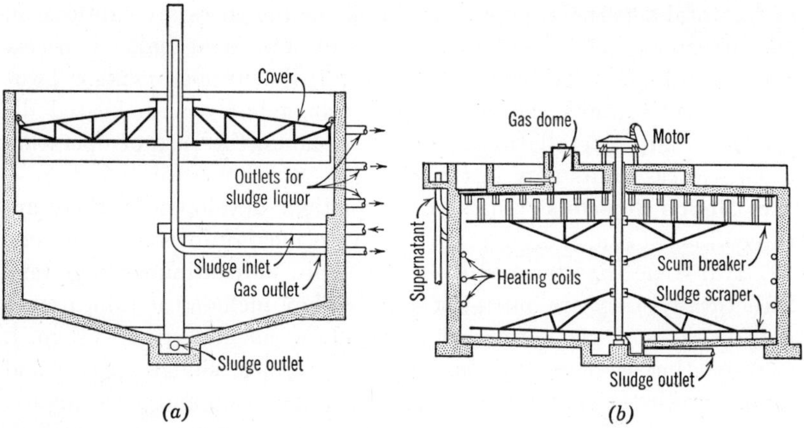

Figure 17-4. Circular sludge digesters: (*a*) tank with floating cover; (*b*) tank with fixed cover, scum breaker, and sludge scraper.

monly 20 ft. Unless the tank is equipped with a sludge scraper, the bottom should slope steeply to the sludge withdrawal pipe. Fresh sludge is normally admitted at or near the top, and digested sludge is withdrawn from the bottom. Supernatant is removed from low-rate and second-stage digesters through a swinging pipe or depth selector, or through lateral outlets, normally 2 to 4 in number, spaced about 2 ft apart vertically, beginning 3 to 4 ft below the flow-line of the tank. All fixed-cover tanks should have at least one unvalved overflow pipe.

The flow-line of low-rate and second-stage digesters fluctuates as fresh sludge is admitted and digested sludge or sludge liquor is withdrawn. To protect the gas-collecting systems against the entrance of air and the formation of explosive air-gas mixtures, tank covers are either designed as floating structures, or gas is evolved under a fixed cover against the back pressure of a gas holder. Floating covers ride on the gas and may be elaborated into gas holders.

Digesters are heated either directly or indirectly by: (1) heat exchangers situated outside the tank and heating the incoming sludge; (2) fixed or movable heating coils inside the tank; (3) steam bled into the tank; (4) sludge gas burnt under water inside the tank; and (5) submerged gas heaters.

The scum that forms in low-rate digesters can be held in check by: (1) mechanical destruction through scum breakers; (2) by sludge liquor or water sprayed onto the scum; and (3) by compressed gas recycled into the digester bottom. Sludge liquor contains about 1,500 mg/l of suspended solids and has a high immediate BOD. As a rule, it is led back to the plant influent. Otherwise it is coagulated chemically and settled, or it is filtered through sand before being discharged into the plant effluent.

17-12. Requisite Capacity of Digestion Tanks. The basic capacity of digestion tanks is a function of the sludge load, time required for digestion, and loss of sludge moisture (sludge liquor). Operational storage of gas and sludge (winter storage) is an added element. Capacities are expressed in a number of different ways, among them: cu ft of tank volume per capita; cu ft per lb of solids (on a dry basis) added daily; and cu ft per lb of volatile solids (on a dry basis) added daily. Operational or loading parameters are the reciprocals of these capacities. The basic per capita capacity is determined in accordance with the general rules laid down in Section 17-10. For low-rate and two-stage digesters, the assumption is generally made that the relative rate of loss of sludge moisture or reduction in sludge volume is substantially constant. Accordingly, progress of decomposition is parabolic, and the average difference in the volume of the fresh and digested solids is about ⅔ the final difference. Formulated,

$$C = [V_f - \tfrac{2}{3}(V_f - V_d)]t \qquad 17\text{-}11$$

where C is the basic tank capacity of low-rate and two-stage digesters in cubic feet per capita; V is the daily per capita volume of sludge in cubic feet (the subscripts f and d denoting the fresh and digested volumes respectively); and t is the time in days required for digestion. The digestion time is a function of tank temperature and method of operation. It can be estimated from studies such as those shown in Figure 17-5 for plain-sedimentation sludge in low-rate digesters. At a normal sewage temperature of 60 F, for example, the digestion period in low-rate digesters extends over 56 days. In high-rate digesters, the time required for digestion is reduced by about 40% and the sludge volume is not changed by withdrawal of sludge liquor.

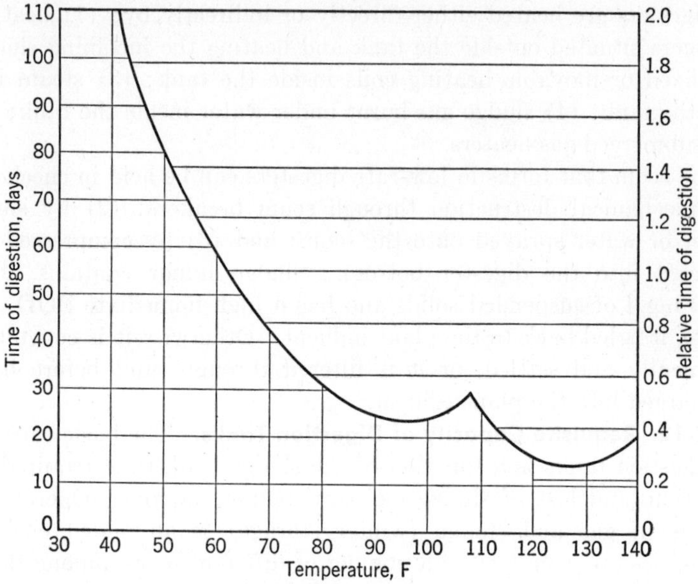

Figure 17-5. **Time required for 90% digestion of plain-sedimentation primary sewage sludge at different temperatures at low rates.**

The design capacity includes, in addition to basic space requirement, an allowance for sludge gas and, in low-rate and second-stage tanks, allowances for sludge liquor and scum. A factor of safety of about 2 is normally applied to the total, and necessary allowance is made for seasonal (usually winter) storage of accumulating sludge. This allowance is high where winters are long.

Example 17-5. Find the basic capacity of (*a*) the sludge compartment of an Imhoff tank in which plain-sedimentation primary sludge is to be digested at an average temperature of 60 F; (*b*) a heated, low-rate digestion tank in which the same sludge is to be digested at 90 F; and (*c*) the capacity of a high-rate digestion tank in which a thickened mixture of primary and activated sludge is to be digested at 90 F. Assume the per capita volumes of sludge calculated for domestic sewage in Example 17-4, namely, 37.8 cu ft of fresh and 9.0 cu ft of digested primary sludge and 32.4 cu ft of thickened fresh and digested combined sludges (about one-half of 65.4 cu ft), all per 1,000 persons daily.

a. The digestion period for primary sludge at 60 F is about 56 days. Hence by Equation 17-11, the required capacity of the Imhoff tank is: $C = [37.8 - \frac{2}{3}(37.8 - 9.0)]56/1{,}000 = 1.0$ cu ft per capita. (Note: allowing for 5 months of winter storage, the design capacity of the Imhoff tank becomes $2 \times 1.0 + 5 \times 30.4 \times 9.0/1{,}000 = 3.4$ cu ft/cap.)

b. The digestion period for primary sludge at 90 F is about 25 days in low rate digesters and the required per capita digester capacity is: $C = 1.0 \times 25/56 = 0.45$ cu ft per capita.

c. The digestion period for combined primary and activated sludge may be estimated at 15 days and the required per capita high-rate digester capacity is: $C = 32.4 \times 15/1{,}000 = 0.49$ cu ft per capita if the combined sludge is thickened to 32.4 cu ft/1,000. The assumption is made in this connection that the mixed sludge digests as rapidly as the primary sludge.

Winter storage equals the daily volume occupied by the fully digested sludge multiplied by the number of storage days.

17-13. Heat Requirements of Digestion Tanks. The heat supplied to heated sludge-digestion tanks must be sufficient (1) to raise the temperature of the incoming sludge to that of the tank; (2) to offset the heat lost from the tank through its walls, bottom, and cover; and (3) to compensate for heat lost in piping and other structures between the source of heat and the tank. The amount of heat entering into the digestion reactions and used up in the evaporation of water into the sludge gases is so small that it need not be taken into consideration in engineering computations.

The specific heat of most sludges is substantially the same as that of water. The heat loss Q through the walls, bottom, and cover of a tank is a function of the temperature difference ΔT, the tank area A, and the coefficient of heat flow C, or

$$Q = CA(\Delta T) \qquad 17\text{-}12$$

The value of C depends upon a number of things: motion of the fluids (sludge inside and air or water outside of the tank), thickness of specific portions of the tank and their relative conductance, and opportunities for radiation. For concrete tanks, rough over-all values for C in Btu/sq ft/hr are 0.10, 0.15, and 0.30 for exposures to dry earth, air, and wet earth respectively. For equal exposure of all parts of a digester, heat is conserved best if the tank geometry conforms as closely as possible to a sphere as structural economy will permit. The largest ratio of sludge volume to tank surface is thereby obtained. For unequal exposures, the portions through which the greatest losses per unit area occur should be kept at a minimum.

Heat transfer from the heating unit to the sludge is analogous to heat loss. For stationary heating surfaces, the coefficient of heat flow in Btu/sq ft/hr has approximate values of 8 to 12 for sludge of ordinary thickness and 35 to 45 for thin sludge or water. Moving surfaces increase the heat flow to about 60 Btu/sq ft/hr. From submerged burners, there is direct absorption of the heat of combustion. Caking of sludge on the surface of heating units is controlled by keeping the temperature of the heating surface at less than 140 F and by moving the unit through the sludge or inducing motion of the sludge past it either mechanically or thermally.

Example 17-6. A cylindrical digester 20 ft in diameter is built of concrete and surrounded by dry earth or provided with equivalent insulation. The side walls are 16 ft high, and the roof rises 1 ft to a central, insulated gas dome and is exposed to the air. The bottom slopes 4 ft to a central sludge-withdrawal pipe. The daily weight of sludge added to the tank is 13,000 lb. Find: (*a*) the daily heat requirements of the tank when the temperatures of the incoming sludge, digesting sludge, earth, and air are 50, 90, 40, and 20 F, respectively, and the coefficient of heat flow is 0.20 Btu per sq ft per hr; (*b*) the required area of stationary heating coils through which water is circulated at an incoming temperature of 130 F and with a temperature drop of 10 F if the coefficient of heat flow is 10 Btu per sq ft per hr; and (*c*) the daily volume of heating water that must be circulated through the coils.

a. Heat requirements.

1. The area of the tank exposed to earth is: $\pi \times 20(16 + \frac{1}{2}\sqrt{10^2 + 4^2}) =$ 1,344 sq ft. The area of roof exposed to air is: $\pi \times 10\sqrt{10^2 + 1^2} = 316$ sq ft.

2. Heat requirements of the incoming sludge: $Q = 13{,}000 \times (90 - 50) =$ 520,000 Btu/day.

3. Exposure loss: $Q = 0.20 \times 24[1{,}344(90 - 40) + 316(90 - 20)] = 430{,}000$ Btu/day.

4. Total heat requirements: $Q = (520{,}000 + 430{,}000) = 950{,}000$ Btu/day.

b. Area of heating coils.

1. Average temperature of heating water: $(130 - 5) = 125$ F.

2. Area of coils: $A = 950{,}000/[24 \times 10(125 - 90)] = 113$ sq ft.

c. Recirculating water.

1. Temperature drop: 10 F = 10 Btu/lb.

2. Weight of water: 950,000/10 = 95,000 lb/day.

3. Volume of water: 95,000/8.34 = 11,400 gpd = 8 gpm.

The calculated heat requirements do not take into account possible losses between the heat source and the digester.

17-14. Utilization of Digester Gas. In addition to methane (combustible) and carbon dioxide (non-combustible), sludge gas always contains water vapor; occasionally hydrogen sulfide; and, more rarely, hydrogen (combustible) and nitrogen (inert). Hydrogen sulfide is an extremely toxic gas. Brief exposure (30 min or less) to concentrations as low as 0.1% by volume may terminate fatally. When hydrogen sulfide is burnt, sulfur dioxide, a very corrosive gas, may be formed. For use in gas engines with exhaust gas heaters, not more than 10 grains of hydrogen sulfide[4] should be present in 100 cu ft of gas (0.015% by volume).

The fuel value of sludge gas can be put to use in various ways both within treatment plants and for non-plant purposes. The following are common: (1) plant-heating purposes—digesters, incinerators, buildings, and hot-water supply; (2) plant-power production—pumping, air and gas compression, and operation of other mechanical equipment; (3) minor plant uses—gas supply to the plant laboratory for gas burners and refrigerators; and (4) motor fuel for municipal cars and trucks. The first two purposes are met by burning the gas (*a*) in a furnace or under a gas-fired hot-water or steam boiler or (*b*) in a gas engine equipped with water jacket and exhaust-gas heat exchanger. The third purpose may be accomplished by direct use of the gas under the available plant pressure or by bottling the gas. The fourth purpose involves bottling the gas under high pressure in steel containers.

Collection, storage, and utilization of sludge gas are economically justified only when the treatment works are of sufficient size to warrant skilled attendance. Gas storage is either included in the design of digesters, or separate holders are provided. The collection, storage, and distribution system must be kept under pressure at all times if the formation of explosive mixtures of gas and air is to be avoided. Combustion of methane takes place as follows: $CH_4 + 2O_2 = CO_2 + 2H_2O$. Since air contains about 21% of oxygen by volume, at least $2/0.21 = 9.5$ cu ft of air are required to burn 1.0 cu ft of methane. If the gas contains 72% methane, therefore, at least $9.5 \times 0.72 = 6.8$ cu ft of air are required to burn the methane in 1.0 cu ft of digester gas. Explosive mixtures of methane and air are obtained over a range of 5.6 to 13.5% of methane by volume. Maximum flame speed occurs at 9.6%. Above 13.5%, the mixture burns quietly after ignition. Violent explosions with loss of life have occurred in sewage works.

The operating, protecting, and regulating devices of gas collection and distribution systems include: (1) condensate traps and drains for water vapor; (2) flame traps that will prevent flash-backs from gas burners and engines; (3) pressure-regulating valves; and (4) waste-gas burners. Gas lines and their appurtenances must be protected against freezing, and all vents must terminate in the open. Gas storage may be effected without compression under a head of 3 to 6

[4] 1 lb = 7,000 grains, and 1 cu ft of H_2S weighs 0.095 lb.

in. of water. The economical pressure for cylindrical and spherical pressure tanks is about 40 psig; for bottled gas about 5,000 psig. Before being compressed, the gas may be passed through scrubbers to remove unwanted constituents: carbon dioxide, hydrogen sulfide, and water vapor.

Hot-water boilers are neither as efficient (about 60%) nor as trouble-free (sulfur dioxide corrosion) as steam boilers with heat exchangers for hot-water heating (about 80%). Gas engines that are equipped for hot-water utilization have a water-heating efficiency of about 50% and a direct power efficiency of 22 to 27% depending upon the engine load (half load to full load respectively). Conversion of gas-engine power into electrical power and use of electric motor-driven equipment entail a loss of about 25% of the engine power. For equal performance in automotive engines about 160 cu ft of sludge gas containing 72% of methane (110,000 Btu) may be substituted for a gallon of gasoline (122,000 Btu).

Example 17-7. If the 13,000 lb of sewage sludge added daily to the digester in Example 17-6 are assumed to contain 5% solids, 72.2% of which are volatile, and if 67% of the volatile matter is assumed to be destroyed in producing gas that is composed of 72% methane and 28% carbon dioxide by volume, estimate: (*a*) the volume of gas produced and its calorific power; (*b*) the power made available from a gas engine equipped with a waste-gas boiler for the purpose of heating the digester and from an electrical generator driven by the engine; and (*c*) the volume of gas that is available for plant purposes other than digester heating (950,000 Btu per day) or that must be burnt in a waste-gas burner.

a. Gas production. The volatile matter destroyed is: $13{,}000 \times 0.05 \times 0.722 \times 0.67 = 315$ lb. At 1.25 lb of gas per lb of volatile matter destroyed and the given gas composition, the gas yield is: $1.25 \times 315/(0.72 \times 0.0446 + 0.28 \times 0.1225) = 5{,}930$ cu ft daily, or $5{,}930 \times 963 \times 0.72 = 4.1 \times 10^6$ Btu daily.

b. Power of gas engine and generator. If the gas engine has a water-heating efficiency of 50%, the daily heat input of the engine must be $950{,}000/0.50 = 1.9 \times 10^6$ Btu. At 2,545 Btu per hp-hr and 0.7457 kw-hr per hp-hr, and at an engine efficiency of 25% and a generator and motor efficiency of 75%, the heat and gas consumed are: $2{,}545/0.25 = 10{,}000$ Btu per brake hp-hr, and $10^4/(963 \times 0.72) = 14.4$ cu ft of gas per brake hp-hr. The engine power is then $(1.9 \times 10^6)/(24 \times 10^4) = 8.0$ hp; and the electrical power $8.0 \times 0.75 \times 0.7457 = 4.4$ kw. [If all of the available gas were supplied to the engine, the engine and generator power would be raised $(4.1 \times 10^6)/(1.9 \times 10^6) = 2.2$ fold.]

c. Volume of excess gas. With $(4.1 \times 10^6 - 1.9 \times 10^6) = 2.2 \times 10^6$ Btu not used by the engine, the volume of excess gas is $(2.2 \times 10^6)/(0.72 \times 963) = 3{,}170$ cu ft daily.

As has been shown in Section 16-11, the energy requirements of diffused-air, activated-sludge units are about 550 hp-hr or 410 kw-hr per million cu ft of free air daily when the air pressure is 7 psig. It follows from the calculations given in Example 17-7 that $550 \times 14.4 = 7{,}900$ cu ft of gas are needed to deliver a million cu ft of air at a pressure of 7 psig by means of an engine-driven compressor or $7{,}900/0.75 = 10{,}500$ cu ft of gas when electric drive is employed. The flexibility of electrical operation, including the possibility of using purchased electricity when the gas supply fails, often justifies the installation of electrical equipment. Stand-by fuel must otherwise be provided in the form of municipal gas, gasoline, or oil. Stand-by equipment varies in accordance with the selected sources of energy.

Since 10^6 cu ft of air daily will treat about 1 mgd of sewage from 10^4 people in activated-sludge units, and since the gas production from primary solids and activated sludge is about 1.25 cu ft per capita, the available gas supply of 1.25×10^4 cu ft daily is normally sufficient to provide the necessary engine (and where wanted electrical) power and to keep the sludge digestion tanks at optimum mesophilic temperatures. Where primary treatment and sludge digestion are employed, the gas yield of about 1 cu ft per capita is normally more than adequate for the principal plant purposes.

Sludge Drying, Incineration, and Disposal

17-15. Chemical Conditioning and Elutriation. Coagulation of the solids dispersed in sludge (called chemical conditioning) increases the rate at which water can be removed from the sludge by filtration through cloth or by drying on sand beds.

a. Chemical conditioning. Common conditioning chemicals for sewage sludge are listed in Table 17-3. In this table, all but lime

TABLE 17-3. Common Conditioning Chemicals for Sewage Sludge

Conditioning Chemical	Chemical Symbol	Molecular Weight
Ferric chloride	$FeCl_3$	162.2
Chlorinated copperas	$FeSO_4Cl$	187.4
Ferric sulfate	$Fe_2(SO_4)_3$	399.9
Aluminum sulfate	$Al_2(SO_4)_3 \cdot 14H_2O$	594.3
Lime	CaO	56.1

are coagulating agents. Before these agents can combine with the solids fraction of the sludge, they must satisfy the coagulant demand of the liquid fraction of the sludge which is exerted by the alkalinity or bicarbonates (Section 14-2). The alkalinities of digested sewage sludges are quite high; in some instances a hundredfold those of fresh sludges. As a precipitant of bicarbonates (Section 14-3), lime may be substituted for the portion of the coagulant that combines with the liquid fraction. Lime does not form floc with this fraction; only a precipitate.

The coagulant or conditioner requirements of sludge are generally expressed as a percentage ratio of the pure chemical to the weight of the solids fraction on a dry basis. In accordance with what has been said, the requirements may be divided into two parts: (1) the liquid-fraction requirement and (2) the solids-fraction requirement. The liquid-fraction requirement is approximated closely by the stoichiometry of the idealized chemical reactions. The solids-fraction requirement is a matter of experience. For ferric chloride, Genter[5] has developed the relationship:

$$p_c = [1.08 \times 10^{-4} Ap/(100 - p)] + 1.6p_v/p_f \qquad 17\text{-}13$$

where A is the alkalinity of the sludge moisture in mg/l of $CaCO_3$, and p_c, p, p_v, and p_f are respectively the percentages of chemical ($FeCl_3$), moisture, volatile matter, and fixed solids in the sludge, all on a dry basis.[6] The term for the solids fraction ($1.6p_v/p_f$) is derived from operating results for the vacuum filtration of ferric-chloride-treated sewage sludge. Since this term is a function of the volatile-matter content of the sludge, coagulant requirements can be reduced in magnitude by digestion of the sludge prior to coagulating it for dewatering. By contrast, the magnitude of the term for the liquid fraction $[1.08 \times 10^{-4} Ap/(100 - p)]$ is greatly increased by digestion. It can be reduced either by the use of lime as a precipitant or by washing out a share of the alkalinity of the sludge with water of low alkalinity. This is called elutriation.

b. Elutriation. The elutriation of sludge can be carried out in single or multiple tanks by single or repeated washings, the wash water being used serially if desired. During washing, the sludge is kept in suspension by air or mechanical agitation. Serial use of wash water is called countercurrent elutriation.

If a total of R volumes of elutriating water with an alkalinity of W mg/l is added for each volume of moisture in the sludge, and the alkalinity of the sludge moisture before elutriation is A mg/l, the

[5] A. L. Genter, Computing coagulant requirements in sludge conditioning, *Trans. Am. Soc. Civil Engrs.*, *111*, 641 (1946).

[6] 1 mg/l $CaCO_3$ (100) combines with ($\frac{2}{3} \times 162.2/100$) = 1.08 mg/l of $FeCl_3$ (162.2) in accordance with the equation: $2FeCl_3 + 3Ca(HCO_3)_2 \rightleftharpoons 2Fe(OH)_3 + 3CaCl_3 + 6CO_2$.

alkalinity of the elutriated sludge moisture E in mg/l can be found by striking a balance between the alkalinities entering and leaving the elutriating tank or tanks. The following examples in which the subscripts denote the sequence of operations will indicate the development of general formulations:

1. Multiple elutriation of sludge in a single tank. In this scheme, $1/n$th of the elutriating water is used in each washing operation. See (*a*) in Figure 17-6. Hence:

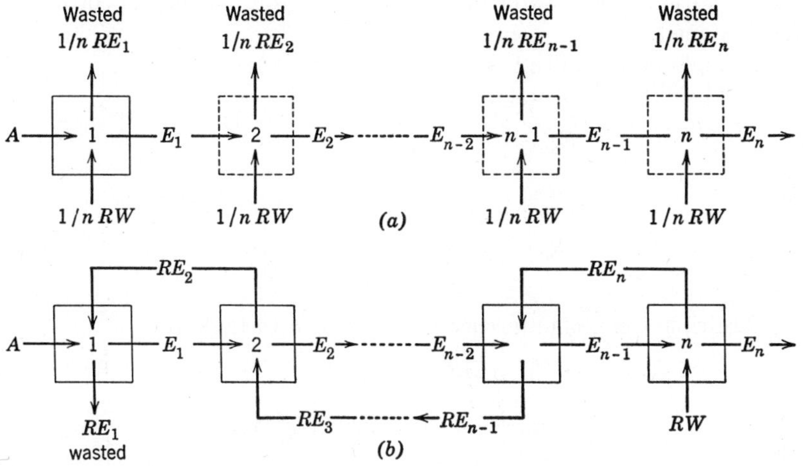

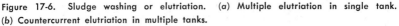

Figure 17-6. Sludge washing or elutriation. (a) Multiple elutriation in single tank. (b) Countercurrent elutriation in multiple tanks.

$$(1/n)RW + A = (1/n)RE_1 + E_1$$

$$(1/n)RW + E_1 = (1/n)RE_2 + E_2$$

$$\cdots\cdots\cdots\cdots\cdots\cdots\cdots\cdots\cdots$$

$$(1/n)RW + E_{n-2} = (1/n)RE_{n-1} + E_{n-1}$$

$$(1/n)RW + E_{n-1} = (1/n)RE_n + E_n$$

2. Countercurrent elutriation in multiple tanks. In this scheme, the clean wash water is introduced into the last tank which receives the partially elutriated sludge from the next to the last tank, the wash water from the last tank being used to wash the sludge coming into the next to the last tank. Proceeding serially in this manner (Figure 17-6*b*), to the first tank:

$$RW + E_{n-1} = RE_n + E_n$$
$$RE_n + E_{n-2} = RE_{n-1} + E_{n-1}$$
$$\cdots\cdots\cdots\cdots$$
$$RE_3 + E_1 = RE_2 + E_2$$
$$RE_2 + A = RE_1 + E_1$$

If we solve respectively for the alkalinity E_n of the final sludge and for the ratio of wash water to sludge R the following general equations are obtained:

1. Single tank, multiple elutriation (n stages):

$$E_n = \frac{A + W[(R/n + 1)^n - 1]}{(R/n + 1)^n} \qquad \text{17-14}$$

and

$$R = n\left[\left(\frac{A - W}{E - W}\right)^{1/n} - 1\right] \qquad \text{17-15}$$

2. Multiple tank, countercurrent elutriation (n tanks):

$$E_n = \frac{A + W(R^n + R^{n-1} \cdots + R)}{R^n + R^{n-1} \cdots + R + 1}$$

or

$$E_n = \frac{A(R - 1) + WR(R^n - 1)}{R^{n+1} - 1} \qquad \text{17-16}$$

and

$$(R^{n+1} - 1)/(R - 1) = (A - W)/(E - W) \qquad \text{17-17}$$

The ratio of elutriating water to wet sludge commonly employed is about 2 to 1. Reduction in the necessary amounts of conditioning chemicals is reflected in increased heat values of the dried cake and reduced heat requirements for drying and incineration. The wash water is treated or disposed of along with digestion-tank and sludge-filter liquor.

Example 17-8. A digested sludge with 45% volatile solids on a dry basis and 90% moisture has an alkalinity of 3,000 mg/l. Find the percentage of ferric chloride that must be added to this sludge prior to vacuum filtration: (a) if the sludge is not elutriated, and (b) if the sludge is elutriated in two tanks by countercurrent operation in a ratio of 3 to 1 with water of 20 mg/l alkalinity. Find also (c) the elutriation ratio that will reduce the alkalinity of the sludge to 300 mg/l by countercurrent and two-stage elutriation.

a. Unelutriated sludge. By Equation 17-13: $p_c = (1.08 \times 10^{-4})\ 3{,}000(\frac{90}{10}) + 1.6(\frac{45}{55}) = 4.22\%$ of $FeCl_3$ on a dry-weight basis.

b. Elutriated sludge, countercurrent operation. By Equation 17-16: $E_2 = (3{,}000 \times 2 + 20 \times 3 \times 8)/26 = 250$ mg/l. By Equation 17-13: $p_c = (1.08 \times 10^{-4})\ 250(\frac{90}{10}) + 1.6(\frac{45}{55}) = 1.55\%$ of $FeCl_3$ on a dry-weight basis.

c. Elutriation ratio. By Equation 17-17: $(R^3 - 1)/(R - 1) = (3{,}000 - 20)/(300 - 20) = 10.64$, or $(R^2 + R + 1) = 10.64$, whence $R = 2.64$ by countercurrent elutriation.

By Equation 17-15: $R = 2\left[\left(\frac{3{,}000 - 20}{300 - 20}\right)^{1/2} - 1\right]$, or $R = 4.54$ for two washings by multiple elutriation. This is 70% more wash water than is needed in the countercurrent operation.

17-16. Vacuum Filtration. The dewatering of sludge by filtration through cloth or metallic strainers is an operation that has been taken over from the chemical industries. The art of dewatering solids has advanced from the batch or discontinuous operation of chamber, or leaf, filter presses to the continuous, automatic operation of vacuum filters. Among these, the revolving-drum filter is most widely used (Figure 17-7). In the cloth filter, the filtering medium is cotton or woolen cloth or synthetic fiber of suitable weight and weave. The cloth is stretched and wired over a supporting layer of copper mesh which covers the sides of the drum and overlies a series of cells running the length of the drum. These cells can be placed under vacuum or pressure. The drum revolves at a peripheral speed of 1 fpm or less. As it revolves, it passes through a reservoir of the sludge that is to be dewatered. A vacuum of sufficient magnitude (12 to 26 in. of mercury) is applied to the submerged cells (from 15 to 40% of the filter surface) to attach a mat of sludge of suitable thickness to the cloth. The emerging mat is placed under a drying vacuum of effective magnitude (20 to 26 in. of mercury), and the sludge liquor is drawn into the vacuum cells and drained from them for treatment and

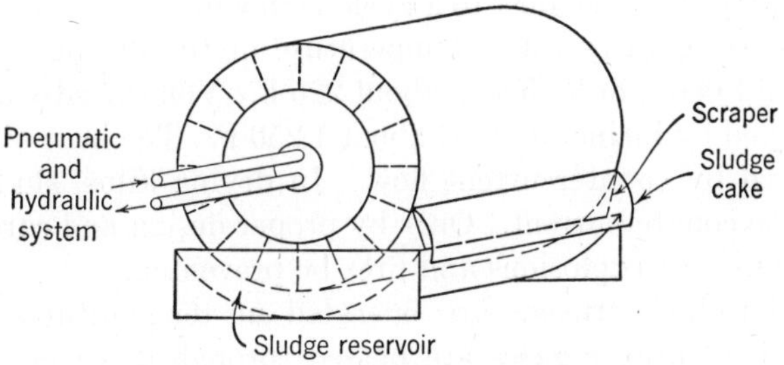

Figure 17-7. Drum vacuum filter. *Dorr Co.*

disposal with other sludge liquors. The dried cake is removed from the drum by a scraper and carried away for heat-drying, incineration, or disposal. If necessary, a slight pressure is applied to the cell of the drum which is just about to engage the scraper. This lifts the cake from the cloth and facilitates its removal. In the coil filter, the cloth is replaced by a series of helically coiled steel springs. The springs are endless and are wound onto and off the drum as it rotates.

The sludge cake is usually from $\frac{1}{16}$ in. to $\frac{1}{4}$ in. thick. Its solids content is as high as 32% for plain-sedimentation sludge (raw or digested) and as low as 20% for raw, activated sludge. Digested, activated sludge may be dewatered to about 25% solids content. Trickling-filter sludge and mixtures of different sludges span the gap. The solids content of dewatered, trickling-filter humus depends upon the length of storage of the sludge in the filter. The cake-producing capacity of vacuum filters varies ordinarily from 2 to 6 lb per sq ft per hr on a dry basis. Low yields are obtained with fresh, chemical sludge and activated sludge, high yields with digested, plain-sedimentation sludge. Filter speeds and vacuums are varied to suit operating conditions. Power requirements of drum filters and ancillary pneumatic and hydraulic equipment lie in the vicinity of $\frac{1}{8}$ hp per sq ft of filter area.

17-17. Heat Drying and Incineration. Sewage sludge is heat-dried to less than 10% moisture when it is to be sold as a commercial fertilizer. Heat-drying may also precede the use of sludge as a fuel for sludge-drying or other plant purposes. The dried sludge is then burnt in a furnace. Two types of rotary driers are in use: the kiln (direct-indirect) drier common to the lime and cement industry, and the cage-mill (flash-drier) system illustrated in Figure 17-8. Drying is promoted by adding a sufficient amount of previously dried sludge to the incoming cake to reduce the moisture of the mixture to about 50%. Drying gases are passed through the tumbling mixture in the cage mill and carry the dried dust to a cyclone in which it is separated from the transporting gases. The temperature of the drying gases is reduced from 1,000 F or higher to about 225 F. Volatilized-sludge odors are destroyed by incineration at about 1,250 F. The heat of the gases is conserved by countercurrent flow. In drying kilns, sludge movement is also countercurrent. Only by proper design and careful management will dust explosions and fires be prevented.

Sludge-burning furnaces are operated at temperatures of about 2,500 F. The furnace gases are passed through a regenerative preheater in which air and the recirculated exhaust gases from the

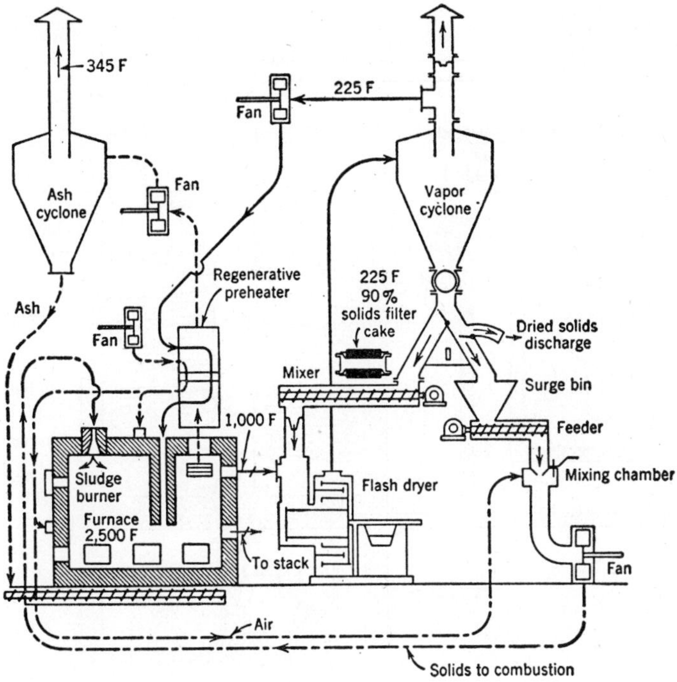

Figure 17-8. Heat-drying and incineration of filter cake. *Combustion Engineering* Co.

flash-drier are brought up to temperature before they are introduced respectively into the drying element and the furnace. Fly ash is removed from the furnace gases in a cyclone.

In the multiple-hearth incinerator shown in Figure 17-9, filter cake is fed onto the topmost hearth and moved (rabbled) from hearth to hearth by plows or teeth attached to horizontal, hollow (for air cooling) arms branching from a vertical, central, hollow shaft. The sludge cake loses moisture, ignites, burns, and cools. Hearth temperatures rise to a maximum in the center of the incinerator. The exhaust gases are passed through a preheater or recuperator for the purpose of heating the air blown into the furnace to support combustion. The cold-air intake is through the hollow shaft to which the rabble arms are attached.

Heat requirements are determined by the temperature of the sludge and its moisture content and by the efficiency of the furnace. If the temperature of the sludge is 60 F, the heat requirements are 1,124 Btu per lb of moisture. Furnace efficiency usually varies between

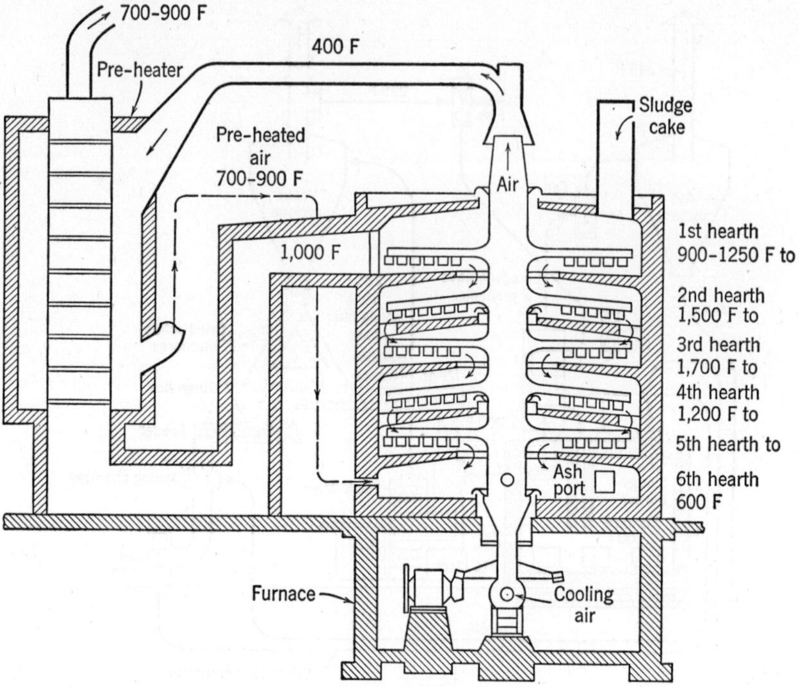

Figure 17-9. Multiple-hearth furnace for the incineration of filter cake. ***Nichols Herreshoff Corp.***

45 and 70% in terms of total heat recovery (including credits on stack gas and latent heat of evaporation) and total heat input. Multiple-hearth furnaces have a combined efficiency of evaporation and incineration of about 55%. Sludge cake produced by the vacuum filtration of chemically conditioned, raw, plain-sedimentation sludge and of mixtures of it with fresh, trickling-filter or activated sludge will ordinarily supply sufficient heat for self-incineration. Digested sludge, on the other hand, is almost always inadequate in heat value to support its own destruction by burning. Auxiliary fuel must be used. Sludge-digester gas may serve this purpose.

Example 17-9. An activated-sludge plant produces 7,000 gpd of excess activated sludge from 1 mgd of sewage. The sludge contains 1.5% solids of which 70% are volatile on a dry basis. In conditioning the sludge for dewatering on a vacuum filter, 6% $FeCl_3$ on a dry basis is added. Find (*a*) the required vacuum filter area and (*b*) the auxiliary heat required to incinerate the filter cake. The specific gravity of the wet sludge may be taken as 1.002.

a. Area of vacuum filter. The daily weight of dry solids is:

$$7{,}000 \times 8.34 \times 1.002 \times 1.5 \times 10^{-2} = 880 \text{ lb}$$

Assuming that each per cent of $FeCl_3$ increases the dry solids in the ratio of the molecular weight of $Fe(OH)_3$ to that of $FeCl_3$, or 106.8 to 162.2, the added chemical increases the weight of sludge by 0.66% for each per cent of ferric chloride. Hence the additional weight is $6 \times 0.66 \times 880/100 = 35$ lb. Assuming an allowable filter loading of 2.5 lb per sq ft per hr, the required filter area is then found to be $(880 + 35)/(24 \times 2.5) = 15.2$ sq ft.

b. Auxiliary heat for incineration. By Equation 17-10, the fuel value of the filter cake is:

$$Q = 107\left(\frac{100 \times 70}{100 - 6 \times 0.66} - 5\right)\left(\frac{100 - 6 \times 0.66}{100}\right) = 7{,}000 \text{ Btu per lb}$$

If the filter cake contains 20% solids and the efficiency of evaporation and incineration is 55%, the heat requirements are $1{,}124(100 - 20)/(20 \times 0.55) = 8{,}100$ Btu per lb. Auxiliary heat must, therefore, be provided in an amount of $(880 + 35)(8{,}100 - 7{,}000) = 1.0$ million Btu per day.

17-18. Air-Drying. Under favorable climatic conditions (dryness and warmth), well-digested sludge will dry in a week or two when it is run onto a porous bed to a depth of 8 to 12 in. No odor troubles are encountered. The drying of fresh sludge, on the other hand, gives rise to bad odors, and the sludge will not dry satisfactorily in layers of reasonable thickness. Therefore, air-drying is more or less confined to well-digested sludges.

Drying beds usually consist of graded layers of gravel or crushed stone beneath 4 to 6 in. of filter sand (see Figure 17-10). Agricultural tile pipes or sewer pipes laid with open joints serve as underdrains in much the same way as in intermittent sand filters (Section 16-1). The beds are subdivided to meet plant-operating conditions. Their width is so chosen that the vehicle used for removing the dried sludge

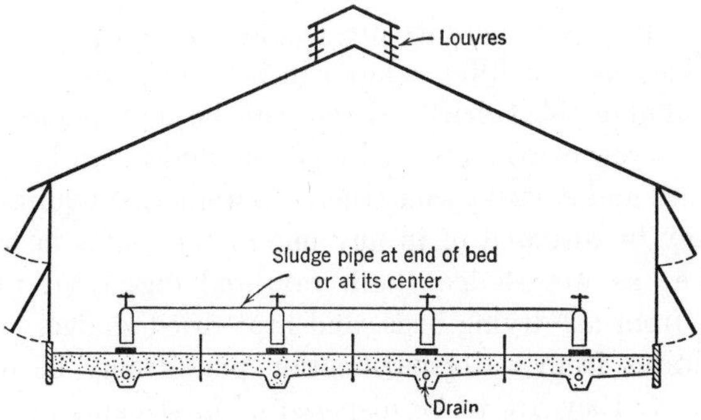

Figure 17-10. Glass-covered sludge-drying beds.

can be loaded conveniently. Common values for small plants are 20 ft or less. The length is generally held below 100 ft. This is the distance sludge may be expected to flow from a single outlet when the surface slope of the bed is 0.5% or less. Concrete posts and reinforced-concrete slabs or cypress planks rising about 12 in. above bed level confine the sludge to the bed and its subdivisions.

Glass enclosures of the greenhouse variety or sheds similar to the platform sheds of railroad stations will protect the sludge against rain. If the enclosures are properly ventilated, the number of dryings per year can be increased by 33 to 100%. In the northern part of the United States, about 5 dryings of 8 in. of wet digested sludge are feasible per year on open beds. Bed-dried, digested sludge contains about 40% solids. Its volume is about half that of the wet sludge. The sludge is removed by hand-forking or by mechanical, sludge loaders or strippers.

In air-drying, moisture is lost to the atmosphere by evaporation and to the bed by percolation. Both are important.

Example 17-10. If the production of digested plain-sedimentation solids is 9 cu ft per 1,000 persons daily (Example 17-4), find (*a*) the area of open sludge-drying bed, in sq ft per capita, that must be provided in the northern United States and (*b*) the volume of sludge cake, in cu yd per capita, that must be removed annually.

a. Area of bed. Assuming 5 dryings of sludge 8 in. in depth annually, the bed area is $(9 \times 365)/(5 \times 1{,}000 \times 8/12) = 1.0$ sq ft per capita. This is a common figure for open beds in the northern United States.

b. Volume of sludge cake. Assuming 50% reduction in volume of sludge during drying, the volume of dried cake becomes $0.5 \times 9 \times 365/(27 \times 1{,}000) = 6 \times 10^{-2}$ cu yd per capita annually.

17-19. Sludge Handling and Disposal. The flow characteristics of wet sludge have been described in Section 9 of this chapter. Both free-flow and pressure conduits are employed. Partially dewatered sludge (sludge paste or filter cake) can be transported on belt conveyors. Granular (heat-dried) sludge can be moved pneumatically or by belt or screw conveyors. All types of sludge can be handled in industrial cars and suitably constructed automotive equipment.

Sludge may be disposed of in any one of the states in which it is produced, i.e., as wet sludge (both raw and digested), filter cake, sludge cake from air-drying beds, and heat-dried sludge. Alum and iron precipitates from water-purification plants may be discharged into sewers. If they are to be disposed of in streams of small size, they should preferably be lagooned before discharge. Lagoons are natural depressions in the ground, or earth basins excavated for that purpose. They may or may not be provided with overflows and underdrains. Heavy precipitates of calcium and magnesium from water-softening plants may be partially dewatered and used as fill for low-lying lands. Their possible reclamation is discussed in Section 14-9. Wet, sewage sludge may be pumped onto land and plowed under. Digested sludge is more suitable for this purpose than raw sludge. In favorable circumstances, sewage sludges may be discharged into water. Seacoast communities may transport either wet or partially dewatered fresh or digested sludge to dumping grounds at sea. Specially designed sludge tankers and scows or barges are used for this purpose. Wet, digested sludge may be discharged into large streams (more particularly in times of flood runoff) without creating a nuisance, or it may be pumped to deep-lying and hydraulically active portions of tidal estuaries. Sludge lagoons may be used both for the digestion of raw sludge and for the storage and consolidation of digested sludge. The odors produced by raw sludge must be taken into cognizance in this connection. Low-lying land can be filled by lagooning or by the dumping of filter-cake or air-dried sludge. Inclusion of partially dewatered sludge or sludge cake in sanitary land fills is a possibility. Air-dried sludge as well as filter cake may be hauled away by farmers to serve as a soil builder. Disintegration of the sludge for this purpose is of some value. As described in Section 17-8, dried sludge is commonly used as a fertilizer or fertilizer base, or it is incinerated. The ash from incinerators can be disposed of as fill, or it can be dumped at sea.

18 Disinfection, Destruction of Aquatic Growths, and Removal of Odors and Tastes

18-1. Safety and Palatability of Water. The safety and palatability of water often hinge upon the elimination or destruction of two groups of living organisms: (1) the pathogenic bacteria and other microorganisms that may infect man through his use of contaminated water and (2) the algae and related water blooms that may render water esthetically unfit for human consumption. The creation or intensification of odors and tastes is, at times, associated with the destruction of these organisms. A discussion of the removal of odors and tastes from water is, therefore, made a part of the present chapter. For convenience in presentation, attention is given, furthermore, to other matters that are allied to the methods of treatment employed, or to the objectives that are to be attained.

Disinfection

18-2. Means of Disinfection. The disinfection of water for general sanitary purposes can be accomplished by many different means. A list of the more common ones is given below:

1. Heat. Raising water to its boiling point and holding it there for 15 to 20 min will disinfect it. Since no important water-borne diseases are caused by spore-forming bacteria, or other heat-resistant organisms, this is a safe practice which is often resorted to as an emergency measure.
2. Light. Exposure of water to sunlight for a protracted period of time is a natural means of disinfection. Irradiation of water by ultraviolet light of suitable wave length offers an intensified and controllable engineering

means. Disinfection is then accomplished by exposure of water in thin films to the emanations from mercury-vapor lamps. These lamps must be encased in quartz or in special glass envelopes that are transparent to the intense and destructive, invisible light of 2,537 angstrom units (A) emitted by the mercury-vapor arc. To insure disinfection, the water must be sufficiently free from suspended matter and other substances that might shade the organisms against the light. Time and intensity of exposure must also be adequate. Other forms of radiant energy, too, are destructive to living organisms, but they have not yet found engineering application.

3. CHEMICAL DISINFECTANTS. Exposure for an adequate length of time to chemicals of the following kinds in adequate concentration will disinfect water:

a. Oxidizing chemicals. For the disinfection of water the following are important: (1) The halogens—chlorine, bromine, and iodine—released in suitable form from suitable sources; and (2) other oxidizing agents such as potassium permanganate and ozone. Of the halogens, liquid chlorine and a number of chlorine compounds have been found to be most generally and most economically useful. Bromine (Br_2) has been employed on a limited scale for the disinfection of swimming-pool water, and iodine has been used for the disinfection of small quantities of drinking water. Elemental iodine (I_2) may be released from tablets of tetraglycine hydroperiodide for such disinfection. Potassium permanganate and ozone have a more limited use because of cost, ozone, in addition, because of difficulty of production and application to water. Ozone is particularly effective in the destruction of odors. It also bleaches color. The oxidizing capacity of a compound is not necessarily a measure of its disinfecting efficiency. Hydrogen peroxide, for example, is a strong oxidant but a poor disinfectant.

b. Metal ions. The ions of silver are notably destructive in minute concentrations,[1] but long periods of exposure are required, and the use of silver is costly. Copper ions are strongly algicidal (Section 18-13) but only weakly bactericidal.

c. Alkalies and acids. Pathogens will not survive in water that is highly alkaline or highly acid, e.g., at very high or very low *p*H values. Destruction of living organisms by caustic lime may be incidental to water softening by lime.

d. Surface-active chemicals. Of these, the cationic detergents are strongly destructive, the anionic detergents only weakly so. The neutral detergents occupy an intermediate position. The disinfecting powers of the detergents have been used only selectively in wash waters and rinse waters. Their toxicity is yet to be fully explored.

For general municipal and industrial water needs, but one of the means included in this list (chlorination) is both of proved efficiency and economy, and but one more (heat) can be resorted to with assurance of success through individual action in times of emergency (when "boil-water orders" are issued by public authorities). Because chlo-

[1] As low as 15 μg/l (micrograms per liter, or closely parts per billion).

rine and some of its compounds meet the general requirements for disinfection so well, and because they are used almost to the exclusion of other disinfecting agents, the discussion of disinfection which is to follow will be concerned very largely with the principles and practice of chlorination.

18-3. Theory of Disinfection. The disinfection of water and waste waters is concerned almost wholly with the destruction of single-celled organisms: bacteria, protozoa, and viruses; more particularly bacteria. This explains, in part, the success that can be attained in chemical disinfection by the addition of disinfecting substances in relatively minute amounts (fractions of a milligram per liter of free chlorine, for example). The fact that the required concentration of disinfectant is small and that much of it is normally inactivated in the course of disinfection or prior to use of the disinfected water, explains, furthermore, why suitably disinfected water can be ingested with impunity by man and the higher animals and why less highly organized living things, such as fish in fishbowls supplied with chlorinated water, are also not harmed.

Green and Stumpf [2] have shown that disinfecting chlorine compounds react with certain of the enzymes that are essential to the metabolic processes of living cells and that death results from the inactivation of these key substances. There are reasons for assuming, therefore, that destruction of these essential links in the life requirements of living cells is the primary action of disinfectants, even when a radical process, such as heat, eventually coagulates the entire protoplasmic content of the cell. Since the enzymes involved are created within the cell plasm, disinfection proceeds theoretically in two steps: (1) penetration of the cell wall by the disinfectant and (2) reaction of the cell enzymes with the disinfectant.

In terms of the gross effects that generally govern engineering practices, the factors that establish the efficiency of disinfection are:

1. The nature of the organisms to be destroyed and their concentration and condition in the water to be disinfected. Non-spore-forming bacteria are less resistant to disinfection than are spore-forming bacteria. But spore formers are, fortunately, of little sanitary significance. Among the bacteria of enteric origin *Esch. coli* appears to be somewhat more resistant than the pathogenic groups. As a result, it is a useful test organism. The cysts of the enteric pathogenic protozoön *E. histolytica* are known to be quite resistant, but little is known about the resistance of the viruses. Concentra-

[2] D. E. Green and P. K. Stumpf, The mode of action of chlorine, *J. Am. Water Works Assoc.*, *38*, 1301 (1946).

tion of organisms enters into the problem of chemical disinfection only when the number of organisms present in a given volume of water is sufficiently high to compete for the disinfectant. Clumping of bacteria, such as the staphylococci, protects the cells inside the clump.

2. The nature and concentration of the disinfectant employed in terms of the products that it releases when it is placed in the water to be disinfected. As will be shown later, for example, chlorine and many of its compounds used in water disinfection may form in water one or more different substances of varying disinfecting efficiency.

3. The nature of the water to be disinfected. Suspended matter will shelter embedded organisms against chemical disinfection and destructive light rays. Organic matter will use up oxidizing chemicals. Other substances will react with chemical disinfectants and change their structure. The resulting compounds may be less efficient and even innocuous.

4. The temperature of the water to be disinfected. The higher the temperature, the more rapid is the kill.

5. The time of contact. The longer the time, the greater is the opportunity for destruction. In pure water of a given temperature, destruction of a given species of organisms by a given species of disinfectant is a time-concentration process. When light is the disinfectant, its intensity at the cell surface is the concentration factor. When heat is the disinfectant, the temperature of the water is itself a measure of the concentration of the disinfectant.

18-4. Kinetics of Disinfection. Under ideal conditions, all cells of a single species of organism will be equally susceptible to a single species of disinfectant; both cells and disinfectant will be uniformly dispersed in the water; the disinfectant will remain substantially constant in concentration throughout the period of contact; and the water will contain no interfering substances. The rate of disinfection, under ideal conditions, is then a function of the following variables: (*a*) the time of contact; (*b*) the concentration of the disinfectant; (*c*) the number of organisms; and (*d*) the temperature of the water.

a. Time of contact. The effect of contact time on the killing of organisms by disinfectants is generally expressed in terms of Chick's law.[3] This states that the number of organisms destroyed, y, per unit time is proportional to the number of organisms remaining, N, the initial number being N_0. Hence

$$dy/dt = k(N_0 - y) \qquad 18\text{-}1$$

where k is the coefficient of proportionality or the rate constant with dimension $[t^{-1}]$. Integration between the limits $y = 0$ at $t = 0$ and $y = y$ at $t = t$ gives the equation

[3] Harriet Chick, Investigation of the laws of disinfection, *J. Hygiene*, *8*, 92 (1908).

$$\log_e \frac{N_0 - y}{N_0} = \log_e \frac{N}{N_0} = -kt \quad \text{or} \quad \frac{N}{N_0} = e^{-kt} \qquad \text{18-2}$$

A plot of log N/N_0 against t, therefore, traces a straight line with slope $-k \log e = -k'$ and intercept 1 (or 100%) at $t = 0$. When $kt = 1$ or $k't = 0.4343$, the rate of survival, or mean lethal dose, is 0.368.

Departures from Chick's law are not uncommon, even when the conditions of test are as nearly ideal as possible. The rate of kill, instead of being constant, may increase or decrease with time. An increase can be explained in at least two ways: (1) as a combination of slow diffusion of chemical disinfectants through the cell wall and a rate of killing dependent upon the rising concentration of disinfecting material inside the cell; and (2) on the assumption that a lethal number of centers in the organism must be reached by the disinfectant. A linear relation may then be created by plotting log N/N_0 against t^m, or of log log N/N_0 against t. The exponent m will have a value greater than unity (Figure 18-1). A decrease is generally explained as being due to variation in resistance of different cells within the same culture of organisms. However, a decline in the concentration of the disinfectant as well as other interfering factors may be responsible. Linear relations may result when, as before, N/N_0 is plotted functionally against t.

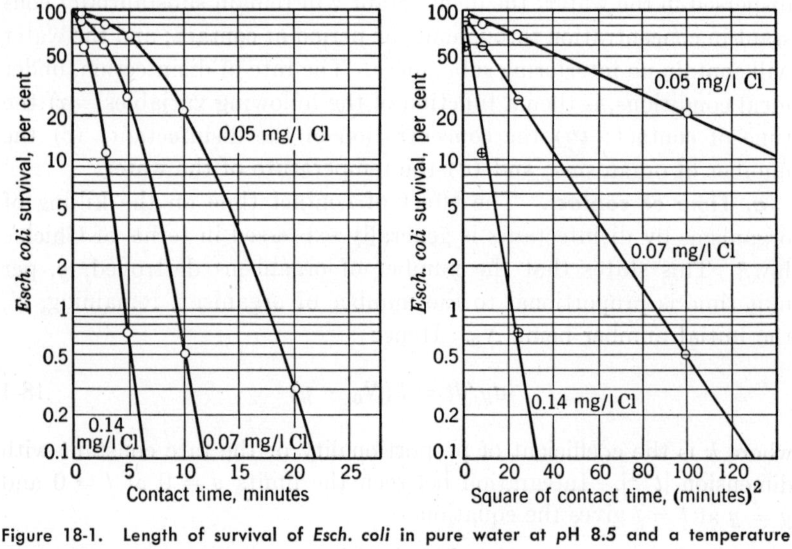

Figure 18-1. Length of survival of *Esch. coli* in pure water at pH 8.5 and a temperature of 2 to 5 C.

b. Concentration of disinfectant. Commonly observed changes in disinfecting efficiency with concentration of the disinfectant can be expressed mathematically by the equation

$$c^n t_r = \text{Constant} \qquad 18\text{-}3$$

Here, c is the concentration of the disinfectant; t_r is the time required to effect a constant percentage kill of the organisms to be destroyed; and the exponent n is generally called the coefficient of dilution. Values of $n > 1$ indicate that the efficiency of the disinfectant decreases rapidly as it is diluted; values of $n < 1$ that the time of contact is more important than the dosage. When $n = 1$, concentration and time are of equal weight.

Equation 18-3 is purely empirical. It plots as a straight line on double logarithmic paper, the slope of the line being $-1/n$ (Figure 18-2).

c. Concentration of organisms. No significant difference is generally observed between the killing of high and low concentrations of organisms. Where a difference is observed, at very great differences in concentration of cell substance, for example, it can be formulated as

$$c^p / N_r = \text{Constant} \qquad 18\text{-}4$$

Here c is again the concentration of the disinfectant; N_r is the concentration of organisms that is reduced by a constant percentage in a given time; and p is the concentration exponent of the disinfectant.

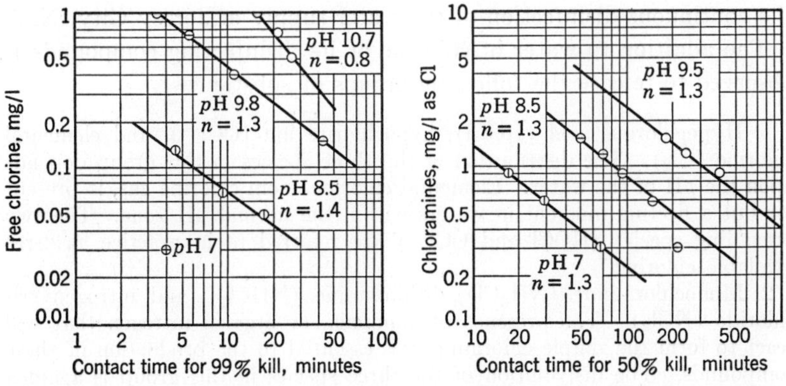

Figure 18-2. Time-concentration relationships in disinfection. (a) Concentration of free available chlorine required for 99% kill of *Esch. coli* at 2 to 5 C. (b) Concentration of combined available chlorine required for 50% kill of *Esch. coli* at 2 to 5 C.

Like Equation 18-3, this equation is merely an expression for the correlation of observations.

d. Temperature of disinfection. If either the rate of diffusion through the cell wall or the rate of reaction with an enzyme determines the rate of disinfection, its variation with temperature is identified most conveniently by the van't Hoff-Arrhenius equation written in the following form:

$$\log \frac{t_1}{t_2} = \frac{E(T_2 - T_1)}{2.303RT_1T_2} = \frac{E(T_2 - T_1)}{4.575T_1T_2} \qquad 18\text{-}5$$

The symbols T_2 and T_1 stand for two temperatures (normally in degrees Kelvin) between which the rates are to be compared; t_1 and t_2 are the times required for equal percentages of kill to be effected at these temperatures and at a fixed concentration of disinfectant; E is the activation energy (normally in calories) and a constant characteristic of the reaction;[4] and R is the gas constant (1.99 cal per deg C, for example). When $T_2 - T_1 = 10$, the ratio t_1/t_2, called Q_{10}, is approximately related to E, in the vicinity of 20 C, as follows:

$$\log Q_{10} = \log t_a/t_b = E/39{,}000 \qquad 18\text{-}6$$

Here t_a and t_b are the times required for equal percentages of kill at temperatures T_a and T_b that are 10 C apart.

18-5. Disinfection by Chlorine. The first use of chlorine as a disinfectant for municipal water supplies in America was in 1908 when George A. Johnson and John L. Leal employed chloride of lime for the continuous disinfection of the water supply of Jersey City, N. J.

The addition to water of chlorine or its disinfecting compounds is observed to release the following groups of substances:

1. Hypochlorous acid (HOCl), hypochlorite ion (OCl^-), and elemental chlorine (Cl_2). The distribution of the three species in this group depends upon the pH of the water. Elemental chlorine, from chlorine gas, is present for but a fleeting moment in waters within the normal pH zone. The two prevailing species (HOCl and OCl^-) are referred to in practice as "free available chlorine."

2. Monochloramine (NH_2Cl), dichloramine ($NHCl_2$), and nitrogen trichloride (NCl_3). The presence of ammonia, or organic nitrogen that will react to form the simple chloramines, is essential to the production of these compounds. The distribution of the three species in this group is again a function of the pH of the water. Nitrogen trichloride is not formed in significant amounts within the normal pH zone unless the "break point"

[4] The higher the value of *E*, the slower is the reaction.

(Section 18-8) is approached. The two prevailing species (NH_2Cl and $NHCl_2$) are referred to in practice as "combined available chlorine."

3. Complex organic chloramines, more especially in sewage.

The disinfecting power of the different species of chlorine compounds varies widely. Therefore, the chemistry of chlorination must be known if chlorine and its compounds are to be employed intelligently and efficiently in the disinfection of water and waste waters.

The concentration in water of free available chlorine and of combined available chlorine is generally determined colorimetrically by the *ortho*-tolidine-arsenite (OTA) test. This test depends upon the fact that free available chlorine reacts much faster with *ortho*-tolidine than does combined available chlorine. For the identification of free available chlorine, therefore, sodium arsenite (a reducing agent) is added to stop the reaction *after* the free available chlorine has reacted and, at least approximately, *before* the combined available chlorine has reacted.

As a strong oxidizing agent, chlorine reacts with reducing substances to produce the so-called "chlorine demand." It is thereby changed into chloride ion or organic chloride, depending upon the nature of the substances present in water. These substances include inorganic Fe^{++}, Mn^{++}, NO_2^-, and H_2S, along with the greater part of the organic material (living and dead) in the water. The reaction of the inorganic reducing substances is generally rapid and stoichiometric; that of the organic material is generally slow, and its extent depends upon the excess of concentration of available chlorine present. Since the amount of organic material in natural waters that serve as drinking-water supplies is closely related to their natural color or stain, the organic chlorine demand of these waters can often be approximately estimated from the depth of color. Similarly, the organic chlorine demand of waste waters bears some relation to their BOD or, more closely, to the oxygen absorbed from permanganate or dichromate.

The occurrence of these reactions is a complicating factor in the use of chlorine as a disinfectant, for one must provide sufficient chlorine to take care of these side reactions along with the disinfecting reactions. It is for this reason that chlorine residuals after a specified time of contact, such as 10 min, are made the basis for standards of accomplishment or comparison. The demand is a function of temperature, concentration, and time. Determination of its magnitude must take all these factors into account. The chlorine used up in disinfection is part of the demand.

18-6. Free Available Chlorine. The solution of elemental chlorine in water is characterized by the following equilibrium equations:

a. Hydrolysis:

$$Cl_2 + H_2O \rightleftharpoons HOCl + H^+ + Cl^- \qquad 18\text{-}7$$

$$(HOCl)(H^+)(Cl^-)/(Cl_2) = K_h \qquad 18\text{-}8$$

b. Ionization:

$$HOCl \rightleftharpoons H^+ + OCl^- \qquad 18\text{-}9$$

$$(H^+)(OCl^-)/(HOCl) = K_i$$

or

$$(OCl^-)/(HOCl) = K_i/(H^+) \qquad 18\text{-}10$$

Solutions of hypochlorites, such as chloride of lime and calcium hypochlorite, establish the same ionization equilibrium in water. When calcium hypochlorite is used, for example, the reactions leading up to this equilibrium are

$$Ca(OCl)_2 \rightarrow Ca^{++} + 2OCl^- \qquad 18\text{-}11$$

and

$$H^+ + OCl^- \rightleftharpoons HOCl \qquad 18\text{-}9$$

The value of the hydrolysis constant K_h, 4.5×10^{-4} (mols/l)^2 at 25 C is of such magnitude that no measurable concentration of Cl_2 exists in solution when the pH value of the chlorinated water is more than about 3.0 and the total chlorine concentration is less than about 1,000 mg/l.

At ordinary water temperatures, the hydrolysis of chlorine is essentially complete within a few seconds, and the ionization of hypochlorous acid produced is an essentially instantaneous, reversible reaction. The value of the ionization constant K_i varies in magnitude with temperature as shown in Table 18-1.

TABLE 18-1. Values of the Ionization Constant of Hypochlorous Acid at Different Temperatures

Temperature, C	0	5	10	15	20	25
$K_i \times 10^8$, mols/l.	1.5	1.7	2.0	2.2	2.5	2.7

The relative distribution of HOCl and OCl^- at various pH values is shown in Figure 18-3. It is calculated from Equation 18-10 and Table 18-1 as

$$\frac{(HOCl)}{(HOCl) + (OCl^-)} = \frac{1}{1 + (OCl^-)/(HOCl)} = \frac{1}{1 + K_i/(H^+)} \qquad 18\text{-}12$$

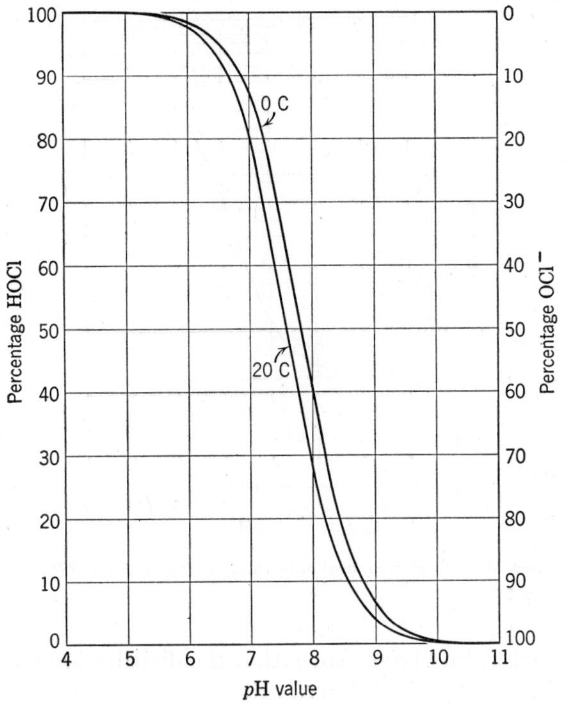

Figure 18-3. Distribution of hypochlorous acid and hypochlorite ion in water at different pH values and temperatures. *After Morris.*

At 20 C and pH 8, for example, the percentage distribution of HOCl is $100 \times [1 + 2.5 \times 10^{-8}/10^{-8}]^{-1} = 100/3.5 = 29\%$. This equilibrium relationship, therefore, permits the identification of the species of chlorine that constitute free available chlorine.

The relative colicidal efficiency (concentration of aqueous, or free available, chlorine required to kill 99% of *Esch. coli* in 30 min at 2 to 5 C) is presented in Figure 18-4. The mirrored images exhibited between Figures 18-3 and 18-4 suggest a higher killing efficiency for HOCl than for OCl^- (in the approximate ratio of 80:1 for the conditions of test).

18-7. Combined Available Chlorine. The most important reaction of chlorine with nitrogen compounds is that of hypochlorous acid with ammonia. This is a stepwise process for which the successive reactions are:

$$NH_3 + HOCl \rightarrow NH_2Cl + H_2O \qquad 18\text{-}13$$

$$NH_2Cl + HOCl \rightarrow NHCl_2 + H_2O \qquad 18\text{-}14$$

$$NHCl_2 + HOCl \rightarrow NCl_3 + H_2O \qquad 18\text{-}15$$

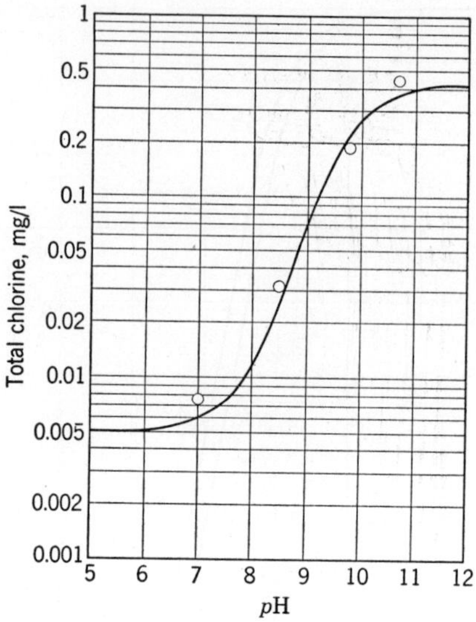

Figure 18-4. Concentration of free available chlorine required for 99% kill of *Esch. coli* in 30 min. at 2 to 5 C.

Morris [5] and Palin [6] have shown that the distribution of the chloramines is governed by the relative rates of formation of monochloramine and dichloramine, which change with the relative concentrations of chlorine and ammonia as well as with pH and temperature. Figure 18-5 shows the distribution at equimolar concentrations of chlorine and ammonia or at a weight ratio of chlorine (Cl_2) to ammonia (N) of 5 to 1.

A comparison of diagrams (*a*) and (*b*) in Figure 18-2 shows that combined available chlorine is a much less efficient colicidal agent than free available chlorine. The value of the dilution coefficient $n = 1.3$ suggests that concentration of the disinfectant is somewhat more important than time of contact, and the magnitudes of $E = 12{,}000$ to $20{,}000$ recorded in experiments lie within the range of chemical reactions.

18-8. Break-Point Reactions of Ammonia. Oxidation of ammonia and reduction of chlorine are noted when the molar ratio of chlorine to ammonia is greater than one. A substantially complete oxidation-reduction process occurs in the neighborhood of a ratio of 2 to 1 and

[5] J. C. Morris, unpublished research, Harvard University, 1951.

[6] A. T. Palin, The estimation of free chlorine and chloramine in water, *J. Inst. Water Engrs.*, 3, 100 (1949).

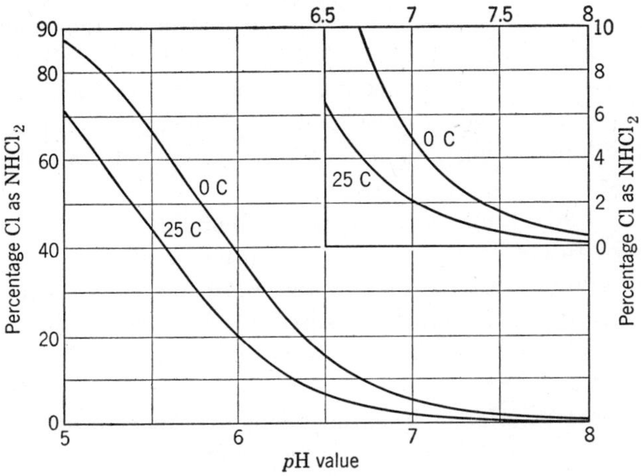

Figure 18-5. Distribution of chloramines at equimolar concentrations of chlorine and ammonia. [Cl_2:NH_3 (as N) = 5]. *After Morris.*

leads, in the course of time, to the disappearance of all the ammonia and oxidizing chlorine from the solution. This phenomenon is called the "break point." It is generally illustrated by a diagram such as that shown in Figure 18-6. Between *A* and *B*, molar ratios of chlorine to ammonia are less than one, and the residual oxidizing chlorine is essentially all monochloramine. Between *B* and *C*, oxidation of ammonia and reduction of chlorine increase, until complete oxidation-reduction occurs at *C*, the break point. In this region, again, the residual oxidizing chlorine is essentially all monochloramine. Beyond *C*, unreacted hypochlorite remains in solution, and the presence of some nitrogen trichloride is observed, depending upon the *p*H.

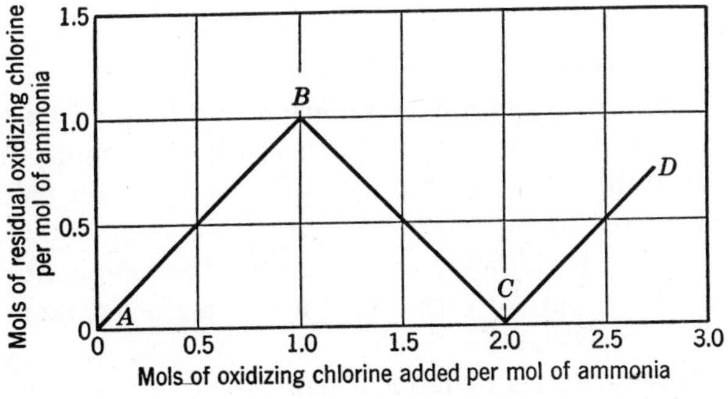

Figure 18-6. Schematic diagram of the break point. *After Morris.*

The rate of the break-point reaction is strongly dependent upon *p*H. A maximum rate occurs between *p*H 7 and 8. However, no clear-cut picture of the complex reactions involved can as yet be presented, and the student must be referred to current publication for up-to-date information. Time requirements are determined in practice by test.

Important advantages of chlorinating to and, if desired, beyond the break point to obtain free available chlorine residuals are: (1) that most odors and tastes normal to water are thereby destroyed and (2) that rigorous disinfection is insured. In the presence of undecomposed urea, nitrogen trichloride is very likely to be found. It gives rise to bad odors and tastes.

18-9. Dechlorination. When large amounts of chlorine have been added to water (for example, to insure disinfection in the time available before the water is to be used or to destroy odors and tastes), unwanted residuals can be removed by dechlorination. Intensive use of chlorine in this manner without the break-point reaction is called "superchlorination and dechlorination." There are a number of methods of dechlorination, among them: the addition of reducing chemicals; passage through beds of granular activated carbon; and aeration. The reducing agents include sulfur dioxide, SO_2; sodium bisulfite, $NaHSO_3$; and sodium sulfite, Na_2SO_3. The bisulfite is ordinarily used in practice, because it is cheaper and more stable than the sulfite. Samples of water that are collected for bacteriological analysis are usually dechlorinated by including sodium thiosulfate ($Na_2S_2O_3$) in the sampling bottles either as a solution or in crystalline form. Granular activated carbon absorbs chlorine into its pores where the chlorine oxidizes the carbon to carbon dioxide. Contact with powdered activated carbon cannot generally be made long enough to produce this result. Chlorine, hypochlorous acid, dichloramine, and nitrogen trichloride are sufficiently volatile to be removed by aeration. Other species of chlorine are not.

18-10. Technical Properties of Chlorine and Related Compounds. Chlorine gas (Cl_2) can be liquefied at room temperatures, at a pressure of 5 to 10 atm, for storage and shipment in steel cylinders or tanks. One pound of the liquid will produce 5 cu ft of gas. Under conditions of use, withdrawal of gas lowers the temperature of the stored fluid. If the rate of withdrawal is to remain constant, the heat loss must be supplied from without. But direct application of heat at temperatures in excess of 125 F is dangerous. Since reliquefaction of chlorine in measuring and dosing equipment produces erratic results, chlorine containers and gas lines must be kept cooler than the dispensing equipment.

The solubility of chlorine gas in water is about 7,300 mg/l at 68 F and 1 atm. Below 49.2 F, chlorine combines with water to form chlorine hydrate ($Cl_2 \cdot 8H_2O$ usually), called chlorine ice. The hydrate interferes with the proper operation of feeding equipment. Feed or sealing water that comes into contact with the gas should, therefore, be kept above 49.2 F.

Chlorine gas is highly toxic and must be handled with due care and adequate safeguards. Its odor threshold in air is about 3.5 ppm by volume. Coughing is induced when its concentration reaches 30 ppm, and exposures for 30 min to concentrations of 40–60 ppm are dangerous. At a concentration of 1,000 ppm, the gas is rapidly fatal.

Where the use of chlorine is large—in municipal water and sewage works, for example—liquid chlorine is the cheapest form of chlorine that can be employed. In small installations and for emergency, or other specialized uses, some of the compounds of chlorine are more satisfactory, among them: the hypochlorites of calcium, $Ca(OCl)_2$, and sodium, ($NaOCl$); chlorinated lime, $CaClOCl$, and certain organic complexes such as Halazone, $HOOC—C_6H_4—SO_2NCl_2$. The purposeful combination of chlorine with ammonia and the release of chlorine dioxide, ClO_2, from sodium chlorite, $NaClO_2$, create other useful chlorine disinfectants. Chlorinated lime (a loose combination of chlorine with slaked lime), calcium hypochlorite, sodium chlorite, and the common organic chlorine compounds are solids. Sodium hypochlorite is produced as a liquid.

Of the substances that may be used in combination with chlorine, or as antichlors (chlorine-reducing substances), ammonia and sulfur dioxide are gases that can be liquefied, stored, handled, and dispensed like chlorine. Ammonia is available also as ammonium hydroxide (aqua ammonia) and ammonium sulfate. Sodium bisulfite ($NaHSO_3$), a solid, may take the place of SO_2.

The strength of chlorine compounds, i.e., their oxidizing power, is commonly expressed in terms of their "available chlorine." Use of this term is analogous to that of alkalinity as $CaCO_3$. "Chlorine equivalent" would be a more accurate designation. The oxidizing power of chlorine compounds is proportional to their amount of chlorine with a valence number greater than -1. Calculation of the percentage of "available chlorine" of a given compound is based on (1) the mols of equivalent chlorine, or number of mols of chlorine that would have an oxidizing capacity equivalent to one mol of the compound; (2) the actual percentage by weight of chlorine present in the compound; and (3) the proportion by weight of the pure compound present in the commercial product. Chlorinated lime, for example, contains as its essential constituent about 62.5% of calcium oxychloride, CaClOCl (molecular weight 127), with Cl_2 mols (molecular weight 71) of equivalent chlorine. Therefore, the actual weight of chlorine present is $62.5 \times 71/127 = 35\%$ of the total, and the available chlorine is also 35%. The oxidizing ability of non-chlorinous compounds can also be expressed in terms of available chlorine.

18-11. Application of Chlorine and Related Compounds. Liquid chlorine, ammonia, and sulfur dioxide are generally added to water in controlled amounts through orifice flow meters called respectively chlorinators, ammoniators, and sulfonators. For a given dosage, the pressure drop across the orifice is kept constant. In devices that are operated under pressure, this is done by providing a pressure-reducing, pressure-compensating valve which keeps the influent pressure constant regardless of pressure changes in the container from which the gas is drawn. In devices that are operated under a vacuum, the drop in pressure across the orifice is regulated by controlling the vacuum on the outlet side of the orifice, the inlet side also being under partial vacuum. The advantages of vacuum-feed devices in lessening gas leakage are obvious. Some pressure devices are based on regulated volumetric displacement of the gas (bubblers).

The measured gas flow may be introduced directly into water through diffusers, or it may be dissolved in a small flow of water that passes through the gas-flow regulating device and carries a solution of the gas to the point of application. Escape of gas through water in direct feed is not uncommon. Solution feed is preferred for this reason. A flow diagram of a vacuum-type, solution-feed chlorinator is presented in Figure 18-7. Portable chlorinators are used to supply chlorine for the disinfection of water mains, wells, tanks, and masonry reservoirs that have been newly constructed or that have undergone repairs. The initial concentration of the chlorine applied for these purposes is about 50 mg/l. Dosage is repeated until a residual of about 1 mg/l is obtained. The structure is then flushed out thoroughly before being placed in service.

Solutions of chlorinating, ammoniating, and sulfonating compounds are commonly fed through chemical reagent feeders (Section 14-8). For the chlorination of new mains, suitable amounts of calcium hypochlorite are sometimes placed in the main during construction. Manufacture of chlorine at the treatment works by the electrolysis of brine

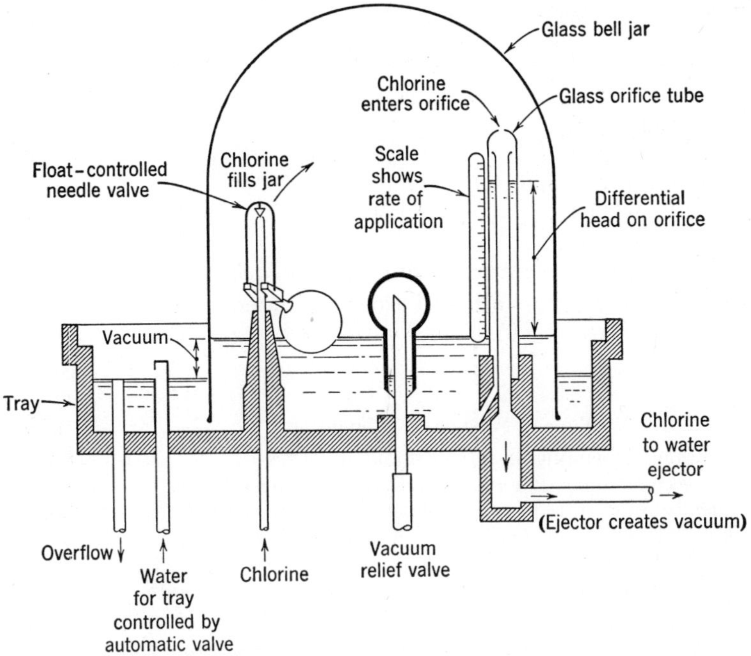

Figure 18-7. Control features of a vacuum-type chlorinator. *Wallace & Tiernan Co.*

in electrolytic cells is possible, but it has not found significant use.

The dosages of chlorine that are generally required in the marginal (minimal) treatment of water and sewage may be gaged from Tables 18-2 and 18-3. Suitable adjustments of the values given must be made for temperature effects and for variations in the quality of different waters or the strength of different waste waters. The capacities of feeding equipment must cover a sufficiently wide span to insure adequate dosage under all the conditions that may be encountered. To the values in Table 18-2 must be added the chlorine demand of the water.

Satisfactory disinfection of secondary sewage effluents, represented by 99.9% destruction of *Esch. coli* and 37 C bacterial count, is generally obtained when the chlorine residuals after 15 to 30 min of contact lie between 0.2 and 1.0 mg/l. A residual of 0.5 mg/l after 15 min appears to be a safe average. Disinfection of sewage with preformed chloramines reduces the loss of active chlorine to nitrogenous substances.[7]

[7] A. G. Friend, Unpublished doctoral dissertation, Harvard University, 1956.

TABLE 18-2. Minimum Chlorine Residuals for Drinking Water at 20 C

After Butterfield

*p*H value	6 to 7	7 to 8	8 to 9	9 to 10	10 to 11
Free available chlorine, mg/l after 10 min	0.2	0.2	0.4	0.8	0.8
Combined available chlorine, mg/l after 60 min	1.0	1.5	1.8	1.8	...

TABLE 18-3. Probable Amounts of Chlorine Required to Secure a Chlorine Residual of 0.5 mg/l after 15 min in Sewage and Sewage Effluents

Type of Sewage or Effluent	Probable Amounts of Chlorine, mg/l
Raw sewage, depending on strength and staleness	6 to 25
Settled sewage, depending on strength and staleness	5 to 20
Chemically precipitated sewage, depending on strength	3 to 20
Trickling-filter effluent, depending upon performance	3 to 10
Activated-sludge effluent, depending upon performance	2 to 20
Intermittent-sand-filter effluent, depending upon performance	1 to 10

In municipal water supplies, chlorination is often the only treatment process. Where other treatment methods are included, disinfecting chlorine may be added to the raw water (prechlorination), the partially treated water, or the finished water (postchlorination). The water may be chlorinated more than once; also after it leaves the plant. Where the distribution system contains open reservoirs, for example, the water may be rechlorinated in the distribution system.

18-12. Other Uses of Chlorine. In the operation of water and waste-water works, chlorine has been found useful for a number of purposes other than disinfection. Some of these are outlined below:

1. Destruction or control of undesirable growths of algae and related organisms in water and waste waters (Section 18-13).
2. Destruction and prevention of growth of iron-fixing and slime-forming bacteria in pipelines and other water conduits and of slime-forming bacteria in sewers and sewage-treatment works.
3. Destruction of filter flies (*Psychoda*) and of ponding slime growths in trickling filters.
4. Improvement of the coagulation of water and waste waters and of the separation of grease from waste waters.
5. Control of odors in water and waste waters.
6. Stabilization of settling-tank sludges in water-purification works.

7. Prevention of anaerobic conditions in sewerage systems and sewage-treatment works, by delaying or reducing decomposition.
8. Control of odors associated with the treatment of sewage sludge, including its drying.
9. Destruction of hydrogen sulfide in water and waste waters, and the protection of concrete, mortar, and paint against the corrosive action of this gas.
10. Reduction of the immediate oxygen requirements of returned activated sludge and of digester liquor returned to the treatment plant.
11. Reduction or delay of the BOD of waste waters that are to be discharged into receiving waters.
12. Preparation at the plant of the coagulant chlorinated copperas.

Destruction of Aquatic Growths

18-13. Control of Plankton. The control of the plankton of lakes, ponds, and reservoirs, and to a lesser extent of streams, is an important and often vexing problem in the management of surface waters that serve as water supplies or as receiving waters. Among the nuisances created by the, often sudden, "blooming" of a single genus or a few genera are: nauseous odors and tastes; killing of fish; interference with stock watering; poisoning of water fowl and cattle; poisoning of mussels; shortening of filter runs in water-purification plants; growths in pipes and other water conduits; and interference with industrial water uses. The characteristics of the odors and tastes associated with different organisms vary widely (Table 18-4). Consumer complaints are ordinarily registered when the concentration of odor-producing organisms lies above 500 to 1,000 areal standard units of 400 square microns. The bitter taste imparted to water by the alga *Synura* becomes objectionable, however, whenever the presence of this organism can be detected. Small amounts of chlorine, intended for disinfection, may intensify the odors and tastes of microorganisms in much the same way as they intensify the tastes due to phenols. On the other hand, high concentrations of chlorine will destroy both the organisms and their odor-producing oils or cell matter.

The use of copper sulfate for the eradication of algae and other microscopic organisms from reservoirs was suggested in 1904 by Moore and Kellerman.[8] Since then, this chemical has been applied more widely than any other algicide. The use of chlorine is supplemental

[8] G. T. Moore and K. F. Kellerman, A method of destroying or preventing the growth of algae and certain pathogenic bacteria in water supplies, *U. S. Bur. Plant Ind.*, Bull. 64 (1904).

rather than competitive. It destroys organisms that are more sensitive to it than to copper ions, oxidizes odors released when plankton growths are killed by copper and undergo decay, and delays decay and consequent depletion of oxygen. Activated carbon has been applied with some success in small reservoirs to shut out the sunlight essential to the growth of chlorophyllaceous organisms. It is useful also in removing odors and tastes due to algae. The addition of lime in amounts sufficient to produce caustic alkalinity deprives the plankton of needed carbon dioxide.

The mechanism and kinetics of destruction of plankton organisms by copper and chlorine are analogous to those of disinfection. However, the rate of kill at the concentrations normally employed is relatively slow. For copper sulfate it is days rather than minutes. Destruction of large growths by copper sulfate and by small concentrations of chlorine is accompanied (1) by an intensification of odors and (2) by a rise in number of the saprophytic bacteria which feed upon the cell substances released by the plankton carcasses. This may cause so serious a depletion of dissolved oxygen that fish are killed. Destruction of one plankton genus may be followed by the rapid rise of another. A treated body of water must, therefore, be watched carefully. Remedial, supplementary treatment of the water with chlorine or activated carbon may be indicated. The amounts of copper sulfate and of chlorine required to kill some of the most troublesome organisms are shown in Table 18-4. The values given in this table apply to relatively soft, warm (15 C, or 60 F) waters. Troublesome organisms are shown in Figure 11-5.

The tolerance of fish to copper sulfate lies between 0.14 mg/l (trout) and 2.1 mg/l (black bass), i.e., within the range of concentrations required to destroy plankton growths. However, the number killed is generally small, because dosage is based, not upon the total volume of water in the body to be treated, but only upon the volume contained within the limited (usually uppermost) strata in which the plankton occurs. Therefore, fish can seek refuge in the untreated waters. When a massive killing of fish follows the destruction, or natural death, of intense algal blooms, the likely causes are the depletion of oxygen due to the decay of the algae and the adherence of dead algal cells to the gills of the fish.

The quantities of copper normally needed for plankton control fall well below the concentration of 3 mg/l allowed under the federal drinking-water standards.

TABLE 18-4. Concentration of Copper and Chlorine Required to Kill Troublesome Growths of Organisms

After Hale

	Organism	Trouble	Copper Sulfate, mg/l	Chlorine, mg/l
Algae				
Diatoms	*Asterionella, Synedra, Tabellaria*	Odor: aromatic to fishy	0.1–0.5	0.5–1.0
	Fragilaria, Navicula	Turbidity	0.1–0.3	....
	Melosira	Turbidity	0.2	2.0
Green	*Eudorina,*Pandorina* *	Odor: fishy	2–10	....
	Volvox *	Odor: fishy	0.25	0.3–1.0
	Chara, Cladophora	Turbidity, scum	0.1–0.5	....
	Coelastrum, Spirogyra	Turbidity, scum	0.1–0.3	1.0–1.5
Blue-green	*Anabaena, Aphanizomenon*	Odor: moldy, grassy, vile	0.1–0.5	0.5–1.0
	Clathrocystis, Coelosphaerium	Odor: grassy, vile	0.1–0.3	0.5–1.0
	Oscillatoria	Turbidity	0.2–0.5	1.1
Golden-brown	*Dinobryon*	Odor: aromatic to fishy	0.2	0.3–1.0
	Mallomonas	Odor: aromatic	0.2–0.5	....
	Synura	Taste: cucumber	0.1–0.3	0.3–1.0
	Uroglenopsis	Odor: fishy. Taste: oily	0.1–0.2	0.3–1.0
Others	*Ceratium*	Odor: fishy, vile	0.2–0.3	0.3–1.0
	Glenodinium	Odor: fishy	0.2–0.5	....
	Peridinium	Odor: fishy	0.5–2.0	....
	Cryptomonas	Odor: aromatic	0.2–0.5	....
Higher bacteria	*Beggiatoa* (sulfur)	Odor: decayed, pipe growths	5.0	....
	Crenothrix (iron)	Odor: decayed, pipe growths	0.3–0.5	0.5
Crustacea	*Cyclops*	†	....	1.0–3.0
	Daphnia	†	2.0	1.0–3.0
Miscellaneous	*Chironomus* (bloodworm)	†	....	15–50
	Craspedacusta (jellyfish)	†	0.3	....

* These organisms are classified also as flagellate protozoa.
† These organisms are individually visible and cause consumer complaints.

18-14. Application of Algicides. Destruction of large pulses of plankton growths should not be necessary. Propagation leading to heavy infestations should be arrested as soon as limnologic and microscopic evidences sound a warning. Prevention of propagation requires adequate sampling and an understanding of the responses of different kinds of organisms to season (heat and light) and water movement. Except for *Synura,* which should be destroyed whenever its presence can be detected, bodies of water from which drinking-water supplies are taken should, as a rule, be treated whenever the concentration of microscopic organisms exceeds 500 to 1,000 areal standard units. The destruction of some organisms like *Synura* is sometimes complicated by their growth under the sheet of ice that covers bodies of water during the winter.

Small reservoirs, more particularly distribution reservoirs, and basins can be protected or treated by adding algicides to their influent waters. Dry-feed or solution-feed apparatus suited to the chemical to be applied are used for this purpose. Seeding of such reservoirs from upland storages can also be prevented by such means. Where large reservoirs, or portions of them, are to be treated, the algicide must be applied from a boat. A common method of applying copper sulfate is to place crystals of this chemical in burlap bags that are dragged through the water. To cover areas of moderate size, the boat may take a zigzag course across the surface, form a "reflected" zigzag pattern on the return run, and cover the shore waters more intensively by finally traversing a perimetral course within about 20 ft of the shore line. For large areas, a pattern of parallel paths 20 to 100 ft apart may be traced first in one direction and then at right angles to it.

The solubility of copper sulfate as $CuSO_4 \cdot 5H_2O$ is high. It varies from 19.5% by weight at 32 F (0 C) to 31.3% at 86 F (30 C). The rate of solution of crystals of copper sulfate (including 5 molecules of water) is sufficiently slow, however, to make the bag method effective. Dry-feed or solution-feed machines may be used instead. Dusters of the orchard-spray variety and special broadcasting equipment have also been employed successfully. Chlorination apparatus of the type described in Section 18-11 is used for the application of liquid chlorine, hypochlorites, and chloramines. A combination of copper sulfate, chlorine, and ammonia will form cupric chloramine and tends to prevent precipitation of the copper. Powdered activated carbon for "blacking out" sunlight from small basins can be dispersed from bags, added to the influent, or ejected onto the surface as a slurry. Its use can be confined to sunny days.

18-15. Destruction of Water Weeds. Most of the higher aquatic plants are perennial and propagate by means of runners, tubers, buds, or stem fragments; few depend upon seed reproduction. Since vegetative propagation is relatively slow and seed reproduction is successful only when the seeds find suitable lodging, objectionable growths of water weeds are relatively rare. Under favorable conditions, however, weeds may propagate so rapidly that they create a serious nuisance, especially in shallow bodies of water. The greatest depth of prevalence of attached weeds is about 40 ft. The discharge of waste waters that are rich in fertilizing elements, such as nitrogen and phosphorus, will promote heavy weed infestation of receiving waters and of oxidation or fish ponds.

There are five ways of destroying higher aquatic growths: draining, dredging, cutting, dragging, and poisoning. If the weeded area can be drained during hot weather, the exposed plants will die, and their roots will be destroyed. Dredging will remove the entire plant. Cutting and dragging offer but temporary relief. Flowering weeds should be cut before they have had a chance to go to seed. Since copper and chlorine in reasonable concentration are not effective against large aquatic plants, other chemical agents must be employed to poison them. Unfortunately, the compounds that are effective may also be toxic to man, or to fish, in the concentrations that must be used. Compounds of chlorinated benzene, although toxic to fish, have been used successfully in bodies of water from which drinking water is drawn. These substances are sprayed upon the water and settle onto the weeds to destroy them. More than one dose must generally be applied to control growth. The killing of fish is kept down by proceeding from the shore outward and thereby causing the fish to migrate into deep water.

Arsenical compounds such as sodium arsenite will destroy a variety of water weeds. Their use is limited to waters that do not serve as sources of drinking water for man or cattle. The development of new herbicides gives promise of eventually providing effective non-toxic weed killers that can be used with safety. Mention should be made in this connection of the growth-regulating substances of the dichlorphenoxyacetic acid type, sodium chlorate and ammonium sulfamate. Some of these have been used successfully for the control of (1) marginal growths, such as willows, that encroach upon bodies of water and (2) emergent vegetation, such as the water hyacinth and water chestnut. The required dosage of sodium arsenite is about 20 lb per 1,000 sq ft, and kill is improved if the weeds are cut before applying the chemical.

Proper design of reservoirs will keep weeds from establishing themselves (Section 4-2); and control of pollution will minimize their prevalence.

18-16. Destruction of Other Organisms. A number of other problems in biological control occur in water supply and waste-water disposal. A few examples will illustrate their range. Copper sulfate has been used in concentrations of 0.5 to 2.0 mg/l to destroy the snail hosts of the flukes that cause swimmer's itch. It has also been employed to control root growths in house sewers. Caustic alkalinity as well as chlorine have been found to kill *Cyclops,* the intermediate host of guinea worm. Chlorine as well as storage of water for a day or two at temperatures prevailing in the tropics have destroyed the cercariae of the pathogenic schistosomes (blood flukes). Chironomid larvae (blood worms) have been screened from returned activated sludge which they were destroying. Insecticides, such as DDT, have found use in the control of adult filter flies (Section 16-3).

Removal of Odors and Tastes

18-17. Available Processes. The processes in which odor and taste removal or control is the principal objective or the specific purpose include: (1) aeration; (2) oxidation by chemicals such as chlorine (including the hypochlorites and chlorinated lime), combinations of chlorine with ammonia, chlorine dioxide, and ozone; and (3) adsorption onto substances such as activated carbon.

Aeration will remove from water only odors and tastes that are dissolved in it as gases or that are otherwise sufficiently volatile (i.e., of low boiling point) to escape rapidly at an air-water interface. The concentration of gases, furthermore, must be such that the water is supersaturated with them in terms of their partial pressure in the air with which the water is brought into contact. Hydrogen sulfide (boiling point −62 C) is the principal odorous gas that can be removed from water to a substantial degree by aeration. The odors associated with algae and related organisms are examples of volatile substances that can often be reduced below their threshold values. But so-called phenolic substances and their chloro compounds, which are created by the marginal chlorination of water containing phenolic substances, are non-volatile and will not respond to aeration. The phenolic compounds involved are hydroxy derivatives of benzene and include phenol, cresol, and similar substances released by chemical industries, gas-manufacturing establishments, and coke plants. The boiling point of phenol (C_6H_5OH) is 182 C and that of *ortho*-chlorphenol ($Cl \cdot C_6H_4 \cdot OH$) 176 C. As previously mentioned, chlorphenols may be objectionable in quantities as low as 1 μg/l.

Destruction of odors by oxidizing chemicals is successful when the chemical reaction involved is such as to produce non-odorous substances. This is not uncommon. One of the simplest oxidizing reactions is that between chlorine and hydrogen sulfide to precipitate sulfur. The stronger the oxidizing agent, the more certain is the destruction of the offending substances. Hence the effectiveness of break-point chlorination. The production of chlorphenol by marginal chlorination and the intensification of tastes when water containing *Synura* or other microscopic organisms is chlorinated speak against halfway measures.

Adsorption of odor- and taste-producing substances is widely effective. Activated carbon possesses especially high adsorptive properties and is almost the only substance used for this purpose in water-works practice. The efficiency of adsorption of a substance from water is inversely proportional to its solubility in water. Since many of the odorous substances in water are organic compounds and but slightly soluble, they are generally adsorbed with ease.

18-18. Aeration. As shown in other chapters of this book, the aeration of water and sewage serves many purposes other than odor removal. Aerating devices used specifically for the removal of volatile substances from water commonly take one of the following three forms: (1) injection aerators in which air is blown into the water in substantially the same way as in activated-sludge aeration units; (2) gravity aerators in which the water cascades over a flight of steps or troughs, flows in a thin sheet over an inclined plane that may be studded with baffles to increase the turbulence of the water, drops through the air from perforated pans or perforated pipes, or percolates through porous materials similar to trickling filters; and (3) fountain aerators in which the water is sprayed upward into the air through perforated pipes or pipes equipped with nozzles. Combinations of fountain aerators and beds of contact material similar to trickling filters have also been employed. Injection aerators or air-diffusion units for the removal of gases or volatile matter are designed in substantially the same way as activated-sludge units. The detention period is seldom less than 15 min or more than 45 min, and the amount of air may be as low as 0.005 and as high as 0.2 cu ft per gallon of water treated.

The most effective fountain aerators take the form of pipes equipped with nozzles that break up the spray into small droplets. Examples of nozzles are shown in Figure 18-8, and an arrangement of piping is sketched in Figure 18-9. Operating heads are seldom less than 4 ft or more than 30 ft. The floating-cone nozzle is particularly useful for variable heads.

The use of aerators for odor and taste removal has decreased markedly since the introduction of powdered activated carbon into water-works practice. Aerators may be expected to find continuing employment, however, for the removal of carbon dioxide and hydrogen sulfide and for the addition of oxygen.

18-19. Rates of Aeration. The rate of absorption of a gas is proportional to its degree of undersaturation (or saturation deficit) in the absorbing liquid, or

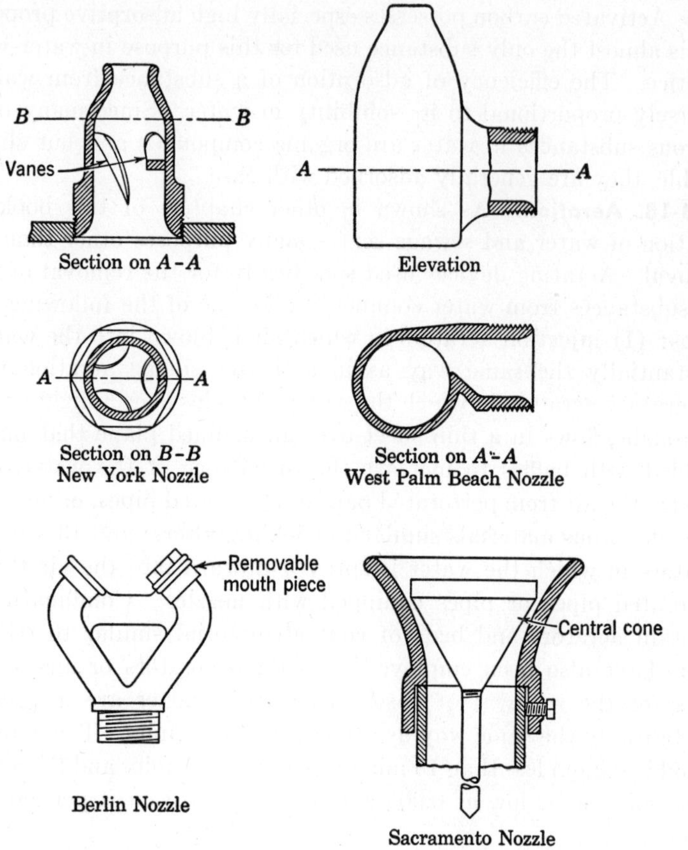

Figure 18-8. Aerator nozzles. The coefficients of discharge of these nozzles vary from 0.85 to 0.92.

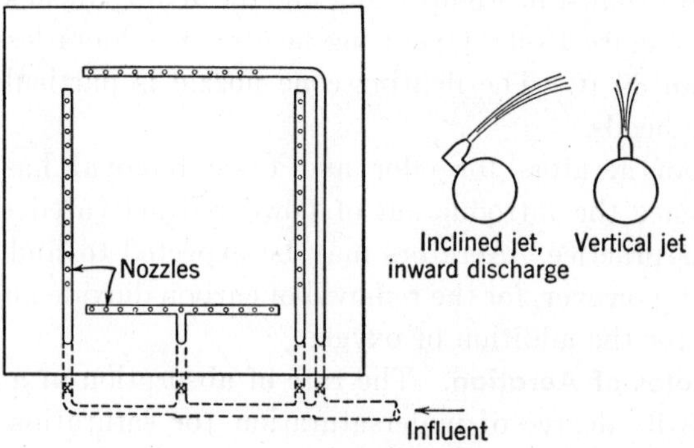

Figure 18-9. Plan of fountain aerator.

$$dc/dt = K_g(c_s - c) \qquad 18\text{-}16$$

Here dc/dt is the change in concentration or the rate of absorption of the gas at time t; c_s is the saturation concentration of the gas at a given temperature; c_t is its concentration at time t; and K_g is the rate constant of solution or gas transfer for the conditions of exposure. Integration between the limits c_0 at $t = 0$ and c_t at $t = t$ yields the equation:

$$c_t - c_0 = (c_s - c_0)(1 - e^{-K_g t}) \qquad 18\text{-}17$$

The magnitude of K_g increases with the temperature. It increases also with the degree of mixing to which the gas and liquid are subjected, i.e., with the rate of renewal of the gas-liquid interface and the degree of eddy diffusion. The temperature effect can be expressed in terms of the van't Hoff-Arrhenius equation (Section 18-4), but the degree of mixing or rate of renewal of the interface and of eddy diffusion is difficult of definition, unless the physical power involved can be identified. Since entrance of a gas into a liquid must take place at the gas-liquid interface, K_g becomes more specific if the area of the interface in its relation to the volume of the liquid can be identified. This can be done, for example, where water is sprayed into the air in droplets, or when air is bubbled through water. The over-all value of K_g is then $k_g A/V$, where k_g is *the gas-transfer coefficient* and A/V is the interfacial area between the gas and liquid per unit volume of liquid.

In contrast to absorption, the rate of precipitation or dissolution of a gas from a liquid becomes proportional to its degree of oversaturation in the precipitating liquid or the saturation surplus. It follows that the equations for rates of absorption should apply also to rates of dissolution. The fact that the saturation concentration c_s will be less than the observed concentration c_0 makes for negative differences that indicate precipitation.

18-20. Chemical Oxidation. Chlorine is used as a chemical oxidant as well as a disinfectant in break-point chlorination and superchlorination (Sections 18-8 and 18-9). It may be applied to water for the specific purpose of odor and taste reduction also as chlorine dioxide (ClO_2), a strong oxidizing agent. Chlorine dioxide, a gas in pure form, is produced as needed from sodium chlorite ($NaClO_2$) by allowing a solution of this solid to react with a strong chlorine solution (7,500 mg/l of Cl_2 or a pH value of <3.5), or more rarely with an acidified solution of calcium or sodium hypochlorite.

$$2NaClO_2 + Cl_2 \rightarrow 2ClO_2 + 2NaCl \qquad 18\text{-}18$$

The theoretical ratio of chlorine to sodium chlorite is 1 to 2.6, but a ratio between 1 to 2 and 1 to 1 is employed in practice with commercial sodium chlorite (82% $NaClO_2$). Common dosages of chlorine dioxide lie between 0.2 and 0.3 mg/l. Although chlorine dioxide is itself a disinfectant, the excess of chlorine normally used in its generation is commonly counted upon to accomplish disinfection. Chlorine dioxide appears to be particularly effective in the destruction of phenolic substances. Against other taste-producing compounds, it has been used with partial or indifferent success.

Ozone is another strong chemical oxidant. Three atoms of oxygen are combined to form a molecule of this gas by the corona discharge of high-voltage electricity through dry air. The relatively small partial pressure of ozone in the air, the resulting difficulty of its solution in water, and the "fixing" of some residual odors in treated water have militated against the exploitation of this otherwise very promising substance. The energy use in producing ozone is 0.2 kw-hr per gram of ozone at 15,000 volts, and but 0.5 to 1% of the air's oxygen is converted into ozone. From 1 to 4 mg/l of ozone are required for deodorizing or for disinfection. Modern ozonizing plants include besides contact tanks the following equipment for the production of ozone: air cleaners, blowers, refrigerative driers, adsorptive driers, ozone generators, and cooling-water services. The power requirement for this ancillary equipment is from 25 to 35% of the power needed for the generation of the ozone. Contact tanks similar in construction to the air-diffusion units of activated-sludge tanks provide a detention of about 10 min for the absorption of the gas.

18-21. Adsorption. Activated carbon is the chief means employed for the removal of odors and tastes from water by adsorption. Although a wide variety of other raw materials can also be employed, activated carbon is generally produced from wood. The raw material is charred at a temperature below 500 C and then activated by slow burning at temperatures above 800 C. The adsorptive capacity of different activated carbons for pure phenol, called their phenol value, offers a basis for their general comparison. However, the phenol value does not necessarily reflect their relative efficiency in removing specific odors and tastes. The phenol value is defined as the mg/l of activated carbon required to reduce 100 μg/l of phenol by 90%. Most commercial carbons used in water treatment possess a phenol value between 15 and 30. Granular activated carbon is generally a millimeter or less in diameter; powdered activated carbon is normally ground to such size that 50% will pass a 300-mesh sieve and 95% a 200-mesh sieve. The adsorptive capacity of finely divided activated carbon can be understood when it is realized that 1 cu ft of this substance is estimated to present a surface of about 3,000,000 sq ft to the water in which it is suspended.

Determination of the phenol value and of the dosage of powdered activated carbon required to reduce odors and tastes to desired threshold values is based upon the relationships expressed by the Freundlich adsorption isotherm. If c_0 is the concentration of odor or phenol in the water to be treated and c is the residual concentration produced by the addition of m units of activated carbon, the equilibrium equation states that

$$\log \frac{c_0 - c}{m} = \log K + \frac{1}{n} \log c \qquad \text{18-19}$$

Hence the values of K and $1/n$ can be read respectively as the intercept at $c = 1$ and as the slope of the straight line of best fit on double logarithmic paper. The coefficient K is a measure of the fundamental effectiveness of the adsorbent; the coefficient n is a measure of the change in rate of effectiveness with relative dosage. It follows from Equation 18-19 that the phenol value includes both the coefficient K and the coefficient n. Specifically, it is expressed as $\log m = 1.9542 - (\log K + 1/n)$ because $c_0 - c = 90$ and $c = 10$.

It is generally simpler and sufficiently precise to find the dosage required to reach a certain threshold odor or taste from a plot of experimental results. Either an arithmetic or a double logarithmic plot can be used. In an arithmetic plot, carbon dosage in mg/l is made the ordinate and threshold odor or taste values the abscissa (see Figure 18-10*a*). In such a plot, the experimental points should straddle the desired threshold value. Satisfactory extrapolation is possible by double logarithmic plotting of $(c_0 - c)/m$ against c (see Figure 18-10*b*). For the data plotted in Figure 18-10, the dosage of activated carbon required to reduce the threshold odor value from 20 to 4 is 7 mg/l.

Activated carbon may be applied to water to correct existing odors and tastes or to prevent their intensification by chlorine. The addition of carbon should be kept flexible. Introduction in advance of coagulation of the raw water allows substantial removal of the carbon particles prior to filtration, stabilization of the precipitated sludge,

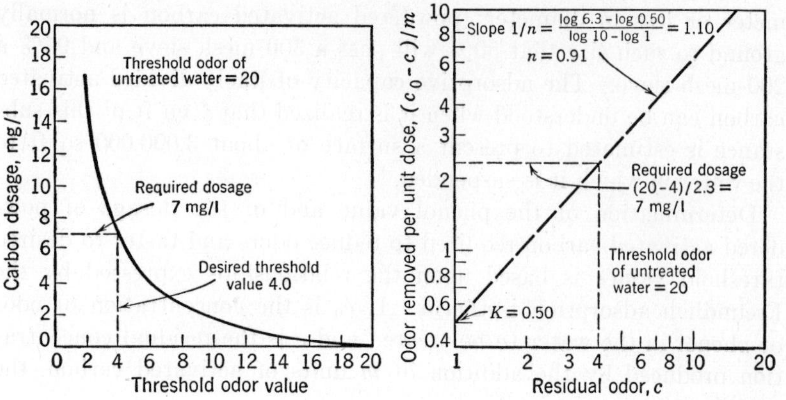

Figure 18-10. Determination of carbon dosage for taste control. (*a*) Arithmetic plotting of experimental results. (*b*) Double-logarithmic plotting of experimental results.

and buffering against rapidly changing water quality in terms of odors and tastes. Deposition of carbon on filter beds is more economical but contributes to more rapid loss of head. Addition of carbon to reservoirs has been mentioned in Section 18-14. Required dosages vary from a few milligrams per liter to over 10 mg/l.

Powdered activated carbon is generally shipped in paper bags. It should be isolated in storage to protect the plant against dust and carbon fires, and it should be kept dry to prevent caking. But it may be fed dry or suspended as a slurry in water.

19 The Natural Purification of Water

19-1. Patterns of Pollution and Natural Purification. When sewage is discharged into water, a succession of changes in water quality takes place. If the sewage is emptied into a lake in which the currents about the outfall are sluggish and shift their direction with the wind, the changes occur in close proximity to each other, move their location sporadically, and cause much overlap. As a result, the pattern of change is not crisply distinguished. If, on the other hand, the water moves steadily away from the outfall, as in a stream, the successive changes occur in different river reaches and establish a profile of pollution and natural purification so well defined that it can be subjected to mathematical analysis and generalization (Section 19-9). In most streams, this pattern is by no means static. It shifts longitudinally along the course of the stream and is modified in intensity with changes in season and hydrography. The intensity rises during the warmer months and at low river stages. It is suppressed in winter and when the stream is in flood. Ice cover imposes a pattern of its own. A decrease in the pollutional load is similar to an increase in stream runoff.

When a single, large charge of sewage or other putrescible matter is poured into a clean stream, the water becomes turbid, sunlight is shut out of the depths, and green plants, which by photosynthesis remove carbon dioxide from the water and release oxygen to it, die off. Scavenging organisms increase in number until they match the food supply. The intensity of their life activities is mirrored by the intensity of the biochemical oxygen demand. The oxygen resources of the water are drawn upon heavily. In an overloaded stream, the dissolved oxygen may become exhausted. Nitrogen, carbon, sulfur, and other important nutritional elements run through their natural cycles (Section 11-7), and sequences of microbic population groups manage to break down the sewage matters in accordance with the nutritional requirements and environmental adaptiveness of the constituent organisms.

Depending upon the hydrography of the stream, suspended matter is carried along with the water or removed to the bottom by sedimentation. The bottom (benthal) deposits may be laid down in thicknesses varying from a thin pollutional carpet to heavy sludge banks. Decomposition of these deposits differs appreciably from that in the flowing water. In the presence of oxygen dissolved in the supernatant water, benthal decomposition changes with depth of deposit from largely aerobic to largely anaerobic conditions. The influence of the benthal factor upon the stream varies accordingly.

The initial effect of pollution, on a stream, is to degrade the physical quality of the water. As decomposition becomes active, there is a shift to chemical degradation that is biologically induced. At the same time, there is a biological degradation in terms of the variety and organization of the living things that persist or make their appearance. In the course of time and flow, however, the energy values of a single charge of polluting substances are used up. The biochemical oxygen demand is decreased in intensity, and the rate of absorption of oxygen from the atmosphere, which at first has lagged behind the rate of oxygen utilization, falls into step with it and eventually overwhelms it. The water becomes clear. Green plants flourish once again and release oxygen to the water by photosynthesis. Other higher aquatic organisms, including game fish, which are notably intolerant to pollution, reappear and thrive as in a balanced aquarium. The stream waters are returned to normal purity. Self-purification is gradually completed. Recovery takes place.

The natural purification of polluted waters is never fast, and heavily polluted streams may traverse long distances during the time required to accomplish a significant degree of purification.

The self-purification of polluted ground waters departs significantly from that of surface waters. The variety of living organisms that seize upon the pollutional substances for food is greatly restricted in the confinement and darkness of the pore space of the soil. But this reduction in biological forces is more than counterbalanced by the introduction of the physical force of filtration. In general, the rate of purification is stepped up greatly, and time and distance of pollutional travel shrink to smaller values.

If pollution is kept within bounds, it will contribute to the fertility of the water. The growth of useful aquatic life may thereby be promoted. Then fish will browse in increased numbers in the aquatic meadows that derive the elements for their growth from the nitrogen and other fertilizing constituents of the waste matters. The use of settled sewage for the fertilizing of fish ponds is an example of controlled pollution, as is the possibility of harvesting proteinaceous plankton from oxidation ponds (Section 19-14). In the fertilization of water by domestic sewage, however, the danger of spreading disease through plant or animal foods must never be lost from sight.

19-2. Parameters of Pollution and Natural Purification. Pollution and natural purification may be measured physically, chemically, and biologically. No single yardstick tells the full story. Depending upon the nature of the polluting substances and the uses that the receiving body of water (or water taken from it) is to serve, measurements may include determinations such as turbidity, color, odor, nitrogen in its various forms, BOD, dissolved oxygen and other gases, mineral substances of many kinds, bacteria, and larger aquatic organisms.

When waters that have been polluted are to be used for municipal purposes or as bathing waters, for example, the progress of bacterial self-purification as measured by the prevalence of the coliform group of organisms may be the principal determinant. The concentration of coliform organisms then reflects (1) the relative hazard of infection incurred by ingesting the water and (2) the degree of purification to which the water must be subjected before it can be used with safety. When pollutional nuisance of receiving waters is to be avoided, the DO and BOD, taken together, are generally relied upon to delineate the profile of pollution and natural purification on which engineering calculations of permissible pollutional loadings are based. The BOD records in a comprehensive manner the pollutional load placed on the receiving water or remaining in it at any time, while the DO identifies the capacity of the body of water to assimilate the imposed load with or without the aid of reaeration by oxygen absorbed from the atmosphere. Requisite standards of water quality (Section 19-16) will serve as a guide to the tests that are meaningful in given circumstances. The significance of biological indicators of contamination and pollution has been discussed in Section 11-16.

A single example [1] of observed changes in terms of some of the generally useful parameters of pollution and natural purification is illustrated in Figure 19-1. The samples on which all but the benthal results are based were collected during midsummer and represent the condition of the stream waters during warm weather when the greatest demands are normally made upon it by the pollutional load. Since bottom deposits are garnered over a long period of time, the bottom-dwelling organisms are characteristic of the average condition of the stream during the period of accumulation. That time of flow, rather than distance of flow, is the controlling factor is strikingly shown by the improvement in water quality effected by passage of the stream through the lake that occupies the lower reaches. The tributaries entering from the left in Figure 19-1 were themselves heavily polluted. The waters of the other tributary were of significantly better quality than that of the main stream.

19-3. Rates of Bacterial Self-Purification. The discharge into a receiving water of sewage and other waste waters that are rich in decomposable matter vastly increases the number and genera of saprophytic bacteria that are essential to self-purification. The multiplying organisms are derived in part from the waste water, in part from the receiving waters. Other saprophytes enter from other sources. Only after they have come into balance with the food supply under the prevailing environmental conditions does the number and variety of saprophytes begin to decline. The density of the more strictly intestinal bacteria isolated from samples of water is also observed to rise appreciably below a sewer outfall during the first 10 to 12 hr of flow. But this may be due, in some extent, to increased capture of organisms by the breaking-up of clumps of bacteria-containing substances and their more uniform dispersion in the water. Below the points of modal concentration of the different bacterial population groups, their numbers drop off at varying rates. The die-away is normally not identical with that observed when pure cultures of representative organisms are suspended in clean water and stored in the laboratory under conditions of light and temperature that are similar to those obtaining in receiving waters. There are several reasons for this. Two are particularly important: (1) the presence, in polluted, natural bodies of water, of predators such as the ciliated protozoa which feed upon bacteria and (2) the biophysical factors

[1] From a survey by the United States Public Health Service of the Mississippi River at Minneapolis and St. Paul before treatment of the metropolitan sewage.

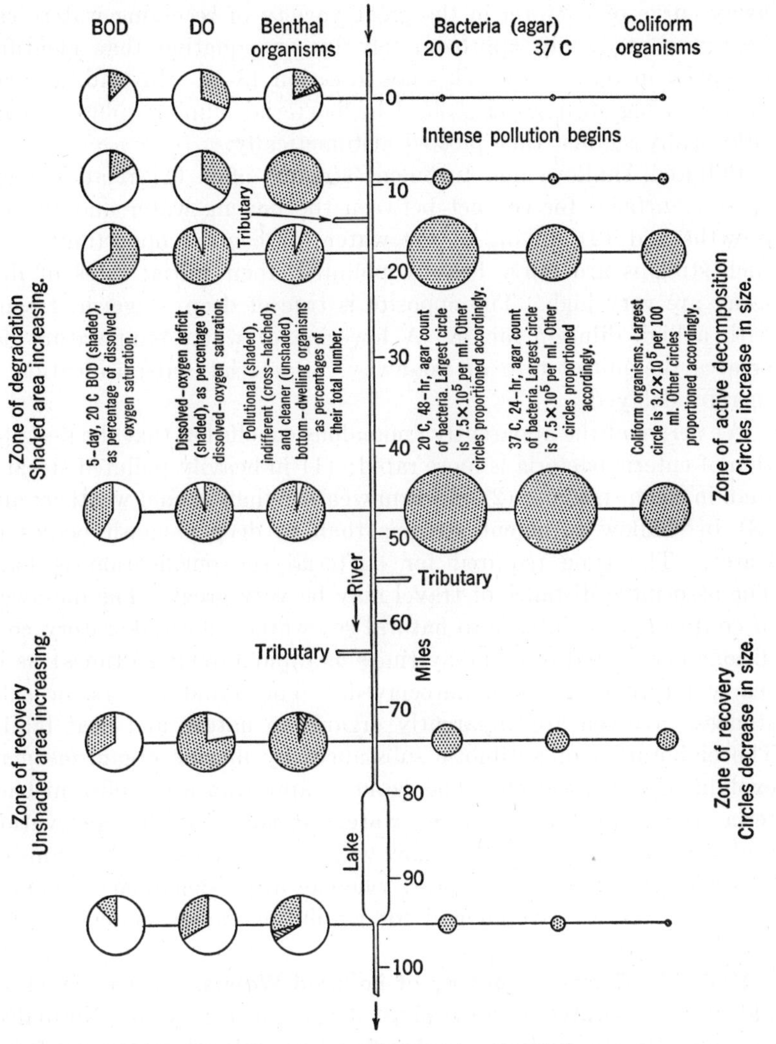

Figure 19-1. Pollution and self-purification of a large stream.

(such as sedimentation and biological flocculation and precipitation) that ally the processes of natural purification to those of a sewage-treatment plant. Conversely, it has indeed been suggested that a sewage-treatment plant is like a river wound up in small space.

If we acknowledge that the bacteria do not die merely for lack of food, but that numerous other factors contribute to their removal from the flowing water and destruction in it, it follows that the die-away curve of bacteria in the great variety of receiving waters can be represented only approximately by an equation that identifies die-away in terms of Chick's law (Section 18-4). Instead, a curve of decreasing steepness is traced by bacterial numbers plotted logarithmically against time plotted arithmetically.

Polluted, shallow, and turbulent streams offer (1) relatively extensive surfaces for contact between the flowing water and surface growths and (2) mixing of the waters or contact opportunity. If such streams are fairly heavily polluted, their initial rates of die-away are very high. The opposite is true of deep, sluggish streams with a high dilution factor. A lowering of water temperature decreases the initial rate of die-away. Bacterial self-purification is thereby delayed.

We arrive at the apparently anomalous conclusion that the destruction of enteric bacteria is more rapid: (1) in heavily polluted streams than in clean streams; (2) in warm weather than in cold weather; and (3) in shallow turbulent streams than in deep sluggish bodies of water. The time required for bacterial self-purification is long. The associated distance of travel may be very great. The die-away of coliforms inoculated into natural sea water under laboratory conditions is reported to be many times as rapid (about 25 times) as in sea water that has been autoclaved.[2] The lethal factors, or substances, involved are apparently organic in nature and heat labile. The elaboration of antibiotic substances by marine organisms may explain this observation. The rapid disappearance of coliform bacteria from sewage-polluted sea water accounts for the observation that a dilution factor of 200 to 250 will reduce the coliform organisms in sewage to 10 per ml or less, whereas dispersion unaccompanied by rapid die-away would call for a dilution factor more than 10^3 times as great.

19-4. The Oxygen Economy of Polluted Waters. In nature, clean waters are saturated with dissolved oxygen, or nearly so. Normally, therefore, waste matters discharged into natural waters undergo aerobic decomposition. Only when the supply of oxygen present in solution or taken into solution—principally from the atmosphere—cannot keep pace with the biochemical oxygen demand of the waste matters does the receiving water, and with it the type of decomposition, become anaerobic. Although the ultimate result of both types

[2] B. H. Ketchum, C. L. Carey, and Margaret Briggs, Preliminary studies on the viability and dispersal of coliform bacteria in the sea, *Limnological Aspects of Water Supply and Waste Disposal*, Am. Assoc. Advance. Sci., Washington, D. C., p. 64, 949.

of decomposition is a purified water, the conditions associated with each are as different as those obtaining in an activated-sludge unit on the one hand and in a septic tank on the other. Under aerobic conditions, the receiving waters remain reasonably clean in appearance and free from odor. Within limits, such waters continue to support their normal animal and plant populations. Under anaerobic conditions, by contrast, the waters become black, unsightly, and malodorous, and their normal fauna and flora are destroyed. A septic receiving water usually creates a nuisance that makes itself felt over long reaches of the stream, because anaerobic decomposition is so much slower than aerobic decomposition.

For the maintenance of normally satisfactory conditions, therefore, the oxygen economy of the receiving water is of paramount consideration. In order to maintain a balanced ledger, biochemical oxygen demand on the debit side must not exceed available oxygen supply on the credit side. Exertion of the BOD results in *deoxygenation* of the receiving waters. Absorption of oxygen from the atmosphere and from oxygen released by green plants during photosynthesis results in *reoxygenation* or *reaeration* of the receiving waters. The interplay between deoxygenation and reaeration produces the dissolved-oxygen profile of a stream called the *oxygen sag* (Section 19-9).

19-5. Deoxygenation of Polluted Waters. It is generally assumed that the demands made upon the oxygen resources of polluted streams by the living organisms engaged in the utilization and the accompanying destruction or stabilization of decomposable substances are the same as those recorded in the laboratory when samples of waste water that have been mixed with convenient amounts of synthetic dilution water are subjected to BOD tests (Section 11-8*b*). This assumption overlooks the fact that the biophysical as well as the biochemical environment of BOD bottles cannot possibly be like that of every kind of stream, even when the temperature of incubation of the bottles is that of the stream water. Fortunately, for engineering predictions of the deoxygenation of large and important streams, the correlation between (1) laboratory observations of the BOD of polluted waters and (2) field investigations of the reaction of such streams to pollution is usually high.

The 5-day, 20 C BOD of domestic sewages upon which engineering calculations of deoxygenation are generally based is shown in Tables 12-2 and 12-3. If the waste waters are composed of combined sewage, or if they contain industrial wastes or other polluting (oxygen-demanding) substances, the pollutional load can be accounted for in terms of the equivalent domestic population. As stated in Section 12-5, the population equivalent of combined sewage from normally industrialized communities is generally of the order of 1.4 times the tributary population. The population equivalents of industrial wastes are discussed in Section 20-7.

19-6. Rate of Deoxygenation by the Suspended and Dissolved Load. As shown in Figure 19-2, the progressive exertion of the BOD

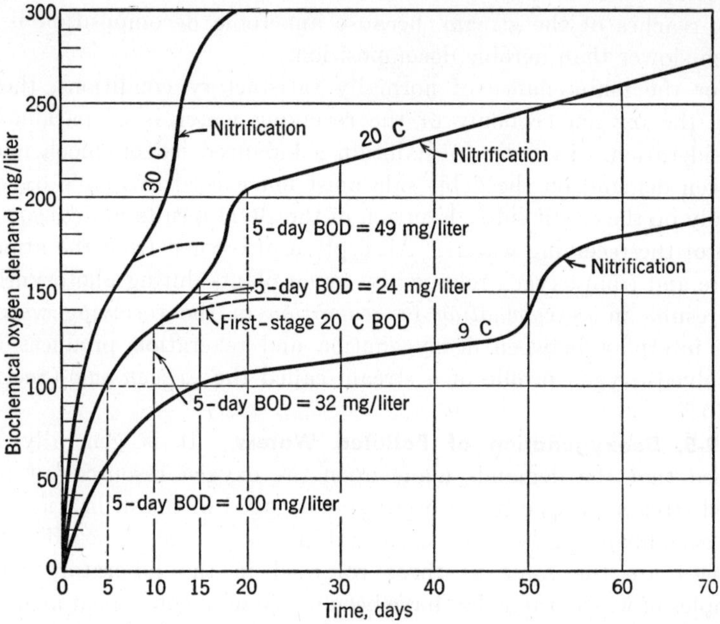

Figure 19-2. Progress of biochemical oxygen demand (BOD) at 9, 20, and 30 C. ***After Theriault.***

of freshly polluted water generally breaks down into two stages: a first stage in which it is largely the carbonaceous matter that is oxidized and a second stage in which nitrogenous substances are attacked in significant amounts and nitrification takes places. If the temperature of freshly polluted water is 20 C, for example, the first stage extends about to the tenth day and is characterized by a progressive falling off of the actual BOD exerted in each interval of time. Analysis of the first-stage experience demonstrates that the amount of BOD exerted in a unit of time relative to the BOD remaining to be exerted during the first stage is substantially constant.

In the succeeding second stage, the BOD rises sharply as nitrification becomes dominant. Oxygen utilization then reaches a fairly uniform rate that is maintained for a protracted period of time.

a. Formulation of the first-stage BOD curve. The first-stage BOD has generally been interpreted as a first-order reaction, dependent on the concentration of oxidizable organic material present, but independent of the oxygen concentration, provided that it is greater than a critical value of about 4 mg/l at 20 C for example. This means that the rate-determining steps in the reaction are not ones that involve oxygen.

The resulting first-order equation may be written in the form

$$dy/dt = k(L - y) \tag{19-1}$$

or

$$y = L(1 - e^{-kt}) = L(1 - 10^{-k't}) \tag{19-2}$$

where L is the initial first-stage BOD of the water, y is the oxygen demand exerted in time t, and k or k' are the rate constants related respectively to a base e and a base 10. The BOD remaining at time t is equal to $(L - y)$, and the proportion of BOD exerted in time t is $y/L = (1 - e^{-kt}) = (1 - 10^{-k't})$, k' being equal to $0.4343k$.

Practical evaluation of this equation is complicated by the fact that L, as well as k or k', is usually unknown. A number of methods for finding the magnitudes of L and k or k' from a series of observations of y and t have been proposed. Of these the "method of moments" developed by Moore, Thomas, and Snow [3] appears to be the most convenient.

b. Temperature effect. For a given sample of water, the rate of reaction k increases with temperature. The observed effect of temperature can be formulated in terms of the van't Hoff-Arrhenius relationship (Section 18-4) and is conveniently expressed as the temperature characteristic C_k (and its power function, the temperature coefficient $\Theta_k = e^{C_k}$), or the temperature quotient $Q_{10} = e^{10C_k} = \Theta_k{}^{10}$, or

$$k/k_0 = e^{C_k(T-T_0)} = \Theta_k{}^{(T-T_0)} \tag{19-3}$$

where T is the temperature and the subscript zero denotes the reference values of k and T. From about 15 to 30 C, the following values obtain: $C_k = 0.046$ per deg C, $\Theta_k = 1.047$, and $Q_{10} = 1.58$. At lower tem-

[3] E. W. Moore, H. A. Thomas, Jr., and W. B. Snow, Simplified method for analysis of BOD data, *Sewage and Ind. Wastes*, 22, 1343 (1950).

peratures, these values increase appreciably. Above 30 C they decrease, probably because of a thermal inactivation of the enzymes responsible for oxidation.

Example 19-1. If the BOD of a waste water has a first-stage value of $L = 188$ mg/l and a reaction velocity constant $k_0 = 0.523$ per day at 20 C what is its expected 5-day BOD at 30 C, assuming that $C_k = 0.046$?

By Equation 19-3, $k = 0.523e^{0.46} = 0.828$ per day.

By Equation 19-2, $y = 188(1 - e^{-0.828 \times 5}) = 185$ mg/l.

c. *Limitations of the formulation.* Theriault[4] found that the value of k was fairly constant for a variety of sewage-polluted waters and possessed a mean magnitude of 0.23 days^{-1} at 20 C ($k' = 0.1$). Later investigations of the behavior of sewage samples have shown, however, that k may vary considerably, ranging from 0.16 to 0.70 days^{-1} at 20 C, and that the mean value is more nearly 0.39. The possible variation in k implies that the 5-day, 20-C BOD is not by itself a complete measure of the strength of sewage or degree of pollution of water because it is not a constant proportion of the L value. The proportion of first-stage demand reached in a 5-day period at the stated variations in k values lies between 55.1 and 97.0%. It follows that comparisons can be drawn between the 5-day, 20-C BOD values of different waters only if their reaction velocity constants are identical.

Other complications occur, too. In unseeded samples (i.e., samples that harbor initially an inadequate flora and fauna to activate the BOD reactions), "lag" periods are experienced before the reactions proceed normally. By contrast, sewages that have undergone partial anaerobic decomposition or that contain reducing chemical substances, such as originate in certain industries, may exert an "immediate" demand (sometimes called a chemical demand) at the beginning of the BOD run. This is not part of the normal BOD.[5] In some instances, furthermore, the values of k diminish as the percentage of reaction increases. This probably results from differences in ease of oxidation of the materials present, the rate decreasing as the more easily oxidized substances are used up. The onset of nitrification, finally, may produce increases in rate in the later stages of the reaction, particularly in highly diluted samples.

Estimation of k and L is more difficult when these complications

[4] E. J. Theriault, The oxygen demand of polluted waters, *U. S. Public Health Service Bull.* 173 (1927).

[5] High initial demands establish a negative lag phase.

occur, but suitable methods have been published to cope with this situation.[6]

The rate of BOD of polluted sea water appears to vary with the concentration of the sea water. In low concentrations (up to about 25%), k is larger than in fresh water. In straight sea water it is less. No change appears to take place in the magnitude of the first-stage demand. A second stage is observed, but it is retarded.[7]

There is, as yet, no satisfactory formulation of the nitrification stage of the BOD curve. The relationship of nitrified sewage effluents to stream sanitation has been discussed in Section 16-8.

19-7. Rate of Deoxygenation by the Benthal Load. Mud and sludge deposits are composites of settleable solids that have been laid down and impounded, generally over long periods of time during which stream currents were too sluggish (1) to prevent the sedimentation of suspended matter or (2) to encourage bottom scour. If the overriding waters contain dissolved oxygen, aerobic conditions are maintained at the surface of the accumulating organic debris. Diffusion of oxygen into the deposits is normally too slow, however, to carry enough oxygen to the deeper strata to keep them from becoming anaerobic.

The sludge-water interface is by no means static. During periods of sedimentation, settling solids form new surface layers. During periods of scour, the deposits are churned up. The entire sludge load may indeed be resuspended and moved away. Some bottom-dwelling organisms, such as the sludge worms and insect larvae (Figure 11-6), ingest subsurface debris and cast their fecal pellets upon the mud surface; other organisms burrow into the deposits and expose the spoil to the flowing water. Gases of decomposition are produced within the sludge. If they are released in sufficient volume, they may buoy some of the sludge into the supernatant water (and even to the water surface). Hydrography determines the degree of deposition as well as the rate of scour, whereas temperature establishes the intensity of decomposition or sludge activity. Because the processes of decomposition in deep deposits are largely anaerobic, their rate of stabilization is normally much slower than that of the suspended and dissolved pollutional load.

[6] H. A. Thomas, Jr., Analysis of the biochemical oxygen demand curve, *Sewage Works J., 12,* 504 (1940). See also the immediately preceding references.

[7] H. B. Gotaas, The effect of sea water on the biochemical oxidation of sewage, *Sewage Works J., 21,* 818 (1949).

The deposition of bottom sludges is not necessarily detrimental to the sanitary economy of a stream. In fact, it may be of considerable help. Transfer of the settleable load to the stream bottom delays the demands made upon the supply of dissolved oxygen and reduces them in proportion to the degree of anaerobic stabilization of the sediments. The winter's accumulation may be washed away by spring freshets (the spring housecleaning of the stream) and give the waters a new start at the beginning of what is usually the most dangerous season: summer, when stream flows are low and rates of decomposition are high.

Although the rate of deoxygenation by the benthal load can be formulated, the magnitudes of the constants that should be applied in different circumstances are not sufficiently well known to make the formulation widely useful. Use of the following approximate relationship is, therefore, suggested for the determination of the maximum, daily, benthal oxygen demand of an accumulating sediment:[8]

$$y_m = 3.14 \times 10^{-2} y_0 C_T w \frac{5 + 160w}{1 + 160w} \sqrt{t_a} \qquad 19\text{-}4$$

Here y_m is the maximum daily benthal oxygen demand in grams per square meter; y_0 is the 5-day, 20-C BOD in grams per kilogram of volatile matter; $C_T = y/y_0$ is the temperature factor, from Equations 19-2 and 19-3, for $t = 5$ days and $T_0 = 20$ C; w is the daily rate of deposition of volatile solids in kilograms per square meter; and t_a is the time in days up to 365 days during which accumulation takes place.

Example 19-2. On a daily per capita basis, the 5-day, 20-C BOD of 39 grams of volatile settleable solids of a domestic sewage is 19 grams (Table 12-2), 10 grams of volatile solids being deposited daily per square meter of stream bottom during a period of 100 days. Find the maximum daily benthal oxygen demand of the accumulating sediment if the water temperature remains constant at 20 C.

Since a BOD of 19 grams produced by 39 grams of volatile solids equals $19 \times 1{,}000/39 = 500$ grams per kilogram of volatile matter, and since the temperature factor C_T is unity at 20 C, Equation 19-4 states that

$$y_m = 3.14 \times 10^{-2} \times 500 \times 1 \times 10 \times 10^{-3} \frac{5 + 160 \times 10 \times 10^{-3}}{1 + 160 \times 10 \times 10^{-3}} \sqrt{100}$$
$$= 4.0 \text{ grams per sq m daily}$$

If the deposits are laid down in equal increments and they remain sufficiently thin to be decomposed aerobically, their maximum daily

[8] G. M. Fair, E. W. Moore, and H. A. Thomas, Jr., The natural purification of river muds and pollutional sediments, *Sewage Works J.*, *13*, 270, 756, 1209 (1941).

rate of deoxygenation will equal the BOD exerted by a single day's accession of settleable solids during a period of time equal to the period of sludge accumulation. This follows from the fact that the deposit will include the following: (1) the first day's batch of solids which is exerting its first-day demand; (2) the preceding day's batch which is exerting its second-day demand; (3) the second preceding day's batch which is exerting its third-day demand, etc., back to the beginning of sludge accumulation. In these circumstances, for example, the solids accumulating in 5 days at a daily rate of 10 grams of volatile matter per square meter of stream bottom and possessing a 5-day, 20 C BOD of 500 grams per kilogram of volatile matter, may be estimated to reach a maximum rate of deoxygenation of $500 \times 10 \times 10^{-3} = 5$ grams per square meter daily if the temperature is 20 C.

19-8. Atmospheric Reoxygenation of Polluted Waters. Aside from the oxygen released by green plants during photosynthesis, the oxygen dissolved in streams and other bodies of water and needed for the maintenance of an aerobic biological environment is derived in nature from the atmosphere with which these waters are in contact. Although photosynthesis may make considerable amounts of oxygen available, oxygenation by green plants is confined: (1) to waters that are not sufficiently degraded by pollution to destroy the green plants, which are fairly intolerant of pollution; (2) to waters that have sufficiently recovered from pollution to reestablish the presence of green plants; (3) to the hours of daylight; and (4) to the warmer (growing) seasons of the year. During the night, green aquatic plants abstract oxygen from the water. There results a diurnal cycle of dissolved oxygen within waters that are rich in vegetation, the amplitude of this cycle varying with the intensity of sunlight and the density of the plant population. For these reasons, this source of oxygen, important as it may be in the total oxygen economy of natural waters, cannot generally be included in engineering calculations of the oxygen balance of polluted waters. Reliance can be placed only on the oxygen absorbed from the atmosphere at the air-water interface. Ice cover shuts off the air contact, and winter conditions may, in certain circumstances, produce worse oxygen deficits than summer conditions, in spite of lowered rates of deoxygenation and higher oxygen-saturation values of cold waters.

The rate at which water that is not saturated with oxygen absorbs this gas from the atmosphere has been discussed in Section 18-18. If, in Equation 18-19, $(c_s - c_0) = D_a$, $(c_s - c_t) = D$, and $K_g = r$, where

D_a is the initial dissolved-oxygen deficit, D is the deficit after time t, and r is the rate of reoxygenation of the body of water, we may write

$$D = D_a e^{-rt} \qquad 19\text{-}5$$

and

$$dD/dt = -rD \qquad 19\text{-}6$$

The magnitude of r is not only a function of water temperature but also of the area of the air-water interface in relation to the volume of water and the renewal of this interface by the film-reducing movements of the water and of the air above it. The variation of r with temperature can be formulated in accordance with the van't Hoff-Arrhenius equation as

$$r = r_0 e^{C_r(T-T_0)} \qquad 19\text{-}7$$

Here C_r is the temperature characteristic of the rate of reoxygenation r, and T is the temperature of the water, the subscript zero designating the reference values. Within the range of normal water temperatures, the magnitude of C_r derived from Becker's observations [9] is about 0.018 when the water temperature is measured in degrees C.

Example 19-3. A large polluted stream flowing at low velocity contains 2.2 mg/l of dissolved oxygen at 15 C. Find: (*a*) the amount of oxygen added during 2 days of flow; (*b*) the maximum rate of reoxygenation if decomposition is sufficiently active to keep the dissolved-oxygen content of the stream at 2 mg/l. Assume a rate of reoxygenation of 0.40 per day at 20 C and a temperature characteristic of 0.018.

The DO saturation value of fresh water at 15 C is 10.2 mg/l (Table A-6). Hence the DO deficit of the stream is: $D_a = (10.2 - 2.2) = 8.0$ mg/l.

a. In accordance with Equation 19-7: $r = 0.40e^{0.018(15-20)} = 0.40 \times 0.91 = 0.36$.

By Equation 19-5, therefore: $D = 8.0e^{-0.37 \times 2} = 8.0 \times 0.47 = 3.8$ mg/l.

b. By Equation 19-6: $dD/dt = -0.37 \times 8 = -3.0$ mg/l per day. In accordance with the statement of the problem, this is also the rate of deoxygenation.

19-9. The Dissolved-Oxygen Sag. The interplay of the deoxygenation of polluted waters (BOD) and their reoxygenation, or reaeration, from the atmosphere creates a spoon-shaped profile of the dissolved-oxygen (DO) deficit along the path of water movement. This profile is called the dissolved-oxygen sag. Its genesis is portrayed in Figure 19-3. The general mathematical properties of the

[9] H. G. Becker, Mechanism of absorption of moderately soluble gases in water, *Ind. Eng. Chem.*, *16*, 1220 (1924).

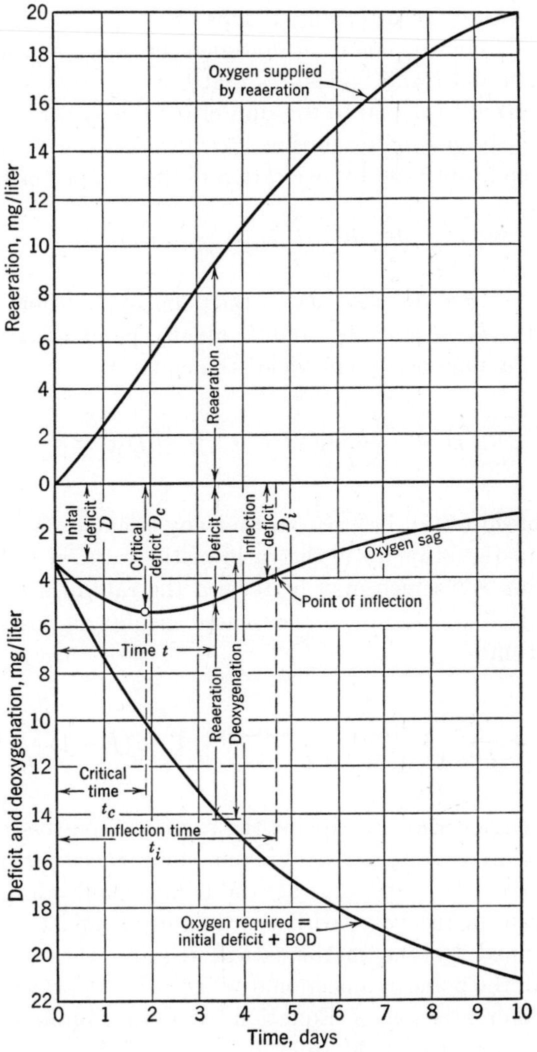

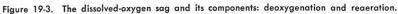

Figure 19-3. The dissolved-oxygen sag and its components: deoxygenation and reaeration.

sag curve, which underlie engineering calculations of the permissible pollutional loading of receiving waters, have been formulated in the classical studies of Streeter and Phelps.[10]

The basic differential equation that identifies the combined action of deoxygenation and reaeration states that the net rate of change in the DO deficit (dD/dt) is equal to the sum of (1) the oxygen utilization by BOD in the absence of reaeration [$dD/dt = k(L_a - y)$] and (2) the rate of oxygen absorption by reaeration in the absence of BOD ($dD/dt = -rD$), or

$$dD/dt = k(L_a - y) - rD \qquad 19\text{-}8$$

Integration between the limits D_a at the point of pollution, or reference point, [$t = 0$, $(L_a - y) = L_a$] and D at any point distant a time of flow t from the reference point yields the equation

$$D = \frac{kL_a}{r - k}(e^{-kt} - e^{-rt}) + D_a e^{-rt} \qquad 19\text{-}9$$

This relationship may be used to find any point on the oxygen-sag curve. If, in Equation 19-9, the ratio of the rates of reaeration and deoxygenation r/k which may be termed the rate of self-purification f of the particular body of water is used insofar as possible, the expression becomes

$$D = \frac{L_a}{f - 1} e^{-kt} \left\{ 1 - e^{-(f-1)kt} \left[1 - (f - 1) \frac{D_a}{L_a} \right] \right\} \qquad 19\text{-}10$$

From an engineering standpoint the sag curve possesses two points of particular interest: (1) the point of maximum deficit, or critical point, with coordinates D_c and t_c and (2) the point of inflection, or point of maximum rate of recovery, with coordinates D_i and t_i. The critical point is defined by the mathematical requirement $dD/dt = 0$ and $d^2D/dt^2 < 0$; the point of inflection by $d^2D/dt^2 = 0$. If we perform the necessary differentiation of Equation 19-9, we obtain the following simplified expressions for the times t_c and t_i and the associated deficits D_c and D_i: [11, 12]

[10] H. W. Streeter and E. B. Phelps, *U.S. Public Health Bull.* 146 (1925).

[11] G. M. Fair, The dissolved oxygen sag—an analysis, *Sewage Works J.*, *11*, 445 (1939).

[12] For the special case $f = 1$,

$$D = (ktL_a + D_a)e^{-kt};\ t_c = (1 - D_a/L_a)/k;\ t_i = (2 - D_a/L_a)/k;\ \text{and}\ t_i - t_c = 1/k$$

$$t_c = \frac{1}{k(f-1)} \log_e \left\{ f \left[1 - (f-1) \frac{D_a}{L_a} \right] \right\} \qquad 19\text{-}11$$

or

$$D_c = L_a e^{-kt_c}/f \qquad 19\text{-}12$$

and

$$t_i = \frac{1}{k(f-1)} \log_e \left\{ f^2 \left[1 - (f-1) \frac{D_a}{L_a} \right] \right\} \qquad 19\text{-}13$$

or

$$D_i = L_a e^{-kt_i}(f+1)/f^2 \qquad 19\text{-}14$$

The coordinates of these two points are related to each other as follows:

$$t_i - t_c = (\log_e f)/[k(f-1)] \qquad 19\text{-}15$$

and

$$D_i/D_c = e^{-k(t_i - t_c)}(f+1)/f \qquad 19\text{-}16$$

Example 19-4. A large stream possesses a rate of self-purification $f = 2.4$ and a rate of deoxygenation $k = 0.23$ per day. The DO deficit of the mixture of stream water and waste water at the point of reference D_a is 3.2 mg/l, and its first-stage BOD L_a is 20.0 mg/l. Find: (*a*) the DO deficit at a point 1 day distant from the point of reference; (*b*) the magnitudes of the critical time and critical deficit; and (*c*) the magnitudes of the inflection time and inflection deficit.

a. By Equation 19-10: $D = \frac{20.0}{1.4} e^{-0.23} \left[1 - e^{-1.4 \times 0.23} \left(1 - \frac{1.4 \times 3.2}{20.0} \right) \right]$ $= 5.0$ mg/l.

b. By Equation 19-11: $t_c = \frac{1}{0.23 \times 1.4} \log_e \left[2.4 \left(1 - \frac{1.4 \times 3.2}{20.0} \right) \right] = 1.93$ days, and by Equation 19-12: $D_c = 20.0e^{-0.23 \times 1.93}/2.4 = 5.3$ mg/l.

c. By Equation 19-15: $t_i = 1.93 + (\log_e 2.4)/(0.23 \times 1.4) = 4.65$ days, and by Equation 19-16: $D_i = 5.3e^{-0.23 \times 2.72}/(3.4/2.4) = 4.0$ mg/l.

The progress of self-purification can also be estimated by empirical procedures based upon straight-line relationships between suitable DO, BOD, and stream-flow parameters.

Le Bosquet and Tsivoglou,[13] for example, have observed a straight-line relationship between the critical DO concentration of large streams and stream flow as follows:

$$c_c = c_s - K/Q \qquad 19\text{-}17$$

[13] M. Le Bosquet, Jr. and E. C. Tsivoglou, Simplified dissolved oxygen computations, *Sewage and Ind. Wastes*, 22, 1054 (1950).

where c_c is the critical DO concentration in mg/l, c_s is the DO saturation value in mg/l,[14] and K is an observed river coefficient that will balance the equation when Q is the stream flow in 1,000 cfs.

Similarly, Churchill[15] has found a straight-line relationship between the DO drop in a given river stretch and the relative BOD loading of the stretch, whereby

$$\Delta c = \Delta c_n + KL_a \tag{19-18}$$

where Δc is the DO drop in mg/l, Δc_n is the normal DO drop in mg/l in the absence of new pollution, and K is an observed river coefficient that will balance the equation when L_a is the 5-day BOD load in lb/day/cfs imposed on the receiving water. A stepwise analysis identifies the DO profile of the stream.

19-10. Allowable BOD Loading of Receiving Waters. Inspection of Equations 19-10 to 19-12 shows that the pollutional load L_a that can be placed upon a particular receiving water is determined by the magnitudes of the following parameters: (1) its deoxygenation constant k; (2) its self-purification constant $f = r/k$; (3) its critical deficit D_c; and (4) its initial deficit D_a.

1. As pointed out in Section 19-6, the value of the deoxygenation constant k may be expected to vary widely in different receiving waters and along the course of these waters. Only the magnitude $k = 0.23$ per day for large streams of normal velocity appears to be well founded. Departure from this value is expected to be particularly great in shallow, swift streams filled with boulders and debris.

2. Present information on the self-purification constant $f = r/k$ supports the values at 20 C listed in Table 19-1.

This classification of different bodies of water is not sharply defined. Each class merges into its adjacent class, and there is appreciable variation within the types described, as well as within different reaches of the same body of water. In accordance with Equations 19-3 and 19-7, the variation of the self-purification constant $f = r/k$ with temperature is given by the relationship

$$f = f_0 e^{(C_r - C_k)(T - T_0)} = f_0{}^{C_f(T - T_0)} \tag{19-19}$$

For values of $C_r = 0.018$ and $C_k = 0.046$ within the range of normal water temperatures, $C_f = -0.028$, i.e., the magnitude of f decreases with rising temperatures and increases with falling temperatures by about 3% compounded per degree C.

[14] Equation 19-17 is best satisfied by DO saturation values 0.9 times the values shown in Table A-6.

[15] M. A. Churchill, Analysis of a stream's capacity for assimilating pollution, *Sewage and Ind. Wastes, 26,* 887 (1954).

TABLE 19-1. Values of the Self-Purification Constant *f*

Nature of Receiving Water	Magnitude of *f* at 20 C
Small ponds and backwaters	0.5–1.0
Sluggish streams and large lakes or impoundments	1.0–1.5
Large streams of low velocity	1.5–2.0
Large streams of moderate velocity	2.0–3.0
Swift streams	3.0–5.0
Rapids and waterfalls	Above 5.0

3. If septic conditions are to be avoided, the maximum magnitude of the critical deficit D_c is the DO saturation value S of the receiving water, e.g., 9.2 mg/l at 20 C in fresh water. For the support of game fish, such as trout, the DO content must not fall below about 5 mg/l, which gives an allowable critical deficit of but 4.2 mg/l at 20 C.

4. For given values of k, f, and D_c, the initial deficit D_a establishes two boundary values for the maximum loading that can be imposed on a receiving water: (*a*) an upper limit associated with zero initial deficit or full DO saturation ($D_a = 0$) and (*b*) a lower limit associated with an initial deficit equal to the critical deficit ($D_a = D_c$). These boundary restrictions allow the important parameters of the sag curve to be generalized in such fashion that their values need to be computed but once. They can then be recorded in tabular form, or graphically as in Figure 19-4. Loading curves between the upper and lower boundary values are included in this figure in order to make this diagram more widely useful.

Example 19-5. Find from Figure 19-4 for a water temperature of 20 C and a minimum DO content of 4.0 mg/l (1) the allowable loading and (2) the coordinates of the characteristic points of the oxygen sag of a stream with a rate of self-purification $f = 2.4$ and a rate of deoxygenation $k = 0.23$ per day under the following conditions: (*a*) maximal, $D_a = 0$, (*b*) minimal, $D_a = D_c$, and (*c*) intermediate, $D_a = 0.50D_c$ (characteristic points by calculation).

Since the DO saturation value at 20 C is 9.2 mg/l, the critical deficit of the stream is: $D_c = (9.2 - 4.0) = 5.2$ mg/l.

1. Allowable loading:

a. Maximal ($D_a/D_c = 0$): $L_a'/D_c = 4.5$; or $L_a' = 4.5 \times 5.2 = 23.4$ mg/l.

b. Minimal ($D_a/D_c = 1.0$): $L_a''/D_c = 2.4$; or $L_a'' = 2.4 \times 5.2 = 12.5$ mg/l.

c. Intermediate ($D_a/D_c = 0.5$): $L_a/D_c = 3.9$; or $L_a = 3.9 \times 5.2 = 20.3$ mg/l.

2. Coordinates of characteristic points:

a. Maximal ($D_a/D_c = 0$): $kt_c' = 0.62$; or $t_c' = 0.62/0.23 = 2.7$ days. $kt_i' = 1.24$; or $t_i' = 1.24/0.23 = 5.4$ days. $D_i/D_c = 0.76$; or $D_i = 0.76 \times 5.2 = 3.95$ mg/l.

b. Minimal ($D_a/D_c = 1.0$): $t_c'' = 0$ by definition. $t_i'' = t_c' = 2.7$ days. $D_i'' = D_i' = 3.95$ mg/l.

c. Intermediate ($D_a/D_c = 0.5$): By Equation 19-12: $e^{kt_c} = L_a/(fD_c) = 3.9/2.4 = 1.63$, and $kt_c = 0.489$; or $t_c = 0.489/0.23 = 2.1$ days. By Equation 19-15: $k(t_i - t_c) = (\log_e f)/(f - 1) = 0.8755/1.4 = 0.625$, and $kt_i =$

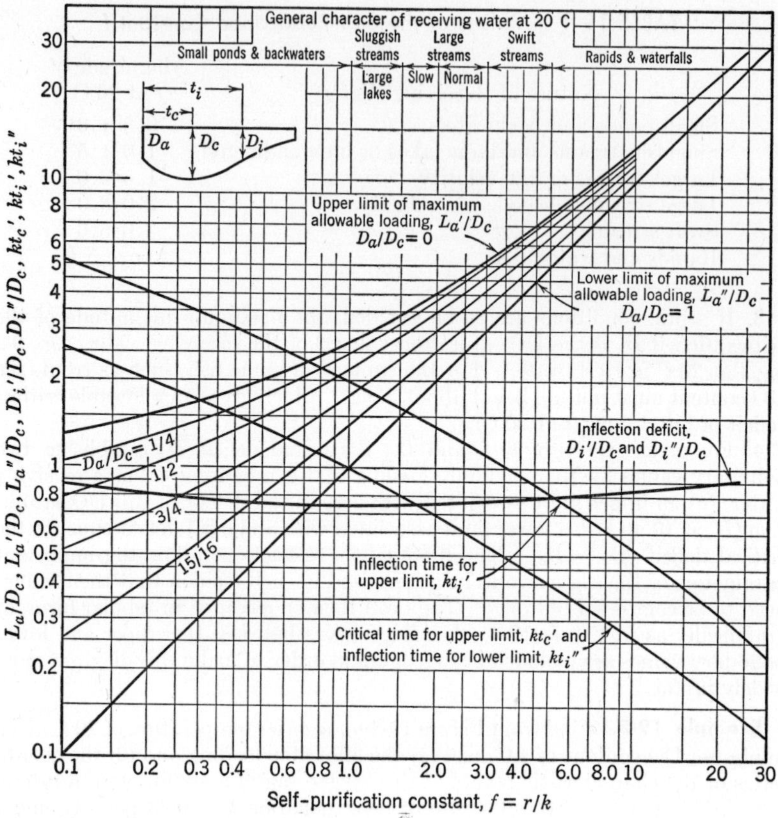

Figure 19-4. Allowable loading of receiving waters and associated coordinates of the critical point and the point of inflection of the dissolved-oxygen sag.

$(0.625 + 0.489) = 1.11$; or $t_i = 1.11/0.23 = 4.8$ days. By Equation 19-16: $D_i/D_c = e^{-0.625}(3.4/2.4) = 0.758$; or $D_i = 0.76 \times 5.2 = 3.95$ mg/l, i.e., D_i is constant.

19-11. Dilution Requirements. The amount of water into which waste matters can be discharged without creating objectionable conditions, or nuisance, is the converse of the allowable pollutional loading of receiving waters. The dilution parameter is commonly expressed as stream flow Q in cubic feet per second per 1,000 population required to avoid odor and related nuisances. Recommended values of Q include: (1) Hazen's estimate of 1898 that a sluggish stream, already partially depleted of oxygen at the point of sewage discharge, may require a diluting runoff of as much as 10 cfs per 1,000 population; (2) Stearns's estimate of 1890 that the lowest required dilution of normal streams is 2.5 cfs per 1,000 population; and (3) a commonly quoted value of 4 cfs per 1,000 population.

If waste matter with a first-stage BOD of L lb per capita daily is discharged into a stream carrying Q cfs per 1,000 population, the BOD loading is $185.5L/Q$ mg/l. For a permissible loading of L_a, therefore, the required stream flow becomes

$$Q = 185.5L/L_a \qquad \text{19-20}$$

Example 19-6. If the first-stage, 20-C BOD of combined sewage is assumed to be 0.25 lb per capita daily, find the needed dilution corresponding to the allowable loadings of Example 19-5, namely, 23.4 mg/l (maximal), 20.6 mg/l (intermediate), and 12.5 mg/l (minimal) for a DO residual of 4.0 mg/l.

By Equation 19-20, $Q = 185.5 \times 0.25/L_a = 46.4/L_a$ cfs or, respectively, 2.0, 2.3, and 3.7 cfs per 1,000 persons daily depending upon the magnitude of the initial deficit (D_a = 0, 2.6, and 5.2 mg/l, respectively).

19-12. Sewage Fields in Lakes and Coastal Waters. The natural progress of dispersion of waste waters in lakes and coastal waters is slow. The turbulence common to streams and other flowing waters is absent. Also, the waste waters are generally lower in density than the receiving waters, because the waste waters are warmer than the receiving waters and the receiving waters possess an inherently greater density when they are salt or brackish. The rate of chemical diffusion being relatively insignificant, natural mixing of the unlike waters then becomes a function of wind, currents, and (in the sea) tide. The work to be done if mixing is to disperse the wastes uniformly in the receiving waters is great. As a result, the proper design of outfalls challenges the ingenuity of the engineer.

A number of different methods are used singly, or in combination, to prevent the formation of a sewage field of considerable thickness and area at the surface of the receiving water: (1) the waste water is discharged in small amounts at a number of different points; (2) the outfall is constructed with multiple outlets that are suitably spaced and designed to accomplish as much mixing as possible; and (3) the outfall is submerged in order to induce vertical as well as horizontal dispersion of the waste matters. Horizontal or inclined, submerged discharge is more effective than vertical discharge, because the longer path followed by the rising sewage or waste water offers better opportunity for mixing. The flow pattern traced by the waste water is much like that of a smoke plume from a chimney. When the rising column of waste water reaches the surface, it spreads out horizontally in the same manner as smoke under conditions of atmospheric inversion.

Observations by the California State Board of Health [16] show that the area of the "sleek" field that is created by the discharge of raw sewage through submerged outfalls into salt water is related to the tributary population roughly as follows:

$$A = P(11.5 - 3.5 \log P) \qquad \text{19-21}$$

where A is the area in acres and $P(\lesseqgtr 1{,}000)$ is the population in thousands. This relationship is useful in making a first estimate of the length of outfall required to keep beach waters free from sleek and associated bacterial contamination. Looking at dilution as a treatment process, it is evident that the areal rate of treatment is relatively small. For a per capita discharge of Q gpd, the areal rate of treatment Q' in gallons per day per acre becomes roughly

$$Q' = 1{,}000Q/(11.5 - 3.5 \log P) \qquad \text{19-22}$$

At best, this is an areal loading of the order of magnitude of intermittent sand filters.

More exactly, the area and configuration of sewage fields is a function of the following physical factors: rate of discharge; diameter, direction, and submergence of outlet nozzle; and speed of water currents. These control the thickness and horizontal spread of the field and the associated mixing or dilution. Use of multiple outlets will normally produce some overlap but will remain advantageous. Empirical formulations of the extent of sewage fields in sea water have been developed by Rawn and Palmer.[17]

19-13. Control Works. The volume of waste water that can safely be emptied into a natural, receiving body of water can be increased not only by the proper location and design of outfalls and by suitable treatment of the waste water before discharge but also by (1) regulation of waste discharge, (2) control of the flow of the receiving water (low-water regulation), (3) strengthening the power for self-purification of the receiving water (aeration and reservoir construction), and (4) limitation of sludge deposition. The husbanding, by suitable control works, of the forces of self-purification that inhere in natural bodies of water is an important engineering responsibility.

[16] *Eng. News-Record, 123,* 690 (1939).

[17] A. M. Rawn and H. K. Palmer, Predetermining the extent of a sewage field in sea water, *Trans. Am. Soc. Civil Engrs., 94,* 1036 (1929).

19-14. Oxidation Ponds and Sewage Lagoons. Oxidation ponds are shallow basins impounded or excavated in the ground for the purpose of purifying settled sewage or other waste water by storage under climatic conditions that favor the growth of algae: namely, warmth and sunshine. Bacterial decomposition of the waste matters releases carbon dioxide; heavy growths of algae develop; ammonia and other plant-growth substances are used up; and dissolved oxygen is kept at a high level. The driving force in this type of self-purification is photosynthesis supported by a symbiosis between saprophytic bacteria and algae.

If oxidation ponds are made 2½ to 3 ft deep and hold the sewage for 2 weeks or more, a remarkable destruction of coliform organisms (possibly due in part to the production of antibiotic substances by the algae) and a satisfactory reduction in BOD are observed. The effluent is high in DO, often supersaturated during the daytime. The pond waters are so rich in algal cells that thought has been given to harvesting these cells as a source of protein for animal feed. Allowable surface loadings approach those of intermittent sand filters, but removal efficiencies are somewhat poorer. BOD loadings in the vicinity of 50 lb of 5-day, 20 C BOD per acre are generally employed. Oxidation ponds must be cleaned after an interval of several years, and weeds must be kept under control (Section 18-15).

Where oxidation ponds have been used for fish culture, settled municipal sewage has been diluted with clean water, and their surface loading has been decreased. Weed growths have then been controlled by raising ducks on the ponds.[18]

Ponds that treat raw sewage, called sewage lagoons, should be provided with central inlets in order to prevent the accumulation of sludge on the banks. Evaporation and percolation reduce the amount of effluent to be disposed of. Sewage lagoons should preferably be kept a mile from town and at least ¼ mile from the nearest habitation. Ponds of this kind should store up to 200 times the daily flow.[19] This is a surface loading of 100 persons per acre in basins about 3 ft deep serving rural communities with a per capita sewage flow of 50 gpd.[20] Since these ponds aim at complete treatment, they are also called stabilization ponds.

[18] In North America, oxidation ponds have found good use in the Southwest. Fish ponds have been managed successfully in western Europe.

[19] W. van Heuvelen and J. H. Swore, Sewage lagoons in North Dakota, *Sewage and Ind. Wastes*, *26*, 771 (1954).

[20] W. W. Towne, A. F. Bartsch, and W. H. Davis, Raw sewage stabilization ponds in the Dakotas, *Sewage and Ind. Wastes*, *29*, 377 (1957).

19-15. Disposal of Digested Sewage Sludge. Digestion of sewage sludge at 95 to 100 F reduces the concentration of coliform organisms by as much as 99.8% and the BOD by 90%. In some situations, this fraction of the pollutional load may be disposed of by pumping it into the plant effluent or by emptying it through a separate outfall. Disposal of digested sludge with effluent from primary treatment (plain sedimentation) is calculated [21] to increase the 5-day, 20 C BOD of the effluent by about 2%, the settleable solids by about 1.5 ml/l, the grease by about 20% (in miscible or emulsified form), and the chlorine requirement by about 5%. The concentration of coliforms, on the other hand, is slightly decreased by dilution.

19-16. Standards of Water Quality for Receiving Waters. Standards of quality for waters that are to serve primarily as recipients of sewage and other waste waters normally look to the preservation of the general attractiveness of natural bodies of water and to the prevention of nuisance. To this end it is usually prescribed by water pollution control agencies that receiving waters must meet the following requirements: (1) they must not contain floating or settleable solids, oil, or sludge deposits attributable to waste waters in amounts that are offensive to the sense of sight; and (2) they must not produce odors that are offensive to the sense of smell. Since the production of objectionable odors is associated most commonly with anaerobic decomposition, the amount of decomposable waste matter added to the water must not be great enough to exhaust the DO content of the water.

It is obvious that the maintenance of desirable standards of water quality implies a proper balance between (*a*) the volume (and where necessary the quality) of the receiving water and (*b*) the volume and strength of the waste water. Attaining a proper balance may require a prescription of the degree of treatment to which sewage and other waste waters must be submitted before discharge.

A classification of receiving waters according to use and requisite quality which includes a statement of needed sewage treatment is presented in Table 19-2. This table is based on a similar compilation by Imhoff and Fair.[22] The suggestions contained in Columns 3, 4, and 5 of this table must be interpreted broadly. They should not be

[21] A. M. Rawn and F. R. Bowerman, Disposal of digested sludge by dilution, *Sewage and Ind. Wastes, 26,* 1309 (1954).

[22] Karl Imhoff and Gordon M. Fair, *Sewage Treatment,* John Wiley and Sons, New York, 2nd Ed., 1956, p. 302.

TABLE 19-2. Classification of Receiving Waters According to Use and Requisite Quality

		Required Treatment of Sewage before Discharge		
Use (1)	Standards of Quality at Low-Water Stage (2)	Normal (3)	Emergency (4)	Required Treatment of Water before Use Shown in Column (1) (5)
Industrial uses not needing a high-quality water; irrigation of crops not subject to contamination when intended for human consumption; and receipt of wastes without the creation of nuisance	Absence of nuisance—odors, slick, and unsightly suspended or floating matters; dissolved oxygen present at outfall	Sedimentation except when receiving waters are large in volume	Chlorination for removal of hydrogen sulfide; addition of nitrate to supply oxygen	Sometimes none; chlorination where needed
Fishing; recreational boating; raising of seed oysters; and industrial use after treatment	Absence of slick, odors, and visible floating and suspended solids DO $\geqq$ 3 mg/l and preferably $\geqq$ 5 mg/l; $CO_2 <$ 40 mg/l and preferably $<$20 mg/l	Sedimentation, chemical precipitation, or biological treatment depending upon degree of dilution	Aeration; addition of diluting waters	Withdrawal of water not implied
Bathing, recreation, and shellfish culture	Clear; no visible sewage matter; a coliform IN less than 100 to 1,000 per 100 ml depending on length of bathing season; DO near saturation	Sedimentation, chemical precipitation, or biological treatment, depending upon degree of dilution; chlorination of effluent	Heavy chlorination	Withdrawal of water not implied
Drinking water and related uses	Chemical standards for substances not removable by common water-treatment methods; clear; DO near saturation; coliform MPN of 50/100 ml when chlorination is the only treatment; up to 20,000/100 ml when treatment is complete	Sedimentation, chemical precipitation or biological treatment depending upon degree of dilution; chlorination of effluent	Heavy chlorination	Chlorination when coliform MPN is less than 50/100 ml; pre- and post-chlorination, coagulation, sedimentation, and filtration when coliform MPN is up to 20,000/100 ml

regarded as rigid rules. A sufficiently long stretch of receiving water must be considered as a whole to permit evaluation of treatment requirements in terms of the indicated standards of water quality and classes of water use.

20 Industrial Water Supply and Waste-Water Disposal

20-1. Water and Waste-Water Problems of Industry. Industries require large volumes of water for cooling purposes, steam generation, manufacturing processes, and sanitation. In the production of basic commodities like metals, chemicals, foods, and textiles, the tonnage of water may well exceed that of other raw materials. Finishing and fabrication processes generally need smaller, but nevertheless appreciable, amounts of water. Most of the water used becomes waste water and may carry a heavy burden of polluting substances. For economy of water supply and waste-water disposal, plants that need large amounts of water are commonly located on sizable rivers, lakes, or tidal estuaries. Upon these they impress their presence in numerous ways that are of concern to the water engineer. The supply of water to a given industry and the removal of its waste waters must be based upon an understanding of the manufacturing processes that require water and produce waste water. A discussion of even the most common industrial processes, however, falls beyond the scope of this book.

Water Supply for Industries

20-2. Quantity and Quality Requirements. The amounts of water used by industry vary widely not only with the type of industrial operation but also with the following: (1) the availability and cost of water; (2) the difficulty of waste-water disposal; (3) the nature of the processes and equipment employed; and (4) the attention given by management and public authorities to water conservation. Among possible measures of conservation by management are: (1) the recirculation of cooling water through ponds or towers; (2) the use of countercurrent washing equipment; (3) the reuse of slightly soiled water (either in the same process after repurification, or in other processes that do not require water of high quality); and (4) the prevention of waste, such as letting flushing lines run continuously. Ranges in amounts of process waters for different industries are given in Table 20-3. To them must be added the water evaporated in the generation of steam for power or other purposes. If the quantities consumed are broken down according to their quality requirements, it may be found that a large percentage of the water, such as cooling water, need not be of high sanitary or chemical quality, although the remaining water, such as high-pressure boiler feed-water and water used in food processing, may have to comply with very strict quality specifications.

The quality tolerances for process waters vary with the manufacturing process and with the quality of the goods to be produced. Many industrial products or operations call for water that is clear, colorless, tasteless, relatively soft, free from iron, manganese, hydrogen sulfide, and organic matter, and of approved bacteriological quality. Examples are: bottled beverages, fine chemicals, canned goods, processed milk, ice, packed meat, edible oils, laundering operations, and the printing and dyeing of textiles. Most municipal soft waters are of this nature. Process waters drawn from a private source, however, may have to be purified. The principles of treatment discussed for municipal water supplies apply equally well to the large body of process waters.

Wash waters should be soft when soap is the detergent and when deposition of residues by evaporating rinse water is to be avoided. Among industries that are sensitive to hardness are laundries, electroplating plants, milk plants, ice plants, and textile mills. They generally soften or demineralize the available water. Breweries, distilleries, and bakeries, on the other hand, require relatively hard water for some manufacturing operations and may have to add hardness. Pulp and paper mills, tanneries, oil refineries, and steel mills do not commonly need water of municipal quality. But they may have other requirements. Paper pulp and low-quality paper can be made with colored water that contains as much as 50 mg/l of turbidity, but it should be low in iron and manganese, hardness, and carbon dioxide. Formation of organic slimes and mineral scales must also be kept under control. By contrast, high-quality paper can be manufactured only with high-quality water. The situation is much the same in tanning. In oil refineries and steel mills, water is used primarily for steam production and cooling. Quality requirements for the cooling water of these industries are much the same as those for cooling waters in general (Section 20-6). In the rolling of steel, however, a chloride content above 150 mg/l in cooling water causes rapid deterioration of rolls. Quality tolerances for a variety of process waters are summarized in Table 20-1. Quality requirements for boiler feed-water are discussed in Section 20-5.

20-3. Selection of Source. Industrial water supplies are either purchased from a municipality or developed privately. Multiple sources of supply are common. Examples are cooling water drawn from a stream, lake, or estuary; process water or water used for special cooling purposes drawn from the ground; and drinking water and, possibly, boiler feed-water purchased from a municipality. Use of multiple sources by large industries may render the planning, design, and management of their supplies quite complex.

Many of the difficulties encountered in industrial water supply stem from the concentration of too many industries in too small an area. Resulting heavy overdrafts on ground-water sources then point to the eventual impairment of water quality and to the possible depletion of the supply. Manufacturers should, therefore, be encouraged to scatter their plants and to anticipate the effects of future expansion of their own and other industries upon the abundance and quality of available water resources.

20-4. Selection of Treatment Processes. The cost of water treatment and the associated economic gain are important elements in comparisons of alternate sources of supply. Necessary studies may be stimulated also by the deterioration of existing supplies or by demands for better quality or quality control of manufactured products. The situation is again more complex than for municipal supplies. Not only may the water have to be "tailored" to fit specific uses, but the number of treatment processes from which a selection can be made is generally larger than for public supplies. By way of illustration, hardness is removed from industrial water supplies, in practice, by at least ten different processes: (1) cold lime, (2) cold lime-soda, (3) cold lime-barium, (4) hot lime-soda, (5) hot phosphate, (6) sodium-cation exchange, (7) lime followed by sodium-cation exchange, (8) hydrogen-cation exchange, (9) hydrogen-cation exchange followed by anion exchange, and (10) distillation.

The ways of purifying water discussed in earlier chapters are ap-

TABLE 20-1. Quality Tolerances for Industrial Process Waters *

All values are expressed in parts per million.

Industry or Use	Turbidity	Color	Hardness as $CaCO_3$	Iron as Fe	Manganese as Mn	Total Solids	Alkalinity as $CaCO_3$	Odor Taste	Hydrogen Sulfide	Other Requirements
Air conditioning	..	..	...	0.5 †	0.5	...	...	Low	1	No corrosiveness or slime formation
Baking	10	10	...	0.2 †	0.2	...	...	Low	0.2	Potable water
Brewing, light beer	10	..	...	0.1 †	0.1	500	75	Low	0.2	Potable, NaCl less than 275 ppm, *p*H 6.5–7.0
dark beer	10	..	...	0.1 †	0.1	1,000	150	Low	0.2	Potable, NaCl less than 275 ppm, *p*H 7.0 or more
Canning, legumes	10	..	25–75	0.2 †	0.2	...	...	Low	1	Potable
general	10	..	...	0.2 †	0.2	...	...	Low	1	Potable
Carbonated beverages	2	10	250	0.2(0.3) †	0.2	850	50–100	Low	0.2	Potable, organic color plus oxygen consumed less than 10 ppm
Confectionery	..	..	...	0.2 †	0.2	100	...	Low	0.2	Potable
Cotton bandage	5	5	...	0.2 †	0.2	...	...	Low	...	
Food, general	10	..	...	0.2 †	0.2	...	...	Low	...	Potable
Ice	5	5	...	0.2 †	0.2	...	...	Low	...	Potable, SiO_2 less than 10 ppm
Laundering	..	..	50	0.2 †	0.2	...	...	....	...	
Paper and pulp, ground wood	50	20	180	1.0 †	0.5	...	...	....	...	No grit or corrosiveness
kraft pulp	25	15	100	0.2 †	0.1	300	...	....	...	
soda and sulfite	15	10	100	0.1 †	0.05	200	...	....	...	
high-grade light papers	5	5	50	0.1 †	0.05	200	...	....	...	No slime formation
Plastics, clear, uncolored	2	2	...	0.02 †	0.02	200	...	....	...	
Rayon (Viscose), pulp production	5	5	8	0.05 †	0.03	100	Total 50, hydroxide 8	....	...	Al_2O_3 less than 8 ppm, SiO_2 less than 25 ppm
manufacture	0.3	..	55	0.0	0.0	...	...	....	...	Cu less than 5 ppm, *p*H 7.8 to 8.3
Tanning	20	10–100	50–135	0.2 †	0.2	...	Total 135, hydroxide 8	....	...	
Textiles, general	5	20	...	0.25	0.25	...	...	....	...	
dyeing	5	5–20	...	0.25 †	0.25	200	...	....	...	Constant composition, residual alumina less than 0.5 ppm
Wool scouring	..	70	...	1.0 †	1.0	...	...	Low	...	

* Progress Report, Committee on Quality Tolerances of Water for Industrial Uses, *J. New Eng. Water Works Assoc.*, *54*, 271 (1940).
† Limit given applies to both iron alone and the sum of iron and manganese.

plicable also to industrial supplies. But there are some treatment processes that are peculiarly suited to specific industrial needs. The preparation of boiler feed-water and of cooling water are examples.

20-5. Feed Water for Boilers. In the operation of boilers, foaming, priming, scale formation, caustic embrittlement, and corrosion mount with operating pressures. Foaming and priming entrain moisture and solids in steam. The solids carried over may then be deposited in steam lines and in turbines and other equipment. The intercrystalline cracking of boiler metal, called caustic embrittlement, is associated (1) with localized stresses that have strained the metal beyond its elastic limit and (2) with a high concentration of caustic soda in the absence of an adequate concentration of sulfate in the feed water. Failure generally occurs at riveted seams and similar places of confined extent that have been subjected to stresses of high intensity. Table 20-2 suggests feed-water tolerances for different pressures. The values listed take into account (1) that reductions in turbidity, color,

TABLE 20-2. Feed-Water Quality Tolerances for Boilers Operated at Different Pressures *

All values but the *p*H value are expressed in parts per million.

	Pressure, psig			
Measure of Quality	0 to 150	150 to 250	250 to 400	Over 400
Turbidity	20	10	5	1
Color	80	40	5	2
Oxygen consumed	15	10	4	3
Dissolved oxygen (O_2) †	1.5	0.1	0	0
Hydrogen sulfide (H_2S) ‡	5	3	0	0
Total hardness ($CaCO_3$)	80	40	10	2
Sulfate carbonate ratio (Na_2SO_4:Na_2CO_3)	1:1	2:1	3:1	..
Aluminum oxide (Al_2O_3)	5	0.5	0.05	0.01
Silica (SiO_2)	40	20	5	0
Bicarbonate (HCO_3^-)	50	30	5	0
Carbonate ($CO_3^{=}$)	200	100	40	20
Hydroxide (OH^-)	50	40	30	15
Total solids §	3,000 to 500	2,500 to 500	1,500 to 100	50
Minimum *p*H value	8.0	8.4	9.0	9.6

* Progress Report, Committee on Quality Tolerances of Water for Industrial Uses, *J. New Eng. Water Works Assoc.*, *54*, 261 (1940).

† Feed-water entering boiler.

‡ Except when odor in live steam is objectionable.

§ Depends on design of boiler.

organic matter (as measured by oyxgen consumed), and total solids decrease foaming and priming; (2) that reductions in hardness, silica, and alumina alleviate scale formation; (3) that maintenance of a high ratio of sulfate to carbonates controls caustic embrittlement; and (4) that elimination of oxygen, reduction of bicarbonate ions, and increase in *p*H suppress corrosion. Municipal water supplies, as well as private water supplies, must generally be suitably prepared for use in high-pressure boilers.

Water suited to the boiler pressure can be, and often is, softened and demineralized by the procedures described in Sections 14-3 and 14-5. Since boiler feed-water must be heated in any event and treatment becomes more efficient at elevated temperatures, hot processes are often substituted for cold processes: chemical reactions are quicker; the solubility of important precipitates is lower; the agglomeration of flocs is prompter; and the rate of settling of precipitates is faster. Whereas a settling period of 8 to 10 hours is required in cold, lime-soda softening, for example, only 2 to 3 hours are needed at 100 F and but an hour at 212 F.

Hot softeners are generally operated at temperatures of 212 F or more. For this reason, reaction tanks are made of steel and covered. As shown in Figure 20-1, the cold water enters the tank through a float-controlled valve that holds the water surface at the desired level. Solutions of chemicals are automatically proportioned to the inflow

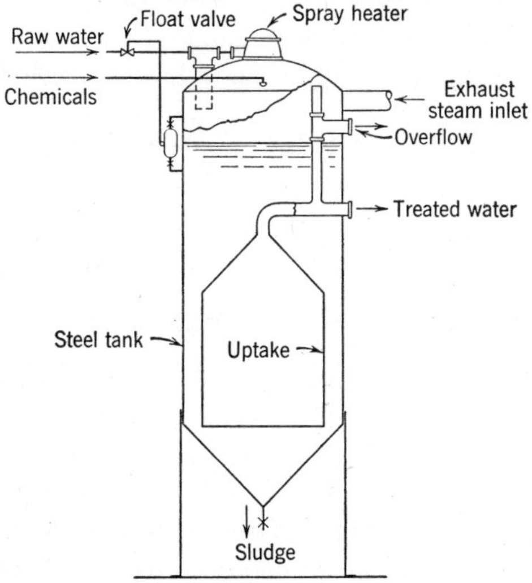

Figure 20-1. Enclosed, heated water softener. ***Permutit Co.***

which is heated by steam as it enters the tank. Tanks are generally elaborated to include a mixing and flocculating chamber, a settling compartment, and a conical sludge hopper. The softened water is drawn from the settling compartment and passed through a pressure filter to remove colloidal precipitates before it is fed to the boiler. Crushed, anthracite-coal or other non-siliceous grains are used as the filtering medium, in order to avoid silica pick-up. The filter is backwashed with hot softened water, and the wash water is returned to the softener. Sludge and boiler blowdown, too, are sometimes recirculated through the softener in order to economize on chemicals.

High boiler pressures, as indicated in Table 20-2, call for more effective silica removal, for deactivation, and for acid treatment to prevent scaling, corrosion, and caustic embrittlement.

a. Softening. The principal methods of softening are hot lime-soda softening and hot phosphate softening. The hot lime-soda process does not differ in its elements from the cold process (Section 14-3*a*), but it is more economical of space and chemicals and produces a softer water.

Phosphates and caustic soda will precipitate calcium as tricalcium phosphate and magnesium as magnesium hydroxide. Magnesium may also be precipitated in the absence of caustic soda; probably by the hydrolysis of magnesium phosphate. The addition of caustic soda has the advantage of removing silicates. Both the calcium and magnesium precipitates are substantially insoluble at elevated temperatures. Water of very low hardness can, therefore, be produced. The reactions which result in precipitation of hardness are:

$$Na_3PO_4 \rightleftharpoons 3Na^+ + PO_4^{\equiv} \qquad 20\text{-}1$$

$$3Ca^{++} + 2PO_4^{\equiv} \rightleftharpoons Ca_3(PO_4)_2 \downarrow \qquad 20\text{-}2$$

$$NaOH \rightleftharpoons Na^+ + OH^- \qquad 20\text{-}3$$

$$Mg^{++} + 2OH^- \rightleftharpoons Mg(OH)_2 \downarrow \qquad 14\text{-}10$$

When hot, phosphate-softened water is passed through equipment such as economizers and closed heaters, in which there is a marked rise in temperature, after-precipitation may occur unless the water has been stabilized by lowering its *p*H value, or the formation of scales is prevented by adding organic inhibitors. Required dosages and resultant water quality are determined in accordance with the principles laid down in Sections 14-3 and 14-6.

b. Removal of silica. Natural waters may contain more than 100 mg/l of silica in solution. This silica forms troublesome scales of calcium and magnesium silicates and analcite ($Na_2O_3 \cdot Al_2O_3 \cdot 4SiO_2 \cdot 2H_2O$) in high-pressure boilers and deposits hard, glassy scales on turbine blades when it is carried over in steam. Silica can be removed by highly basic anion exchangers after the decarbonation step of the common, ion-exchange, demineralizing process. Fluosilicates are also removed. Distillation frees water from silica along with all other minerals. The principles of ion exchange and distillation have been discussed in Section 14-5. Quite different in action is the adsorption of silica on hydrous precipitates of magnesium and iron oxides.

Hot-process removal of silica by magnesium is ordinarily ancillary to hot lime-soda or hot phosphate softening. Separate treatment of cold as well as hot water is also effective. The compounds employed include magnesium sulfate, dolomitic lime, calcium magnesite, magnesium carbonate, and magnesium oxide. Magnesium oxide is preferred for the hot removal of silica because of its high effectiveness, and because its use does not increase the dissolved-solids content of the water or call for an increase in lime and soda when the water is to be softened. The natural magnesium hardness of the water which is precipitated in softening assists in the removal of silica.

Because their solubility increases with temperature, hydrous ferric oxides are normally added only to cold water. From 10 to 20 mg/l of ferric sulfate are required for each mg/l of silica to be removed. Considerable quantities of anions are released. This, together with the expense, limits the application of ferric hydroxide to feed waters that are turbid and must be coagulated in any case.

c. Deactivation. In order to control corrosion, oxygen is removed from boiler feed-water by de-aeration, external chemical treatment, or internal chemical treatment. Polyphosphates are widely used for internal treatment because of their corrosion-inhibiting properties. As sequestering agents, they reduce scaling by causing boiler salines to precipitate as soft sludges that can be removed by blowdown.

De-aeration of boiler water to remove oxygen and carbon dioxide, and incidentally nitrogen, is accomplished by boiling or atomizing the water at elevated temperatures. De-aerating heaters (Figure 20-2) may be operated above, at, or below atmospheric pressure. For hot-process softening, a de-aeration unit is ordinarily built into the feed-water heater. As shown in Figure 20-2, feed water, which has been warmed in a vent condenser that recovers most of the steam used for heating and de-aeration, is sprayed into the steam chamber at the top

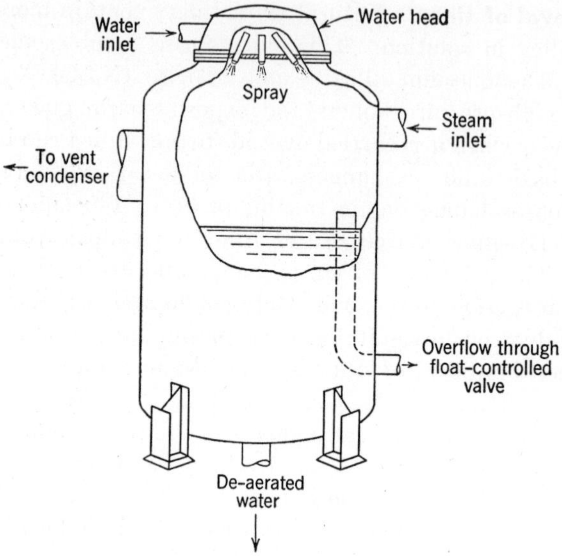

Figure 20-2. De-aerating heater. *Permutit Co.*

of the heater along with trap returns. The water is heated by the steam and loses all but about 0.4 mg/l of its dissolved oxygen. The hot water then passes in countercurrent flow against the incoming steam through a scrubber. More heat is added, and the dissolved oxygen is further reduced. The now slightly superheated water falls into the de-aerated water-storage compartment, where flashing completes the removal of oxygen usually to less than 0.007 mg/l. Gases escape from the system through the vent condenser, along with a small amount of steam.

Residual dissolved oxygen may be removed by maintaining in the boiler water an excess of up to 30 mg/l of sodium sulfite (Na_2SO_3, mol. wt. 126.1). The oxidation-reduction reaction is

$$2Na_2SO_3 + O_2 \rightarrow 2Na_2SO_4 \qquad 20\text{-}4$$

and it proceeds quite rapidly in hot water, especially in the presence of an excess of sodium sulfite.

d. Reduction of alkalinity and pH. Boiler feed-waters (in particular sodium-cation-exchange, softened waters) are treated with acid to reduce their alkalinity and to increase their sulfate-to-carbonate ratio. Acid is added either before or after softening. The acid can also be introduced by passing a portion of the water through a cation exchanger operated on the hydrogen cycle (split treatment). Sulfuric acid will not only acidify the water but will also increase the sulfate to carbonate ratio. The acid reacts with alkaline constituents of the water to form carbon dioxide. This is removed in the de-aerating heater. The total dissolved-solids content of the water is little affected.

When part of the water is softened in a sodium-cation exchanger and the balance is passed through a hydrogen-cation exchanger, the sulfuric and hydrochloric acid produced will destroy the alkalinity of the mixed water. The quality of the mixture can be controlled by varying the proportions of water treated in each kind of exchanger. If the sulfate content of the raw water is quite low, sodium sulfate may have to be added to the softened water in order to reach the desired sulfate-carbonate ratio.

20-6. Cooling Water. Cooling water should not form scales, deposit sediment, promote the growth of slimes, or cause corrosion. However, the most troublesome "contaminant" of cooling water is often the heat which raises the temperature of natural waters that must serve one industry after another along a water course. In the processing of food and beverages, cooling water should be as good as drinking water in bacterial purity and freedom from toxic metals. Otherwise, almost any source of water, including sea water, treated sewage, and polluted river water can be used for cooling purposes. Because of their seasonally uniform and low temperature, ground waters are drawn upon heavily as cooling waters. During the winter, a shift is sometimes made to surface waters.

Cooling-water systems are of three types: (1) once-through systems, (2) open recirculating systems, and (3) closed recirculating systems. Means for the control of scale formation and corrosion vary accordingly.

In once-through systems, the water can be stabilized (Section 14-6) at a point at which protective layers of calcium carbonate are maintained on cooling surfaces, and a sequestering or surface-active agent can be added to prevent excessive deposition at points of high temperature. Included in the surface active agents are polyphosphates (Section 14-7), tannins, starches, and lignins. These can be used singly or in different combinations. They broaden the solubility range of scale-forming substances and counterbalance the oversaturation of scale-forming minerals.

In open recirculating systems, the evaporation of water in cooling ponds or towers increases its dissolved-solids concentration, while windage loss removes dissolved solids from the system.[1] The cycles of concentration through which the water passes equal the sum of the evaporation and windage losses divided by the windage loss, all expressed as proportions or percentages of the total water use. If the windage loss is not high enough, the mineral concentration can be held within desired limits (1) by bleeding recirculating water from the system, (2) by softening or demineralizing the make-up water, or (3) by lowering the alkalinity of the recirculating water with acid. In other respects, scaling and corrosion can be reduced as in once-through systems. However, larger concentrations of surface-active agents (30 to 100 mg/l) are usually needed to offset the increased dissolved-solids concentration of the recirculating water.

In closed cooling systems, there is but little make-up water, and scaling is reduced. Corrosion is decreased for the same reason and because the water is not aerated. Corrosion may be further reduced by stabilization, deactivation, vacuum de-aeration, or the addition of inhibitors.

Slime and algal growths in condensers and other heat exchangers may seriously impair their operation. Where such growths are allowed to develop, they must be cleaned out periodically. This is a costly operation when it requires dismantling of the equipment. It is generally cheaper to add to the cooling water chemicals, such as copper sulfate, chlorine, and chloramine, that will either prevent the formation of growths or destroy existing growths (Chapter 18). Ordinarily, the chemicals are added intermittently in heavy doses. An example is the application of chlorine in amounts that will produce an excess of several milligrams per liter of free available chlorine for 30 min a day to prevent slime growths in the main condensers of a power plant.

Disposal of Industrial Waste-Waters

20.7. Nature of Industrial Waste-Waters. Most industrial waste-waters are derived from cooling, washing, flushing, extracting, impregnating, chemical treatment, and similar operations. They are as varied in quantity and nature as the products and processes of the mills from which they drain. Their spectrum ranges from the discharge of great volumes of cooling water that is "contaminated" only

[1] Evaporation loss is about 1% for each drop in temperature of 10 F through the pond or tower. Windage losses are 1.0 to 5.0% for spray ponds, 0.3 to 1.0% for atmospheric towers, and 0.1 to 0.3% for mechanical-draft towers.

with heat to the emptying of relatively small but concentrated baths that are so loaded with inorganic and organic substances as to be on the verge of jelling. Quite different in origin are the drainage waters from coal mines and the brines from oil fields. Coal-mine drainage may continue to give trouble long after the working of the mines has been stopped.

The discharge or treatment of the waste waters of certain industries has been known to cause far worse difficulties than the discharge or treatment of the domestic sewage of the community in which the industries are situated. Toxic metals and chemicals may destroy the biological activity of streams and municipal sewage-treatment works and render receiving waters unfit for further use. In the manufacture of organic chemicals, the wastes may impart to receiving waters tastes and odors that are almost impossible of removal in water-purification plants. Strong acids and alkalies may render receiving waters corrosive and expensive to purify. Suspended solids may settle in receiving waters and smother aquatic life. Excessive concentrations of organic matter may overtax municipal sewage-treatment works and rapidly exhaust the natural purifying capacity of receiving waters. Oils, dyes, and floating solids may render receiving waters and their banks unsightly and interfere with the rights of riparian owners.

The tests that identify the strength and characteristics of domestic sewage cannot be applied to the analysis of industrial waste-waters, unless this is done with an understanding of their limitations and unless they are supplemented by tests that evaluate more specific properties of the waste waters. Toxic wastes, for example, may have a high chemical demand for oxygen but exert a biochemical oxygen demand that is quite low, although much organic matter is present. Reduction of toxic constituents below threshold limits (by dilution in the laboratory or in receiving waters) will permit biological activity to establish itself. The total oxygen demand may then increase with increasing dilution of the waste, although the chemical oxygen demand is decreased. To cite another example, the chemical tests commonly included in a sanitary water analysis will not record the presence or danger of toxic metals or of toxic organic and inorganic complexes. Higher organisms, such as fingerlings or minnows, may have to be placed in graded dilutions of the waste-water with receiving water in order to measure the nature and intensity of poisoning effects. Since toxic chemicals are often specific in their physiological action, even such tests may be of but limited value. The ecology of a receiving water is affected by the destruction of any one group of the many living organisms through which the food chain of self-purification is maintained. The synergistic, or combined, effect of different toxic chemicals may be more marked than their isolated actions.

The quantity and strength of waste waters from a given industry vary within wide limits depending on the manufacturing processes employed and the methods of their control in different plants. The approximate composition of waste waters that possess high BOD values is listed in Table 20-3. The total weight of BOD discharged from a plant employing relatively few people may equal that of the domestic sewage from a city of fair size. As stated in Section 12-5, the population equivalent of the BOD of industrial waste waters is the ratio of their BOD to the per capita BOD normally exerted by domestic or combined sewage. Similar comparative values can be calculated for suspended solids and other characteristic pollutants.

20-8. Reduction, Recovery, and Re-Use of Water and Waste Matters. In critical situations, or in the interest of preserving water assets and reducing the cost of sewage treatment, the pollution of receiving waters or the loading of sewage-treatment works by industrial waste-waters can be reduced in a variety of ways: (1) by altering manufacturing processes to decrease the volume and concentration of waste waters, (2) by developing means for the recovery of useful and marketable by-products from the waste waters or industrial processes, and (3) by treatment and re-use of process waters within the plant. Only when these possibilities have been exhausted should the waste waters be allowed to be (1) discharged into municipal sewers (either in their raw state or after treatment) or (2) treated by themselves preparatory to direct disposal into available receiving waters or onto land.

A significant reduction in the volume and concentration of waste waters can be effected in almost all industries in which draining, rinsing, and spillage are important sources of waste matters. The following are illustrative examples: (1) reduction of the loss of milk, whey, and buttermilk in the manufacture of milk products (*a*) by fuller drainage of cans, churns, and other vessels prior to washing, and (*b*) by introduction of a preliminary, low-volume, cold-water rinse from which food products can be recovered by evaporation; (2) adequate drainage (assisted by shaking) of plated pieces upon their removal from electroplating baths and use of preliminary, low-volume, rinse waters to make up or replenish the baths; (3) reduction of spillage in dyeing, printing, chemical treating, food processing, as

TABLE 20-3. Approximate Quantities and Concentration of Industrial Waste-Waters

After E. W. Moore

Waste Water	Production Unit	Gallons per Unit	Suspended solids, mg/l	5-Day BOD, mg/l	Special Characteristics
Beet sugar *	1 ton beets	3,000–4,000	800	450	Without Steffens' waste †
	...	...	...	700–2,000	With Steffens' waste
Brewery	1 barrel beer	300–1,000	250–650	500–1,200	...
Cannery	1 ton stock	2,500–8,000	200–3,000	300–4,000	...
Coal washing	1 ton coal	600–2,400	3,000–150,000	...	Fine coal
Distillery	1 bushel grain	45–55	20,000–40,000	15,000–20,000	Starchy
	100 gal molasses	200–300	...	20,000–30,000	High in potash
Gas and coke	1 ton coal	200–400	200–3,000	1,000–6,000	Phenols 1,000–5,000 mg/l in untreated liquor
Laundry	100 lb clothes	1,500	400–1,000	300–1,000	Alkaline
Malthouse *	100 bushel barley	800	...	400	...
Milk plant	1,000 lb milk	100–225	...	300–2,000	Lactose, sours readily
Oil-well brine	100 gal oil	4–2,800	...	...	Total solids 11,000 to 325,000 mg/l
Packing house, small	1 hog ‡	1,000–1,500	500–1,500	600–2,000	High in fats, proteins
large	1 hog ‡	500–800	400–1,000	350–1,000	...
Paper-making	1 ton paper	5,000–100,000	150–1,000	20–100	Fiber, clay
Paper pulp, ground-wood	1 ton pulp	0–12,000	500	20	...
sulfite	1 ton pulp	30,000–100,000	100–150	400	...
sulfite cooker-liquor	1 ton pulp	2,000–3,600	...	16,000–25,000	Lignin, sulfites
Tannery	100 lb hides	600–700	1,000–5,000	500–5,000	High in lime
Textile, cotton kier §	100 lb goods	120–250	...	1,000–1,600	High in caustic alkali
kier-liquor only	100 lb goods	30	...	4,000–8,000	...
cotton kier and bleach	100 lb goods	1,000–1,600	...	100–200	High in oxidizing agents
Flax retting *	1 ton straw	5,300	...	1,800–2,800	...
Fulling *	...	...	4,000	520	...
Silk boiling *	100 lb silk	850	100–500	700–1,000	...
Sulfur dye (dye-bath only)	100 lb goods	500–1,800	...	1,000–2,000	Sulfides
Wool-scouring, batch	100 lb wool	160–500	1,000–170,000	200–10,000	Wool grease
countercurrent	100 lb wool	40–100	1,000–170,000	200–10,000	Wool grease

* Data from one source only.

† The Steffens process precipitates tricalcium sucrate from beet juices that have yielded their crystallizable sugar. Steffens' waste is the liquor filtered from the sucrate.

‡ 1 steer = 2.5 hogs; 1 sheep or calf = 1 hog.

§ A kier is a tub.

well as other operations, in which floor washings become water-carried wastes; and (4) use of countercurrent washing and rinsing of wool, which reduces the amount of water by 80%.

Examples of the recovery of salable or usable industrial wastes are the recovery of (1) copper and sulfuric acid from spent copper-pickling liquor, (2) copperas from spent steel-pickling liquor, (3) alkalies from mercerizing processes, (4) feed from distillery slop, (5) fiber from paper-mill wastes, and (6) palm oil from cold-rolling-mill wastes. Economic factors that may militate against recovery of waste materials are: (1) fluctuating or glutted markets and (2) the necessity for establishing separate marketing organizations for by-products because they are so unlike the articles of manufacture themselves.

Examples of process waters that can be re-used are: (1) the white waters of paper mills,[2] the development of objectionable slime growths being controlled by chlorination; (2) the flume and wash waters of the beet-sugar industry after sedimentation or lagooning; and (3) the spent dye baths or rinse waters of textile mills. The last-named waters can be used for the preparation of dye solutions.

20-9. Disposal with Domestic Sewage. The discharge of industrial waste-waters into municipal sewerage systems may be advantageous (1) when the waste waters become more amenable to treatment after they have been mixed with domestic sewage; (2) when treatment of combined wastes is more economical because of the increased size of the operation; and (3) when treatment of the combined wastes is more effective and economical because of the technical and sanitary supervision available in the municipal works. Waste waters should not be emptied into public sewers when there is evidence that their admission would result in (1) nuisances or hazards, (2) clogging or damage to the sewers, or (3) interference with existing treatment processes. Greases and oils, flammable solvents, hot liquids, concentrated acids and alkalies, poisonous substances, putrescent materials, and large and heavy solids are examples of objectionable waste matters. They may have to be removed from waste waters or modified by preliminary treatment at the industrial plant before discharge into the public sewerage system. Sometimes the blending of different wastes or the regulated release of waste waters (either uniformly or in proportion to the flow of domestic sewage) is all that is needed.

[2] White water contains fiber, size, dye, and loading materials that have passed through the wires, showers, and felts of paper-making machines. They will support heavy growths of slime-forming organisms, both lower and higher bacteria.

Biological treatment processes have a marked ability to adapt themselves to toxic wastes, especially when the concentration of toxic substances is raised gradually and a sufficiently long breaking-in period is allowed. Shock loads, however, may be fatal. Of the biological growths, trickling-filter slimes are quite resistant to variable loadings; activated sludges are not. High BOD, suspended-matter content, or volume of industrial waste-waters may demand additional plant capacity to handle the industrial load.

In the public interest, operating authorities should be empowered: (1) to exclude objectionable or dangerous wastes from sewerage systems; (2) to specify the manner of waste-water discharge into such systems; (3) to require pretreatment of industrial waste-waters; and (4) to determine, negotiate, and levy appropriate charges upon industry for acceptance and disposal of water-carried industrial wastes.

20-10. Methods of Separate Treatment and Disposal. Available methods for treating and disposing of industrial waste-waters by themselves are generally quite like those for domestic sewage. They include: screening; lagooning; sedimentation with or without neutralization, coagulation, or precipitation; biological treatment; and ultimate disposal of the treated liquids into receiving waters or onto land.

Racks find some use. More often, however, fine screens take their place in order to recover fibers or stock and to remove gross suspended matters. In paper mills and in food-processing plants, for example, screens with 20 to 60 meshes to the inch or more, and of the self-cleaning, shaker or drum type, are widely employed (Figure 20-3). Useful screenings are recovered; waste screenings are buried, burned, or spread on land.

Plain sedimentation and storage in lagoons is common in the canning, mining, and chemical industries. If the waste solids are pre-

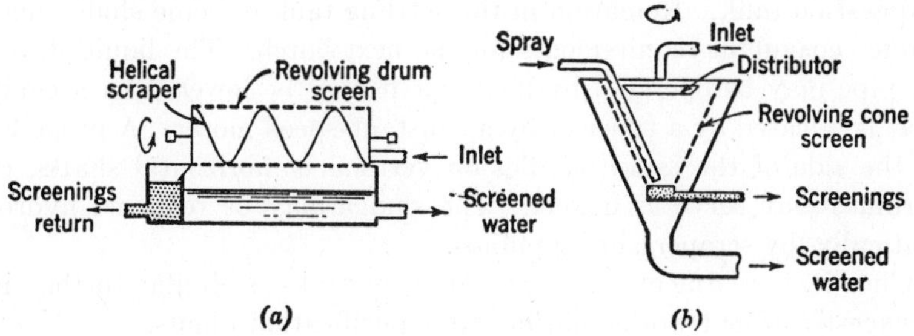

Figure 20-3. Screens or save-alls: (a) *Shevlin* revolving drum; (b) *Whitman* revolving cone.

dominantly organic, their decomposition may exhaust the dissolved oxygen of the lagooned waters and give rise to foul gases including hydrogen sulfide. Nitrates may then have to be added. The oxygen in nitrates is more readily available to living organisms than that in sulfates.

For treatment beyond screening and plain sedimentation, most industries resort to chemical precipitation because of its flexibility and because of the expense of constructing and maintaining biological treatment units. The common water coagulants (alum, ferrous sulfate and lime, ferric sulfate and ferric chloride) are generally employed. But some wastes respond better to other chemical precipitants. Examples are: calcium chloride for laundry wastes, and alkalized starches for coal-washing wastes. The types and dosages of effective coagulants cannot be predicted. Experimentation in the laboratory and in pilot plants is, generally, necessary. Neutralization or adjustment of *p*H is accomplished with chemicals such as lime, soda ash, sulfuric acid, and carbon dioxide.

Both fill-and-draw and continuous-flow settling tanks find use. The former are often best suited to small plants or works in which the characteristics of the waste water fluctuated rapidly; the latter where flows are large and wastes are quite uniform in amount and character. Fill-and-draw plants usually consist of two or more tanks equipped with mixers and with liquid and sludge draw-off pipes (Figure 20-4). When a tank unit has been filled, the waste water is mixed to uniform consistency. The quantities of chemical required for the batch are determined by jar tests and added to the tank. Mixing is continued until a good floc has formed. The tank contents are then allowed to come to rest, and the solids are permitted to settle. After that, the supernatant liquid is siphoned off through a draw-off pipe that sinks automatically with the liquid surface. The sludge is discharged to a drying bed, to a sludge lagoon, or, if it is putrescible, to a digestion tank. Retention in the settling tank of some sludge may reduce coagulant requirements for the next batch. The liquid draw-off pipe may be operated by floats, or it may be lowered on a chain that is released by a timer or by a constant-speed motor. A propeller in the side of the tank, paddles on vertical or horizontal shafts, or turbines may serve as mixers. The sludge may be removed hydrostatically, by scrapers, or by pumps.

Chemical treatment in continuous-flow tanks is similar to that in sewage-treatment works and in water-purification plants.

The loading and operation of biological treatment units are func-

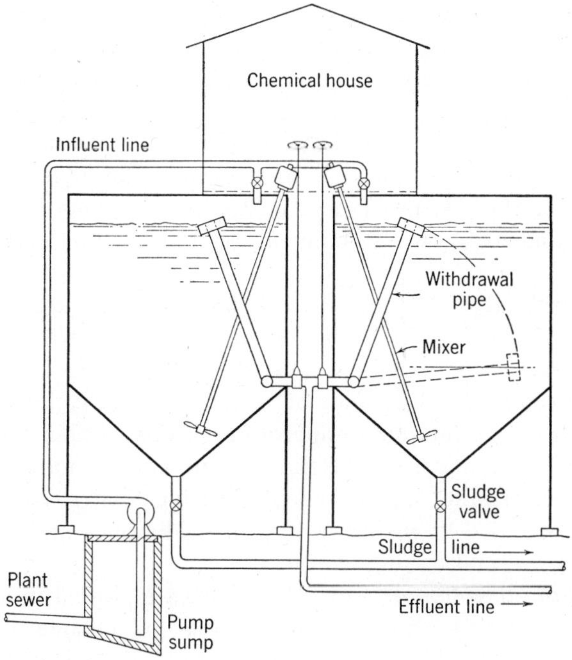

Figure 20-4. Fill-and-draw plant for the clarification of industrial waste-waters by chemicals.

tions of the strength of the wastes and the nature of their constituents. As is true with sewage, the weight of BOD removed by a unit area or volume of filter ordinarily increases with the loading, whereas the percentage removal declines. Commonly, there are advantages in recirculating effluent when the BOD of the waste waters approaches 1,000 mg/l. Trickling filters can handle a number of toxic wastes quite satisfactorily. Among them are phenol, formaldehyde, cyanide, and sulfide wastes. In order to distribute the loading and acclimate the filter to the permissible load, the waste may have to be diluted for some time with sewage or with waste water that is free from toxic materials. Pilot tests will identify permissible loadings and the effects of substances that may produce slime growths or precipitates that clog the filter. Activated-sludge treatment should rarely be tried without pilot tests, even when it has been applied successfully to similar waste waters. Foaming and bulking may be too severe in the presence of strong or toxic industrial wastes.

Suitably screened or settled effluents may be sprayed onto land when industries are situated far from satisfactory receiving waters.

Spray disposal is particularly useful when manufacturing operations reach their peak during the summer and fall or at a time when evapotranspiration is high and the water table is low. Waste waters from vegetable and fruit canneries are examples. Portable irrigation pipes equipped with rotating nozzles are often used. Rates of application and frequency of change of area are determined by irrigation experience and from field tests. Industrial waste-waters may also be carried onto land in the ways commonly employed for the disposal of sewage.

Sludge disposal is generally in accordance with sewage-plant practice. The sludge removed from many industrial waste-waters is relatively stable and can be disposed of without digestion. Where space is available, the lagooning of sludge is generally favored.

20-11. Wastes Containing Mineral Impurities. Examples of waste waters that contain large or detrimental amounts of mineral impurities are steel-pickling liquors, copper-bearing wastes, electroplating wastes, gas- and coke-plant wastes, oil-field brines and petroleum-refinery wastes, and mining wastes.

a. Steel-pickling liquors. Steel and iron are pickled in acid (normally sulfuric acid) prior to cold working, galvanizing, plating, or similar operations. The acid concentration of the pickling bath declines from an initial value of 5 to 15% to one of 1.5 to 5% while its concentration of ferrous iron rises as high as 4 to 30%. Neutralization of the spent pickling liquor, which contains other impurities as well, is costly and leaves large volumes of sludge. Processes for the recovery of ferrous sulfate or acid include: (1) evaporation of water to crystallize impurities; (2) crystallization of ferrous sulfate by cooling or by the addition of organic solvents; (3) use of scrap iron to neutralize residual acidity followed by evaporation to recover copperas; (4) recovery of sulfur and iron oxides by roasting recovered copperas; (5) electrolytic recovery of iron; and (6) dewatering and processing of the sludge after neutralization with lime to produce building and insulating materials. Diluteness of the waste, presence of extraneous impurities, and a limited market for ferrous sulfate impose formidable barriers to profitable recoveries.

b. Copper-bearing wastes. Pickling and washing of copper and its alloys after hot working and annealing leaves copper in the waste liquors. Very small amounts of copper (less than 1 mg/l) will interfere with the life of streams and biological sewage-treatment works. The relatively high cost of copper makes its recovery more profitable than that of ferrous sulfate or iron. Available methods are: (1) electrolytic treatment of the pickling liquor to recover copper and regenerate the acid; (2) crystallization of copper sulfate, which may require neutralization of spent acid with copper oxide scale; (3) lime neutralization followed by sedimentation; and (4) passage through iron turnings or other scrap iron or steel, iron being dissolved and an equivalent amount of copper being precipitated as recoverable metal.

c. Wastes containing chromates and cyanides. Chromates, or hexavalent chromium ($CrO_4^=$ and $Cr_2O_7^=$), and sodium cyanide (NaCN) are widely used in electroplating and other electrolytic operations. The concentration and composition of the toxic waste waters vary widely. About 1 mg/l of chromate (as Cr) or cyanide (as CN) appears to be the permissible limit of these substances in sewage that is to be treated biologically. Reduction of spillage, draining of processed pieces, prewashing, use of wash waters to make up new solutions, and recovery of spent baths are measures of control. Chromates may be removed by precipitation with a barium salt and an alkali or with ferrous sulfate. They may be reduced to the relatively non-toxic trivalent chromic or chromite forms (Cr^{+++} or CrO_2^-) by passage over scrap iron. Cyanides can be volatilized by acidification and aeration provided that safeguards are taken against the poisonous effects of the hydrogen cyanide (HCN) that is released. Cyanides can be precipitated with ferrous sulfate and lime. Chlorination in alkaline solution will convert them to less toxic cyanates such as NaOCN. Further chlorination results in the decomposition of cyanates to carbon dioxide and nitrogen.

d. Gas- and coke-plant wastes. Vapor condensates from manufactured gas and from the quenching of coke throw considerable quantities of ammonia, phenols, cresols, sulfides, cyanides, and thiocyanates into the waste waters. They have a high oxygen demand, are toxic, and impart to receiving waters tastes and odors that are difficult to remove. Phenol appears to be the principal offender (Section 18-21). Acclimated trickling filters can oxidize phenolic waters that contain several hundred milligrams per liter of phenol. Activated sludge is less tolerant, but 50 mg/l will not cause injury in favorable circumstances.

Recovery of ammonia from gas- and coke-plant wastes is common. The spent liquors, which contain lime used to free the ammonia as well as most of the remaining contaminants, may then be evaporated or subjected to phenol recovery: (1) by solvents, such as benzol, benzene, pyridine, and tricresyl phosphate; (2) by adsorption on activated carbon; or (3) by distillation. Otherwise the wastes may be treated on trickling filters, either with domestic sewage or after dilution with treated sewage effluents or other waters.

e. Oil-field brines and petroleum-refinery wastes. Oil-field brines, which average about 3.3 times the amount of oil pumped, contain as much as 32.5% total solids and 20% chlorides. Their solids load may indeed be ten times that of normal sea water. Although they are usually less heavily mineralized than this, most oil-field brines are sufficiently saline to destroy fresh-water life unless they are highly diluted. Since heavy concentrations of dissolved solids can be removed satisfactorily only by distillation at great expense, the economical disposal of brines remains a challenge. Methods of disposal include: (1) storage in ponds for evaporation and seepage and (2) recharge of deep saline strata by pumping, often as a means of increasing the yield of oil. Seepage from lagoons may render ground waters salty and clog water-bearing formations. The oil in brines and refinery wastes may be removed by flotation and skimming. Gas flotation increases the yield. Hydrogen sulfide, mercaptans, phenols, and similar substances may have to be removed when receiving waters serve as sources of water supply.

f. Mining wastes. Mining wastes include (1) the mineralized and acid water pumped or drained from mines and (2) the waste waters from the washing and processing of coal or ore. Acid coal-mine drainage and coal-washing wastes are a widespread source of trouble. The acidity and iron content of coal-mine drainage is due to the oxidation of iron pyrites (FeS) to ferrous sulfate and sulfuric acid. No satisfactory method for reducing the acid load has as yet been found. Included in methods tried are: (1) the flooding of abandoned mines; (2) the sealing of mine entrances with water traps to exclude the oxygen needed to form acids; (3) the reduction of seepage into mines by diversion of surface streams or by other drainage works; and (4) the neutralization of the drainage waters by the addition of lime or by their passage through beds of limestone. The application of inactivating coatings to exposed surfaces is in the experimental stage.

The suspended matter in coal-washing wastes can be removed by sedimentation with or without coagulation. An alkalized solution of potato starch is a good coagulant.

20-12. Wastes Containing Organic Impurities. The most important organic wastes are produced by milk-processing plants, meat-packing establishments, breweries and distilleries, and canneries.

a. Milk-processing wastes. Milk-plant wastes contain washings (1) from cans, pasteurizers, coolers, churns, and other equipment, and

(2) from the plant floor. Their BOD is high (up to several thousand milligrams per liter), and their decomposition is rapid. Reduction of spillage, fuller drainage of cans and equipment, and recovery of solids from first rinsings will reduce losses. Treatment methods include: (1) chemical precipitation with lime and iron in dosages up to 500 mg/l; (2) activated-sludge treatment, possibly aided by small amounts of iron coagulant; and (3) trickling filtration. Treatment on trickling filters is common. Dosing rates range from 0.5 to 1.5 mgad without recirculation of effluent and from 2 to 6 mgad (net) with recirculation. The liquid going to the filter should have a BOD of less than 400 mg/l. If the effluent BOD must be low, the BOD of the applied waters must be reduced. Double filtration with alternation of the leading filter has been quite successful. It provides relief for the leading filter after it has been dosed for a time with concentrated wastes.

b. Meat-packing wastes. Packing-plant and abattoir wastes contain blood, grease, excreta, paunch contents, liquors from rendering and other processing operations, and floor washings. The larger the plant, the more economical does recovery become, and the smaller is the resulting weight of solids lost per animal slaughtered. Meat-packing wastes are treated in ways common to the treatment of domestic sewage. Consideration must be given to the strength of the applied wastes. This may be high.

c. Brewery and distillery wastes. The principal waste material of breweries and distilleries is spent grain. The food values of this residue are high and can be recovered profitably as a feed for hogs and cattle either as liquid slop or as dry feed. Alternate methods of disposal are: (1) use as fertilizer; (2) re-use of part of the distillery slop to make up new mash; and (3) anaerobic fermentation. Wastes that contain less suspended but more dissolved organic matter (for example, steepings and washings) may possess such high BOD values that they must be evaporated or treated biologically. Suspended solids are generally removed by sedimentation prior to biological treatment.

d. Vegetable- and fruit-processing wastes. The characteristics of vegetable- and fruit-processing wastes vary within wide limits with the raw materials and the process. BOD values range up to 60,000 mg/l, and the wastes may be strongly acid or alkaline. Treatment and disposal are peculiarly difficult because of the seasonal nature of the industry and because of the shifting from one vegetable or fruit to another as the season advances. Screening and lagooning or irrigation are used most often. Screenings are buried, burned, spread on land, or used for feed. Lagoons, less than 5 ft deep, should hold 125% of the seasonal volume of waste waters. About 25% of these waters is stored over the winter in order to dilute and seed the next year's batch. Water is discharged from the lagoons by evaporation and seepage and by withdrawal into receiving waters during spring freshets. Nuisances due to the depletion of oxygen can be combated by the addition, to waste waters of average strength, of sodium nitrate at a rate of 200 lb or less for each pack of 1,000 No. 2 cases. Disposal by irrigation requires suitable land areas. Waste water to depths as high as 600 in. per year has been sprayed onto sandy areas covered with underbrush and forest litter.

20-13. Wastes Containing Both Organic and Mineral Impurities. Examples of such wastes are those of the textile industry, laundries, tanneries, and paper mills.

a. Textile wastes. These wastes are derived from deterging and fiber preparation, and from dyeing, printing, and finishing processes. The variety of fibers (wool, cotton, silk, linen, synthetics, etc.) is great, and the kinds and colors of goods produced are numerous. As a result, textile waste waters vary in composition and strength more than other industrial waste-waters. Only a few examples of their disposal are given below.

The scouring of wool produces a water-carried waste that contains dirt, manure, burrs, spent soap, and large amounts of wool grease. Grease can be recovered by lowering the *p*H of the settled waste with sulfuric acid to a value of 3 or 4 (acid cracking) to break the soap emulsion. In the acid tanks, most of the fat settles as a sludge, the remainder rises to the surface. Chlorination, aeration, coagulation, pressing, and centrifuging also find use in the recovery process. Extraction by solvents prior to scouring yields wool grease of high quality (lanolin).

Cotton kiering is the boiling of woven goods in water containing 0.5 to 3.0% of caustic and soda. Gums, pectins, vegetable impurities, and sizing are separated from the fiber. The resulting waste water is highly alkaline and has a BOD of thousands of milligrams per liter. Neutralization with sulfuric acid or carbon dioxide must precede biological treatment on filters. Alkaline bleaching wastes will neutralize or decolorize acid or colored wastes. Bleaching wastes may also be combined with kier liquors for disposal. Mercerizing wastes are sufficiently concentrated to justify recovery of the caustic by dialysis or evaporation.

Dye wastes are deeply colored. High acidity or alkalinity, or the dye itself, may render them destructive to aquatic life. They can be treated chemically (by coagulation, bleaching, or absorption) or biologically (on trickling filters or in activated-sludge units). Decolorization is rarely complete. Waste waters from dyeing, printing, and finishing operations are so variable in volume and composition that experimentation should precede the selection of a plan of treatment.

b. Laundry wastes. Laundry wastes contain (1) spent soaps, synthetic detergents, bleaches, and (2) dirt and grease. They respond to coagulation with alum or ferric coagulants in combination with calcium chloride or sulfuric acid. Dosages range from 1 to 5 lb per 1,000 gal.

c. Tannery wastes. Roughly half of the BOD (several thousand mg/l) of tannery wastes is concentrated in liquors from the preliminary processes of soaking, liming, dehairing, and fleshing the hides ("beamhouse wastes" [3]), and the other half from the tanning and finishing processes. Preliminary processing removes highly putrescible materials; final processing introduces toxic chemicals, such as sulfides and chromates, as well. Variations in the characteristics of the wastes within a given tannery and between tanneries are high. Treatment methods include screening, flocculation, sedimentation, and biological filtration. Success of treatment depends on adequate blending and neutralization of the various waste waters.

d. Paper-mill wastes. Production of wood pulp by the sulfite, soda, or sulfate (kraft) processes is common. Wastes from sulfite mills do the most damage to receiving waters and are the most difficult to treat. Ponding, digestion, and evaporation have been tried in addition to patented processes that recover sulfur dioxide or sulfites. Caustic soda is usually recovered from soda- and sulfate-pulping liquors. "Black liquor" containing wastes cooked from the wood fibers is evaporated, and the solids are burned to produce "black ash." This material is added to fresh soda ash to make up "green liquor" which, in turn, is causticized with quicklime, settled, and filtered to produce "white liquor," which is used in the pulping process. Activated carbon is a salable by-product. It is prepared from residues of soda recovery.

Waste waters from the reclamation of old paper carry ink and clay filler removed from the paper, as well as spent caustic and soda ash

[3] From the process of working or dressing hides over a beam or in a beaming machine.

from the processing baths. Recovery of chemicals from these waste waters has not been found profitable.

The wastes from beaters, refiners, and paper-making machines ("white waters") contain about 5% fiber and 45% clay. These are recovered by screening and sedimentation, or the water is recirculated after it has been chlorinated to prevent the development of slime growths.

20-14. Radioactive Wastes. Radioactive materials comprise all isotopes,[4] the nuclei of which undergo spontaneous disintegration. The quantity of radioactivity is measured by the number of disintegrations that take place in a unit of time. The standard unit, called a curie, is 3.7×10^{10} disintegrations per second. This is the rate of nuclear transformation of 1 gram of radium. Each radioisotope decays at a characteristic rate that is unaffected by heat or pressure. The transformation is described by Equation 18-2 when N is the quantity of the isotope remaining at time t measured from the instant when N_0 was present. Rates are conventionally expressed in terms of the "half-life" rather than the rate constant k of the element. The half-life of a radioisotope is the time required for half of it to decay. Solution of Equation 18-2 for $N/N_0 = 0.5$ gives $k = 0.69/\text{half-life}$. The half-lives of radioisotopes range from 10^{-11} sec to more than 10^{10} years.

Radioactive waste waters originate primarily (1) in hospitals and research laboratories and in the laundries serving them and (2) in water-cooled nuclear reactors and in chemical plants that process reactor fuels. The radioactivity of fuel-processing wastes is of a much higher order of magnitude than that of radioactive waste waters from hospitals, laboratories, and laundries. Curies [5] must be dealt with rather than microcuries, μc.

Fuel-processing wastes are now stored in tanks, usually after concentration by evaporation. How these wastes will be contained ultimately and whether they can be safely and economically discharged into the atmosphere or disposed of in the ocean are matters that are yet to be determined.

Radioactive phosphorus (P^{32}) and iodine (I^{131}) are frequently used as tracers in research work. Their half-lives are 14.3 and 8 days respectively. P^{32} and I^{131} can be disposed of into sewers if transient concentrations in excess of 100 μc/l are avoided by regulated release,

[4] Isotopes are chemical elements that differ slightly in atomic weight but occupy the same place in the periodic system and possess the same nuclear charge.

[5] One curie = 10^6 microcuries.

dilution, or storage prior to disposal. Storage for 10 half-lives reduces the concentration of isotopes with short half-lives to about 0.1% of their original amount.

The permissible increase in radioactivity of public waters is currently set at 10^{-7} μc/ml for unknown mixtures of isotopes. For specific isotopes, the permissible limit is much higher: 2×10^{-4} μc/ml for P^{32} and 3×10^{-5} μc/ml for I^{131}. These figures are useful guides [6] in judging the amounts of radioactivity that can safely be discharged into natural waters.

Other limitations on the disposal of radioisotopes in sewage are: (1) the contamination of plumbing systems; (2) hazards to personnel at treatment plants; and (3) the use of sludge and effluent in the cultivation of crops. Algae and higher plants will concentrate in their cells numerous chemical elements from both water and fertilizers. Radioactive elements, such as P^{32}, may be included. However, if the half-life of the radioisotope is short, radioactive decay will greatly reduce the activity of the element before it can find its way back into the food supply of man.

Radioactive substances can be removed from water and waste water in a number of different ways, the selection of which must depend on the nature of the substances involved and their physical condition in the water or waste water. Straub [7] lists the following methods: evaporation, carrier precipitation (coagulation), sand filtration, ion exchange (including natural clays), electrodialysis, metallic displacement or scrubbing, differential volatility, electrolytic separation, solvent extraction, biological processes, and crystallization.

The maximum removal of radioactivity in biological sewage-treatment systems is about 95%. A much lower removal is experienced for radioisotopes that are not utilized by, or readily adsorbed on, biological slimes, or that occur in company with an abundance of nonradioactive atoms of the same element.[8]

[6] National Bureau of Standards, Maximum permissible amounts of radioisotopes in the human body and maximum permissible concentrations in air and water, *Handbook 52* (1953).

[7] Conrad P. Straub, Observations on the removal of radioactive materials from waste solutions, *Sewage and Ind. Wastes, 23,* 188 (1951).

[8] C. C. Ruchhoft and L. R. Setter, Application of biological methods in the treatment of radioactive wastes, *Sewage and Ind. Wastes, 25,* 48 (1953).

Problems

CHAPTER 2. QUANTITIES OF WATER AND WASTE WATER

2-1. *Estimate of midyear population* (Section 2-4). Using the 1940 and 1950 census figures for Detroit, Mich.,[1] estimate the 1945, 1955, and 1960 midyear populations by both the arithmetic and the geometric increase method.

2-2. *Population forecasts* (Section 2-4). Estimate the 1960, 1970, and 1980 population of Detroit by plotting the data for 1910 onward on arithmetic coordinate paper and extending the curve by eye.

2-3. *Population forecasts* (Section 2-4). Plot the percentage growth rates of Detroit against time and extend the resulting curve to predict the 1960, 1970, and 1980 populations of the 142-sq mile area now within the central city.

2-4. *Population forecasts* (Section 2-4). From a knowledge of the nature of Detroit and its industries, discuss the economic and geographic factors that may influence its future growth and make qualitative predictions of the kind and extent of this influence.

2-5. *Factors affecting consumption* (Section 2-6). Of the 10-mgd average consumption in a community of 70,000 population, 1.5 mgd are estimated to be lost through leaks in mains, services, and plumbing fixtures. If it is assumed that these leaks behave as orifices, estimate how much water can be saved by reducing the average pressure in the street mains from 50 psig to 30 psig.

2-6. *Economics of metering* (Section 2-6). Only the services to single-family dwellings of a community are unmetered. The annual consumption per unmetered service is estimated to be 0.1 mg. If the annual expense for installing, maintaining, and reading a meter is \$8.00 and the annual expense for each additional mgd of water supplied is \$150.00, how much water would have to

[1] In this and the three succeeding problems, data for any other community may be substituted.

be saved per single-family dwelling to make extension of metering an economically sound operation?

2-7. *Variations in demand* (Section 2-7). Determine the required capacity of the constituent structures of the four water-works systems shown in Figure 2-3, assuming that each serves a community of 20,000 people where the average annual consumption is 3 mgd.

2-8. *Sources of flow in sanitary sewers* (Section 2-8). Estimate the amount of storm-water flow in sanitary sewers in an area where houses 25 × 25 ft on 50 × 125-ft lots are occupied by 5 persons, assuming that the rainfall intensity is 2 in./hr and that roof drainage from 1 house in 50 is illegally discharged into the sanitary sewer. Express the answer in gpcd and gpd/acre.

2-9. *Variations in flow* (Section 2-9). A sanitary sewer serves 50,000 people whose average water consumption is 140 gpcd and whose community occupies 6 sq miles. Estimate the average and peak rates of flow in the sewer.

CHAPTER 3. HYDROLOGY

3-1. *Evaporation* (Section 3-4). Estimate the evaporation from the surface of a large reservoir during a month in which the following averages existed: water temperature, 75 F; air temperature, 80 F; wind velocity, 11 mph; relative humidity, 65%.

3-2. *Variations in annual rainfall* (Section 3-10). If the mean annual rainfall is 40 in. and the coefficient of variation in annual rainfall is 0.15: (*a*) How often on the average will the annual rainfall be in excess of 52 in.? (*b*) How often will it be less than 25 in.? (*c*) What percentage of the time would it be expected to fall between 30 and 40 in.? (*d*) What magnitude of annual rainfall will be exceeded once on the average in every 10 years? (*e*) What magnitude of annual rainfall will not be reached once on the average in 50 years? Assume that the statistical distribution is arithmetically normal.

3-3. *Normal frequency analysis of annual rainfall* (Section 3-10). Make a statistical analysis of the following 29-year record [2] of annual rainfalls in inches to determine: (*a*) the mean; (*b*) the median; (*c*) the standard deviation; and (*d*) the coefficient of variation.

43.30, 53.02, 63.52, 45.93, 48.26, 50.51, 49.57, 43.93, 46.77, 59.12, 54.49, 47.38, 40.78, 45.05, 50.37, 54.91, 51.28, 39.91, 53.29, 67.59, 58.71, 42.96, 55.77, 41.31, 58.83, 48.21, 44.67, 67.72, 43.11.

3-4. *Probability paper analysis of annual rainfall* (Section 3-10). Determine the geometric mean and geometric standard deviation by plotting the data of Problem 3-3 on logarithmic probability paper and drawing, by eye, the line of best fit.

3-5. *Statistical analysis of annual runoff* (Section 3-10). Plot the following 34-year record [3] of average annual runoffs in cfs on arithmetic and logarithmic

[2] Coldbrook gage on the watershed of Esopus Creek, N. Y., 1918–1945. Substitute for this record any other desired.

[3] Esopus Creek at Coldbrook, N. Y., 1914–1947. Drainage area 192 sq miles. Substitute for this record any other desired.

probability paper and determine: (*a*) the arithmetic mean; (*b*) the arithmetic standard deviation; (*c*) the geometric mean; and (*d*) the geometric standard deviation.

393, 504, 498, 445, 379, 471, 571, 406, 407, 445, 528, 403, 385, 675, 510, 493, 284, 403, 484, 519, 419, 383, 448, 645, 551, 318, 529, 286, 494, 466, 267, 593, 300, 425.

3-6. *Comparison of annual rainfall and annual runoff* (Section 3-10). (*a*) Prepare a table similar to that in *a* of Example 3-2 for the records given in Problems 3-3 and 3-5. (*b*) Determine and assemble the information and discuss the points considered in *c* of Example 3-2.

3-7. *Intensity of storms* (Section 3-12). Given the rain gage record of Table P-1 for successive periods of a storm,[4] find the arithmetic mean intensity of precipitation for various durations.

TABLE P-1. Intensity of Storms (Problem 3-7)

Time from beginning of storm, min	5	10	15	20	25	30	35	40
Cumulative rainfall, in.	0.23	0.60	0.65	0.70	0.71	0.72	0.73	0.74

3-8. *Frequency of intense storms* (Section 3-13). Given the number of occurrences of intensities of various durations for a 42-year record,[5] determine by interpolation in Table P-2 the time-intensity values for the 10-year storm, and plot the resulting intensity-duration-frequency curve on arithmetic paper.

TABLE P-2. Frequency of Intense Storms (Problem 3-8)

Duration, min	Number of Times the Stated Intensities (in./hr) Were Reached or Exceeded													
	0.75	1.0	1.25	1.5	2.0	2.5	3.0	3.5	4.0	4.5	5.0	6.0	7.0	8.0
5									65	39	28	10	3	1
10								45	25	16	11	3		
15						69	38	22	12	8	5	2		
30					38	16	6	3	2	1				
60		69	39	24	5	2	1							
120	33	13	6	2										

3-9. *Intensity-duration-frequency relationships* (Section 3-13). Develop intensity-duration-frequency curves for the 1-, 5-, 10-, 20-, and 50-year frequencies for the data given in Problem 3–8, assuming that the average frequency of recurrence of intensities of equal or larger magnitude is the record in years divided by the number of times an intensity has been reached or exceeded. Plot the given data on log-log paper, then read off values for and plot the intensity-duration-frequency curves on arithmetic coordinate paper.

3-10. *Graphical formulation of intensity-duration-frequency* (Section 3-13). Determine graphically the constants for Equation 3-5 to fit the data in Table P-3 derived from a frequency analysis of intense rainfalls:

[4] Storm of April 29, 1951, Baltimore, Md.
[5] Baltimore, Md., 1905–1946.

TABLE P-3. Intensity of Storms of Varying Frequency (Problem 3-10)

Duration, min	Intensity of Rainfall for Storms of Stated Frequency, (in./hr) 1-yr	5-yr	10-yr	20-yr
10	3.6	5.1	5.8	6.6
20	2.5	3.8	4.4	5.0
30	1.9	2.9	3.4	3.9
40	1.6	2.4	2.9	3.3
50	1.4	2.1	2.5	2.9
60	1.2	1.9	2.2	2.6

3-11. *Statistical analysis of flood flows* (Section 3-14). Plot the following 21 maximum 24-hr average annual floods [6] in csm on log probability paper, and from the straight line of best fit determine the geometric mean and geometric standard deviation. What is the maximum 24-hr flood expected once in 2, 10, 100, and 1,000 years?

7.3, 4.5, 6.6, 41.5, 15.3, 9.0, 13.2, 13.3, 32.4, 10.4, 11.8, 4.7, 12.3, 9.8, 22.4, 12.0, 26.5, 4.7, 8.9, 11.3, 8.4.

3-12. *Graphical analysis of flood flows* (Section 3-14). Given the following 21-year record of 24-hr floods [7] that reached or exceeded 1,100 cfs on the 165-sq mile watershed of Problem 3-11, plot the recurrence intervals on log-log paper and, from the curve of best fit drawn by eye, determine the 24-hr flood expected to be reached or exceeded once in 2, 10, 100, and 1,000 years. Compare these values with those obtained in Problem 3-11 and discuss the differences observed.

1,200, 1,100; none; none; 6,850, 4,340, 1,420, 1,240, 1,200; 2,520, 1,620; 1,480, 1,150; 2,180, 1,600, 1,420; 2,170, 1,870; 5,340, 2,230; 1,720; 1,940, 1,210; none; 2,020, 1,680; 1,610, 1,610, 1,160; 3,540, 2,790; 1,980; 4,370, 1,640, 1,110; none; 1,460, 1,300, 1,270, 1,180, 1,110; 1,860, 1,790, 1,320, 1,200; 1,380.

3-13. *Estimates of maximum runoff rates from rainfall rates* (Section 3-15). For the region studied in Problem 3-8, estimate the 1-, 10-, and 50-year flood runoff for an area of 2 sq miles on the assumption that C_{max} in Equation 3-8 is 0.75 and the time of concentration, t, is 90 min.

3-14. *Unit hydrographs* (Section 3-15). Determine the distribution graph for a unit storm on a 1,000-sq mile watershed for which the observed total flow and estimated base flow are shown in Table P-4.

3-15. *Estimates by unit hydrograph method* (Section 3-15). Given the average percentage distribution of runoff shown in Table P-5 for unit rainfalls on a 1,000-sq mile watershed, calculate the compounded runoff or total hydrograph for the stated sequence of rainfall.

[6] Patapsco River near Marriotsville, Md., 1930–1950.

[7] Only the greatest 24-hr rate is taken from the record for each flood rise, and only one of two consecutive flood rises is counted if the intervening minimum 24-hr flow is greater than 90% of the smaller of the two rises. Analysis of all floods above a selected minimum flood is based on 24-hr average flows because the USGS records only one peak discharge for each year. Other peak flows can ordinarily be obtained only from the original charts taken from the gage.

TABLE P-4. Flows for a Unit Storm (Problem 3-14)

Sequence of Time Units (1)	Observed Rainfall, in. (2)	Runoff, cfs: Observed Total (3)	Runoff, cfs: Estimated Base Flow (4)
1	0.86	1,440	400
2	0.00	4,030	430
3	0.00	3,040	470
4	0.00	1,580	510
5	0.00	890	550
6	0.00	740	600
7	0.00	620	580
8	0.00	560	560

TABLE P-5. Distribution of Rainfalls (Problem 3-15)

Sequence of time units	1	2	3	4	5	6	7	8	9
Average distribution per unit, %	12	40	30	12	4	1	1	0	0
Allowance for base flow, csm	1.5	1.6	1.8	2.1	2.5	2.6	2.6	2.5	2.4
Sequence of rainfalls for consecutive time units, in.	0.8	3.0	1.4	1.0	0	0	0	0	0
Estimated loss, in.	0.6	1.6	0.6	0.3	0	0	0	0	0

CHAPTER 4. Collection of Surface Water

4-1. *Freeboard* (Section 4-4). An earth dam in the northeastern United States which impounds water from a 100-sq mile watershed is protected from floods by a 300-ft side channel spillway. If the fetch is 3 miles, the average reservoir depth 30 ft, and the design wind velocity 50 mph, what amount of freeboard should be provided above the spillway crest?

4-2. *Gravity masonry dam* (Section 4-4). Estimate the cubic yards of concrete required per foot length of a gravity concrete dam 60 ft high and 10 ft wide at the top.

4-3. *Water intakes* (Section 4-5). Sketch a plan and an elevation for an intake tower to be built on the upstream face of a masonry dam and designed to discharge 25 mgd. Maximum water depth at overflow elevation is 60 ft. Show size and location of ports, screens, downtake shaft and all appurtenances, including any arrangements provided for cleaning or repairing gates, screens, or other equipment.

4-4. *Spillways* (Section 4-6). Design a side-channel spillway to discharge 40,000 cfs under a 12-ft head into a rectangular (or approximately so) receiving channel. Make a sketch showing the channel dimensions and the elevation of the channel bottom relative to that of the spillway crest at each end of the overflow section. Assume free discharge at the outlet end of the receiving channel. See Section 15-9 for the hydraulics of receiving channels.

4-5. *Spillways* (Section 4-6). What is the minimum bottom slope of the exit channel required to prevent backwater in the receiving channel of the spillway of Problem 4-4?

4-6. *Spillways* (Section 4-6). A circular morning-glory spillway is to discharge 10,000 cfs under a 10-ft head into a 2,000-ft conduit that has an outlet 50 ft below the spillway crest. What should be the diameter of the spillway at its crest and the diameter of the conduit? See Section 6-2.

4-7. *Storage to maintain a constant draft* (Section 4-7). Find the storage required to maintain a constant draft of 85 mgd from a 170-sq mile watershed for the record of monthly mean runoff values shown in Table P-6.

TABLE P-6. Monthly Mean Runoff Values (Problem 4-7)

	Feb.	Mar.	Apr.	May	June	July	Aug.	Sept.	Oct.	Nov.	Dec.	Jan.	Feb.
Runoff, mgd/sq mile	1.35	0.42	0.35	0.37	0.35	0.45	0.32	0.25	0.41	0.46	0.36	0.57	1.46

4-8. *Storage to maintain a variable draft* (Section 4-7). Find the storage required to maintain an adequate supply of water during a period for which the monthly mean runoff and draft values are shown in Table P-7.

TABLE P-7. Monthly Mean Runoff and Draft Values (Problem 4-8)

	June	July	Aug.	Sept.	Oct.	Nov.	Dec.	Jan.	Feb.	Mar.	Apr.
Runoff, mgd	310	133	97	109	79	79	118	424	450	204	280
Draft, mgd	207	220	214	214	204	192	187	197	196	190	188

4-9. *Permissible draft from a given reservoir* (Section 4-7). Find the draft rate which will exhaust 75% of the total storage available in a 20-billion gallon reservoir, on a 300-sq mile watershed, if the reservoir is full at the beginning of the dry period and the runoff is as shown in Table P-8. During what month will the reservoir refill?

TABLE P-8. Monthly Mean Runoff Values (Problem 4-9)

	Jan.	Feb.	Mar.	Apr.	May	June	July	Aug.	Sept.	Oct.	Nov.	Dec.
First-year runoff, mgd/sq mile	0.87	0.95	1.02	0.95	0.54	0.67	0.46	0.26	0.17	0.20	0.27	0.41
Second-year runoff, mgd/sq mile	0.36	0.61	0.68	0.71	0.77	0.60	0.55	1.74	0.77	1.43	1.06	1.23

4-10. *Draft-storage-frequency curves* (Section 4-8). From the mass diagram for a 71-year record of streamflow in the eastern United States, the largest storage requirements were determined for the stated draft rates, as shown in Table P-9. (*a*) Construct the draft-storage-frequency curves for exceedance intervals of 20, 50, and 100 years. (*b*) What is the safe yield of a 37-billion-gallon reservoir which impounds water from 303 sq miles of the watershed? (*c*) What size reservoir would be required to provide a safe yield of 100 mgd from 165 sq miles of the watershed?

TABLE P-9. Storage Values Required to Maintain Stated Drafts during the 11 Greatest Droughts in 71 Years (Problem 4-10)

Draft, mgd/sq mile	Storage, mgd/sq mile
0.50	127, 79, 58, 39, 36, 30, 28, 24, 21, 17, 16,
0.55	129, 97, 74, 58, 47, 39, 37, 33, 30, 29, 25,
0.60	214, 131, 99, 76, 63, 56, 47, 44, 42, 39, 31,
0.65	259, 177, 135, 109, 91, 70, 63, 56, 53, 47, 45,
0.70	305, 218, 176, 151, 118, 106, 88, 83, 74, 68, 56,

4-11. *Generalized storage values* (Section 4-9). Using Hazen's generalized storage values, find the safe yield of a 37-billion-gallon reservoir on a stream that has a mean annual flow at the dam of 270 mgd and a coefficient of variation of 0.33.

4-12. *Loss by evaporation* (Section 4-10). A mean draft of 100 mgd is to be developed from a 170-sq mile catchment area. The reservoir area is estimated to be 4,000 acres at the flowline. The mean annual rainfall is 40 in., the mean annual runoff is 16 in., and the mean annual evaporation is 48 in. Find (*a*) the revised mean annual runoff; (*b*) the equivalent mean draft; (*c*) the equivalent land area; and (*d*) the adjusted flowline.

4-13. *Flood routing* (Section 4-12). (*a*) Given the reservoir and spillway characteristics shown in Table P-10, prepare a set of flood routing curves. (*b*) For the inflow data of Table P-11, construct the outflow hydrograph.

TABLE P-10. Reservoir and Spillway Characteristics (Problem 4-13)

Spillway head, ft	0	1	2	3	4	5	6	7	8
Area, acres	6,230	6,400	6,564	6,730	6,900	7,060	7,230	7,400	7,566
Outflow, cfs	0	700	1,980	3,640	5,600	7,850	10,300	12,960	15,840

TABLE P-11. Rate of Inflow (Problem 4–13)

Date	Time	Runoff, cfs	Date	Time	Runoff, cfs
Aug. 22	2 P.M.	600	Aug. 24	2 P.M.	5,800
	8 P.M.	1,100		8 P.M.	2,800
Aug. 23	2 A.M.	1,900	Aug. 25	2 A.M.	1,600
	8 A.M.	3,300		8 A.M.	1,100
	2 P.M.	6,000		2 P.M.	940
	8 P.M.	20,000		8 P.M.	920
Aug. 24	2 A.M.	39,000	Aug. 26	2 A.M.	900
	8 A.M.	18,400		8 A.M.	850

4-14. *Spillway capacity and flood routing* (Section 4-12). If the maximum 24-hr flood of Problem 4-13 is 20,000 cfs and the maximum allowable spillway head is assumed to be 8 ft, estimate the outflow rate by use of Fuller's generalized values. Is calculation of outflow by the flood routing method warranted?

CHAPTER 5. Collection of Ground Water

5-1. *Coefficient of permeability* (Section 5-4). If 2 mgd of water flow vertically downward through 1 acre of a natural sand filter 3 ft deep with a head loss of 2 ft at 60 F, what is the coefficient of permeability of the sand?

5-2. *Darcy's Law* (Section 5-4). Estimate the discharge through a 1-ft width of aquifer 60 ft thick under a gradient of 50 ft per mile when the water temperature is 50 F and the standard coefficient of permeability is 200 gpd/sq ft.

5-3. *Measurement of permeability* (Section 5-4). A 2-in. inside-diameter, falling-head permeameter contains 6 in. of silt. If the head across the sample falls from an initial value of 45 cm to a final value of 15 cm in a 5-cm inside-diameter head tube in 20 min and the temperature is 60 F, what is the coefficient of permeability in gpd/sq ft?

5-4. *Field measurement of permeability* (Section 5-4). The measured mean interstitial velocity in the ground is 10 ft/day when the water table slope is 4×10^{-2} and the ground water temperature is 50 F. If the porosity ratio is estimated to be 0.4 and k_f as 0.6, what is the coefficient of permeability in gpd/sq ft?

5-5. *Infiltration galleries* (Section 5-5). An underground infiltration system consists of 2 perforated pipes laid in parallel rows 22 ft apart at the bottom of an 8-ft natural sand bed that rests on relatively impervious clay. The water level in a midway, intermediate, parallel feed trench, 2 ft wide and 8 ft deep, stands 2 ft below the ground surface. If the water level lies 1 ft above the clay at the intake pipes, what total length of intake piping is needed to produce 0.5 mgd of water? Assume a coefficient of permeability of 5×10^2 gpd/sq ft.

5-6. *Unconfined steady flow into wells* (Section 5-6). An 18-in. well penetrates a free ground water body that is 40 ft deep and has a water table slope of 2×10^{-3}. The coefficient of permeability of the water-bearing material is 6×10^{-4} fps. If the well is pumped sufficiently long for the drawdown to approach a constant value of 20 ft: (*a*) Estimate the diameter of the circle of influence. (*b*) Calculate the discharge from the well.

5-7. *Unconfined steady flow into wells* (Section 5-6). If the slope of the undisturbed water table in Problem 5-6 increases to 2×10^{-2}, what will be: (*a*) the diameter of the circle of influence; and (*b*) the discharge? Assume that all other factors remain unchanged.

5-8. *Confined steady flow into wells* (Section 5-7). A single 12-in well, pumped at a rate of 200 gpm, penetrates the full 20-ft depth of an extensive artesian aquifer for which the undisturbed piezometric surface has a uniform slope of 52.8 ft per mile. The average coefficient of permeability is 4×10^{-4} fps and the aquifer is assumed to be incompressible. (*a*) What width of aquifer is required to supply the well? (*b*) If pumping lowers the piezometric surface significantly for a distance from the well equal only to the width of aquifer from which water is collected, what is the drawdown at the well? (*c*) What is the drawdown 100 ft from the well? (*d*) Draw the flow net and use it as a basis for calculating the drawdown 100 ft from the well. (*e*) What is the distance from the well to the point of stagnation?

5-9. *Unsteady flow into well* (Section 5-8). An 18-in. well penetrating a 60-ft thick aquifer was pumped at a uniform rate of 300 gpm for 10 days. The drawdown of the piezometric surface was measured at an observation well 1,000 ft from the pumped well with the results shown in Table P-12. Use the Theis

TABLE P-12. Drawdown of Observation Well (Problem 5-9)

Time, days	0.04	0.1	0.2	0.5	1.0	2.0	4.0	10.0
Drawdown, ft	4.2	5.8	7.2	9.2	10.5	11.7	13.0	15.0

method for analysis of unsteady flow data to determine the coefficient of permeability and the storage coefficient for the aquifer.

5-10. *Interference of wells* (Section 5-9). Two 12-in. wells 1,000 ft apart are pumped simultaneously for a period of 7 days, one well at a rate of 300 gpm, the other at a rate of 600 gpm. The storage coefficient for the aquifer is 3×10^{-5} and the coefficient of transmissibility is 20,000 gpd/ft. What is the drawdown in each well, if screen and casing losses are neglected?

5-11. *Contact with salt water* (Section 5-11). Water stands at 1-ft depth in an infiltration gallery having an invert elevation lying 5 ft above sea level in the fresh-water lens of a sandy island. If the original water table was 20 ft above sea level, what reduction in thickness of the lens resulted from installation of the gallery?

5-12. *Contact with salt water* (Section 5-11). The undisturbed surface of the fresh-water lens near the center of a large island is flat and stands 30 ft above the level of the ocean. A 12-in. well is pumped at a rate of 200 gpm for a sufficient length of time to have the drawdown at the well reach 25 ft. If the average porosity of the island material is 0.4, and it is assumed that the salt-water bulge below the well is an amplified reflection of the drawdown curve and that there is no recharge, estimate the volume of water that will have been removed when the drawdown is 25 ft. Assume that the circle of influence is 4,000 ft across and that the drawdown curve is defined by ¼ of an ellipse with its major axis ending at the water level in the well and its minor axis ending at the circle of influence. How long must the well be pumped in order to produce this volume of water?

CHAPTER 6. Transmission of Water

6-1. *Hydraulics of conduits* (Section 6-2). Find the head lost in 10,000 feet of 48-in. pipeline carrying 30 mgd of water. Use the Hazen-Williams diagram and assume $C = 100$.

6-2. *Hydraulics of conduits* (Section 6-2). (*a*) Given: $d = 12$ in., $C = 120$, $l = 4{,}500$ ft, and $Q = 1.8$ mgd, find the head loss, H. (*b*) Given: $d = 18$ in., $C = 70$, $l = 3{,}000$ ft, and the total head loss, $H = 12$ ft, find the rate of discharge, Q. (*c*) Given: $H = 30$ ft, $C = 110$, $l = 8{,}000$ ft, and $Q = 15$ mgd, find the diameter of the pipeline, d. (*d*) Given: $d = 20$ in., $l = 1{,}500$ ft, $Q = 4$ mgd, and $H = 2$ ft, find the value of the Hazen-Williams coefficient, C.

6-3. *Hydraulics of conduits* (Section 6-2). Use the Hazen-Williams diagram to find the head loss in a square conduit 3 ft on a side and 100 ft long, with a C of 120, when carrying 20 mgd.

6-4. *Capacity and size of conduits* (Section 6-3). Given the data in Table P-13 on the three pipes to be used in series in a transmission main designed to

TABLE P-13. Characteristics of Pipes (Problem 6-4)

			Pipe Diameter, in.					
			84	96	108	120	132	144
			Cost in Place, dollars/ft					
Pipe No.	Length, ft	C						
1	25,000	120	67	81	96	114	138	175
2	20,000	120	76	92	111	132	162	203
3	10,000	120	87	105	130	157	193	240

carry 240 mgd of water with a total head loss of 40 ft, find the most economical diameter for each pipe.

6-5. *Capacity and size of conduits* (Section 6-3). A transmission main 40,000 ft long, $C = 120$, is to carry 240 mgd of pumped water. If the capital cost per foot is the same as for Pipe No. 1 in Problem 6-4, the maintenance cost is the same for all diameters, interest and depreciation are 5% per year, power costs 1 cent/kw-hr, motor and pump efficiency is 80% wire to water, and the first cost and maintenance of the pumping station are independent of the head difference due to change in diameter, what is the most economical pipe diameter to use?

6-6. *Strength of conduits* (Section 6-6). What should be the thickness of a steel pipeline 48 in. in diameter to withstand a maximum pressure of 300 psig?

6-7. *Location of conduits* (Section 6-7). Two alternate routes for crossing a valley are to be compared. The longer route, staying on higher ground, requires 10,000 ft of Pipe No. 1 in Problem 6-4, and the shorter requires 6,000 ft of Pipe No. 1 and 3,000 ft of Pipe No. 2. Which is the most economical location if 200 mgd of water are to be pumped through the conduit? Assume $C = 120$ and that all cost and other data required are those given in Problems 6-4 and 6-5.

6-8. *Initial leakage of conduits* (Section 6-8). A new 12-in. bell-and-spigot, cast-iron pipeline, constructed of 12-ft lengths of pipe, is tested under a pressure of 100 psig and found to leak at a rate of 10 gph. What is the acceptable amount of leakage?

6-9. *Air valves* (Section 6-9). A 60-in. concrete pipeline is equipped with two 6-in. air valves and a gate valve at each summit. Estimate the maximum vacuum in inches of water that will exist inside the line when it is emptied at a rate of 50 mgd.

6-10. *Anchorages* (Section 6-9). What single external force must be applied to a 24-in., 90-deg, cast-iron bend in a leaded-joint, bell-and-spigot pipeline in order to prevent movement of the bend, if the maximum internal pressure is 200 psig? Neglect the resistance of the joints.

6-11. *Anchorages* (Section 6-9). A 60-in. steel pipeline coming down into a valley changes from a slope of 30 deg with the horizontal to a slope of 45 deg with the horizontal. The maximum water pressure is 250 psig. What weight of concrete anchor block is necessary to resist the horizontal and vertical thrust on the vertical bend? Assume a coefficient of friction between the block and its foundation of 0.7. The line is not laid in trench.

6-12. *Pumping units* (Section 6-10). What type of pump would be selected to pump 60 mgd of water against a 20-ft head differential, if the pump is to operate at 360 rpm?

6-13. *Pumping units* (Section 6-10). Select three suitable pumps for a station in which the maximum demand is 10 mgd, the minimum demand is 2 mgd, the maximum and minimum static differentials are 70 and 60 psig respectively, and the dynamic pressure varies with the station discharge as shown in Table P-14. For purposes of this problem only, assume that pumps with the characteristics given in Table P-14 can be found for any desired combination of shut-off head and rated discharge.

TABLE P-14. Station and Pump Data (Problem 6-13)

Station discharge, mgd	0	2	4	6	8	10	
Dynamic pressure, psig	0	2	6	12	20	30	
Discharge, % of rated capacity	0	20	40	60	80	100	120
Efficiency, %	0	39	63	78	88	91	83
Head differential, % of shut-off head	100	98	95	90	84	75	56

Prepare a table similar to Table 6-4 showing the operating characteristics of the station for the average system head curve.

CHAPTER 7. DISTRIBUTION OF WATER

7-1. *Hydrant flow tests* (Section 7-4). In a residential area of one-story, ranch-type houses on large lots, a fire-flow test was made by opening the two outlets on a fire hydrant and measuring the residual pressure nearby. With the hydrant closed, the residual pressure was 38 psig. With both 2½-in. outlets opened, the residual pressure was 12 psig and the velocity head pressure at the outlets 5 psi. How much water will the hydrant deliver at 20 psig residual? Is this adequate for fire fighting?

7-2. *Distribution system analysis by method of sections* (Section 7-5). The pipe network in Figure P-1 serves 20,000 people. The fire draft is 4,300 gpm in

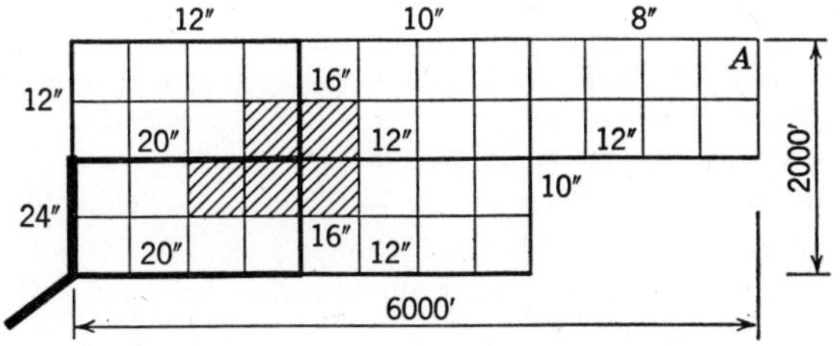

Figure P-1. Pipe network (Problem 7-2).

the shaded area and 1,500 gpm elsewhere. The coincident draft of 140 gpd is uniformly distributed. Study the system by Hazen's method and make recommendations for additional pipes where needed. All lines not marked otherwise are 8 in. in diameter.

7-3. *Distribution system analysis by method of balancing flows* (Section 7-5). Balance the network shown in Figure 7-7 by applying the Hardy Cross method of balancing flows. Heads at the input and take-off points are as follows: $A = 100$ ft, $B = 90$ ft, $C = 80$ ft, $D = 70$ ft, and $E = 60$ ft.

7-4. *Distribution system analysis by method of balancing heads* (Section 7-5). Balance the network shown in Figure 7-8 by applying the Hardy Cross method of balancing heads. Flows at input and take-off points are: $A = 1$ mgd, $C = 2$ mgd, and $F = 3$ mgd.

7-5. *Distribution system analysis by method of balancing heads* (Section 7-5). Find, for a fire flow of 1.5 mgd, the pressure at the intersection of the 2 8-in. pipes in the lower right-hand corner of Figure 7-5*b* when the pressure at the intersection of the 24-in. with the 2 20-in. pipes is 75 psig. In solving this problem, neglect all 6-in. lines and assume that each square in the figure is 400 ft on a side; further, divide the domestic load of 2.2 mgd to the intersections of the grid to be analyzed and apply the Hardy Cross method of balancing heads.

7-6. *Analysis by method of balancing flows* (Section 7-5). Find the total flow at the intersection of the 16-in. and 20-in. pipes with the 12-in. and 10-in. pipes at the center of Figure 7-5*b* when the pressure at this intersection is 60 psig, and the pressure at the point where the 24-in. pipe joins the system is 75 psig. In solving this problem, neglect all 6-in. lines, disregard domestic loads or consider them part of the total load at the intersection in question, assume each square in the figure is 400 ft on a side, and apply the Hardy Cross method of balancing flows.

7-7. *Analysis by equivalent pipe method* (Section 7-5). In Figure 7-8, remove the inflow and given elevation at point C and remove line DE. For the remaining system find the flow from point A to point F by the method of equivalent pipes.

7-8. *Equalizing, or operating, storage* (Section 7-7). Determine the equalizing storage for the drafts shown in Table P-15: (*a*) when the inflow is uniform

TABLE P-15. Draft Rates at Stated Times on Peak Day (Problem 7-8)

Time, hr	0	2	4	6	8	10	12	14	16	18	20	22	24
Draft, mgd	2	1	1	2	5	5	5	5	5	7	7	3	2

during 24 hr; and (*b*) when the inflow to the system is confined to the 18-hr period from 6 A.M. (6 hr) to midnight (24 hr). Assuming that the inflow is by pumping, what pumping rate is required in each case?

7-9. *Service storage* (Section 7-7). A residential zone is supplied by pumps from the large distribution reservoir of a lower zone. If the population of the upper residential zone is 100,000, what amount of distribution storage should be provided for the upper zone?

7-10. *Service storage* (Section 7-7). The drafts listed in Problem 7-8 plus a fire draft of 5 mgd are supplied to a load center near the midpoint of a 20,000-ft, 18-in. diameter line running from a pumping station at the inflow end to a 1-mg elevated tank at the far end. The maximum pressure at the pumping station is limited to 125 psig, but this pressure can be maintained continuously if necessary. The elevations are: 72 ft at the pump center line, 200 ft at the ground surface at the load center, 260 ft at the ground surface at the tank, 340 ft at the tank overflow, and 315 ft at the tank bottom. (*a*) For fire draft plus average peak day draft, what will be the pressure at the load center (1) with the tank full, (2) just before the tank empties, and (3) after the tank has emptied? (*b*) Would the storage be expected to be adequate to meet normal variations in peak day consumption? (*c*) Assuming that the pump pressure is constant at 125 psig, between what elevations will the water level in the tank fluctuate after a few days of peak draft? (*d*) What will be the fluctuations of pressure at the load center for the conditions found in (*c*)?

CHAPTER 8. COLLECTION OF WASTE WATER

8-1. *Collection of sanitary sewage* (Section 8-2). If the minimum design velocity is 2 fps, the peak flow 250 gpcd, the population density 30 per acre, and $n = 0.015$, find: (*a*) the grade at which the minimum size sanitary sewer should be laid; (*b*) the capacity of this sewer; (*c*) the number of people it can serve; and (*d*) the area it will drain.

8-2. *Collection of sanitary sewage* (Section 8-2). A sewer, $n = 0.015$, is designed to carry at 2 fps the sanitary sewage of 10,000 people. If the peak flow in the sewer is 10 times the minimum flow, what will be the velocity in the sewer during periods of minimum flow? (See graph showing hydraulic elements of partially filled pipes, Figure 9-2.)

8-3. *Collection of storm water* (Section 8-3). A storm sewer draining 100 acres and designed to be surcharged not oftener than once in 5 years is to be laid on a slope of 0.0019. The average 45-min (time of concentration) rainfall intensity for the 5-year storm is 2.5 in./hr. If the peak runoff rate is assumed to be 40% of the design rainfall rate and $n = 0.015$, what should be the size of the sewer?

8-4. *Collection of combined sewage* (Section 8-4). Estimate the ratio of storm runoff to dry-weather flow in a combined sewer draining 500 acres when the design rainfall rate is 3 in./hr, the runoff coefficient is 0.70, and the population density is 60 per acre.

8-5. *Inverted siphons* (Section 8-4). Select the pipe sizes for a siphon to carry a minimum dry-weather flow of 0.2 cfs, a maximum dry-weather flow of 2 cfs, and a storm flow of 60 cfs. State the velocities in each pipe at each of these flows.

CHAPTER 9. FLOW IN SEWERS AND THEIR APPURTENANCES

9-1. *Transporting velocities* (Section 9-2). Find the minimum velocity and gradient required to transport ¼-in. gravel through a square drain 3 ft on a side if $n = 0.015$ and $k = 0.04$.

9-2. *Flow in filled sewers* (Section 9-3). Construct a diagram for Manning's formula similar to that for the Hazen-Williams formula at the back of the book. Use $n = 0.012$ and express the flow in cfs.

9-3. *Flow in filled sewers* (Section 9-3). (*a*) Given $Q = 6$ cfs, $n = 0.012$, $v = 2.5$ fps, find d and s. (*b*) Given $Q = 6.2$ cfs, $n = 0.015$, $s = 0.001$, find d and v. (*c*) Given $d = 30$ in., $n = 0.013$, $s = 0.0004$, find Q and v. (*d*) Given $Q = 4$ cfs, $n = 0.012$, $d = 18$ in., find s and v.

9-4. *Flow in partially filled sewers* (Section 9-4). The ratio of maximum to minimum flow in a 12-in. sewer ($N = 0.012$) is 5:1. If the sewer is designed to support a velocity of 2.5 fps when it flows full, what will be the depth of flow and velocity at minimum flow? Assume a variable n.

9-5. *Flow in partially filled sewers* (Section 9-4). Design a sewer to maintain a velocity of 1.5 fps when it carries 1 cfs and flows at 0.1 full depth. Assume $N = 0.013$ at full depth.

9-6. *Flow in partially filled sewers* (Section 9-4). A 12-in. sewer is to flow at 0.2 depth on a grade that will insure a degree of self-cleaning equivalent to that in a full sewer at 2.0 fps. Find the required grades and associated velocities and rates of discharge at full depth and 0.2 depth for $N = 0.012$ at full depth.

9-7. *Flow in partially filled sewers* (Section 9-4). A 10-in. sewer is to discharge 0.2 cfs at a velocity equivalent in self-cleaning action to that of a sewer flowing full at 2.0 fps. Find the depth and velocity of flow and the required slope for $N = 0.012$.

9-8. *Flow in sewer transitions* (Section 9-5). Flow from an 8-in. sewer, $N = 0.013$, $S = 20 \times 10^{-3}$, and $Q = 0.21$ cfs, and from a 10-in. sewer, $N = 0.012$, $S = 3.3 \times 10^{-3}$, and $Q = 1.36$ cfs, enters a manhole from which sewage discharges into a sewer to be designed to flow full at a velocity of 2.0 fps. (*a*) What are the diameter and slope of the outgoing sewer? (*b*) If the elevation of the invert of the 8-in sewer is taken as 10.00, what should be the invert elevations of the other two sewers at points where they join the manhole?

9-9. *Alternate stages and critical depth of flow* (Section 9-6). Between what slopes will the flow be unstable in a rectangular channel 3 ft wide carrying 17 cfs, if $N = 0.015$?

9-10. *Alternate stages and critical depth of flow* (Section 9-6). Given $q = 35$ cfs, $D = 36$ in., $N = 0.012$, and $S = 0.010$, will the flow be in the upper or lower alternate stage?

9-11. *Alternate stages and critical depth of flow* (Section 9-6). Given a discharge of 35 cfs in a 3-ft sewer, find: (*a*) the critical depth; (*b*) the alternate stages for an energy head of 3.6 ft; and (*c*) the upper alternate stage associated with a lower alternate stage of 1.5 ft.

9-12. *Backwater curve* (Section 9-7). A 6-ft circular sewer, $N = 0.012$, carrying 23 cfs on a gradient $S = 0.0008$ discharges into a screen chamber in which water rises to an elevation of 5 ft above the invert of the incoming sewer. Determine the profile of the water surface relative to the sewer invert back to the point of uniform flow for maximum level in the screen chamber.

9-13. *Drawdown curve* (Section 9-7). A long rectangular sewer discharges at its downstream end by free overfall. If the bottom slope $i = 0.2 \times 10^{-3}$, $N = 0.014$, interior height $a = 5$ ft, and the bottom width $b = 10$ ft, trace the water surface profile for a steady flow of 100 cfs.

9-14. *Side weirs* (Section 9-8). At maximum flow in a 4-ft circular intercepter, $N = 0.012$, $i = 0.0015$, $Q_1 = 40$ cfs, and $Q_2 = 20$ cfs upstream and downstream from a side channel weir. (*a*) Design a side channel weir to produce the desired relationship between Q_1 and Q_2. (*b*) At what flow in the intercepter will sewage begin to spill over the side weir?

9-15. *Capacity of street inlets* (Section 9-9). What is the flow into an undepressed curb inlet 8 ft long in a street with a 1% grade and a 1:24 crown, when 0.8 cfs flows in the gutter?

CHAPTER 10. Design of Drainage Systems

10-1. *Design velocity* (Sections 10-2 and 9-2). If the design storm runoff is 1.55 cfs/acre and the average domestic sewage flow is 10,000 gpd/acre, what design velocity should be used for a 24-in. combined sewer, $n = 0.015$, in order that the velocity at average domestic sewage flow will be capable of initiating scour of sand having a diameter of 0.5 mm?

10-2. *Common elements of sewer design* (Section 10-2). Design sewers for the five sets of conditions listed in Table P-16 and for the following design criteria: minimum velocity = 2 fps, minimum depth = 7 ft, and $n = 0.015$. Assume that there is no change in sewer diameter at the upstream manhole. State diameter, slope, velocity, capacity, and invert elevations and depths at upper and lower ends.

TABLE P-16. Flow Conditions (Problem 10-2)

Sewer No.	Length, ft	Flow, cfs	Surface Elevation, ft		Invert Elevation, Upper End, ft
			Upper End	Lower End	
(1)	(2)	(3)	(4)	(5)	(6)
1	400	1.5	137.6	137.1	129.60
2	350	1.5	326.6	323.1	317.44
3	350	1.5	241.2	238.9	231.67
4	400	3.0	176.9	176.3	168.42
5	350	3.0	194.8	191.3	186.80

10-3. *Design of sanitary sewerage systems* (Section 10-4). Determine the size, slope, and hydraulic characteristics of the various sections of the sanitary sewer for which data are given in Table P-17. Design sewers for a minimum velocity of 2 fps, a minimum depth of 8 ft, and $n = 0.015$. The sewer entering manhole No. 12 is a 12-in. line with invert elevation at 238.1 ft.

TABLE P-17. Sewerage System (Problem 10-3)

Sewer Section	Manhole Number		Length, ft	Surface Elevations, ft		Flow, cfs
	Upper End	Lower End		Upper End	Lower End	
(1)	(2)	(3)	(4)	(5)	(6)	(7)
1	12	13	275	247.6	246.5	2.3
2	13	14	354	246.5	243.1	2.6
3	14	15	348	243.1	241.2	4.8
4	15	16	406	241.2	235.6	5.0
5	16	17	215	235.6	235.9	5.9

10-4. *Capacity design of storm drainage systems* (Section 10-5). A relatively flat, mixed commercial and residential district has an area of 92 acres. Estimate the time of concentration and the runoff coefficient for such an area and calculate the runoff rate for the 5-year storm shown in Figure 3-6.

10-5. *Time zone method of estimating design capacity* (Section 10-5). Given the data of Table P-18 for a relatively flat, mixed commercial and residential area, calculate the runoff by using the time zone method. Assume the design is for the 5-year storm shown in Figure 3-6 and that Horner's curves in Figure 10-4 apply for the pervious and impervious areas respectively.

TABLE P-18. Areas and Times of Flow (Problem 10-5)

Time zone, No.	1	2	3	4	5
Time to point of concentration, min	5	10	15	20	25
Area in zone, acres	5	12	18	25	32
Impervious area, % of total	90	80	75	50	40

10-6. *Weighted average runoff coefficient method* (Section 10-5). Calculate by the weighted average coefficient method the runoff from the area for which data are given in Problem 10-5, assuming that the time of concentration for the entire area is 25 min. Use Horner's curves, Figure 10-4, and the 5-year curve, Figure 3-6. Compare the answers with those obtained in Problems 10-4 and 10-5.

10-7. *Capacity design of inlets* (Section 10-5). An inlet receives water from 1.5 acres of which 40% is impervious. The time of concentration for the impervious area is 5 min and for the pervious area 15 min. Estimate the peak flow at the inlet for the 5-year curve in Figure 3-6.

10-8. *Design of storm-drainage systems* (Section 10-7). Calculate the runoff and design storm drains for the area for which data are given in Table P-19. Use the following design criteria: minimum $v = 2.5$ fps, minimum depth $= 4$ ft, $N = 0.012$, 10-year storm of Fig. 10-6, and time of concentration to first manhole $= 35$ min.

TABLE P-19. Characteristics of Area To Be Drained (Problem 10-8)

Manhole		Length, ft	Incremental Area, acres	Runoff Coefficient for Incremental Area, %	Surface Elevations, ft	
From	To				Upper End	Lower End
1	2	225	23.0	40	57.2	56.6
2	3	450	11.0	52	56.6	56.3
3	4	450	17.4	57	56.3	62.4
4	5	450	5.8	58	62.4	54.6
5	6	450	8.7	63	54.6	55.1

CHAPTER 11. Examination of Water and Waste Water

11-1. *Alkalinity and related quantities* (Section 11-9). The total alkalinity of a sample of water with a *p*H of 11.0 is 200 mg/l. Find the distribution of the alkalinity as (*a*) bicarbonate, (*b*) carbonate, and (*c*) hydroxide alkalinity in mg/l as $CaCO_3$. Assume a water temperature of 25 C and that the effect of salinity can be neglected.

11-2. *Alkalinity and related quantities* (Section 11-9). The total alkalinity of a sample of water with pH 6.0 is 3.0 mg/l. Find the concentration of CO_2 in mg/l. Assume a water temperature of 25 C and that the effect of salinity can be neglected.

11-3. *Hardness* (Section 11-10). (*a*) The total hardness of a sample of water is 300 mg/l. Its bicarbonate alkalinity is 12 mg/l and its carbonate alkalinity is 137 mg/l. Find the amounts of carbonate and non-carbonate hardness. (*b*) The total hardness of a sample of water is 150 mg/l. Its bicarbonate alkalinity is 105 mg/l and its carbonate alkalinity is 45 mg/l. What is the carbonate hardness and what the non-carbonate hardness?

11-4. *Bacteriological indicators of contamination* (Section 11-15). If the USPHS standard of approximately 1 coliform organism in 100 ml of water is assumed to be associated with a regional typhoid morbidity of 10 per 100,000, how should the standard be modified for use in a region where the case rate from typhoid is 200 per 100,000, in order that the probability of water-borne typhoid will be the same in both regions?

11-5. *Bacteriological tests* (Section 11-16). A test for coliform organisms produced the following results: 5 of 5 100-ml portions positive, 2 of 5 10-ml portions positive, and 0 of 5 1-ml portions positive. Find the MPN per 100 ml.

11-6. *Bacteriological quality* (Section 11-16). Tests for determining coliforms in the drinking-water supply of 5 towns gave the results shown in Table P-20.

TABLE P-20. Tests for Coliforms in 5 10-ml Portions (Problem 11-6)

Town (1)	Population (2)	Samples Examined in Month (3)	Number of Positive Portions (4)	Number of Samples in Which 3 or More Portions Were Positive (5)
A	10,000	12	5	1
B	20,000	33	11	0
C	100,000	86	35	2
D	100,000	123	71	6
E	100,000	100	32	3

Five 10-ml portions were tested per sample. In which towns did the water fail to meet the USPHS standards?

11-7. *Bacteriological quality* (Section 11-16). Tests for determining coliforms in the drinking-water supply of 5 towns gave the results shown in Table P-21.

TABLE P-21. Tests for Coliforms in 5 100-ml Portions (Problem 11-7)

Town (1)	Population (2)	Samples Examined in Month (3)	Number of Positive Portions (4)	Number of Samples in Which All Portions Were Positive (5)
A	10,000	11	19	1
B	20,000	22	50	3
C	100,000	108	320	31
D	100,000	135	250	16
E	100,000	100	360	25

Five 100-ml portions were tested per sample. In which towns did the water fail to meet the USPHS standards?

CHAPTER 13. Screening, Sedimentation, and Flotation

13-1. *Settling velocities of discrete particles* (Section 13-3). (*a*) A sphere 4.2 cm in diameter of specific gravity 2.5 is observed to settle in water at 10 C at a rate of 150 cm/sec; find its settling rate if its specific gravity is changed to 1.5. (*b*) A sphere 0.042 mm in diameter of specific gravity 2.5 is observed to settle in water at 10 C at a rate of 0.1 cm/sec; find its settling rate if its specific gravity is changed to 1.5.

13-2. *Settling velocities of discrete particles* (Section 13-3). Sand particles 0.23 mm in diameter and of specific gravity 2.5 settle through 24 cm of water at 20 C in 8.0 sec. Prove that this observation is in agreement with the laws of sedimentation.

13-3. *Settling and rising velocities of discrete particles* (Section 13-3). Write an equation for the eddying resistance at high Reynolds numbers (10^4 to 10^5) of cylinders the length of which equals 5 diameters.

13-4. *Reduction in basin efficiency by currents* (Section 13-7). Find the settling velocity (cm/sec) of particles suspended in water subjected to sedimentation when the overflow rate of the basin is 1,000 gpd/sq ft and 90% of the particles are removed, if the basin is a good one.

13-5. *Reduction in basin efficiency by currents* (Section 13-7). What should the surface loading of an ideal fill-and-draw basin be reduced to if the basin is converted into a continuous-flow basin that is still to remove 90% of the particles of a given size? Assume that the continuous-flow basin will operate poorly.

13-6. *Reduction in basin efficiency by currents* (Section 13-7). Before the introduction of a perforated baffle, a settling tank effected 70% removal of suspended solids. (*a*) Estimate the effect of the baffle, on the assumption that the basin was poor before new construction and became good afterwards. (*b*) By how much must the loading be reduced in order to attain 90% removal in the baffled basin?

13-7. *Bottom scour of deposited sludge* (Section 13-8). A grit chamber is to remove 90% of the particles of specific gravity 2.65 and diameter 0.02 cm at a water temperature of 20 C (settling velocity = 2.5 cm/sec). Assuming a channel friction factor $f = 0.03$, a grit characteristic $k = 0.06$, and a channel depth of 3 ft, find: (*a*) the requisite length of the channel; and (*b*) the requisite width for a flow of 2 mgd. Assume that the operation of the channel as a settling basin is poor.

13-8. *Inlets* (Section 13-11). A series of parallel settling tanks is supplied with water through 10 equal openings. The frictional resistance between the first and the tenth opening is 0.1 ft, and the loss of head through the first opening is 1 ft. What is the rate of discharge through the tenth opening relative to that through the first?

13-9. *Outlets* (Section 13-12). A settling tank discharges 2 mgd over 2 20-ft weirs attached to a horizontal outlet trough 18 in. wide and 20 ft long. The trough terminates in a channel the water level of which rises 6 in. above the invert of the trough. Find the requisite depth of the trough (in.) to ensure free discharge over the weir.

13-10. *Grit chambers* (Section 13-15). A grit chamber is divided into 2 compartments controlled by proportional-flow weirs. Design requirements call for 90% removal of particles of specific gravity 2.5 and diameter 0.1 cm (settling velocity = 16 cm/sec) when a maximum rate of flow of 10 cfs is distributed equally between the two compartments. Assuming a discharge through the proportional-flow weirs of $Q = 2.5h$, find: (*a*) the maximum displacement velocity for a grit characteristic $k = 0.06$ and a channel friction factor $f = 0.03$; (*b*) the maximum depth of flow and width of channel; and (*c*) the required length of channel if the surface area is made 5 times that of an ideal basin in order to allow for turbulence.

13-11. *Grit chambers* (Section 13-15). If flow from a grit chamber were to be controlled by a right-angled triangular weir, what would be the required width of the chamber at a depth of 0.0, 0.5, and 1.0 ft? Flow through this type of weir is represented by the equation $Q = 2.64h^{5/2}$, where Q is the rate of discharge in cfs and h is the head on the apex in ft. Assume that the velocity of flow in the chamber is to be 0.75 fps.

CHAPTER 14. CHEMICAL TREATMENT

14-1. *Chemical coagulation* (Section 14-2). Water is treated with 2 grains/gal of alum. Find: (*a*) the approximate amount of reacting alkalinity; (*b*) the approximate amount of conversion from carbonate to sulfate hardness; and (*c*) the approximate amount of carbon dioxide released.

14-2. *Determination of coagulant dose* (Section 14-2). Prepare operator instructions for the jar test control of alum coagulation in a water plant using dry feed to treat 5 mgd of water, assuming that the alum requirement varies from 0.75 to 2 grains/gal. Give: (*a*) size of sample; (*b*) number of jars; (*c*) strength of alum solution; (*d*) amount of solution in each jar to produce stated doses; (*e*) mixing time and speed; (*f*) basis for choosing dose; and (*g*) when test should be made. If the chosen dose is 1.25 grains/gal, explain how the feed rate should be checked by test and by keeping records of chemicals used.

14-3. *Mineral constituents of water* (Section 14-3). Find the total hardness, alkalinity, and non-carbonate hardness expressed as $CaCO_3$ of a sample of water, analyzing as follows: Ca = 66 mg/l, Mg = 22 mg/l, Na = 76 mg/l, HCO_3 = 160 mg/l, CO_3 = 0 mg/l, OH = 0 mg/l, SO_4 = 200 mg/l, Cl = 56 mg/l, and CO_2 = 30 mg/l.

14-4. *Chemical precipitation, lime softening* (Section 14-3). Estimate the amount of hardness that can be removed from the water of Problem 14-3 by use of lime alone. What is the amount of lime required?

14-5. *Lime-soda softening* (Section 14-3). What are the amounts of chemicals required for the lime-soda softening of the water of Problem 14-3?

14-6. *Flocculation* (Section 14-4). A baffled flocculation chamber has a volume of 6,000 cu ft. When 2 mgd of water pass through it, the loss of head is 3 ft. Find: (*a*) the temporal mean velocity gradient; (*b*) the detention time;

and (*c*) whether the chamber may be expected to perform well. Assume a water temperature of 50 F.

14-7. *Flocculation* (Section 14-4). Alum is introduced into a pipeline 10,000 ft long and 12 in. in diameter discharging at a rate of 1.55 mgd. Find the flocculation characteristics of the line and state whether they are acceptable. Assume a viscosity of 3×10^{-5} lb sec/sq ft.

14-8. *Flocculation* (Section 14-4). Compressed air is employed in a flocculator to impart a spiral velocity of 1.6 fps to water at 50 F. If 10 mgd of water are passed through the flocculator and the tank volume is 3,200 cu ft, find: (*a*) the velocity gradient in fps/ft; and (*b*) the detention period in min. State whether in your opinion the conditions for flocculation are satisfactory.

14-9. *Flocculation* (Section 14-4). A diffused-air flocculator with a capacity of 8,000 cu ft is provided with 100 cfm of compressed air when it flocculates 6 mgd of water. The tank is 10 ft deep, and the water temperature is 10 C (50 F). Find: (*a*) the velocity gradient in fps/ft; (*b*) the detention period in min; and (*c*) the product of (*a*) and (*b*). Then state whether or not the conditions of flocculation are presumably satisfactory.

14-10. *Flocculation* (Section 14-4). (*a*) Design a paddle flocculator for a flow of 5 mgd. (*b*) Calculate the hydraulic power and energy consumption. (*c*) Estimate the total power and energy consumption.

14-11. *Flocculation* (Section 14-4). A paddle-operated flocculator is found to be relatively ineffective. How can the efficiency of the installation be increased without making major structural alterations or adding new units?

14-12. *Ion exchange, zeolite softening* (Section 14-5). A synthetic zeolite is used to treat, in dual units, 0.2 mgd of water containing the following: Ca = 30 mg/l, Mg = 6 mg/l, and Fe = 0.3 mg/l. Calculate: (*a*) the size of the units required; (*b*) the length of the period between regenerations; and (*c*) the amount of salt required to regenerate one unit once.

14-13. *Ion exchange, removal of chlorides* (Section 14-5). Split treatment in cation-anion exchangers is used to reduce the Cl ion in the following water to 250 mg/l: Ca = 90 mg/l, Mg = 12 mg/l, Na = 400 mg/l, HCO_3 = 122 mg/l, SO_4 = 48 mg/l, and Cl = 710 mg/l. If H_2SO_4 costs $100 per ton and NaOH $100 per ton, calculate the cost of regenerating chemicals per mg of water treated.

14-14. *Chemical stabilization* (Section 14-6). Find the saturation indexes at 25 C and 60 C and the excess CO_2 for the waters listed in Table P-22.

TABLE P-22. Composition of Water (Problem 14-14)

	Ca, mg/l ($CaCO_3$)	Alkalinity, mg/l ($CaCO_3$)	Suspended Solids, mg/l	*p*H
A	252	164	284	7.9
B	17	8	37	6.8
C	40	32	60	10.1

CHAPTER 15. FILTRATION

15-1. *Preparation of filter sand* (Section 15-4). A "run of bank" sand is to be converted into a useful filter sand with an effective size of 0.05 cm and a uniformity coefficient of 2.0. An analysis of the sand shows that 20% by weight is smaller than the desired effective size and 60% by weight is smaller than the 60-percentile size. Find: (*a*) the percentage of sand that can be used as filter sand; (*b*) the percentage of fine sand that must be wasted; (*c*) the percentage of coarse sand that must be wasted.

15-2. *Hydraulics of filtration* (Section 15-5). The loss of head through a clean bed of uniform sand 0.05 cm in diameter is 1 ft when the rate of filtration is 2 gpm/sq ft (0.135 cm/sec) and the water temperature is 10 C. Find the loss of head for a rate of filtration of 3 gpm/sq ft and a temperature of 30 C.

15-3. *Hydraulics of filtration* (Section 15-5). The rate of filtration through a bed of uniform sand 0.06 cm in diameter is to be stepped up from 2 gpm/sq ft to 3 gpm/sq ft. What will be the relative loss of head at the higher rate if the water temperature is 10 C?

15-4. *Hydraulics of filter washing* (Section 15-6). A bed of crushed anthracite of specific gravity 1.5, 30 in. deep, with 40% pore space, is backwashed at a rate of 24 in./min (1.016 cm/sec). Find: (*a*) the percentage expansion of the bed, if the settling velocity of the anthracite is 5.08 cm/sec; (*b*) the time of settling of the bed after washing has been completed; and (*c*) the velocity gradient G in cm/sec/cm for an expansion of 60% and a settling velocity of 4 cm/sec at 4 C.

15-5. *Hydraulics of filter washing* (Section 15-6). A bed of sand 30 in. deep with 40% pore space is backwashed at a rate of 24 in./min (1.016 cm/sec). Find: (*a*) the percentage expansion of the bed, if the settling velocity of the constituent uniform sand is 10.16 cm/sec; (*b*) the time of settling of the bed after washing is completed; and (*c*) the approximate time of rise during backwashing.

15-6. *Hydraulics of filter washing* (Section 15-6). Uniform sand 24 in. deep underlies a layer of uniform crushed anthracite. The settling velocity of the sand is 10.0 cm/sec, that of the anthracite 6.0 cm/sec. Find the percentage expansion of the bed at a backwash velocity of 24 in./min (1.016 cm/sec). Assume an initial porosity of 42%.

15-7. *Hydraulics of filter washing* (Section 15-6). (*a*) How close to the settling velocity of its sand grains is a water filter that is 50% expanded, the porosity of the unexpanded bed being 40%? (*b*) How long will it take this bed to settle after expansion if the unexpanded bed is 30 in. deep and the rate of wash is 30 in./min?

15-8. *Hydraulics of filter washing* (Section 15-6). Write an equation for the expansion of a bed of sand, assuming that the loss of head in expansion is proportionate to that in filtration and that the flow is turbulent.

15-9. *Required depth of filter* (Section 15-7). A rapid sand filter with porous-plate underdrainage is composed of uniform sand 0.08 cm in diameter. The terminal loss of head of this filter is to be 8 ft and the rate of filtration is to be

2 gpm/sq ft. Estimate the requisite depth of this filter for average conditions of raw-water quality and pretreatment.

15-10. *Filter underdrains* (Section 15-8). A rapid sand filter is to be equipped with perforated pipe laterals. The perforations, 20 in number, are placed 6 in. on centers. Assuming a loss of head of 0.2 ft between the first and the tenth opening, find the magnitude of the controlling loss of head in the first opening that will make the discharge of the last opening no less than 99% of the first.

15-11. *Filter underdrains* (Section 15-8). The loss of head in the underdrainage system of a rapid filter is 1.5 ft between the nearest and farthest orifices when the filter is being washed. Find the head on the nearest orifice that will keep the flow differential between the two orifices below 5%.

15-12. *Filter underdrains* (Section 15-8). (*a*) What is the loss of head associated with orifices constituting 0.2% of the sand area of beds that are washed at a rate of 24 in./min? (*b*) What is the ratio of the loss of head in half the length of a perforated pipe relative to that in the full length?

15-13. *Wash-water gutters* (Section 15-9). Troughs 15 ft long, 1 ft wide, and spaced 6 ft on centers collect the wash water from a filter that is washed at a rate of 24 in./min. Find: (*a*) the depth of the troughs for free discharge and level invert; and (*b*) the height of the troughs above the sand if a 30-in. bed is to be expanded 50%.

CHAPTER 16. Biological Treatment

16-1. *Recirculation* (Section 16-5). An activated-sludge unit is operated with 25% recirculation of sludge. Assuming a weighting factor of 90%, find: (*a*) the average number of passes; (*b*) the average number of effective passes through the treatment unit; (*c*) the recirculation ratio needed to produce a maximal value of effective passes; and (*d*) the resulting ratio of the magnitude of this value to that of the average number of passes.

16-2. *Recirculation* (Section 16-5). If the treatability of a waste water on a trickling filter is reduced by 25% in each passage through the filter and the loading of the filter is 2,000 lb/acre-ft daily on a once-through basis, find the efficiency of the bed that could be obtained by optimum recirculation.

16-3. *Recirculation* (Section 16-5). Prove that the average number of effective passes through a biological sewage treatment plant reaches a maximum value when $R/I = (2f - 1)/(1 - f)$.

16.4. *Treatment efficiency* (Section 16-7). A flow of 1 mgd of sewage containing 307 mg/l of BOD is passed through a primary settling tank, which removes 35% of the BOD, before being applied to a trickling filter and secondary settling tank. If the filter surface is 0.370 acre and its depth is 6.0 ft, estimate the over-all percentage reduction in BOD and the BOD remaining in the plant effluent: (*a*) for once-through operation of the filter; and (*b*) for recirculation of 1.5 mgd of plant effluent to the trickling filter. Compare these figures with the results of Example 16-2.

16-5. *Treatment efficiency* (Section 16-7). An activated-sludge unit receives a BOD load of 1,665 lb/day from 1 mgd of sewage. The sewage is aerated for 6 hr and the suspended-solids-concentration is maintained at 2,500 mg/l. Find the efficiency of BOD removal.

16-6. *Activated-sludge units* (Section 16-10). Estimate the concentration of suspended solids (mg/l) needed in an activated-sludge tank to effect 75% purification of 2 mgd of sewage under a BOD load of 3,500 lb/day when the period of aeration is 6 hr.

16-7. *Air supply for diffused-air units* (Section 16-11). How much free air can a new 18-in. main, 1,500 ft long, carry with a pressure loss of 1.5 psi when the line pressure is 8 psig?

16-8. *Air supply for diffused-air units* (Section 16-11). Find the frictional resistance in psi offered by 2,000 ft of 12-in. pipe to 3,000,000 cu ft of free air per day compressed adiabatically to a pressure equivalent to 20 ft of water. Assume a pipe friction factor of 0.03.

16-9. *Air supply for diffused-air units* (Section 16-11). Find the theoretical horsepower required to compress adiabatically 3,000,000 cu ft of air per day to a pressure equivalent to 20 ft of water.

CHAPTER 17. SLUDGE TREATMENT AND DISPOSAL

17-1. *Sludge moisture-weight-volume relationships* (Section 17-4). An activated sludge containing 99% moisture is thickened until it contains but 95% moisture. Assuming a fundamental specific gravity of 1.05 for volatile matter and of 2.35 for fixed residue and that the sludge contains 70% volatile matter on a dry basis, estimate: (*a*) the specific gravity of the solids on a dry basis; (*b*) the specific gravities of the wet sludges before and after thickening; (*c*) the relative decrease in volume of the sludge to be handled; and (*d*) the fuel value of the dry solids.

17-2. *Fuel value* (Section 17-7). A sewage to which 30 mg/l of $FeCl_3$ are added precipitates 2,150 lb of dry solids from 1,000,000 gallons of sewage. Assuming that the $FeCl_3$ precipitates as $Fe(OH)_3$, find the fuel value of the sludge if the sludge contains 65% volatile matter.

17-3. *Heat requirements of digestion tanks* (Section 17-13). Primary sludge (2,000 cu ft/day) is to be digested in a heated tank. Assuming that the tank has a surface area of 10,000 sq ft, find the daily heat needed to keep the tank at 90 F if the weighted average temperature outside the tank is 40 F and the temperature of the incoming sludge is 50 F. Assume a coefficient of heat transfer from the tank of 0.2 Btu/sq ft/hr.

17-4. *Utilization of digester gas* (Section 17-14). A high-rate digester receives a solids load of 11 lb/cu ft/month. Estimate the rate of gas evolution in cu ft/sq ft/day in a tank 20 ft deep. Assume that the sludge contains 70% volatile matter, 67% of which is destroyed by digestion, and that the gas contains 72% CH_4 and 28% CO_2.

17-5. *Utilization of digester gas* (Section 17-14). (*a*) A sludge digester releases 40,000 cu ft of gas daily. The gas is measured at a temperature of 77 F and at a pressure of 0.3 psig. Find the volume of gas at 32 F and 14.7 psia. (*b*) If the gas contains 67% methane, what is the daily available energy from this source? (*c*) If the gas is fed to a gas engine with 25% power efficiency, what is the available horsepower?

CHAPTER 18. Disinfection, Destruction of Aquatic Growths, and Removal of Odors and Tastes

18-1. *Aeration* (Section 18-20). A fountain aerator exposes water containing 45 mg/l of CO_2 for 2 seconds. Assuming a saturation value of 1 mg/l, an average droplet size of 0.4 cm, and a gas transfer coefficient of 200 cm/hr, find the terminal CO_2 concentration of the water in mg/l.

18-2. *Aeration* (Section 18-20). Water containing 1.5 mg/l of dissolved oxygen at 15 C is aerated in a fountain aerator. Droplets averaging 0.8 cm in diameter are released. Assuming a gas transfer coefficient of 120 cm/hr, find the time required to raise the DO concentration to 7.5 mg/l.

18-3. *Aeration* (Section 18-20). Spray aeration for deferrization exposes water devoid of oxygen to air for 1 second. The temperature of the water is 10 C and the droplet size 0.5 cm. Assuming a gas transfer coefficient of 150 cm/hr, find the rise in oyxgen concentration of the water in mg/l.

18-4. *Aeration* (Section 18-20). Estimate the oxygen concentration that will be obtained in a diffused-air aerator in which 0.1 cu ft of air is used per gallon of water treated in a tank 10 ft deep if the air bubbles are 0.187 cm in diameter and rise at a uniform velocity of 22 cm/sec. The initial oxygen concentration is 2.5 mg/l and the temperature 20 C. Neglect surface aeration, and assume that the oxygen content of the bubbles remains constant and that the oxygen transfer coefficient is 10 cm/hr.

18-5. *Aeration* (Section 18-20). What will be the oxygen concentration obtained with a spray aerator that throws droplets 0.2 cm in diameter 8 ft upward into the air, if the initial oxygen concentration is 3 mg/l, the temperature 20 C, and the gas transfer coefficient is estimated to be 100 cm/hr? Assume that air resistance can be neglected.

CHAPTER 19. The Natural Purification of Water

19-1. *Formulation of the first-stage* BOD *curve* (Section 19-6). If the 5-day, 20-C BOD of a waste water is 210 mg/l and the rate constant, k, at 20 C is 0.4 per day, find: (a) the total first-stage demand at 20 C; (b) the rate constant at 25 C; (c) the first-stage demand at 25 C; and (d) the 3-day, 25-C BOD.

19-2. *Calculation of* BOD (Section 19-6). The 5-day, 20-C BOD of a waste water is 200 mg/l and its temperature is 80 F. The 5-day, 20-C BOD of the water in a stream is 3.0 mg/l and its temperature is 60 F. What will be the first-stage BOD of the stream when its flow is 10 cfs and 0.2 mgd of the waste water is discharged into it? Assume that the BOD rate is constant, that k at 20 C is 0.3 for both the stream and the sewage, and that the temperature characteristic of the rate constant is 0.046 per deg C.

19-3. *Deoxygenation of polluted waters* (Section 19-5). If all of the 8 mg/l of DO in a clean stream flowing at good velocities and shallow depths can be counted on for biochemical oxidation of organic matter in domestic sewage (leaving reaeration as a factor of safety against nuisance), what should be the dilution factor in cfs per 1,000 population if the sewage flow is 100 gpcd and its biochemical oxygen demand is 200 mg/l?

19-4. *Rate of deoxygenation by the benthal load* (Section 19-7). Raw sewage from a community of 10,000 population discharges into the upstream end of a pool which is 2,000 ft long, 100 ft wide, and 5 ft in average depth. Find the maximum benthal oxygen demand after sludge has accumulated for 30 days during a period in which the flow was 50 cfs. Assume uniform deposition of 40% of the settleable solids and an average temperature of 20 C.

19-5. *Atmospheric reoxygenation of polluted waters* (Section 19-8). A shallow stream contains 6 mg/l of DO at 20 C. Find the rate of reoxygenation if during an 8-hr period the oxygen content rises to 8 mg/l and the BOD rate during this period is estimated to be 3 mg/l/day.

19-6. *Dissolved-oxygen sag* (Section 19-9). The minimum DO downstream from a waste discharge is found to be 4 mg/l at a point estimated to be 1 day's time of flow from the outfall. At the outfall the DO and 5-day BOD of the mixture of stream water and waste water are found to be 7 mg/l and 15 mg/l respectively. Find: (*a*) the rate of self-purification, f, and the rate of deoxygenation, k; and (*b*) the magnitudes of the critical time and critical deficit if the BOD at the outfall is raised to 30 mg/l by an additional waste discharge. Assume all temperatures are 20 C.

19-7. *Allowable* BOD *loading of receiving waters* (Section 19-10). For a minimum DO content of 2 mg/l and a temperature of 20 C, find the allowable loading of a stream which has a self-purification rate $f = 4.0$ and a deoxygenation rate $k = 0.2$ per day for the conditions: (*a*) $D_a = D_c$; and (*b*) $D_a = D_c/4$.

19-8. *Dilution requirements* (Section 19-11). A clean stream containing 8 mg/l of DO is judged to have a self-purification rate of $f = 3.5$. What should be the dilution factor in cfs per 1,000 population for 100 gpcd of sewage having a 5-day BOD of 200 mg/l in order that the DO of the stream shall not fall below 4 mg/l?

19-9. *Dilution requirements* (Section 19-11). A sluggish stream, in passing through an industrial area, has been polluted to the extent that its DO content has dropped to 6 mg/l and it then carries organic materials that exert a BOD of 4 mg/l. If the minimum stream flow is 100 cfs, what measures will need to be taken to prevent a nuisance, if the domestic sewage from 20,000 people must also be discharged to the stream?

19-10. *Dilution requirements* (Section 19-11). The low flow of a sluggish stream is 60 cfs. Estimate the extent to which domestic sewage from a community of 10,000 people must be treated before discharge to the stream. What is the ratio of sewage flow to stream flow, if the per capita production of sewage is 100 gpd?

Tables

TABLE A-1. Abbreviations

The abbreviations used in this book are shown in the following schedule. There is no differentiation between the singular and the plural unless it is noted.

Chemical symbols are listed in Table A-5.

A	angstrom units
atm	atmosphere
A.M.	before noon
ave	average
bbl	barrel
Bé	Baumé degree
BOD	biochemical oxygen demand (in 5 days at 20 C, unless otherwise stated)
Btu	British thermal unit
C	Centigrade degree
cal	calorie
cc	cubic centimeter
cfm	cubic foot per minute
cfs	cubic foot per second
cgs	centimeter-gram-second system
cm	centimeter
csm	cubic foot per second per square mile
cu	cubic
deg	degree
DO	dissolved oxygen
F	Fahrenheit degree
fpm	foot per minute
fps	foot per second
ft	foot
gal	gallon
gpad	gallon per acre per day
gpcd	gallon per capita per day
gpd	gallon per day
gph	gallon per hour
gpm	gallon per minute
hp	horsepower
hr	hour
in.	inch
kw	kilowatt
l	liter
lb	pound
MAF	mean annual flow
m	meter
mg	million gallons, also milligram
mgad	million gallons per acre per day
mgd	million gallons per day
min	minute
ml	milliliter

TABLE A-1. Abbreviations (*Continued*)

mm	millimeter	ppm	part per million
mol	gram molecular weight	psi	pound per square inch
mols	gram molecular weights	psia	pound per square inch, absolute
mph	mile per hour	psig	pound per square inch, gage
MPN	most probable number	rpm	revolution per minute
μ	micron	sec	second
μc	microcurie	sq	square
μg	microgram	U. S.	United States
No.	number	wt	weight
p.	page	yd	yard
P.M.	after noon		
ppb	part per billion		

TABLE A-2. Weights and Measures

The American and English weights and measures referred to in this book are alike except for the gallon. The U. S. gallon is employed. The U. S. billion, which equals 1,000 million, is also employed.

Length

Miles	Yards	Feet	Inches	Centimeters
1	1,760	5,280	..	.....
..	1	3	36	91.4
..	.....	1	12	30.5
..	.....	.....	1	2.54

1 m = 100 cm = 3.28 ft

Area

Square Miles	Acres	Square Feet	Square Inches	Square Centimeters
1	640	......	...	......
..	1	43,560	...	......
..	...	1	144	929
..	...	......	1	6.45

1 sq m = 10.8 sq ft

Volume

Cubic Feet	Imperial Gallons	U. S. Gallons	U. S. Quarts	Liters	Cubic Inches
1	6.23	7.48	29.92	28.32	1,728
..	1	1.2	4.8	4.536	277.4
..	....	1	4	3.785	231
..	....	....	1	0.946	57.75
..	....	....	1.057	1	61.02

1 cu m = 35.3 cu ft

1 Imperial gal weighs 10 lb   1 U. S. gal weighs 8.34 lb

1 cu ft of water weighs 62.4 lb

TABLE A-2. Weights and Measures (*Continued*)

Velocity

Miles per Day	Feet per Second	Inches per Minute	Centimeters per Second
1	0.0611	44	......
..	1	720	30.5
..	......	1	0.043

Time

Days	Hours	Minutes	Seconds
1	24	1,440	86,400
..	1	60	3,600
..	..	1	60

Weight

Tons	Pounds	Grams	Grains
1	2,000	...	....
..	1	454	7,000
..	.....	1	15.43

1 grain per gal = 17.1 mg/l = 142.9 lb per mg
1 ppm = 1 mg/l = 8.34 lb per mg

Discharge

Cubic Feet per Second	Million Gallons Daily	Gallons per Minute
1	0.646	449
1.547	1	694

1 mgd per acre ft = 0.430 gpm per cu yd

Pressure

Pounds per Square Inch	Feet of Water	Inches of Mercury
1	2.31	2.04
0.433	1	0.883
0.491	1.133	1

1 atm = 14.7 psia = 29.9 in. Hg

Power

Kilowatts	Horsepower	Foot-Pounds per Second
1	1.341	738
0.746	1	550

TABLE A-2. Weights and Measures (*Continued*)

Work and Energy

Kilowatt-Hours	Horsepower-Hours	British Thermal Units
1	1.341	3,410
0.746	1	2,540

Temperature

Degree Fahrenheit = $32 + \frac{9}{5} \times$ degrees Centigrade

0	5	10	15	20	25	30	35	40	45	50	55	60	C
32	41	50	59	68	77	86	95	104	113	122	131	140	F

TABLE A-3. Viscosity and Density of Water

Calculated from International Critical Tables, 1928 *and* 1929

Temperature, C	Density ρ, γ (grams/cm^3), also s	Absolute Viscosity μ, centipoises *	Kinematic Viscosity ν, centistokes †
0	0.99987	1.7921	1.7923
2	0.99997	1.6740	1.6741
4	1.00000	1.5676	1.5676
6	0.99997	1.4726	1.4726
8	0.99988	1.3872	1.3874
10	0.99973	1.3097	1.3101
12	0.99952	1.2390	1.2396
14	0.99927	1.1748	1.1756
16	0.99897	1.1156	1.1168
18	0.99862	1.0603	1.0618
20	0.99823	1.0087	1.0105
22	0.99780	0.9608	0.9629
24	0.99733	0.9161	0.9186
26	0.99681	0.8746	0.8774
28	0.99626	0.8363	0.8394
30	0.99568	0.8004	0.8039

* 1 centipoise = 10^{-2} (gram mass)/(cm)(sec). To convert to (lb force)(sec)/(sq ft) multiply centipoise by 2.088×10^{-5}.

† 1 centistoke = 10^{-2} cm^2/sec. To convert to (sq ft)/(sec) multiply centistoke by 1.075×10^{-5}.

TABLE A-4. Vapor Pressure of Water and Surface Tension of Water in Contact with Air

Temperature, C	0	5	10	15	20	25	30
Vapor pressure (p_w), mm Hg *	4.58	6.54	9.21	12.8	17.5	23.8	31.8
Surface tension (σ), dyne/cm	75.6	74.9	74.2	73.5	72.8	72.0	71.2

* To convert to in. Hg divide by 25.4.

TABLE A-5. Atomic Numbers, Weights, and Valences of Some Chemical Elements *

Element	Symbol	Atomic Number	International Atomic Weight (1952)	Valence
Aluminum	Al	13	26.98	3
Arsenic	As	33	74.91	3, 5
Barium	Ba	56	137.36	2
Boron	B	5	10.82	3
Bromine	Br	35	79.92	1, 3, 5, 7
Cadmium	Cd	48	112.41	2
Calcium	Ca	20	40.08	2
Carbon	C	6	12.01	2, 4
Chlorine	Cl	17	35.46	1, 3, 5, 7
Chromium	Cr	24	52.01	2, 3, 6
Cobalt	Co	27	58.94	2, 3
Copper	Cu	29	63.54	1, 2
Fluorine	F	9	19.00	1
Gold (*aurum*)	Au	79	197.2	1, 3
Hydrogen	H	1	1.008	1
Iodine	I	53	126.92	1, 3, 5, 7
Iron (*ferrum*)	Fe	26	55.85	2, 3
Lead (*plumbum*)	Pb	82	207.21	2, 4
Magnesium	Mg	12	24.32	2
Manganese	Mn	25	54.93	2, 3, 4, 6, 7
Mercury (*hydrargyrum*)	Hg	80	200.61	1, 2
Nickel	Ni	28	58.69	2, 3
Nitrogen	N	7	14.01	3, 5
Oxygen	O	8	16.00	2
Phosphorus	P	15	30.98	3, 5
Platinum	Pt	78	195.23	2, 4
Potassium (*kalium*)	K	19	39.10	1
Selenium	Se	34	78.96	2, 4, 6
Silicon	Si	14	28.09	4
Silver (*argentum*)	Ag	47	107.88	1
Sodium (*natrium*)	Na	11	23.00	1
Strontium	Sr	38	87.63	2
Sulfur	S	16	32.07	2, 4, 6
Tin (*stannum*)	Sn	50	118.70	2, 4
Zinc	Zn	30	65.38	2

* Elements encountered in radioactive wastes are not included. For a complete list, see *Handbook of Chemistry and Physics*, Chemical Rubber Publishing Company, Cleveland, Ohio.

TABLE A-6. Saturation Values of Dissolved Oxygen in Fresh and Sea Water Exposed to an Atmosphere Containing 20.9% Oxygen under a Pressure of 760 mm of Mercury *

Calculated by G. C. Whipple and M. C. Whipple from measurements of C. J. J. Fox

Temperature, C	Dissolved Oxygen (mg/l) for Stated Concentrations of Chloride, mg/l					Difference per 100 mg/l Chloride
	0	5,000	10,000	15,000	20,000	
0	14.62	13.79	12.97	12.14	11.32	0.0165
1	14.23	13.41	12.61	11.82	11.03	.0160
2	13.84	13.05	12.28	11.52	10.76	.0154
3	13.48	12.72	11.98	11.24	10.50	.0149
4	13.13	12.41	11.69	10.97	10.25	.0144
5	12.80	12.09	11.39	10.70	10.01	.0140
6	12.48	11.79	11.12	10.45	9.78	.0135
7	12.17	11.51	10.85	10.21	9.57	.0130
8	11.87	11.24	10.61	9.98	9.36	.0125
9	11.59	10.97	10.36	9.76	9.17	.0121
10	11.33	10.73	10.13	9.55	8.98	.0118
11	11.08	10.49	9.92	9.35	8.80	.0114
12	10.83	10.28	9.72	9.17	8.62	.0110
13	10.60	10.05	9.52	8.98	8.46	.0107
14	10.37	9.85	9.32	8.80	8.30	.0104
15	10.15	9.65	9.14	8.63	8.14	.0100
16	9.95	9.46	8.96	8.47	7.99	.0098
17	9.74	9.26	8.78	8.30	7.84	.0095
18	9.54	9.07	8.62	8.15	7.70	.0092
19	9.35	8.89	8.45	8.00	7.56	.0089
20	9.17	8.73	8.30	7.86	7.42	.0088
21	8.99	8.57	8.14	7.71	7.28	.0086
22	8.83	8.42	7.99	7.57	7.14	.0084
23	8.68	8.27	7.85	7.43	7.00	.0083
24	8.53	8.12	7.71	7.30	6.87	.0083
25	8.38	7.96	7.56	7.15	6.74	.0082
26	8.22	7.81	7.42	7.02	6.61	.0080
27	8.07	7.67	7.28	6.88	6.49	.0079
28	7.92	7.53	7.14	6.75	6.37	.0078
29	7.77	7.39	7.00	6.62	6.25	.0076
30	7.63	7.25	6.86	6.49	6.13	.0075

* For other barometric pressures the solubilities vary approximately in proportion to the ratios of these pressures to the standard pressures.

TABLE A-7. Values of the Exponential e^{-x} for x Ranging from 0.00 to 10.00

x	0	1	2	3	4	5	6	7	8	9
0.0	1.000	0.990	0.980	0.970	0.961	0.951	0.942	0.932	0.923	0.914
0.1	0.905	.896	.887	.878	.869	.861	.852	.844	.835	.827
0.2	.819	.811	.803	.794	.787	.779	.771	.763	.756	.748
0.3	.741	.733	.726	.719	.712	.705	.698	.691	.684	.677
0.4	.670	.664	.657	.651	.644	.638	.631	.625	.619	.613
0.5	.607	.600	.595	.589	.583	.577	.571	.566	.560	.554
0.6	.549	.543	.538	.533	.527	.522	.517	.512	.507	.502
0.7	.497	.492	.487	.482	.477	.472	.468	.463	.458	.454
0.8	.449	.445	.440	.436	.432	.427	.423	.419	.415	.411
0.9	.407	.403	.399	.395	.391	.387	.383	.379	.375	.372
1.0	.368	.364	.361	.357	.353	.350	.347	.343	.340	.336
1.1	.333	.330	.326	.323	.320	.317	.313	.310	.307	.304
1.2	.301	.298	.295	.292	.289	.287	.284	.281	.278	.275
1.3	.273	.270	.267	.264	.262	.259	.257	.254	.252	.249
1.4	.247	.244	.242	.239	.237	.235	.232	.230	.228	.225
1.5	.223	.221	.219	.217	.214	.212	.210	.208	.206	.204
1.6	.202	.200	.198	.196	.194	.192	.190	.188	.186	.185
1.7	.183	.181	.179	.177	.176	.173	.172	.170	.169	.167
1.8	.165	.164	.162	.160	.159	.157	.156	.154	.153	.151
1.9	.150	.148	.147	.145	.144	.142	.141	.139	.138	.137

x	e^{-x}	x	e^{-x}	x	e^{-x}	x	e^{-x}	x	e^{-x}
2.00	0.135	3.00	0.0498	4.00	0.0183	5.00	0.00674	6.0	0.00248
2.05	.129	3.05	.0474	4.05	.0174	5.05	.00641	6.2	.00203
2.10	.122	3.10	.0450	4.10	.0166	5.10	.00610	6.4	.00166
2.15	.116	3.15	.0429	4.15	.0158	5.15	.00580	6.6	.00136
2.20	.111	3.20	.0408	4.20	.0150	5.20	.00552	6.8	.00111
2.25	.105	3.25	.0388	4.25	.0143	5.25	.00525	7.0	.000912
2.30	.100	3.30	.0369	4.30	.0136	5.30	.00499	7.2	.000747
2.35	.0954	3.35	.0351	4.35	.0129	5.35	.00475	7.4	.000611
2.40	.0907	3.40	.0334	4.40	.0123	5.40	.00452	7.6	.000500
2.45	.0863	3.45	.0317	4.45	.0117	5.45	.00430	7.8	.000410
2.50	.0821	3.50	.0302	4.50	.0111	5.50	.00409	8.0	.000335
2.55	.0781	3.55	.0287	4.55	.0106	5.55	.00389	8.2	.000275
2.60	.0743	3.60	.0273	4.60	.0101	5.60	.00370	8.4	.000225
2.65	.0707	3.65	.0260	4.65	.00956	5.65	.00352	8.6	.000184
2.70	.0672	3.70	.0247	4.70	.00910	5.70	.00335	8.8	.000151
2.75	.0639	3.75	.0235	4.75	.00865	5.75	.00319	9.0	.000123
2.80	.0608	3.80	.0224	4.80	.00823	5.80	.00303	9.2	.000101
2.85	.0578	3.85	.0213	4.85	.00783	5.85	.00288	9.4	.000083
2.90	.0550	3.90	.0202	4.90	.00745	5.90	.00274	9.6	.000068
2.95	.0523	3.95	.0193	4.95	.00708	5.95	.00261	9.8	.000055
3.00	.0498	4.00	.0183	5.00	.00674	6.00	.00248	10.0	.000045

Chemicals for Water and Waste-Water Treatment

Information compiled from table prepared by B.I.F. Industries

1. *Activated carbon,* C; Aqua Nuchar, Hydrodarco, Norit; available as powder and granules in 35-lb bags, 5- and 25-lb drums, and carloads; dusty, arches in hoppers; weighs 8 to 28 lb/cu ft, averaging 12; fed dry or as slurry of 1 lb/gal maximum; handled dry in iron or steel, wet in stainless steel, rubber, Duriron, and bronze.

2. *Activated silica,* —SiO_2—; Silica Sol, produced at site from sodium silicate, Na_2SiO_3, and alum, ammonium sulfate, chlorine, carbon dioxide, sodium bicarbonate, or sulfuric acid; 41° Bé sodium silicate is diluted to 1.5% SiO_2 before activation; insoluble, will gel at high concentrations; fed as 0.6% solution to prevent gel formation; handled in iron, steel, rubber, and stainless steel.

3. *Aluminum sulfate,* $Al_2(SO_4)_3 \cdot 14H_2O$; alum, filter alum, sulfate of alumina; available in ground, rice, powder, and lump form in 100- and 200-lb bags, 325- and 400-lb barrels, 25-, 100-, and 250-lb drums, and carloads; dusty, astringent, only slightly hygroscopic; weighs 60 to 75 lb/cu ft; should contain at least 17% Al_2O_3; fed dry in ground and rice form; maximum concentration 0.5 lb/gal; handled dry in iron, steel, and concrete, wet in lead, rubber, Duriron, asphalt, cypress, and stainless steel 316; available also as 50% solution.

4. *Anhydrous ammonia,* NH_3; available in steel cylinders containing 50-, 100-, and 150-lb, also in 50,000-lb tank cars; pungent, irritating odor, liquid causes burns; 99 to 100% NH_3; fed as dry gas and aqueous solution through gas feeder or ammoniator; handled in iron, steel, glass, nickel, and Monel.

5. *Calcium oxide,* CaO; quicklime, burnt lime, chemical lime, unslaked lime; available as lumps, pebbles, crushed or ground, in 100-lb, moisture-proof bags, wooden barrels, and carloads; unstable, caustic, and irritating; slakes to calcium hydroxide with evolution of heat when water is added; weighs 55 to 70 lb/cu ft; should contain 70 to 90% CaO; best fed dry as 3/4-in. pebbles or crushed to pass 1-in. ring; requires from 0.4 to 0.7 gal of water for continuous solution; final

dilution should be 10%; should not be stored for more than 60 days even in tight container; handled wet in iron, steel, rubber hose, and concrete.

6. *Calcium hydroxide,* $Ca(OH)_2$; hydrated lime, slaked lime; available as powder in 50-lb bags, 100-lb barrels, and carloads; must be stored in dry place; caustic, dusty, and irritant; weighs 35 to 50 lb/cu ft; should contain 62 to 74% CaO; fed dry, 0.5 lb/gal maximum, and as slurry 0.93 lb/gal maximum; handled in rubber hose, iron, steel, asphalt, and concrete.

7. *Calcium hypochlorite,* $Ca(OCl)_2 \cdot 4H_2O$; HTH, Perchloron, Pittchlor; available as powder, granules, and pellets in 115-lb barrels, 5-, 15-, 100-, and 300-lb cans, and 800-lb drums; corrosive and odorous; must be stored dry; weighs 50 to 55 lb/cu ft; should contain 70% available Cl_2; fed as solution up to 2% strength (0.25 lb/gal); handled in ceramics, glass, plastics, and rubber-lined tanks.

8. *Chlorine,* Cl_2; chlorine gas, liquid chlorine; available as liquefied gas under pressure in 100- and 150-lb steel cylinders, ton containers, cars with 15-ton containers, and tank cars of 16-, 30-, and 55-ton capacity; corrosive, poisonous gas; should contain 99.8% Cl_2; fed as gas vaporized from liquid and as aqueous solution through gas feeder or chlorinator; dry liquid or gas handled in black iron, copper, and steel, wet gas in glass, silver, hard rubber, and tantalum.

9. *Copper sulfate,* $CuSO_4 \cdot 5H_2O$; available ground and as powder or lumps in 100-lb bags and 450-lb barrels or drums; poisonous; weighs 75 to 90 lb/cu ft ground, 73 to 80 lb/cu ft as powder, and 60 to 64 lb/cu ft as lumps; should be 99% pure; best fed ground and as powder; maximum concentration 0.25 lb/gal; handled in stainless steel, asphalt, Duriron, rubber, plastics, and ceramics.

10. *Ferric chloride,* $FeCl_3$ (anhydrous and as solution), $FeCl_3 \cdot 6H_2O$ (crystal); chloride of iron, ferrichlor; available as solution, lumps, and granules in 5- and 13-gal carboys and in tank trucks; hygroscopic; solution weighs 11.2 to 12.4 lb/gal, crystals 60 to 64 lb/cu ft, anhydrous chemical 85 to 90 lb/cu ft; solution should contain 35 to 45%, crystals 60%, and anhydrous chemical 96 to 97% $FeCl_3$; fed as solution containing up to 45% $FeCl_3$; handled in rubber, glass, ceramics, and plastics.

11. *Ferric sulfate,* $Fe_2(SO_4)_3 \cdot 3H_2O$ and $Fe_2(SO_4)_3 \cdot 2H_2O$; Ferrifloc, Ferriclear, iron sulfate; available as granules in 100-lb bags, 400- and 425-lb drums, and carloads; hygroscopic, must be stored in tight containers; weighs 70 to 72 lb/cu ft; $Fe_2(SO_4)_3 \cdot 3H_2O$ should contain 18.5% Fe, $Fe_2(SO_4)_3 \cdot 2H_2O$ should contain 21% Fe; best fed dry, 1.4 to 2.4 lb/gal, detention time 20 min; handled in stainless steel 316, rubber, lead, ceramics, and Duriron.

12. *Ferrous sulfate,* $FeSO_4 \cdot 7H_2O$; copperas, iron sulfate, sugar sulfate, green vitriol; available as granules, crystals, powder, and lumps in 100-lb bags, 400-lb barrels, and bulk; weighs 63 to 66 lb/cu ft; should contain 20% Fe; best fed as dry granules, 0.5 lb/gal, detention time 5 min; handled dry in iron, steel, and concrete, wet in lead, rubber, iron, asphalt, cypress, and stainless steel.

13. *Sodium carbonate,* Na_2CO_3; soda ash; available as crystals and powder in 100-lb bags, 100-lb barrels; 25- and 100-lb drums, and carloads; weighs 30 to 65 lb/cu ft extra light to dense; should contain 58% Na_2O; best fed as dense crystals 0.25 lb/gal, detention time 10 min, more for higher concentrations; handled in iron, steel, and rubber hose.

14. *Sodium chloride,* NaCl; common salt, salt; available as rock, powder, crystals, and granules in 100-lb bags, barrels, 25-lb drums, and carloads; rock weighs 50 to 60 lb/cu ft, fine weighs 58 to 70 lb/cu ft; should contain 98% NaCl; fed as saturated brine; handled in galvanized iron, rubber, and Monel.

15. *Sodium fluoride,* NaF; fluoride; available as granules (crystals) and powder in 100-lb bags, 25-, 125-, 375-lb drums; powder weighs 66 to 100 lb/cu ft, granules weigh 90 to 106 lb/cu ft; should contain 43 to 44% F; best fed as granules 1 lb to 12 gal; handled dry in iron and steel, wet in rubber, plastics, stainless steel, asphalt, and cypress.

16. *Sodium silicate,* $Na_2O(SiO_2)_{3.25\ \mathrm{approx}}$; water glass; available as liquid in 1-, 5-, and 55-gal drums, in ton trucks and tank cars; weighs about 11.7 lb/gal; should contain about 9% Na_2O and 29% SiO_2; fed in solution as received; handled in cast iron, steel, and rubber.

17. *Sulfur dioxide,* SO_2; available as liquefied gas under pressure in 100-, 150-, and 200-lb steel cylinders; 100% SO_2; fed as gas, handled dry in steel, wet in glass, rubber, and ceramics.

Bibliography

REFERENCE WORKS

Municipal Water Supply

American Water Works Association, *Water Quality and Treatment,* published by the Association, New York, 2nd Ed., 1950.

Babbitt, H. E., and J. J. Doland, *Water Supply Engineering,* McGraw-Hill Book Co., New York, 4th Ed., 1949.

Baker, M. N., *The Quest for Pure Water,* American Water Works Association, New York, 1948.

Hardenbergh, W. A., *Water Supply and Purification,* International Textbook Co., Scranton, Pa., 3rd Ed., 1952.

Hoover, C. P., *Water Supply and Treatment,* National Lime Association, Washington, D. C., 1943.

Institution of Water Engineers, *Manual of British Water Supply Practice,* W. Heffer and Sons, Cambridge, England (American Water Works Association, New York), 1950.

Ryan, W. J., *Water Treatment and Purification,* McGraw-Hill Book Co., New York, 2nd Ed., 1946.

Turneaure, F. E., and H. L. Russell, *Public Water Supplies,* John Wiley and Sons, New York, 4th Ed., 1940.

Municipal Sewerage

Babbitt, H. E., *Sewerage and Sewage Treatment,* John Wiley and Sons, New York, 7th Ed., 1953.

Escritt, L. B., *Sewerage and Sewage Disposal,* Contractors Record Ltd., London, 1956.

Hardenbergh, W. A., *Sewerage and Sewage Treatment,* International Textbook Co., Scranton, Pa., 3rd Ed., 1950.

Imhoff, Karl, and G. M. Fair, *Sewage Treatment,* John Wiley and Sons, New York, 2nd Ed., 1956.

Keefer, C. E., *Sewage Treatment Works,* McGraw-Hill Book Co., New York, 1940.

Metcalf, Leonard, and H. P. Eddy, *American Sewerage Practice,* McGraw-Hill Book Co., New York, 3 Vols., 1915 to 1935.

Rudolfs, Willem, *Principles of Sewage Treatment,* National Lime Association, Washington, D. C., 1941.

Municipal Water Supply and Sewerage

Escritt, L. B., and Sidney F. Rich, *The Work of the Sanitary Engineer,* Macdonald and Evans, London, 1949.

Fair, G. M., and J. C. Geyer, *Water Supply and Waste-Water Disposal,* John Wiley and Sons, New York, 1954.

Isaac, P. C. G., *Public Health Engineering,* E. and F. N. Spon, London, 1953.

Maxcy, K. F., *Rosenau, Preventive Medicine and Public Health,* Appleton-Century-Crofts, New York, 8th Ed., 1956. Sections on water by E. W. Moore; section on sewage by G. M. Fair.

Phelps, E. B., *Public Health Engineering* (Vol. 1, Part 2, in collaboration with C. J. Velz), John Wiley and Sons, New York, 1948.

Steel, E. W., *Water Supply and Sewerage,* McGraw-Hill Book Co., New York, 3rd Ed., 1953.

Water Supply and Drainage of Buildings

Babbitt, H. E., *Plumbing,* McGraw-Hill Book Co., New York, 2nd Ed., 1950.

Day, L. J., *Standard Plumbing Details,* John Wiley and Sons, New York, 1938.

Plum, Svend, *Plumbing Practice and Design,* John Wiley and Sons, New York, 1943.

Industrial Water Supply and Waste-Water Disposal

Besselievre, E. B., *Industrial Waste Treatment,* McGraw-Hill Book Co., New York, 1952.

Betz, W. H. and L. D., *Handbook of Industrial Water Conditioning,* published by the authors, Philadelphia, 1950.

Eldridge, E. F., *Industrial Waste Treatment Practice,* McGraw-Hill Book Co., New York, 1942.

Gurnham, C. F., *Principles of Industrial Waste Treatment,* John Wiley and Sons, New York, 1955.

Nordell, Eskell, *Water Treatment for Industrial and Other Uses,* Reinhold Publishing Corp., New York, 1951.

Rudolfs, Willem, Editor, *Industrial Wastes,* Reinhold Publishing Corp., New York, 1953.

Southgate, B. A., *Treatment and Disposal of Industrial Waste Waters,* H. M. Stationery Office, London, 1948.

Rural Water Supply and Waste-Water Disposal

Ehlers, V. M., and E. W. Steel, *Municipal and Rural Sanitation,* McGraw-Hill Book Co., New York, 4th Ed., 1950.

Wright, F. B., *Rural Water Supply and Sanitation,* John Wiley and Sons, New York, 2nd Ed., 1956.

STATISTICAL METHODS

Croxton, F. E., *Elementary Statistics,* Prentice-Hall, New York, 1953.

Hoel, P. G., *Introduction to Mathematical Statistics,* John Wiley and Sons, New York, 1947.

Yule, G. U., and M. G. Kendall, *Theory of Statistics,* J. B. Lippincott Co., London, 1940.

HYDROLOGY

Blair, T. A., *Weather Elements,* Prentice-Hall, New York, 1946.

Foster, E. E., *Rainfall and Runoff,* The Macmillan Co., New York, 1948.

Grover, N. C., and A. W. Harrington, *Stream Flow,* John Wiley and Sons, New York, 1943.

Johnstone, Don, and W. P. Cross, *Elements of Applied Hydrology,* Ronald Press Co., New York, 1949.

Linsley, R. K., M. A. Kohler, and J. L. H. Paulhus, *Applied Hydrology,* McGraw-Hill Book Co., New York, 1949.

Mead, D. W., *Hydrology,* McGraw-Hill Book Co., New York, 2nd Ed., 1950.

Meinzer, O. E., *Hydrology,* McGraw-Hill Book Co., New York, 1942.

Muskat, Morris, *Flow of Homogeneous Fluids through Porous Media,* McGraw-Hill Book Co., New York, 1937.

Thomas, H. E., *The Conservation of Ground Water,* McGraw-Hill Book Co., New York, 1951.

Tolman, C. F., *Ground Water,* McGraw-Hill Book Co., New York, 1937.

Wisler, C. O., and E. F. Brater, *Hydrology,* John Wiley and Sons, New York, 1949.

HYDRAULICS AND STRUCTURES

Creager, W. P., J. D. Justin, and Julian Hinds, *Engineering for Dams,* John Wiley and Sons, New York, 1945.

Davis, C. V., Editor, *Handbook of Applied Hydraulics,* McGraw-Hill Book Co., New York, 2nd Ed., 1952. Sections on water by T. R. Camp; sections on sewage by S. A. Greeley and W. E. Stanley.

Kristal, F. A., and F. A. Annett, *Pumps,* McGraw-Hill Book Co., New York, 2nd Ed., 1953.

National Resources Committee, *Low Dams,* U. S. Government Printing Office, Washington, D. C., 1939.

Rouse, Hunter, Editor, *Engineering Hydraulics,* John Wiley and Sons, New York, 1950.

PHYSICS AND CHEMISTRY

American Society for Testing Materials, *Manual on Industrial Water,* published by the Society, Philadelphia, 1953.

American Public Health Association and American Water Works Association, *Standard Methods for the Examination of Water and Sewage,* American Public Health Association, New York, 9th Ed., 1949, 10th Ed., 1955.

Bull, H. B., *Physical Biochemistry,* John Wiley and Sons, New York, 2nd Ed., 1951.

Hodgman, C. D., Editor, *Handbook of Chemistry and Physics,* Chemical Rubber Publishing Co., Cleveland, 34th Ed., 1952.

Clark, W. M., *Topics in Physical Chemistry,* Williams and Wilkins, Baltimore, 1952.

Daniels, Farrington, *Outlines of Physical Chemistry,* John Wiley and Sons, New York, 1950.

Dorsey, N. E., *Properties of Ordinary Water Substance,* Reinhold Publishing Corp., New York, 1940.

Frost, A. A., and R. G. Pearson, *Kinetics and Mechanism,* John Wiley and Sons, New York, 1953.

Glasstone, Samuel, *Textbook of Physical Chemistry,* D. Van Nostrand and Co., New York, 2nd Ed., 1946.

Gurney, R. W., *Ionic Processes in Solution,* McGraw-Hill Book Co., New York, 1953.

Taylor, E. W., *The Examination of Waters and Water Supplies,* Blakiston Co., Philadelphia, 6th Ed., 1949.

Weiser, H. B., *Colloid Chemistry,* John Wiley and Sons, New York, 2nd Ed., 1949.

Biology

Frobisher, Martin, Jr., *Fundamentals of Bacteriology,* W. B. Saunders Co., Philadelphia, 4th Ed., 1950.

Maxcy, K. F., *Rosenau, Preventive Medicine and Public Health,* Appleton-Century-Crofts, New York, 8th Ed., 1956.

Muenscher, W. C., *Aquatic Plants of the United States,* Comstock Publishing Co., Ithaca, N. Y., 1944.

Needham, J. G. and P. R., *A Guide to the Study of Fresh-Water Biology,* Comstock Publishing Co., Ithaca, N. Y., 1938.

Pratt, H. S., *A Manual of the Common Invertebrate Animals,* Blakiston Co., Philadelphia, 1935.

Prescott, S. C., C-E. A. Winslow, and Mac Harvey McCrady, *Water Bacteriology. With Special Reference to Sanitary Water Analysis,* John Wiley and Sons, New York, 6th Ed., 1946.

Robbins, W. W., A. S. Crafts, and R. N. Raynor, *Weed Control,* McGraw-Hill Book Co., New York, 1942.

Smith, G. M., *The Fresh-Water Algae of the United States,* McGraw-Hill Book Co., New York, 1933.

Stephenson, Marjory, *Bacterial Metabolism,* Longmans, Green and Co., London, 2nd Ed., 1939.

West, T. F., J. E. Hardy, and J. H. Ford, *Chemical Control of Insects,* John Wiley and Sons, New York, 1952.

ZoBell, C. E., *Marine Microbiology,* Chronica Botanica Co., Waltham, Mass., 1946.

Limnology and Stream Sanitation

Phelps, E. B., *Stream Sanitation,* John Wiley and Sons, New York, 1944.

Welch, P. S., *Limnology,* McGraw-Hill Book Co., New York, 1935.

Welch, P. S., *Limnological Methods,* Blakiston Co., Philadelphia, 1948.

Whipple, G. C., G. M. Fair, and M. C. Whipple, *The Microscopy of Drinking Water,* John Wiley and Sons, New York, 4th Ed., 1927.

SERIAL PUBLICATIONS

Professional Societies

American Chemical Society: *Industrial and Engineering Chemistry,* monthly.

American Geophysical Union: *Transactions,* bimonthly.

American Public Health Association: *American Journal of Public Health,* monthly; *Yearbook.*

American Society of Civil Engineers: *Transactions,* annual; *Proceedings,* printed as separates, formerly monthly; *Civil Engineering,* monthly; *Manuals of Engineering Practice.*

American Water Works Association: *Journal,* monthly.

British Waterworks Association, London: *Journal,* several times a year.

Federation of Sewage and Industrial Wastes Associations: *Sewage and Industrial Wastes* (formerly Sewage Works Journal), monthly; *Manuals of Practice.*

Institute of Sewage Purification, London: *Journal and Proceedings,* annual.

Institution of Civil Engineers, London: *Journal,* monthly.

Institution of Public Health Engineers, London: *Journal,* several times a year.

Institution of Water Engineers, London: *Journal,* 6 to 8 times a year.

New England Water Works Association: *Journal,* quarterly.

Governmental Agencies

U. S. Geological Survey: *Water Supply Papers.*

U. S. Public Health Service: *Public Health Reports,* monthly; *Public Health Engineering Abstracts,* monthly; *Public Health Bulletins.*

U. S. Weather Bureau: *Climatological Data,* monthly; *Monthly Weather Review.*

Water Pollution Research Laboratory, Department of Scientific and Industrial Research, Britain: *Water Pollution Research, Summary of Current Literature,* monthly.

Magazines

Case-Sheppard-Mann Publishing Co., New York: *Wastes Engineering,* monthly; *Water Works Engineering,* monthly.

McGraw-Hill Publishing Co., New York: *Engineering News-Record,* weekly.

Public Works Journal Corp., New York: *Public Works,* monthly.

Scranton Publishing Co., Chicago: *Industrial Wastes,* bimonthly; *Water and Sewage Works,* monthly.

Index

Use of Hazen-Williams diagram

a. Given Q and d; to find s.
b. Given d and s; to find Q.
c. Given d and s; to find v.
d. Given Q and s; to find d.
e. Given Q and h_1 to find Q for different h.
f. Given Q and h_1 to find h for different Q.

For C other than 100, (1) multiply given Q or v by (100/C) to find s; or
value of Q or v by (C/100) for given s.

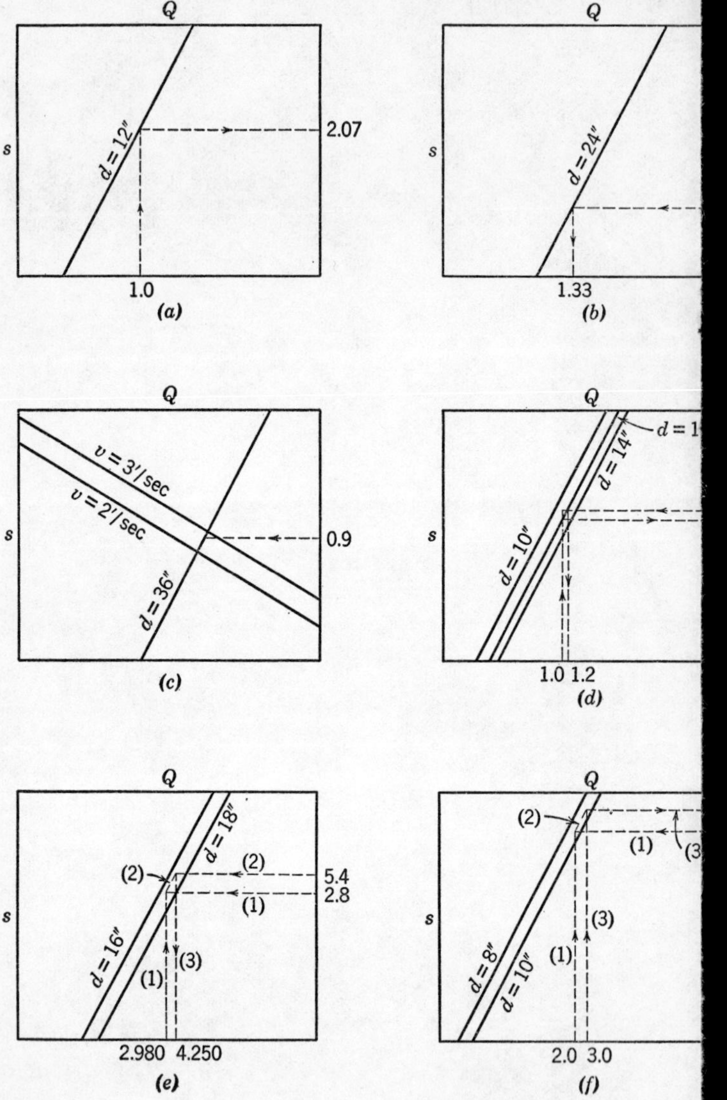

Use of Hazen-Williams diagram

a. Given Q and *d*; to find *s*.
b. Given *d* and *s*; to find Q.
c. Given *d* and *s*; to find *v*.
d. Given Q and *s*; to find *d*.
e. Given Q and *h*; to find Q for different *h*.
f. Given Q and *h*; to find *h* for different Q.

For C other than 100: (1) multiply given Q or v by (100/C) to find *s*; or value of Q or v by (C/100) for given *s*.

Flow of water in pipes—H
Discharge

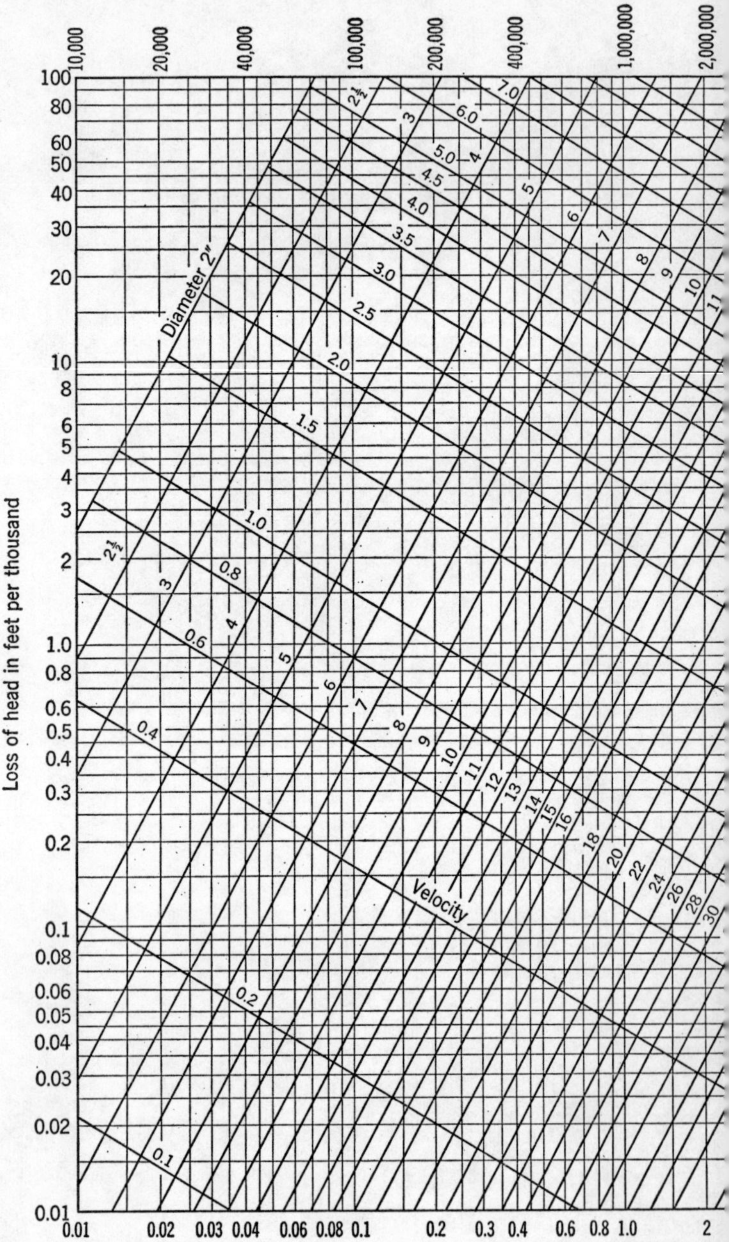

Discharge in n
Velocity ir

0.12

2″

2.9
2.1

54.0
25.3

nultiply found

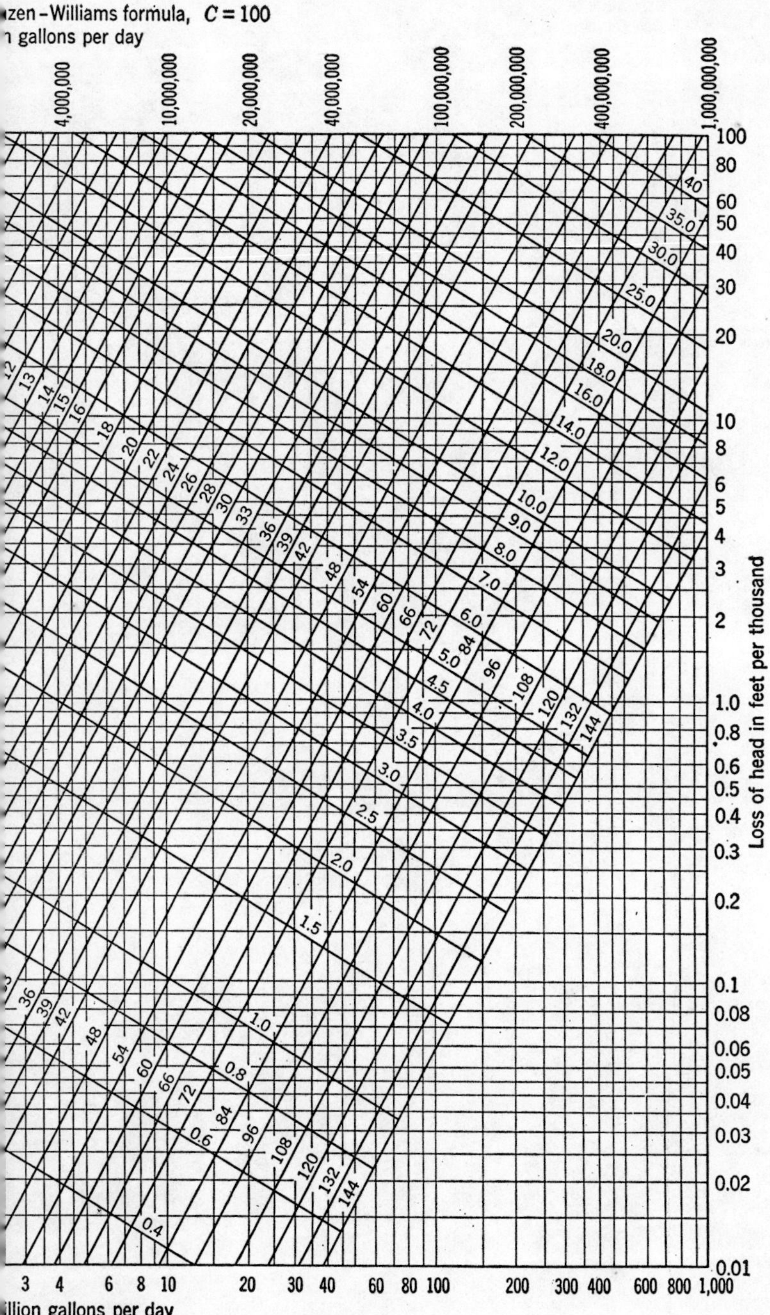
zen – Williams formula, C = 100
n gallons per day
4,000,000
10,000,000
20,000,000
40,000,000
100,000,000
200,000,000
400,000,000
1,000,000,000
Loss of head in feet per thousand
100
80
60
50
40
30
20
10
8
6
5
4
3
2
1.0
0.8
0.6
0.5
0.4
0.3
0.2
0.1
0.08
0.06
0.05
0.04
0.03
0.02
0.01
3
4
6
8
10
20
30
40
60
80
100
200
300
400
600
800
1,000
illion gallons per day
feet per second